A REFERENCE GUIDE
TO P
ELECTR

Other Titles of Interest

BP53	Practical Electronics Calculations and Formulae
BP144	Further Practical Electronics Calculations and Formulae
BP254	From Atoms to Amperes
BP286	A Reference Guide to Basic Electronics Terms

A REFERENCE GUIDE TO PRACTICAL ELECTRONICS TERMS

by
F. A. WILSON
C.G.I.A., C.Eng., F.I.E.E., F.B.I.M.

BERNARD BABANI (publishing) LTD
THE GRAMPIANS
SHEPHERDS BUSH ROAD
LONDON W6 7NF
ENGLAND

Please Note

Although every care has been taken with the production of this book to ensure that any projects, designs, modifications and/or programs etc. contained herewith, operate in a correct and safe manner and also that any components specified are normally available in Great Britain, the Publishers do not accept responsibility in any way for the failure, including fault in design, of any project, design, modification or program to work correctly or to cause damage to any other equipment that it may be connected to or used in conjunction with, or in respect of any other damage or injury that may be so caused, nor do the Publishers accept responsibility in any way for the failure to obtain specified components.

Notice is also given that if equipment that is still under warranty is modified in any way or used or connected with home-built equipment then that warranty may be void.

First Published – August 1992

British Library Cataloguing in Publication Data
Wilson, F. A.
A reference guide to practical electronics terms
I. Title
621.381014

ISBN 0 85934 232 8

Printed and bound in Great Britain by Cox & Wyman Ltd, Reading

Preface

What is all knowledge too but recorded experience, and a product of history; of which, therefore, reasoning and belief, no less than action and passion, are essential materials?

Thomas Carlyle

Electronics is passing through a period of relentless expansion, it is creeping into just about everything, from the watches on our wrists to the manufacture and even driving of our cars. There are far reaching domestic and social implications to the extent that some of us with our calculators and computers are in danger of being taken over. How often therefore do we of the enquiring mind wish we knew a little more about what is going on. This book has been written with this in mind. Some theoretical background is given but generally lengthy proofs are avoided and the mathematics is kept at a reasonable level.

For those wishing to gild the lily there is a companion book entitled "A Reference Guide to Basic Electronics Terms" which considers the more fundamental aspects. However each book stands on its own and relies on its companion no more than any technical publication relies on other work to fill in the gaps. Both books have their own system of references and those terms in the same book are preceded by an asterisk (*), those in the companion book by >> (see the example below).

The references are no more than enlightened suggestions, the reader can choose which, if any, should be explored further. Certainly by following them from term to term one can easily get down to the real roots of any concept.

Modern equipment is often little more than a cluster of unfathomable integrated circuits so we learn better from circuits of discrete components. Accordingly these are frequently used for illustration even though in the practical world integrated circuits have taken over.

A reminder about the references:

(* Cathode-Ray Tube, Deflection Sensitivity >> Magnetic Field)

other terms in this book for extra clarification as required

a term in "A Reference Guide to Basic Electronics Terms" – not essential but may be of interest.

Please note an Index appears on page 425.

F. A. Wilson

ABSORPTION WAVEMETER is an instrument for measuring the frequency of a radio wave. Power for its operation is derived from the wave itself – see Wavemeter.

ACCELERATING ELECTRODE is an electrode in an electron tube (e.g. cathode-ray tube) which is held at a positive potential relative to the electron source. Through its creation of an electric field it imparts energy to electrons in the electron beam and therefore accelerates them. The 1st and 3rd anodes in Figure E6 are for this purpose

See also Electron Gun which includes an example of calculation of electron speeds.
(* Cathode-Ray Tube >> Electric Field, Kinetic Energy)

ACCELERATOR is a device used to accelerate charged particles to high energies. The most commonly found is that used in a cathode-ray or similar electron tube. An electrode carrying a high positive potential increases the velocity of electrons emitted from a cathode. A typical system is illustrated in Figure E6. For nuclear research much higher velocities are required for the production of high energy beams.

The *Van de Graaff electrostatic generator* (after Robert Van de Graaff, an American physicist) is capable of producing up to around 30 MV. It functions by spraying an electric charge onto a moving insulated belt which carries the charge up to an insulated dome. The dome picks up the charge through a set of metal points and so the charge continually builds up. This type is known as a *direct voltage accelerator.*

The *linear accelerator* is a resonance type in which electrons are emitted from an electron gun and then accelerated through an electron tube. In this tube electrodes along its length are so placed that a radio frequency potential connected to them is able to accelerate the electrons by a series of relatively small accelerating voltages. The frequency of the applied potential and the distance between the electrodes are so arranged that when the wave is positive the electrons are accelerated across the electrode gaps but travel through the electrode itself while the wave is negative (inside the electrode there is little field). The electrons therefore continually receive pulses of energy as they travel along the tube.

The *cyclotron* reduces the dimensions required by a linear accelerator by making the paths of the charged particles circular using a magnetic field. The frequency of the accelerating radio frequency field can then be adjusted so that a pulse of energy is supplied twice during the rotation of each particle. Higher energies still are obtained using a further development, the *betatron*.
(* Electron Gun, Cathode-Ray Tube, Van de Graaff Generator, Linear Accelerator >> Charge)

ACOUSTIC FEEDBACK is positive feedback at an audio frequency from a loudspeaker to a microphone at the input of the system. The result is an unwanted howling noise from the loudspeaker, frequently heard on PA systems. It is usually at the first frequency at which the gain of the system loop (microphone → amplifiers → loudspeaker(s) → airpath back to microphone) reaches unity. Amplifier gains must therefore be reduced until the loop is stable. Directional microphones and/or loudspeakers may also be used to alleviate the problem.
(* Microphone, Loudspeaker, Instability >> Amplifier, Feedback)

ACOUSTIC WAVE DEVICE This arises from the discovery in the early 1960's that when an acoustic wave is set up in a single crystal of cadmium sulphide, it can be influenced by a flow through the crystal of charge carriers. The material must be a semiconductor with piezoelectric properties and for example, both cadmium sulphide and gallium arsenide fall into this category.

As an acoustic wave propagates through the crystal, the stresses it produces induce a similarly changing electric field, compressive stresses induce a field in one direction whereas tensile stresses (the wave rarefactions) induce a field in the opposite direction. The net effect is that drifting charge carriers tend to bunch at points where the field is minimum and that when a charge carrier loses velocity, kinetic energy is given up to the acoustic wave. Alternatively when a charge carrier gains velocity, the higher kinetic energy is obtained by the extraction of energy from the wave. Control of the process of energy interchange is effected by application of a d.c. electric field (the *bias*) and it has been found that suitable control of the drift field can produce either loss or gain in the wave propagation.

The technique is therefore to generate acoustic waves in the material by applying electrical signals and to control the drift velocity of conduction electrons within the material by application of a d.c. electric field. There is then interaction between the wave and the electrons, resulting in amplification or attenuation of the input signal according to the bias value.

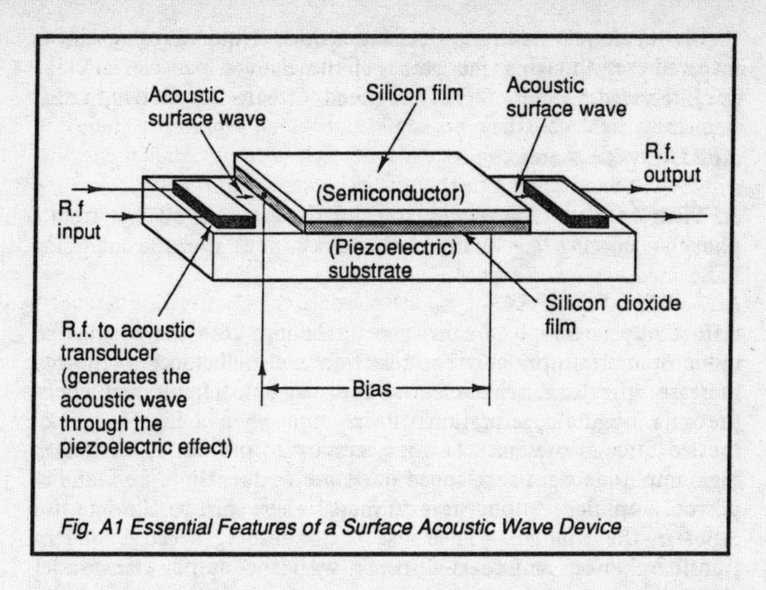

Fig. A1 Essential Features of a Surface Acoustic Wave Device

A further development is the *surface acoustic wave device* (SAW). In this the acoustic wave propagates along the piezoelectric substrate surface. A thin film of semiconductor is placed just above this surface so that the electric field due to the acoustic waves in the piezoelectric substrate extends into the semiconductor slice above it and interacts with the conduction electrons there. A sketch showing the construction of such a device is given in Figure A1. The length is no more than a centimetre or two. Control of the charge carriers and therefore the amplification is effected by connecting the bias potential across the semiconductor slice. It is possible to obtain gains of up to 100 dB at frequencies up to a few GHz.

The acoustic wave technique is applicable not only to amplifiers but can be adapted as shown above for r.f. attenuation. Also owing to the relatively slow speed of an acoustic wave, the device is ideal as a delay line. It is also used in filters (e.g. SAW filters in t.v. receivers), oscillators and many other applications.
(* Delay Line >> Acoustic Wave, Crystal, Piezoelectric Effect, Drift Velocity)

ACTIVE LOAD is a load consisting of an active device, usually a transistor. In the manufacture of integrated circuits, especially those containing mainly MOS transistors, it is frequently much simpler to use transistors for loads instead of plain resistors since

the latter require extra processing work. Note that no gain is involved even though a transistor is employed.
(* Integrated Circuit, MOS Integrated Circuit >> Active, Load)

AERIAL – see Antenna

AFTERGLOW The continuation of the emission of light from a phosphor coating (e.g. as in a cathode-ray tube) after the energising has ceased – see Persistence.

AIR GAP Simply a small gap introduced into the core of an inductor or transformer. The relatively high reluctance of the gap increases the total reluctance of the magnetic circuit and hence prevents magnetic saturation of the core when a high magnetomotive force is present. This is necessary to prevent distortion on high amplitude signals. Gapped cores are frequently to be found in power amplifier output transformers where direct current also flows in the winding. Their use is diminishing because modern transistor power amplifiers dispense with the output transformer altogether.
(* Power Amplifier >> Magnetomotive Force, Reluctance, Distortion)

AIR ISOLATION – a technique used in integrated circuit design to insulate elements from one another – see Isolation.

ALKALINE CELL (ALKALINE-MANGANESE CELL) – a primary cell based on the Leclanché principle, of high capacity and capable of supplying continuous heavy loads. It is commonly used as a superior dry battery and as might be expected, is more expensive than the standard one. The positive electrode is formed from manganese dioxide, the negative is the metal zinc. The electrolyte is a strong solution of potassium hydroxide, an alkali, hence the name of the cell. As a dry cell it is manufactured as a direct replacement for zinc chloride or normal Leclanché types, voltage 1.5.
(>> Primary Cell, Electrolyte, Leclanché Cell)

ALTERNATOR is an a.c. generator of which there are many different types. The basic principle is illustrated in Figure A2(i). Here a permanent magnet rotates within a single turn of a coil and so generates one complete cycle of electromotive force (e.m.f.) in the coil per revolution. The e.m.f. induced in a single turn is very small hence in practice several windings, each of many turns are used, the

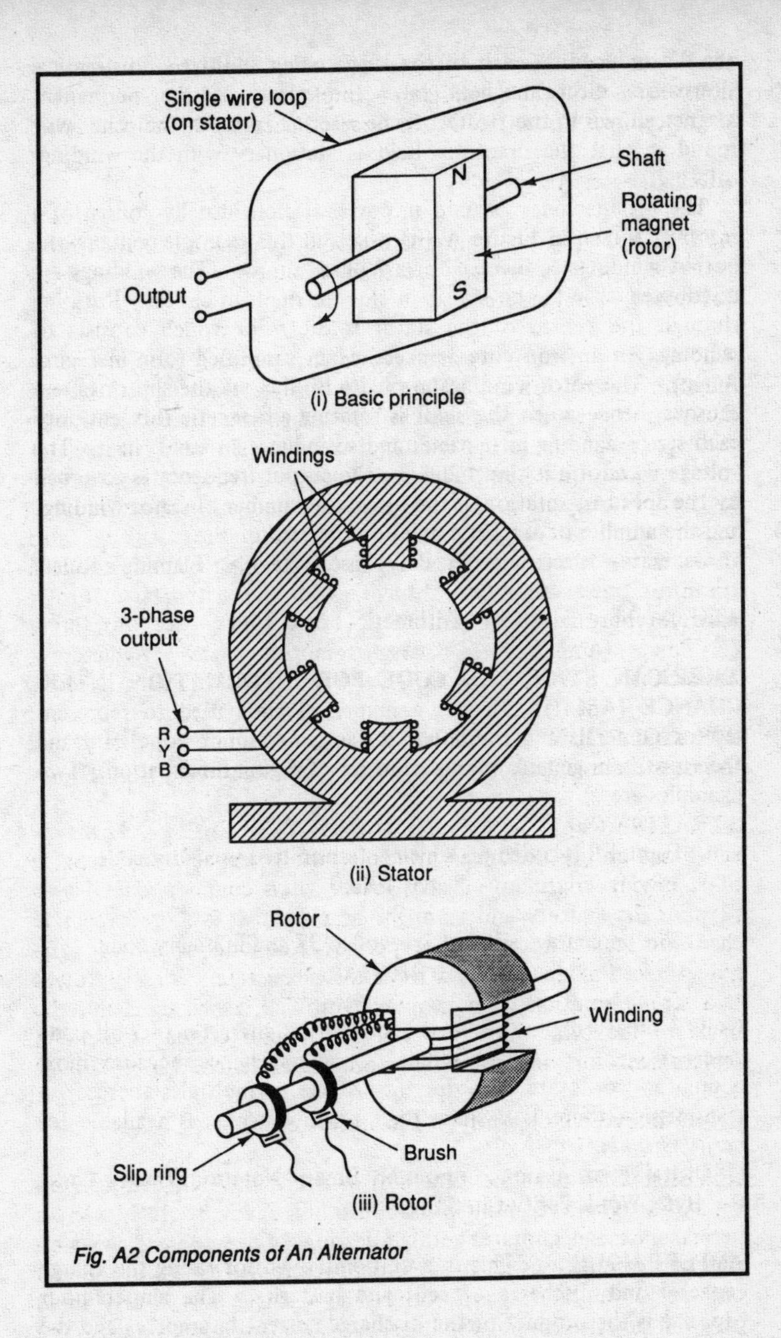

Fig. A2 Components of An Alternator

e.m.f.'s induced in each of the turns being additive. In practical alternators electromagnets take the place of the permanent magnet shown in the figure. Some alternators work the other way round in that the magnetic field is stationary with the windings rotating.

The big machines as used in power stations usually consist of a *stator* as shown in Figure A2(ii) which in this example contains the output windings connected for a 3-phase supply. The windings are distributed around the stator in slots in the iron circuit. Rotating through the centre of the stator is the *rotor* which consists of windings on an iron core as sketched in simplified form in Figure A2(iii). The rotor windings are fed with d.c. via the slip rings and brushes, hence when the shaft is rotating a magnetic flux envelops each stator winding as it passes and so induces an e.m.f. in it. The voltage waveform is sinusoidal and the output frequency is governed by the speed of rotation of the rotor, the number of stator windings and the number of magnetic poles on the rotor.
(* Generator, Electromagnet, Polyphase System >> Fleming's Rules)

ALU – abbreviation of Arithmetic Logic Unit – see this term.

AMERICAN STANDARD CODE FOR INFORMATION INTERCHANGE (ASCII) This is a numerical code used to represent letters, numerals and symbols. It has gained much popularity and therefore is in general use for transfer of digital information. Two examples are:

Capital B is coded 66 which is transmitted in binary code as 1000010

The percentage symbol % is coded 37 and in binary code is 0100101

Only 7 binary digits (bits) are required per character (a 7-bit code caters for $2^7 = 128$ different characters) hence because most computer words are in bytes, i.e. 8 bits or multiples thereof, in transmission there is a spare digit position which is available for *parity checking.*
(* Digital Transmission, Computer, Binary Notation, Binary Code, Bit, Byte, Word, Parity Checking)

AMPERE-HOUR This is a unit employed for rating the charge capacity and discharge of cells and batteries. The ampere-hour capacity is the product of the discharge current in amperes and the time in hours for which the current can be drawn. With many types of cell it depends to a small extent on the rate of discharge, hence it is often necessary to quote this. As an example, a battery may be said to have a capacity of 20 ampere-hours (A h) at the 5-hour rate (which in this case would be a continuous current of 4 amperes). (>> Cell, Battery, Ampere)

ANALOGUE-TO-DIGITAL (A/D) CONVERSION Analogue data which has to be transcribed into the digital form takes many shapes, from the complex ones of speech, music and television signals to the simple slow variation with time of say, a thermocouple indicating temperature. The conversion process involves sampling the analogue signal and from the samples producing a binary code corresponding to the sample level. With the more complex waveforms which change rapidly the *sampling-rate* must be high otherwise much of the information contained in the analogue signal is lost.

There are many methods of performing A/D conversion, mostly provided by a single or a group of integrated circuits, the complexity depending on the speed and accuracy of conversion required. The digital output of the converter can be either serial (one bit at a time) or parallel (all bits of a word appearing simultaneously). Parallel systems are generally much faster than serial.

As a single example of a parallel method, *simultaneous conversion* operates by presenting each sample of the analogue signal to a parallel bank of logic voltage comparators, each one in the bank responding to a discrete level of voltage slightly above or below that of its neighbour. The logic system is arranged so that all comparators at or above the sample voltage level produce a logical output of 1 whereas all below the level have an output of 0. Subsequent logic gates convert the comparator outputs into the appropriate binary code.

See also for an example, Pulse Code Modulation.
(* Sampling, Binary, Bit, Word, Binary Code, Digital Logic, Integrated Circuit, Digital-to-Analogue Conversion >> Analogue Signal)

AND GATE A logic gate which has an output of logic 1 only when all the inputs are at logic 1 – see Digital Logic.

ANTENNA is an arrangement of conductors or conducting materials designed for transmission or reception of electromagnetic waves. A radio wave will induce an e.m.f. in any conducting body (the Eiffel Tower, a bicycle or even ourselves), conversely any conductor carrying an alternating current will radiate energy. Needless to say, much greater efficiencies are obtained by purposeful design according to the range of frequencies at which the antenna is to operate. There is a multitude of different designs hence only a hint of the constructions in general use can be given:

(i) *Long wire* – these are used mainly for long and medium wavelength transmissions. The simplest is a length of wire running horizontally and suspended high up as sketched in Figure A3(i). The "Marconi" antenna however runs vertically and ideally such an antenna should be one-quarter wavelength high. Even at 3 MHz this needs 25 metres (hardly suitable for home use) so a shorter vertical length may be used "loaded" by a horizontal length at the top (i.e. a T or inverted L antenna). Generally directivity is only modest except when special layouts are used, e.g. when the wires are arranged on poles in the form of a rhombus as in (ii) of the figure.

(ii) *Rod* – this type is used for higher frequencies than for (i) where the wavelength is down to a more manageable size. Typical of these are the television u.h.f. antennas usually consisting of a dipole with directors and a reflector to enhance the pick-up (Yagi antenna). This is shown in (iii) of the figure. In (iv) is a sketch of a ferrite-rod antenna which is based on a rod small enough to be enclosed in a portable radio receiver. It is used for reception only.

(iii) *Loop* – antennas are highly directive and are used for direction finding. These consist of a coil of wire wound on a square or circular frame. Reception is greatest when the loop is turned end-on to the direction of the incoming wave, see (v).

(iv) *Dish* – a "dish" is in fact a parabolic antenna used with microwaves (above about 1 GHz). It has no signal e.m.f. induced in it but serves to focus the radio waves onto a "feed horn". This type is highly directional and is used in telephony systems and for the reception of t.v. by satellite. A sketch is shown in Figure A3(vi).

(v) *Horn* – again used for microwaves, especially for transmitting, see (vii) of the figure. The horn is actually an extension of a waveguide carrying the transmission and in a way funnels the wave into the atmosphere.

(vi) *Slot* – a slot or round hole of a size as determined by the wavelength and cut in a conducting surface acts as an antenna. For receiving the signal pick-up is small but many slots may be cut in a plate and connected together in such a way that the output is the sum from all the individual slots. A slot might be about half a wavelength long, i.e. at 10 GHz, some 15 mm (see viii).

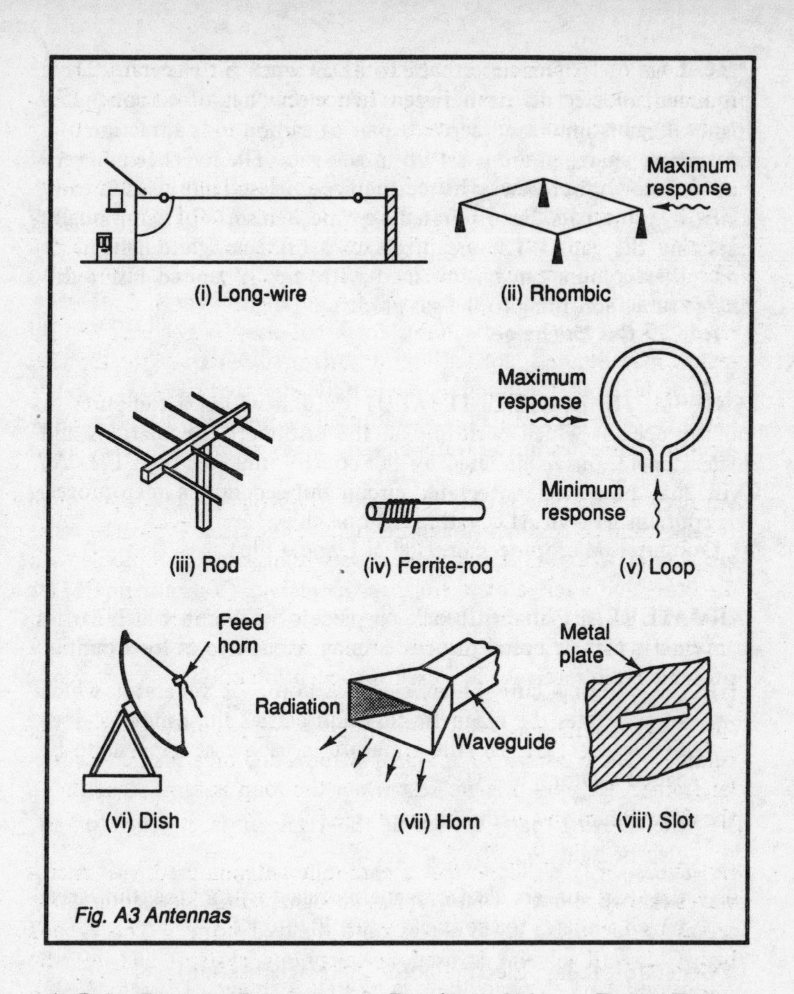

Fig. A3 Antennas

(* Polar Diagram, Isotropic . . . Dipole . . . Yagi . . . Ferrite-Rod . . . Artificial . . . Folded Dipole . . . Loop . . . Parabolic Antenna, Broadside Array, End-Fire Array >> Antenna, Electromagnetic Radiation, Electromagnetic Wave, Reciprocity Theorems, Waveguide, Antenna Gain)

APPLETON LAYER is one of the layers of ionized atmosphere (see the F layer in Fig.I13). It is named after E. V. Appleton, one of the scientists who first investigated the ionized layers. This layer is from some 150 kilometres high upwards, it is strongly ionized and the ionization persists throughout day and night – see Ionosphere.

ARC LAMP This dates back to 1809 when Sir Humphry Davy produced an electric arc between two electrodes of carbon. If a high voltage is impressed across a pair of carbon rods a fraction of a centimetre apart, an arc is set up in the gap. The rods become very hot and slowly burn away hence the type of arc lamp used in early cinema projectors incorporated a mechanism for continually adjusting the gap. The arc produces a brilliant white light in air and other colours can be obtained with arcs generated inside discharge tubes according to the gas used.
(* Arc >> Gas Discharge)

ARITHMETIC LOGIC UNIT (ALU) is a unit within a computer or microprocessor which performs all the arithmetic calculations and logical operations as directed by the control unit (see Fig.C17). An ALU may be a single integrated circuit but generally a microprocessor contains its own ALU within the one chip.
(* Computer, Microprocessor, Digital Logic, Chip)

ARMATURE is a shaped block or piece of soft iron which carries a magnetic flux. Several devices employ armatures as for example:

(i) the rotating core of an electric motor or generator which concentrates the magnetic flux and carries the windings – see Figures A2, E1, P8 (the armature in each case happens to be called a *rotor*);

(ii) the moving part to which the hammer is attached of an electric bell;

(iii) the part of an electromagnetic relay within the flux path which actuates the contacts – see Figure R6.

(* Generator, Relay, Electric Motor >> Magnetisation)

ARTIFICIAL ANTENNA is a network comprising resistance and reactance used to simulate the electrical characteristics of a real antenna but one which does not radiate energy. It is a testing device used mainly:

(i) on radio receivers in which case the artificial antenna is connected between the output of a signal generator (modulated r.f. oscillator) and the antenna terminals of the receiver. A simple one consists of a resistor and a capacitor only. Very low r.f. powers are involved (microwatts to milliwatts) accordingly the component sizes are small;

(ii) for testing radio transmitters the artificial antenna is connected to the transmitter output terminals in place of the actual antenna. Tests can then be made without energy being radiated and causing interference with other transmissions. In this case the artificial antenna network must be capable of dissipating the power which would normally be delivered to the antenna (one or two to many kilowatts).

(* Antenna, Radio Receiver, Transmitter >> Network)

ASCII stands for American Standard Code For Information Interchange – see this term.

ASPECT RATIO is the ratio between the width of a television picture and its height, commonly 4:3 but tending to change with the advent of high-definition television systems.
(* Television Receiver)

ASTABLE MULTIVIBRATOR A multivibrator which cannot latch in either of its two states – see Multivibrator.

ATTENUATION EQUALIZER An equalizer designed to provide compensation over a specified frequency range for the attenuation/frequency distortion of a particular system.
(* Equalization >> Attenuation, Attenuation/Frequency Distortion)

ATTENUATOR This is a piece of equipment designed to attenuate an electrical signal without introducing distortion. It can either be a single resistive network (fixed attenuator) or comprise a series of networks which are switchable (variable attenuator). A fixed attenuator is frequently called a *pad*. The attenuation or loss introduced is usually quoted in decibels and the design is normally such that the attenuator can be inserted into a circuit without upsetting the existing impedance matching or if necessary to match unequal impedances.

Attenuators exist in several forms, generally in L, T or π configurations, the T and π are shown in Figure A4(i). *Symmetrical* networks provide attenuation between equal impedances, *asymmetrical* networks are used when the impedances are not equal. When *balanced*, the series resistance is divided equally between the two through connections, conversely for the *unbalanced* attenuator the series resistance is in one through connection only. The *L-type attenuator* is the simplest and it is capable of matching two different

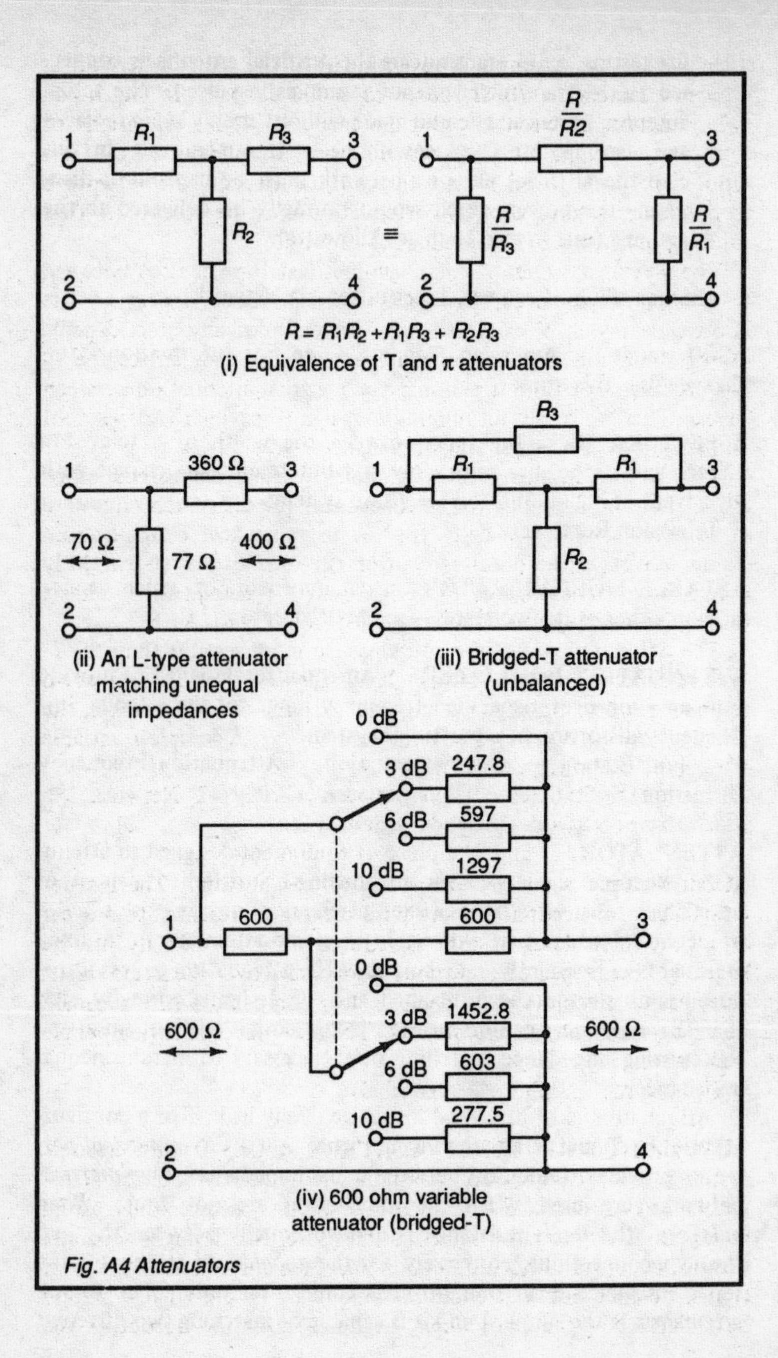

(i) Equivalence of T and π attenuators

(ii) An L-type attenuator matching unequal impedances

(iii) Bridged-T attenuator (unbalanced)

(iv) 600 ohm variable attenuator (bridged-T)

Fig. A4 Attenuators

impedances. An example is given in (ii) of the figure where an L-type pad matches a 70 Ω source to a 400 Ω load. In fact it can only function between unequal impedances. The attenuation for any given matching ratio is fixed and varies from some 2.5 dB for a ratio of 1:1.1 to 16 dB for a ratio of 1:10. Hence if the network is to provide matching, a certain attenuation must be accepted. That for the pad shown in (ii) has a loss of 13.2 dB.

The *T-type attenuator* in its symmetrical form is used between two equal impedances, hence its insertion does not upset the impedance match already existing. Asymmetrically it is capable of matching together two unequal impedances and, unlike the L-type, at the same time it can insert a specified attenuation between them. There is a certain minimum design loss which is dependent on the ratio of the terminating impedances.

The *π-type attenuator* has similar electrical characteristics to the T, but the formulae for calculation of the resistance values are more complicated, especially for the asymmetrical configuration. Design can therefore be directly from the formulae or alternatively it may be less complicated to design for a T-type and then convert to a π. How simple this is can be judged from Figure A4(i).

The *Bridged-T attenuator* contains one more resistor than the T-type as shown in Figure A4(iii). It has the advantage that only two resistors need to be changed in order to vary the attenuation, the bridging resistor R_3 and the shunt resistor R_2. A complete variable attenuator design is given in (iv).
(* Matching, Star-Delta Transformation, Bridged-T Network >> Attenuation, Network, Image Impedance)

AUDIOMETER is an instrument for testing hearing. The listener wears a pair of headphones and pure tones are presented to one ear at a time. The level of tone is reduced until it can only just be heard. This is repeated at various frequencies over the audio range. The results are plotted as decibels loss compared with "normal" hearing on a graph (an *audiogram*). The main use is in fitting people with hearing aids.
(* Hearing Aid, Earphone >> Decibel)

AUTOMATIC FREQUENCY CONTROL (a.f.c.) is an electronic system which automatically maintains the frequency of an oscillator within certain specified limits. A.F.C. circuits are especially useful in superheterodyne radio receivers to ensure that tuning is accurate. Control necessitates both detection and then correction of the error (the difference between what the frequency is and what it should be). Typically the error might be detected at the output of the system by a frequency discriminator which first expresses the frequency deviation as a phase shift, then transforms this to an amplitude variation so the greater the frequency error, the greater the direct voltage output. This voltage has a sign depending on the direction of the frequency drift and is fed back to the input end of the receiver for control of the local oscillator. This might be accomplished by applying the control voltage to a varactor, i.e. a semiconductor diode which changes its capacitance according to the bias voltage. The varactor is part of the capacitance element of the oscillator resonant circuit hence the oscillator frequency is altered in such a way as to minimize the frequency error.

In such systems, although the error may be reduced considerably, some residual error must remain, the better the system, the less the residual error.
(* Radio Receiver, Frequency Discriminator, Varactor >> Superheterodyne Reception, Resonance)

AUTOMATIC GAIN CONTROL (a.g.c.) is a method of maintaining a substantially constant audio frequency (a.f.) output from a radio receiver irrespective of the strength of the incoming signal and the setting of the gain (volume) control. It is also applied to t.v. receivers to avoid changes in picture contrast. Figure R2(iii) shows a basic method as applied to a superheterodyne receiver. The mixer and intermediate frequency (i.f.) amplifier gains are varied by application of a voltage to their input circuits such that the higher the voltage, the less the gain. The voltage is derived at the output of the demodulator and fed back. If the radio signal strength increases, the voltage on the a.g.c. line also tends to increase. As it does so however, it automatically reduces the amplifier gains, so reducing the demoulator output. Conversely if the radio signal strength is reduced, the amplifier gains increase, hence increasing the demodulator output to compensate. By this means the signal fed to the audio amplifier is kept reasonably constant.

Frequently a.g.c. is designed to operate only above a certain level of demodulator output, this ensures that the overall gain of the receiver is not reduced unless the normal demodulator output is exceeded. This is called *delayed a.g.c.* (the application of a.g.c. is delayed until the signal reaches a certain level).
(* Radio Receiver >> Superheterodyne Reception)

AUTOMATIC GRID BIAS is used with thermionic valves. Although generally transistors have taken over, the thermionic valve still has its part to play when very large output powers are required. The function of the automatic bias is to ensure that the valve operates

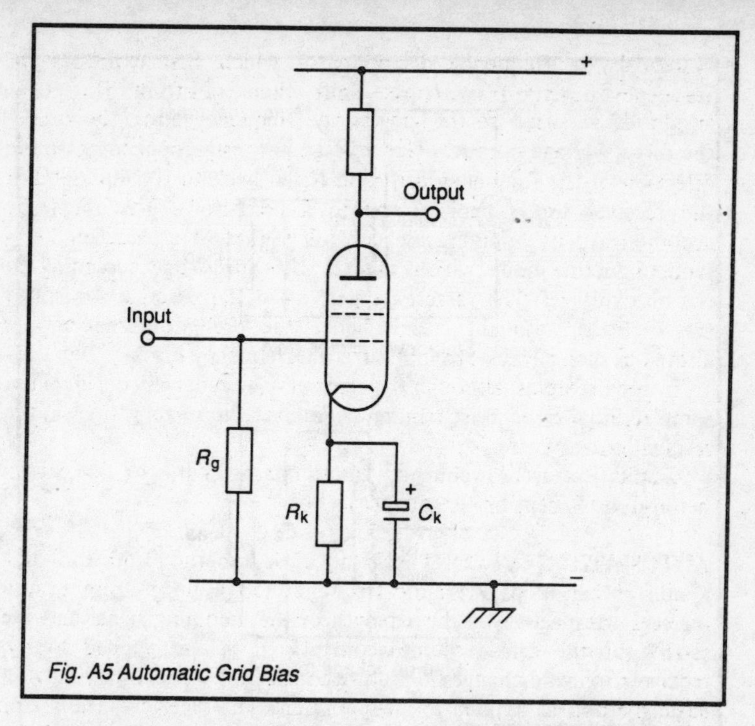

Fig. A5 Automatic Grid Bias

over the required portion of its input characteristic and it is "automatic" in the sense that it is derived from the flow of cathode current and no external bias supply is needed. In the circuit shown in Figure A5 the bias voltage is developed across the resistor R_k in the cathode circuit. Because the voltage drop across R_k makes the cathode positive relative to the negative line, then the grid is made negative relative to the cathode via resistor R_g. This has a high value (1 MΩ or so) to avoid shunting the input circuit. The d.c. bias applied must not fluctuate with the cathode current otherwise negative feedback arises so C_k is connected across R_k. C_k is of high value (several hundred microfarads). The value of R_k for a particular thermionic valve is determined by the cathode current commensurate with the grid bias required as shown by the input characteristic (grid voltage/anode current).
(* By-Pass Capacitor >> Thermionic Valve, Bias)

AUTOTRANSFORMER In most cases transformers have windings which are completely separate from each other. With these therefore the circuits connected to the primary and secondary windings can be arranged to have no direct metallic connection between them. Such *isolation* is useful for example in mains transformers where any

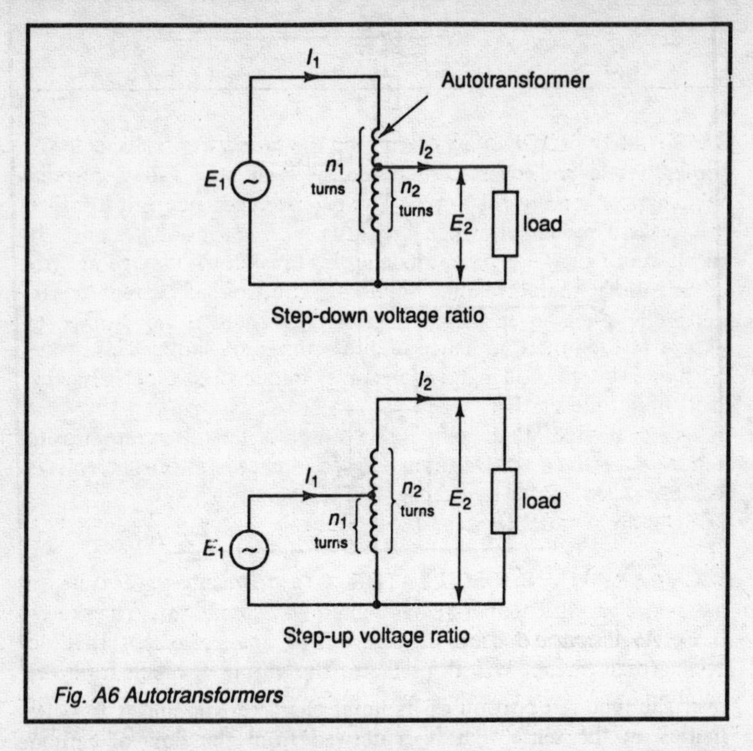

Fig. A6 Autotransformers

direct connection between the secondary circuit and the mains could be dangerous. Where isolation is not required an autotransformer can be used which is simply a single winding, tapped as required. Circuits are shown in Figure A6 and following normal transformer theory:

$$\frac{E_1}{E_2} = \frac{I_2}{I_1} = \frac{n_1}{n_2}$$

Any number of secondary tappings may be used and in fact variable ratio autotransformers are available in which a carbon brush is moved along the winding for the output voltage to be varied.
(>> Transformer)

B

BACKWARD DIODE is a variation on the *tunnel diode*, using lower doping levels and characterised by the peak and valley currents being approximately the same. The reverse resistance is lower than the forward resistance which contrasts with the normal diode. In fact it is not unlike a zener diode with a breakdown voltage of zero. In this diode therefore the "forward" direction of current occurs when the p-region is biased negatively. There is no storage of carriers at the junction, hence response times are short. This makes the diode suitable for high (microwave) frequencies, especially with small amplitude signals.

The backward diode also has a lower temperature coefficient compared with a conventional diode, hence its current/voltage characteristic shows little change with temperature.
(>> Doping, Tunnel Diode, Zener Diode)

BACKWARD-WAVE OSCILLATOR is a travelling-wave tube (a microwave amplifier) operated as a microwave oscillator. The sketch of a travelling-wave tube of Figure T16 applies except that no attenuator is fitted. As an oscillator the output is taken from the coupling at the electron gun end of the slow-wave structure. The correct technical explanation is that there is interaction between the electron stream and the radio frequency wave whose phase and group velocities are 180° apart, however we can look upon it more simply from the point of view that the axial direction of the wave is opposite to that of the electron beam. The interaction produces radio frequency waves travelling in the backward direction compared with the normal travelling-wave tube which amplifies in the forward direction. In fact the oscillator can be made to act as an amplifier with the input coupled to the end of the slow-wave structure adjacent to the collector.
(* Travelling-Wave Tube >> Electromagnetic Wave, Phase Velocity, Group Velocity)

BAFFLE – usually a rigid board with a central hole over which a moving-coil loudspeaker is mounted. The board is of such size that low frequency sound waves radiated from the rear of the loudspeaker travel around it to meet the waves generated from the front of the loudspeaker in phase. By this technique the low frequency response of the loudspeaker is enhanced – see Loudspeaker.

BALANCED CIRCUIT normally implies *electrically* balanced. We encounter balancing in several different ways but always with the intention of reducing or eliminating an undesired quantity such as current or voltage.

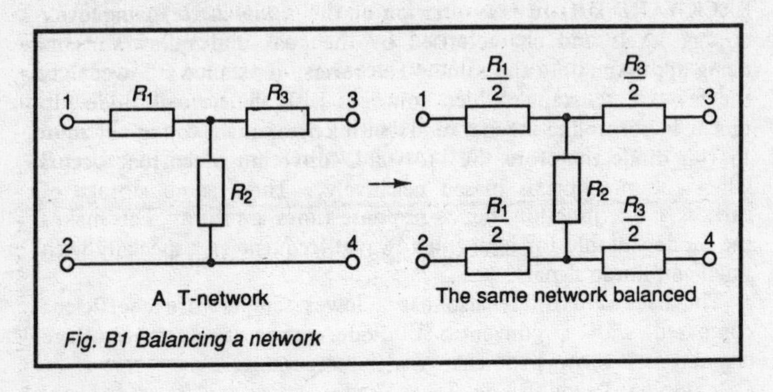

Fig. B1 Balancing a network

(1) In the case of attenuators, filters and the like, balancing means the connection of equal component values in the through wires as illustrated typically in Figure B1 in which a symmetrical T network is balanced as shown. Any interference voltages induced in the 1-3 wire are balanced out by similar voltages induced in the 2-4 wire since they act in opposition in the terminations.

(2) Whole circuits may be balanced with reference to some common point, an example is given by the ring modulator of Figure R9(i) where the input and output circuits are balanced with reference to the centre-taps of T_1 and T_2 to avoid the carrier voltage reaching the output. Another example is given by the push-pull amplifier as shown in Figure P13. Unless the circuits of T_1 and T_2 are balanced with respect to the chassis line, "out-of-balance" currents flow in the load with consequent distortion.

(3) Underground transmission lines may be balanced by the addition of resistance or capacitance (usually the latter) so that the characteristics of the two wires are equal and they are electrically symmetrical with respect to earth. Such lines are also known as *balanced-wire circuits.* If interference currents affecting both wires equally are picked up on the way, then they can be arranged to cancel in the line terminations.

(4) Three-phase electricity supply circuits are balanced as far as possible so that little or no current flows in the neutral.

(* Ring Modulator, Push-Pull Operation, Polyphase System, Balun >> Network, Transmission Line)

BALANCED MODULATOR For suppressed-carrier amplitude-modulated systems, normal modulation techniques followed by a filter to suppress the carrier are difficult to design because the carrier only differs from the sidebands by the lowest modulating frequency, hence a very sharp cut-off filter is necessary. The problem is more easily solved by balancing out the carrier in the modulator first. The basic features of a circuit are given in Figure B2.

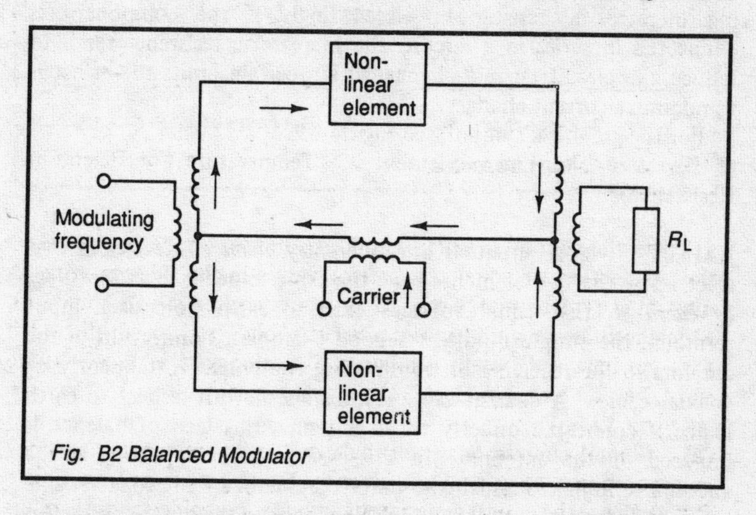

Fig. B2 Balanced Modulator

The arrows show the direction of the carrier currents at some instant and it is evident that as far as the load, R_L is concerned, they cancel. This assumes of course that the upper and lower halves of the circuit are balanced electrically. On the other hand the modulating frequency is transmitted to R_L when the non-linear elements (usually diodes or transistors) have low impedance. The carrier voltage is sufficient to switch the elements "on" and "off" thereby chopping the modulating frequency at the carrier frequency. It can be shown by Fourier analysis that this results in an output consisting of the modulating frequency together with the lower and upper sidebands plus harmonics but no carrier.

This is the simple balanced arrangement, more complicated ones are used, including the *double-balanced* or *ring* modulators in which the modulating frequency is also suppressed. Double sideband operation is then converted to single-sideband by means of a band-pass filter.

(* Ring Modulator, Single-Sideband Transmission >> Modulation, Filter, Fourier Analysis)

BALANCING TRANSFORMER – see Balun.

BALLAST RESISTOR is a device used to regulate current in a circuit. It is a resistor manufactured from a wire or a material, each chosen for its high positive temperature coefficient of resistance. As the current through the resistor increases so its temperature rises because of the power dissipated. There is therefore an accompanying increase in resistance. Accordingly if the component is connected in series in a circuit, the increase in resistance tends to reduce the circuit current, hence within certain limits the effect is to minimize current changes.

For the graphical symbol, see Figure N2.
(* Barretter, Non-Linear Element >> Temperature Coefficient of Resistance)

BALUN Most antennas are inherently *balanced* devices in that electrically the two elements have the same impedance *with respect to earth* so that equal voltages exist to earth from each input terminal, the simple dipole is a good example. Connection of the antenna to the receiving or transmitting equipment is frequently by coaxial cable. A coaxial cable is *unbalanced* with respect to earth hence if connected directly to an antenna, this lack of balance is imposed on the antenna. In this case, voltages appearing at the antenna terminal to which the outer conductor of the coaxial cable is connected create currents which flow back in the outer conductor. Skin effect ensures that these currents remain on the outside of the outer conductor and hence they give rise to unwanted radiation. Generally with receiving antennas such as for television, this is of little concern but for transmitting systems where powers are much greater the result may be that the radiation pattern is modified and depending on the phase relationship between the wanted and unwanted radiations there may be a power loss.

The cure is to provide the antenna with a balanced feed with respect to earth by inserting a device which converts the unbalanced output of a coaxial cable to the balanced conditions required by the antenna. The device is known as a *balun*, an acronym for *bal*anced to *un*balanced transformer.

A balun may take one of several forms. The simplest is perhaps one using a short-circuited quarter-wave ($\lambda/4$) section of transmission line attached to the coaxial cable as sketched in Figure B3. Such a section theoretically has an infinite impedance at the

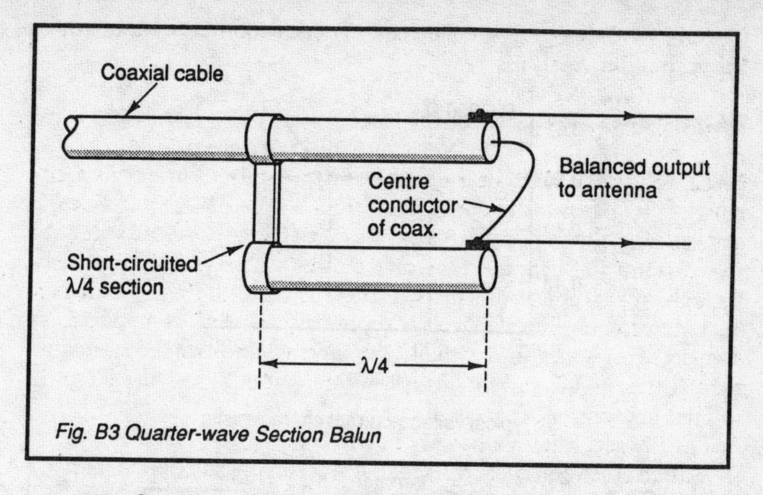

Fig. B3 Quarter-wave Section Balun

operating frequency. The balanced output is therefore decoupled from the coaxial cable outer conductor by a very high impedance, hence parasitic currents on this conductor are minimized.

Modifications to this simple arrangement are possible, for example a λ/4 coaxial sleeve may be used instead. Other designs also allow for some impedance step-up. Even choke coils may be used.

(* Antenna, Quarter-Wave Line, Dipole Antenna, Coaxial Cable, Balanced Circuit, Skin Effect, Choke >> Phase)

BARRETTER is a current stabilizer in the form of a lamp with a special filament having a high positive temperature coefficient of resistance (e.g. pure iron). The glass envelope is usually filled with a gas such as hydrogen to prevent oxidation of the wire. Compared with a ballast resistor, its operation in stabilizing the current in a circuit is similar but the working current is generally lower.

An illustration in round figures of the effect of a barretter in stabilizing the current in a circuit is given in Figure B4. At (i) is shown a typical voltage-current characteristic from which we will assume that the current is 0.5 A over the range 100 to 150 V. At (ii) is shown a circuit in which the load resistance, R_L = 200 Ω. Next suppose that R_L is halved to 100 Ω. Normally the current would rise but to compensate, the barretter resistance increases as shown in (iii) and the current remains almost the same. The word "almost" is used because there must be a slight rise in the current otherwise the barretter resistance would not increase.

Barretters were much used in earlier telephone systems, mainly in an attempt to regulate the current fed out from the exchange

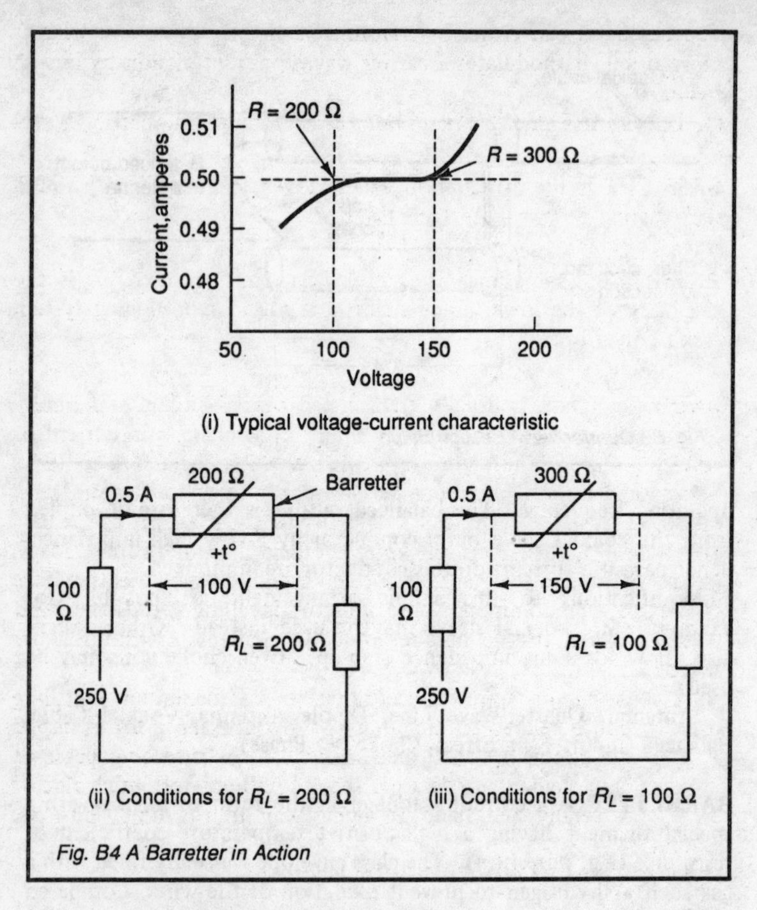

Fig. B4 A Barretter in Action

to each telephone set, irrespective of the resistance of the line. They are now superseded for many applications by semiconductors. (* Non-Linear Element >> Temperature Coefficient of Resistance)

BARRIER-LAYER PHOTOCELL A type involving a metal-semiconductor junction, producing an electromotive force when light falls on the cell.
(>> Schottky Diode, Schottky Barrier)

BASEBAND In the transmission of information (speech, music, t.v., data) over a channel, the baseband is the range of frequencies initially generated, e.g. for music it is the range appearing at the output of a microphone or for t.v. it is the output of the camera.

The baseband can either be transmitted directly by line or what is more usual, it modulates a carrier wave for transmission by line or radio.
(* Television Camera, Microphone >> Modulation, Carrier Wave)

BASS CUT is the attenuation of the lower frequencies in a sound reproducing system – see Tone Control.

BASS LIFT (sometimes the term *bass boost* is used) – is the emphasis of the lower frequencies in a sound reproducing system – see Tone Control.

BAUD Data is usually transmitted over a circuit in a binary format (on paper symbolized by 0 and 1) as changes in current or voltage. One of the earliest systems by which characters could be represented in this form was developed for telegraph transmission (although what we now call 1 and 0 was then known as "mark" and "space"). This was known as the *Baudot code* (after J. M. E. Baudot, a French telegraph engineer). Baudot's name was therefore chosen for the commonly used unit of signalling *speed*, the *baud* which is equal to the number of code elements transmitted per second.

A data circuit is rated according to its maximum signalling speed which is related to the circuit bandwidth hence for example, a 200 baud circuit has sufficient bandwidth for it to be capable of carrying 200 elements or *bits* per second without too much risk of error. Generally the baud is giving way to the unit "bits per second".
(* Binary, Binary Code, Bit >> Bandwidth)

BEAT FREQUENCY OSCILLATOR is an oscillator comprising two radio frequency oscillators, one at a fixed frequency, the other variable. Their outputs are added (heterodyned) to produce a beat frequency.
(>> Beat Frequency, Heterodyne)

BEATING is the addition of two sinusoidal waves so that a periodic signal arises through interference of one wave on the other. The periodic signal generated is known as the *beat frequency* which is equal to the difference between the frequencies of the original waves. The amplitude of the beat frequency is equal to the sum of the original amplitudes.
(>> Beat Frequency, Heterodyne)

BIDIRECTIONAL TRANSISTOR is a bipolar transistor which can have the connections to emitter and collector electrodes interchanged with little or no effect on the operation. For the bulk of bipolar transistors the emitter and collector are of different sizes and doping so the device can only be used in one direction. Conversely a bidirectional transistor has its emitter and collector of similar construction.
(>> Transistor, Doping)

BIFILAR WINDING is a winding which consists of two insulated wires wound together in close proximity on a former as shown in Figure B5. By this method the current in the two adjacent wires is the same and in opposite directions, hence the magnetic fields cancel. Ordinary wire-wound resistors normally have some inductance when the wire is in the form of a coil, however if a bifilar winding is used, the inductive effects are minimized.
(>> Magnetic Field, Inductance)

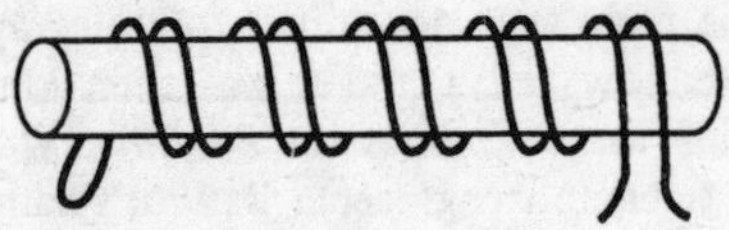

Fig. B5 A Bifilar Winding

BIMETALLIC STRIP is a device constructed from two thin lengths of metal such as iron and brass rivetted together. The two metals have different coefficients of thermal expansion. When the strip is cold both metals are the same length but as temperature rises one lengthens more than the other (the brass in this example) so causing the rivetted pair to bend into an arc – see Figure B6. If one end of the combination is fixed, the other free end can be made to operate contacts (this is how most thermostats are constructed) or, for example, to move a pointer over a scale.

Another application is in the *thermal overcurrent trip*. Current to a motor passes through a heating coil wrapped round a bimetallic strip. On heavy overload the increased current heats the strip sufficiently for it to bend and disconnect the supply.

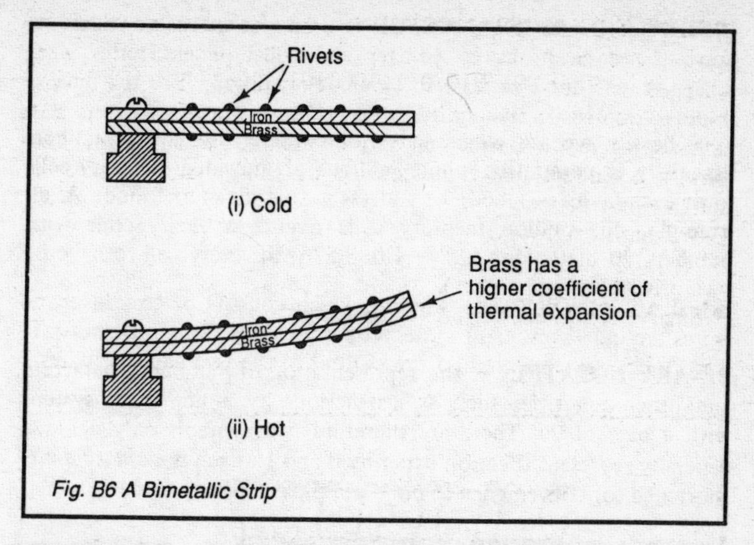

Fig. B6 A Bimetallic Strip

BINARY means "of two" just as *denary* or *decimal* means "of ten". In electronics the two binary states are usually denoted by the numbers 0 and 1, lifted from the decimal system. Generally 0 is indicated by no (or very little) voltage, 1 by some voltage, usually about 5 V for computers but varying according to the system. For electronic systems the near certainty of being able to decide between two states only (voltage or no voltage, pulse or no pulse, etc.) makes binary essential for most digital work.

A binary number therefore consists of a string of 0's and 1's and it has a decimal equivalent. As an example the binary number 100110 has a decimal equivalent of 38 made up as follows:

$$(1 \times 2^5) + (0 \times 2^4) + (0 \times 2^3) + (1 \times 2^2) + (1 \times 2^1) + (0 \times 2^0)$$
$$32 + 0 + 0 + 4 + 2 + 0$$

(note that $2^0 = 1$ and $2^1 = 2$), just as 38 is made up from $(3 \times 10^2) + (8 \times 10^1)$.

BINARY CODE is a system of binary numbers used to represent information, e.g. in computers binary codes represent characters and instructions, in digital transmission systems they represent analogue waveforms. Each character (or digit) in the binary code can have only one of two possible values, labelled 0 and 1.

The number of different combinations available from a binary coding system in which each binary number consists of n binary digits (0 or 1) is 2^n, for example if each number comprises 3 digits, there are $2^3 = 8$ possible combinations:

000, 001, 010, 011, 100, 101, 110, 111 .

Generally we are concerned with considerably larger numbers especially in computing where millions of individual memory cells must each be given a code or address so that it can be found. As an example, one million memory cells require a binary code with numbers 20 digits long (2^{20} = 1,048,576) for every cell to have its own private binary number).
(* Binary, Computer, Digital Transmission)

BINARY NOTATION is the representation of numbers, characters and other quantities such as instructions by a numerical system with a base of 2. There are therefore two symbols only and we generally represent them on paper by 0 and 1. Each is a *binary digit*, shortened for convenience to *bit* – see Binary, Binary Code.

BISTABLE MULTIVIBRATOR A multivibrator which has two latching states – see Multivibrator.

BIT (1) data is usually transmitted in binary, the elementary signal employed is known as a *binary digit* or *bit* for short.
See Binary, Binary Code, Binary Notation.

(2) a *bit* is also the smallest quantity of information which can be transmitted. It has the form of yes or no only and therefore has some parallel with the binary digit.
(>> Information Theory)

BLACK BOX This is an ingenious technique used to analyse an electronic system in terms of what is delivered from the system for a given input. The box is supposedly black so that we cannot see inside it but by measurements made of both voltage and current on the input and output terminals, an *equivalent circuit* of what is inside and its electrical performance can be determined. Figure H3 illustrates this and also shows the equivalent circuit of a bipolar transistor in the box. Complete analysis of the transistor characteristics is achieved through measurements on the four terminals.
(* Equivalent Circuit, Hybrid Parameters)

BLANKING is the term used when the grid potential of an electron gun is made sufficiently negative with respect to the cathode for the electron beam to be cut off – see Electron Gun.

BLOCKING CAPACITOR This is a capacitor used to block d.c. in one part of a circuit from affecting another part. This is possible because the reactance of a capacitor at zero hertz (d.c.) is infinite but lower at higher frequencies. Capacitors C_1 and C_2 in Figure D2 provide an example, C_1 blocks direct current from the previous stage from flowing into the base circuit of the transistor. In the same way C_2 blocks d.c. from the collector circuit of the transistor so that it cannot affect anything connected to the output terminal. Alternating currents pass through C_1 and C_2 which must both be of sufficiently high capacitance so as not to present a high reactance at the lowest frequency passing.
(>> Capacitance, Capacitive Reactance)

BLOCKING OSCILLATOR This is a particular type of *relaxation oscillator*, i.e. one which has a large amount of positive feedback coupled via a time constant circuit, such as a capacitance and resistance in parallel. In one type, as soon as oscillation commences, the active device (usually a transistor) is cut off by a charge built up on the capacitor. The circuit then relaxes until the capacitor has discharged sufficiently through the resistance and oscillation is again possible.

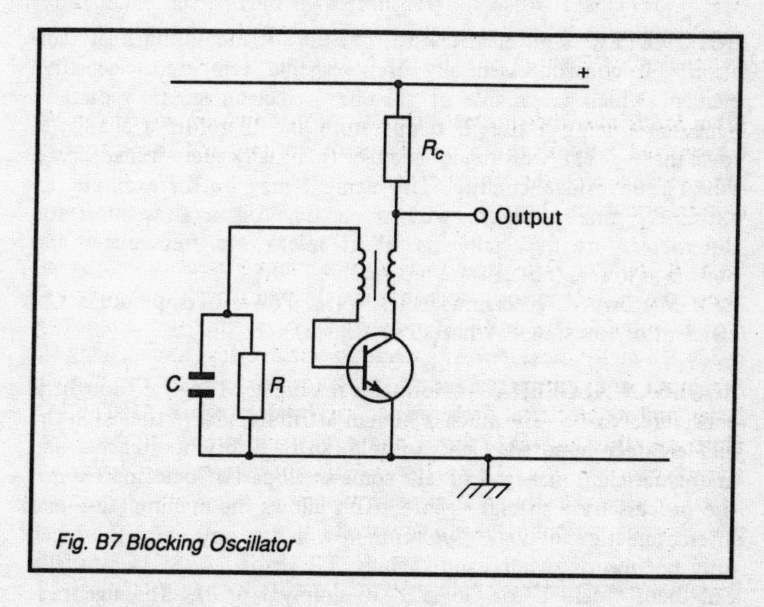

Fig. B7 Blocking Oscillator

The elements of such a blocking oscillator are shown in Figure B7. The transformer provides positive feedback and the circuit bursts into oscillation. Capacitor C charges negatively from the base current and eventually cuts off the transistor. C discharges through R until the oscillations recommence when again C becomes charged. The cycle therefore repeats continuously. Each time the transistor is turned "on", collector current flows through R_c and the potential at the output terminal falls negatively. In this circuit the pulse repetition frequency is controlled mainly by the time constant CR but also by the coupling between the windings of the transformer.

Such a circuit is, in fact, a pulse generator and it is also used in television receivers to generate scanning waveforms.

(* Relaxation Oscillator, Scanning, Television Receiver >> Time Constant, Pulse)

BODE DIAGRAM This provides a convenient method of analysis of simple negative feedback systems. The diagram consists basically of a plot of the gain and phase angle of the system against frequency. From the diagram the Bode technique enables stability to be estimated. Bode's theorem is a direct extension of the Nyquist criterion and is based on the relationship between phase angle and rate of change of gain.

(* Nyquist Diagram >> Complex Notation, Feedback)

BOLOMETER is an electrical instrument for measuring heat radiation. It consists essentially of a resistive, temperature-sensitive element which is capable of absorbing electromagnetic radiation, hence producing a rise in temperature and therefore a change in resistance. The resistance change is usually determined by a Wheatstone bridge circuit. The element may be for example, an extremely fine platinum wire or a film on a glass substrate. Bolometers are especially useful at microwave frequencies and powers as low as 0.01 μW are measurable.

(>> Microwave, Electromagnetic Wave, Power, Temperature Coefficient of Resistance, Wheatstone Bridge)

BOOLEAN ALGEBRA Normally reasoning or logical thought is considered to be very much a human attribute. Nevertheless in the mid eighteen-hundreds George Boole (an English schoolteacher and mathematician) managed to take some small part of logic and express the process by a special algebra. This allows the manipulation and interconnection of logic *functions* in which at any point there can only be one of two possible values, TRUE or FALSE (we usually call them "logic 1" or "logic 0" or simply 1 or 0). The algebra is useful in the design of binary switching circuits for complex networks as are used in computers, usually with the aim of reducing

circuitry to a minimum when providing a certain function. A *truth table* is used to illustrate the final outcome.
(* Binary, Logic, Digital Logic, Logic Gate)

BOOTSTRAPPING An intriguing name for a technique used mainly in amplifier stages in which positive feedback is applied to cause an earlier point in the circuit to be "raised as if by its own bootstraps". The technique may be used to increase the input impedance of a stage or stages usually by reducing the effect of base biasing resistors shunting the signal path. Boostrapping methods are employed in many different types of circuit, however the principle can be understood by consideration of the simple bootstrapped amplifier shown in Figure B8.

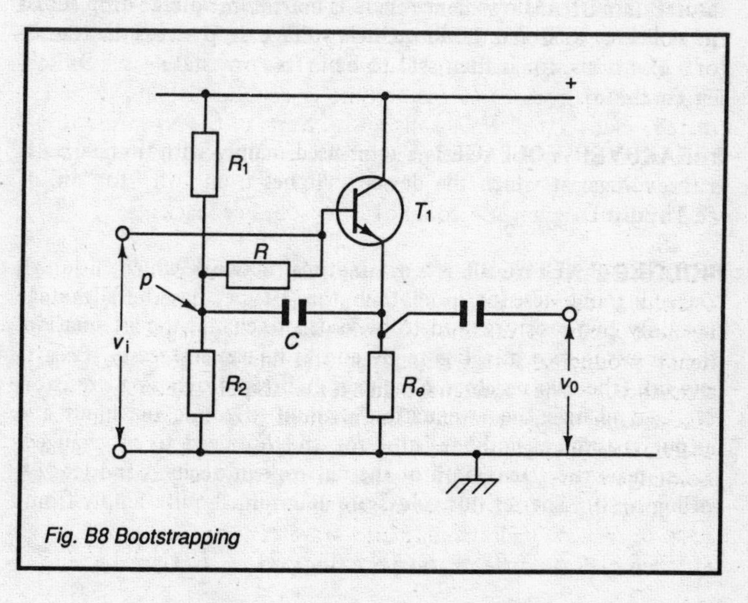

Fig. B8 Bootstrapping

T_1 is connected as an emitter-follower. The base is biased by R_1, R_2 in conjunction with the series resistor, R. Consider an input signal, v_i. Because the emitter-follower has approximately unity voltage gain, then the output voltage, v_o developed across R_e is the same as v_i. Consider next the feedback path via capacitor C to point p and let C present a low reactance over the frequency range for which the circuit is required. The signal at p is approximately equal in magnitude and phase to v_o, hence to v_i. This therefore makes the signal potentials at both ends of R almost the same. Only a minute signal current can therefore flow through R, hence there is minimum signal loss through the biasing chain. In other words, R represents a very high resistance, typically running into 100 or so megohms. Figure B8 shows a bipolar transistor but similar conditions apply when a field-effect transistor is used.

Bootstrapping is also employed in sawtooth generators to improve the linearity and in digital logic circuits to increase the voltage change between logic 1 and logic 0.
(* Emitter-Follower, Sawtooth Waveform, Digital Logic >> Amplifier, Feedback)

BOTTOMING occurs in an active device such as a transistor when the current under the particular operating conditions reaches saturation level. For example, when a switching transistor is "bottomed", saturation current flows hence there is maximum voltage drop across the collector load and therefore little voltage drop across the transistor. The transistor is then said to be in its "on" state – see Switching Transistor.

BREAKOVER VOLTAGE is a term used mainly with thyristors. It is the voltage at which the device switches from "off" to "on" – see Thyristor.

BRIDGED-T NETWORK is a symmetrical network which, although containing one resistor more than the T-type, has the advantage that only two resistors need to be varied to change the attenuation. The circuit is shown in Figure B9 and as its name suggests, it is a T-network (the two resistors, R_1 plus R_2), bridged by a single resistor, R_3. To change the attenuation without affecting the input and output resistances, only resistors R_2 and R_3 need to be changed.

Let α be the attenuation of the network in decibels and let $N = \text{antilog } \alpha/20$. The resistor values are determined quite simply from:

$$R_1 = R_0, \quad R_2 = R_0/(N-1), \quad R_3 = R_0(N-1).$$

For a given network therefore the resistors R_1 are unchanged whatever the attenuation, hence a practical variable attenuator of this type with n different attenuations needs a single 2-pole, n-way switch only as shown in (ii) of the figure.
(* Attenuator >> Network, Decibel)

BRIDGE RECTIFIER A special arrangement of rectifiers connected in a bridge format. The circuit provides full-wave rectification.
(>> Rectification)

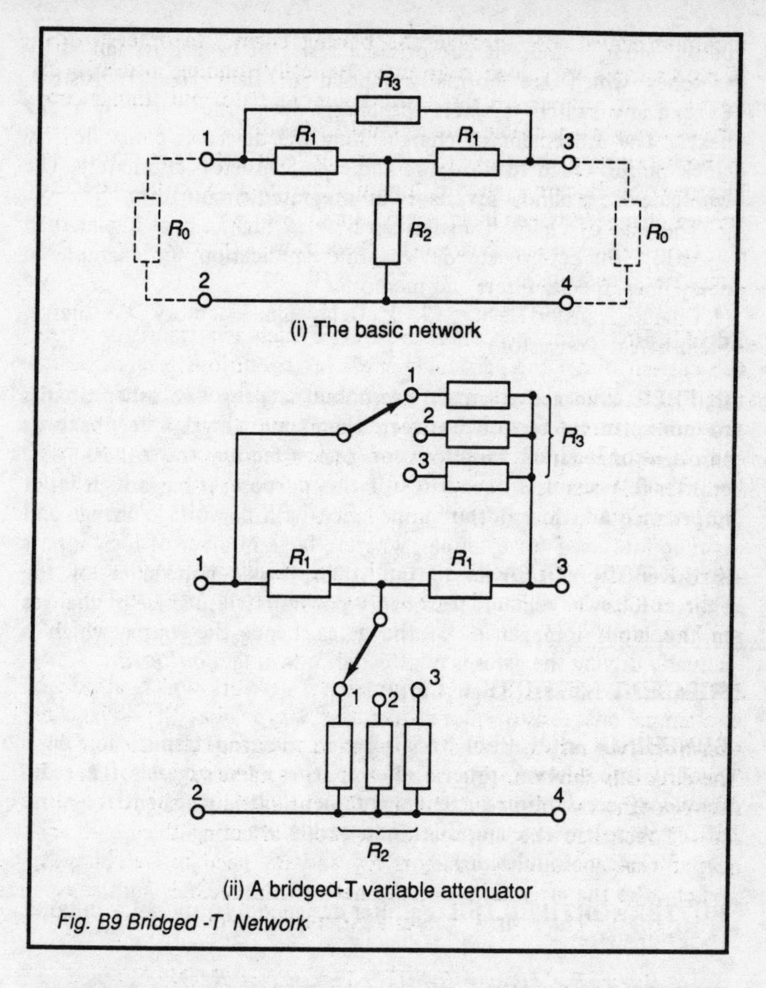

Fig. B9 Bridged -T Network

BROADSIDE ARRAY consists of a number of antennas spaced equally along a straight line and all excited in the same phase. The array has enhanced directional characteristics compared with a single antenna in that there is a concentration of radiation in a plane at right angles to the line and a tendency to cancel radiation in other directions.

See also End-Fire Array.
(* Antenna >> Antenna, Phase, Phase Angle)

BUCKET-BRIGADE DEVICE (BBD) is aptly named for it is basically a charge transfer device in which discrete packets of charge are passed along a line. It comprises a series of capacitors linked by switches which are normally bipolar or field-effect transistors. Closing any switch transfers the charge from one capacitor to the next. The movement of charge along the device is controlled by clock pulses which turn on odd and even transistors alternately. The whole device is almost invariably in integrated circuit form.

The rate of charge transfer can be very high, e.g. at higher than 1 MHz. Bucket-brigade devices find application for example in delay lines, special filters and memories.
(* Charge Transfer Device, Clock, Delay Line, Memory >> Charge, Field-Effect Transistor)

BUFFER is an active circuit interposed between two other circuits to minimize interaction between them, e.g. through feedback or through impedance variations of one affecting the other. The emitter-follower is a favourite for this purpose, it has a high input impedance and low output impedance with no voltage change and is therefore used for example, where a large number of logic inputs is driven from a single output. The input impedance of the emitter-follower remains reasonably constant irrespective of changes in the input impedances of the gates, hence the source which is actually driving the gates is unaffected, it is in fact *buffered.*
(* Emitter-Follower, Logic Gate)

BUNCHING arises from variations in electron transit time in a velocity modulation process due to the introduction of a radio frequency conduction current component. It is an essential feature of certain microwave amplifiers and oscillators.
(>> Velocity Modulation)

BUTTERWORTH FILTER is a filter designed by a special technique.
(>> Filter)

BY-PASS CAPACITOR is a capacitor which is connected in parallel with other components in a circuit so as to provide a low reactance path to signals within a certain frequency range. By-pass capacitors are found in many amplifier circuits, e.g. the capacitor C_k in Figure A5. Here C_k by-passes most of the signal which would otherwise flow through R_k. It must therefore have a low reactance at the lowest frequency to be by-passed, e.g. a reactance of some one-tenth of the value of R_k.
(* Automatic Grid Bias >> Reactance)

BYTE is a group of consecutive binary digits (usually 8) treated as a processing unit in data processing and computers – see Figure M7(i).

There are 2^8 different combinations available using an 8-bit (one byte) unit.

Memories are classified according to the number of bytes they hold, generally expressed in *kilobytes* (e.g. 512 K means 512 kilobytes) where 1 kilobyte = 2^{10} = 1024 bytes. The *megabyte* is also used, i.e. 2^{20} = 1,048,576 bytes or 1024 kilobytes. In a computer one byte represents a letter, numeral, punctuation mark, other symbol or an instruction.

(* Binary, Binary Code, Computer, Word, Memory)

C

CAMERA TUBE is a device which from its early beginnings has been subject to continuous development. It is the essential component of a television camera which looks at the scene to be televised and produces video signals commensurate with what it sees. A scanning process is obviously involved. The two main types of camera tube are the *image orthicon* based on photoemission as the light/video signal transducer and the *vidicon*, based on photoconductivity. A camera tube has three essential components, illustrated in Figure C1(i) for the image orthicon:

(i) the *image section* in which at any instant details of the scene are transcribed on a *target* which develops an electric charge image of the scene. The light which is first focused onto a photocathode causes electrons to be emitted according to the light intensity. These emitted electrons are directed onto the target which consists of a thin glass sheet with a fine wire mesh on the photocathode side. This causes secondary electrons to be emitted from the target so leaving a positive charge pattern on it. The secondary electrons are removed from the wire mesh through a connection to the power supply.

(ii) the *scanning section* in which a low velocity electron beam repetitively scans the back of the target. On hitting the target, electrons in the beam are taken up in neutralizing the positive areas, hence the beam is modulated by the picture information as it scans the target. The target charge is therefore automatically erased by the beam. The modulated beam is reflected by the target and is guided back by a selective electrode system (not shown in the figure).

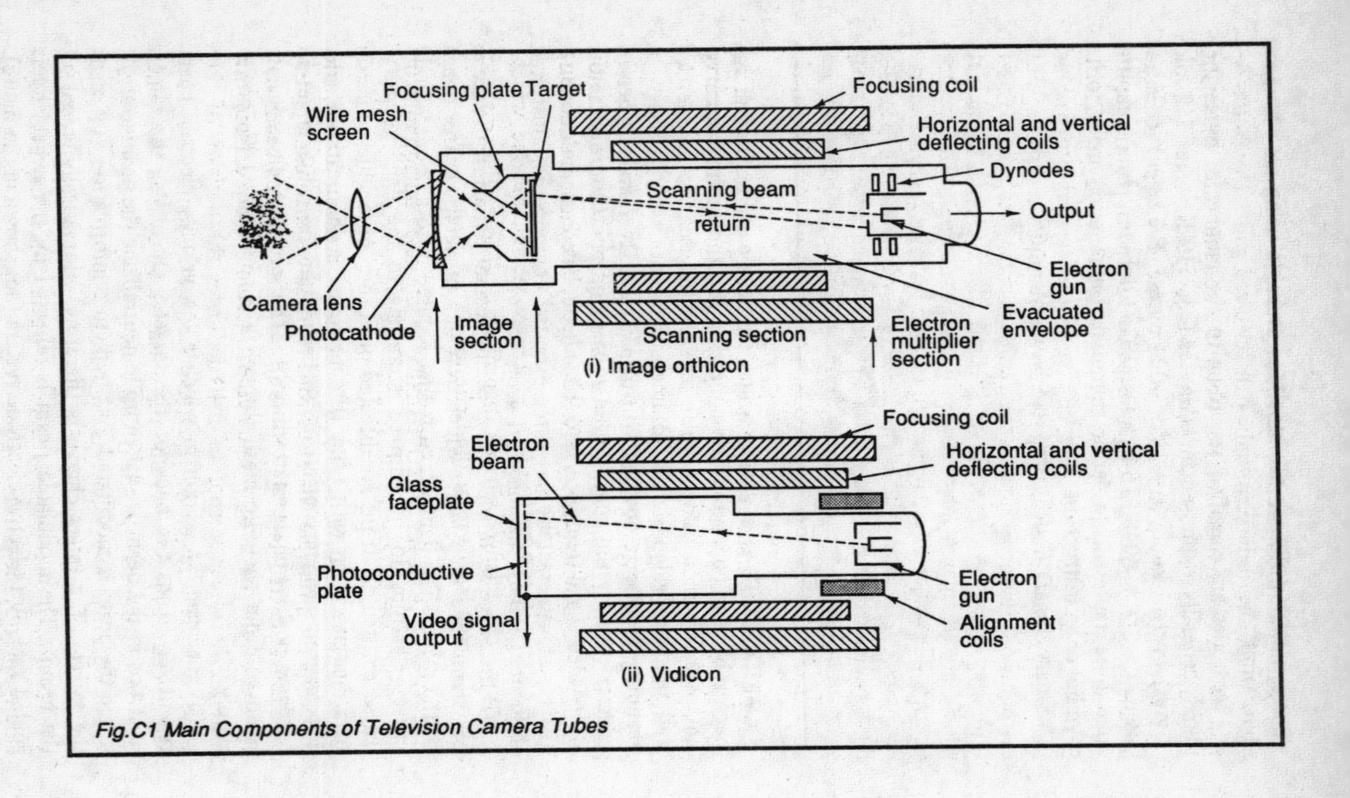

Fig.C1 Main Components of Television Camera Tubes

(iii) the *multiplier section* which receives the returned electron beam on an electrode surrounding the electron gun. This electrode acts as the first dynode of the electron multiplier with a gain of 1000 or more and an output of several microamperes.

The vidicon camera tube is generally less bulky than the image orthicon, differing mainly in the image section and in that no return electron beam is required. A sketch is shown in Figure C1(ii). Because of its smaller size, the vidicon may be favoured for colour television where three or four tubes are required together. For the photoconductor, antimony trisulphide is extensively used. Light from the image of the scene is focused directly onto the target which is a transparent plate coated with the material. This creates electron-hole pairs so changing the conductivity through the target thickness, the resistance of each elemental area therefore depending on the incident light. As the target is scanned by the electron beam therefore, current flow is a function of the resistance of the target at that particular point. The video signal output is taken directly from the photoconductive layer.

Many other arrangements of camera tube are in use, depending on the application, for example, television, industrial, security, research.

See also Iconoscope.

(* Television, Television Camera, Video Signal, Electron Gun, Scanning, Electron Multiplier, Thermal Imaging >> Charge, Photoemission, Photoconductivity, Photocathode, Secondary Emission)

CAPACITOR MICROPHONE A type of microphone which functions by changes in its capacitance – see Electrostatic Microphone under the term Microphone.

CARBON-GRANULE MICROPHONE A type of microphone in which sound waves vary the resistance – see Microphone.

CATHODE-RAY TUBE (c.r.t.) This is an electron tube which works on the principle that electrons released by thermionic emission from a heated cathode can be formed into a pencil beam and directed at the back of a luminescent screen. Viewed from the front of the screen a spot of light indicates the position of the beam. Electric or magnetic fields generated by the applied signal are used to deflect the beam so that the screen shows a visible representation of the signal. On this system cathode-ray tubes as used in oscilloscopes and television sets are based. Two different types of c.r.t. are shown in Figure C2. Details of the electron gun are given in Figure E6. This generates the electron beam which moves at high velocity towards the screen.

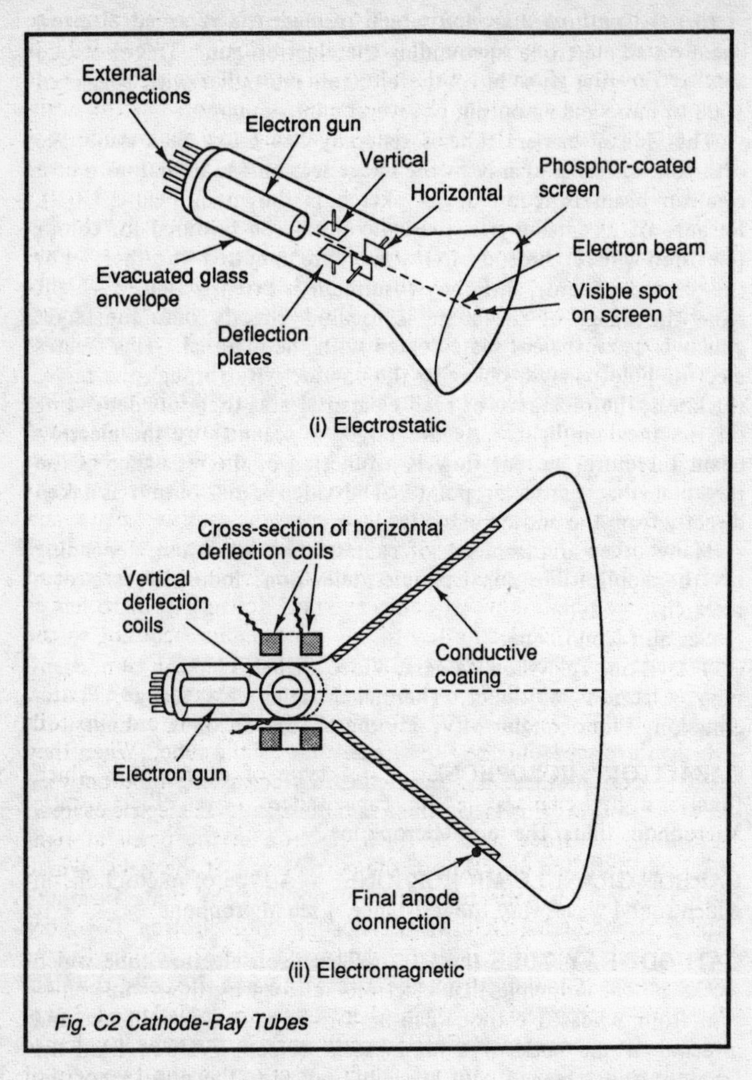

Fig. C2 Cathode-Ray Tubes

The indication of the position of the electron beam on the screen at any instant is through *luminescence*, meaning that it has the ability to emit light without getting hot. This is accomplished by coating the screen inside with certain phosphors which are materials capable of emitting light when electrons strike with high energy. Various colours are obtainable including red, blue, green, yellow-green, orange and white. The brightness of the display depends on the energy of the electron beam when it arrives. This is dependent on the strength of the electric field through which the electrons are accelerated and the square of their final velocity. When light is emitted by the phosphor, this is known as *fluorescence* which is at a constant level while the electron beam is present. As the beam moves on however, the light decays, during the decay time it is known as *phosphorescence.* The decay time is known as the *persistence.*

Because the electron beam strikes the screen at very high velocity, secondary electrons may be released hence giving rise to the accumulation of an electric charge. This opposes the beam and effectively decreases the accelerating voltage. The effect is called *sticking* and is reduced by coating the screen on the inside with a very thin layer of aluminium, connected to the final anode.

Electrostatic Deflection – in (i) of the figure a tube containing two sets of deflection plates is shown. If a potential is applied across one set of plates there will be an electric field between them and the negatively charged electrons in the beam on their way through will be attracted towards the positive plate and repelled from the negative plate. The electron beam is therefore deflected from its straight path towards the centre of the screen and hits at some point above or below (vertical deflection) or to left or right (horizontal deflection) or at any other point according to the combined deflection plate potentials.

Electromagnetic Deflection – consider for example the vertical deflection coils as shown in (ii) of the figure. There are two coils which are placed outside and at each side of the tube. When they carry a current there is a magnetic field across the tube between them. Electrons flowing in the beam constitute an electric current, accordingly a force acts on each electron in the beam at right angles to both the direction of the current and of the field. Which way the beam is deflected can be determined by using Fleming's Rules, remembering that we are dealing with electron flow, not conventional current, hence the right-hand rule is appropriate. As an example, if looking from the screen towards the coils, the field direction is from left to right, then the beam is deflected downwards. The horizontal deflection coils work in the same way hence according to the currents and their directions in the two sets of coils, the beam can be deflected to produce a spot at any position on the screen. One advantage of magnetic deflection is that it permits a wider deflection angle, hence a shorter necked tube can be used, desirable for example for television sets to avoid a large depth of cabinet.

See also Scanning and Time Base.
(* Scanning, Time Base, Electron Gun, Television Receiver,

Oscilloscope >> Thermionic Emission, Electromagnetic Motor Action, Fleming's Rules, Kinetic Energy, Secondary Emission)

CATHODE SPUTTERING is the deposition of metal from a cathode onto an anode – see Sputtering.

CAVITY MAGNETRON The essential component of one type of microwave oscillator – see Magnetron.

CAVITY RESONATOR is a device containing a space bounded by conducting walls within which resonant electromagnetic fields can be set up. Although it can be considered as the microwave equivalent of an *LC* parallel resonant circuit, the action can perhaps be best understood by considering the cavity as a waveguide short-circuited at both ends. If the guide is half a wavelength long a signal at the resonance frequency can be injected into it and a standing wave pattern set up. This operates similarly to a high Q parallel resonant circuit. Typically Q may be many thousands when the cavity is unloaded but when couplings are added it may fall to a few hundreds. Many arrangements are possible but the simplest is known as the TE_{111} mode. For this the cavity is cylindrical in shape and has dimensions so chosen that half wavelength standing wave patterns are obtained as shown in Figure C3. In this drawing only the electric field lines are shown, the magnetic lines are not included but they are perpendicular to the electric lines.

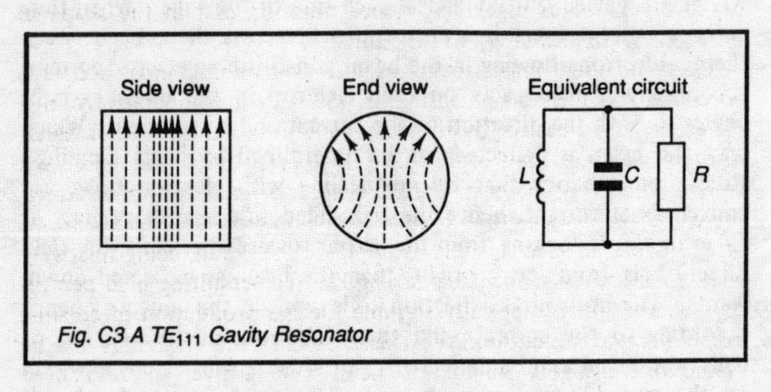

Fig. C3 A TE_{111} Cavity Resonator

For a tuned amplifier it can be shown that:

$$\Delta f = f_r/Q$$

where Δf is the bandwidth and f_r is the resonance frequency.

Hence at 1 GHz, with Q = 500, the bandwidth is 2 MHz.

The radio frequency energy for excitation must be obtained from an outside source such as an antenna or amplifier. This entails setting up the required field in the cavity. For this a *probe* or wire loop is used to produce electric and magnetic fields with lines approximately parallel to those of the fields of the desired mode. (>> Mode, Resonant Circuit, Waveguide, Standing Wave, Q-Factor)

CCD Abbreviation for Charge-Coupled Device – see this term.

CENTRAL PROCESSING UNIT (CPU) is that part of a computer which controls the operation of the whole system. It is a most complex unit, almost invariably in integrated form, usually within a microprocessor of which it forms the main part. In most computer systems the CPU comprises two units, the *control unit* which (i) accepts programming information and data and organizes the data flow and program execution (see Fig.C17) and (ii) the *arithmetic logic unit* which does all the calculations and logical operations. (* Computer, Microprocessor, Arithmetic Logic Unit, Digital Logic)

CERAMIC is derived from the Greek *keramos*, pottery. Ceramics play a great part in electronics for they have high insulating and dielectric properties and may also be piezoelectric. One difficulty with ceramics is that, being so hard and pottery-like, they cannot be filed, drilled or machined, hence must be cast in the shape in which they are ultimately to function.

Many different materials are used, one known to most people is *porcelain*, excellent as an insulator but with a comparatively high dielectric loss because of its glass content. On the other hand, *alumina* ceramics not only have high resistivity but also low dielectric loss. There is also a range of *ferroelectric* ceramics, these are the ones in which some domains grow at the expense of others when an electric field is applied, the result being relatively high polarization at low field strengths. The resulting high permittivity makes them especially suitable for the production of ceramic capacitors and miniature filters. Basic ceramic materials may also be mixed with a highly conducting metal such as silver and then fired to produce a *cermet* (*cer*amic + *met*al). These are used in thick and thin film technology, especially as resistors where the value can easily be controlled according to the mix.
(* Thick Film Circuits, Thin Film Circuits, Ceramic Capacitor >> Dielectric, Piezoelectric Effect, Electric Polarization, Permittivity, Ferroelectricity)

CERAMIC CAPACITOR is one which employs a ceramic as the dielectric. Usually a *ferroelectric* ceramic is used and generally there are two classes of capacitor:

(i) those with permittivities up to about 500. These have good stability and are therefore suitable for example for precision oscillator circuits; and

(ii) those with permittivities exceeding 500 and perhaps up to 10,000. These exhibit much higher capacitance (the capacitance is directly proportional to the permittivity of the dielectric) but are less stable and have higher losses. They are therefore more likely to be found in applications where miniaturization is important but stability is less so, for example, as by-pass or coupling capacitors.

Metallized ceramic plate capacitors are available with capacitances up to some 0.02 μF. For a miniature type, monolithic ceramic construction leads to capacitances up to as high as 0.47 μF but at noticeably higher cost. There are also many types of disc ceramic capacitors with working voltages from a few volts up to 1000 or more.
(* Ceramic, By-Pass Capacitor >> Ferroelectricity, Dielectric, Permittivity)

CERMET A combination of ceramic and metal used in thick and thin film applications – see Ceramic.

CHANNEL This is a term frequently used in electronics to describe a signal or communication path, for example over a pair of wires or over a particular limited frequency band within a (multi-channel) telephony system. The term is also used for a radio or t.v. link or even a link at audio frequencies through the air. Transmission is frequently in one direction only and in television for example, each available channel is identified by a channel number.
(* Telecommunication System, Television >> Radio)

CHARGE-COUPLED DEVICE (CCD) This in essence is a string of MOS capacitors, each of which consists basically of a metal gate electrode coupled electrostatically to a substrate via a silicon dioxide dielectric as shown in Figure C4(i). CCD's are therefore of integrated circuit format and have uses especially in computer processing and memories, certain types of filter and because their inputs are sensitive to light they are also used in optical imaging, for example, in the solid-state camera.

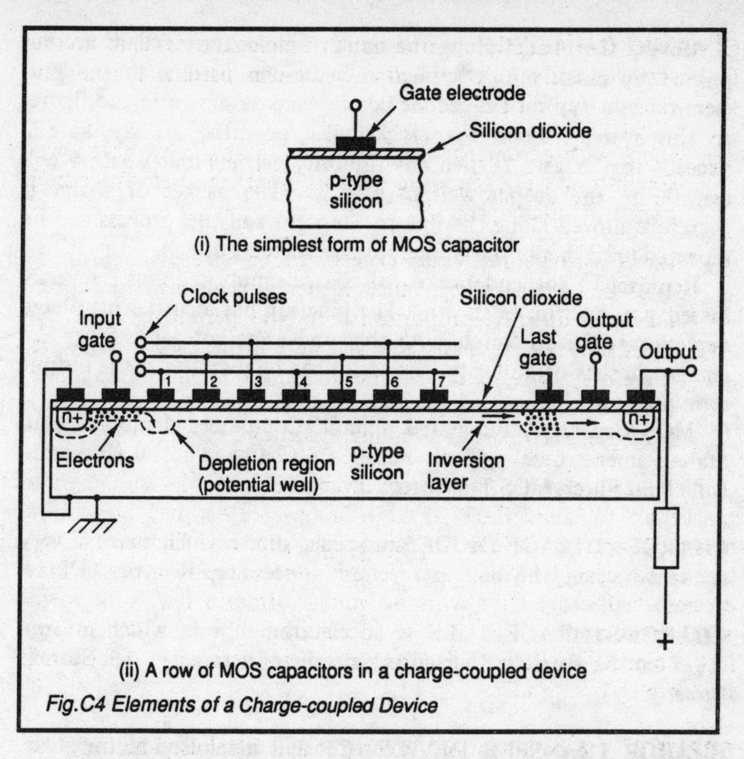

Fig.C4 Elements of a Charge-coupled Device

In (i) of the figure, if a positive potential is applied to the gate electrode, mobile holes in the p-type silicon are repelled, forcing acceptor atoms to give up electrons so that an equal and opposite charge to that on the gate electrode is formed just below the silicon dioxide layer. This can be looked upon as a "well" of electrons or even as a "packet of charge". In addition minority carriers (the electrons in p-type) are attracted to the p-type material surface by the positive potential on the gate and they form an *inversion layer* which has the effect of reducing the size of the potential well. Nevertheless within the p-type silicon and underneath the gate electrode a packet of negative charge now exists.

The CCD consists of a row of the elementary units of (i) of the figure as shown in (ii). Charges are injected into the first well, for example as shown to the left in the diagram. The heavily doped n-region provides a flow of minority carriers. This is controlled by the channel beneath the input gate (as with a MOSFET). Here optical inputs are also possible because incident photons create electron-hole pairs with the electrons being collected into the first well.

Moving the charge along the bank of elementary cells is accomplished by clock pulses applied in a certain pattern to the gate electrodes, a typical system of connections is shown in the figure. In this system, when the clock pulse potential at, say, gate 2 exceeds that at gate 1, then any minority carriers under gate 1 will transfer to the deeper well of gate 2. The packet of charge is therefore moved along the line to the right and this process can be repeated until finally the charge reaches the output end.

Removal of the end packet of charge simply requires a reverse-biased p-n junction as shown. The junction has a sufficiently large depletion region to couple with that under the last gate. Since the charge consists of minority carriers, it can be removed at the output terminal.
(* MOS Capacitor, Integrated Circuit, Computer, Memory, Solid-State Camera, Clock, Clock Pulse >> Charge, Photon, Electron-Hole Pair, Filter, MOS Transistor, Inversion Layer)

CHARGE-STORAGE DIODE is a special diode which cuts off very suddenly when the bias is reversed – see Step-Recovery Diode.

CHARGE-STORAGE TUBE is an electron tube in which information can be stored as a charge pattern on a target – see Storage Tube.

CHARGE TRANSFER DEVICE (CTD) is a semiconductor structure in which discrete packets of charge are transferred from one location to the next along a line. There are two main types, *bucket brigade devices* and *charge-coupled devices* – see these terms.

CHEBYSHEV FILTER is a filter designed by a special technique.
(>> Filter)

CHIP is a tiny piece of semiconductor material grown as a single crystal and usually of the element silicon. Ingots are pulled from a silicon melt and then cut into slices (the wafers) somewhat less than 1 mm thick and up to some 80 mm diameter. Each wafer is then polished, processed and finally diced into as many as several thousand chips, each square and of area from one up to a few square millimetres. To get a realistic idea of the actual size, Figure C5 shows part of an 80 mm diameter wafer with the slicing for chips each of area 4 mm^2.

A chip when processed can contain either a single component such as a transistor or many thousands as in an integrated circuit. Chips are protected from damage by mounting them in special cases

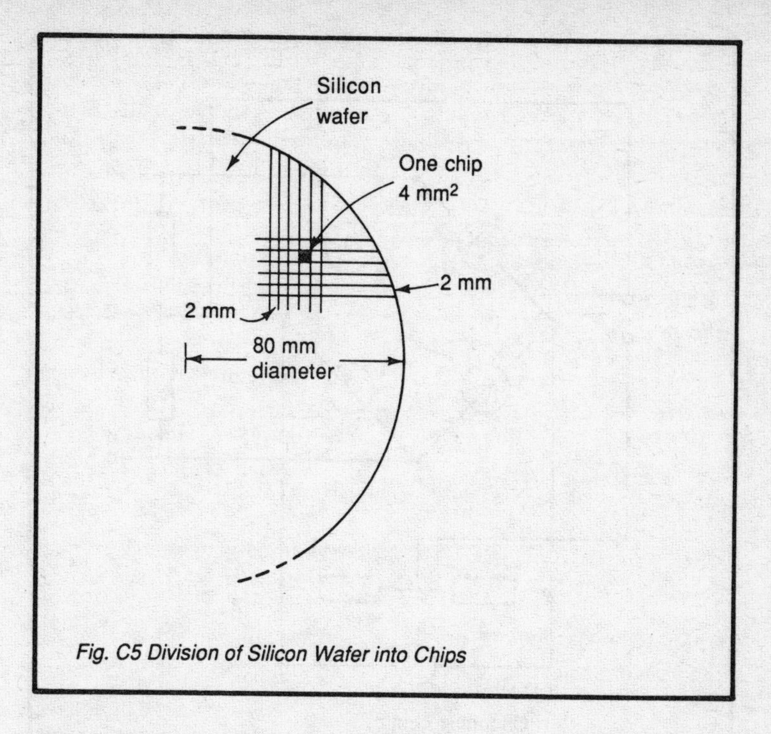

Fig. C5 Division of Silicon Wafer into Chips

with external connecting tags. Within the case fine wires are bonded to the chip and connected to the tags (see Fig.I9).
(* Integrated Circuit >> Silicon, Semiconductor, Transistor)

CHOKE is simply another name for an inductor used to present a high impedance to a.c. over a particular range of frequencies. Radio frequency chokes are often connected in between two separate circuits to reduce interaction between them. As an example it may be necessary to block radio frequency currents from entering an audio circuit. Such a choke might have an inductance of the order of a few millihenries so presenting a high impedance to radio frequencies but low to audio frequencies.

A *smoothing choke* is employed in rectifier circuits as all or part of the ripple filter (smoothing circuit). This type requires a high inductance (several henries) because the frequencies to which it must present a high impedance are low.
(* Ripple Filter >> Inductance, Impedance)

CHOPPER is a device which periodically interrupts an electrical input (usually a direct current) thereby presenting a "chopped"

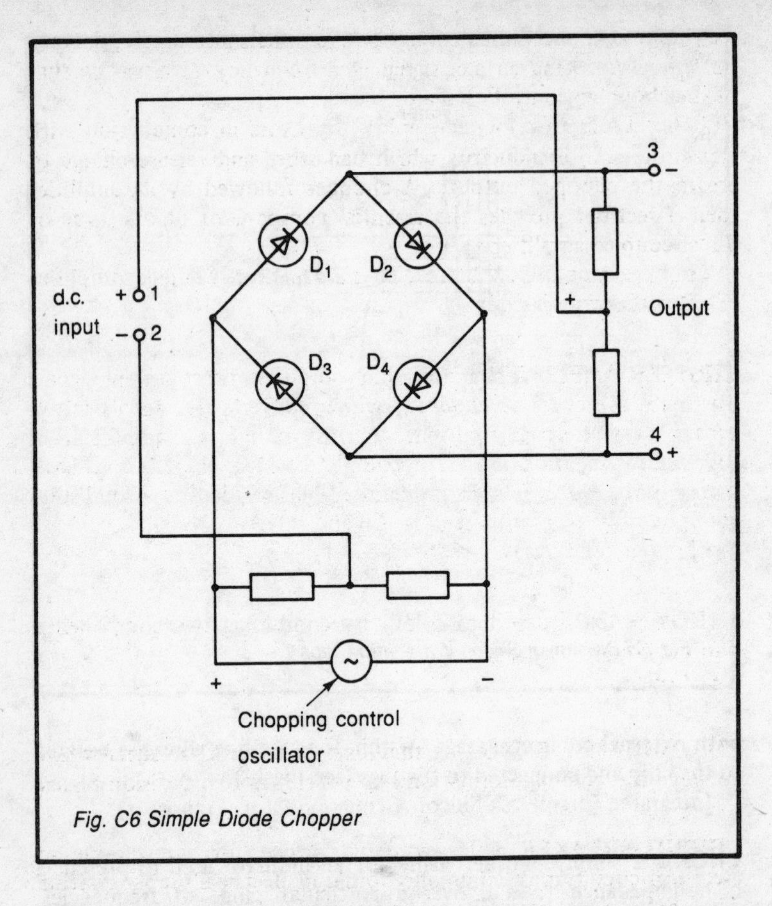

Fig. C6 Simple Diode Chopper

output. The main component is either solid-state or a vibrating relay, generally known as a *vibrator*. Choppers are mainly employed in converting low voltage d.c. to a higher voltage as part of a *chopper amplifier*. Many different types of chopper circuit are in use, perhaps the simplest to understand is the diode chopping circuit, shown in its elementary form in Figure C6. The four diodes are connected in bridge form and the a.c. chopping control signal which may be, say 100 Hz or more, is provided by the oscillator shown. Operation of the circuit can be followed from the polarities shown for one half-cycle of the control signal. In this case diodes D_1 and D_2 both conduct hence the negative pole of the d.c. supply (terminal 2) is connected to the output terminal 3. When the control oscillator reverses its polarity, D_3 and D_4 conduct whereupon terminal 2 is connected to output terminal 4. Accordingly the d.c. input is connected to the output terminals alternately, the output therefore being an a.c. signal at a frequency governed by that of the chopping control oscillator.

Other types of chopper employ thyristors in conjunction with capacitors and/or inductors which can store and release charge to create the chopped output. A chopper followed by an amplifier then a rectifier provides the essential components of one type of direct-coupled amplifier.
(* Chopper Amplifier, Vibrator, Thyristor, Direct-Coupled Amplifier >> Rectification, Diode)

CHOPPER AMPLIFIER is one which amplifies direct current signals by firstly a process of *chopping* which converts the signals into a square wave alternating current, then by normal a.c. amplification followed by rectification. The complete system therefore achieves d.c. amplification. The chopping may be provided by a solid-state chopper or by a vibrator (see Figs C6 and V3).
(* Chopper, Vibrator)

CHROMINANCE describes colour by combining two components, hue and colour intensity.
(>> Colour)

CHROMINANCE SIGNAL is that part of a television signal which conveys the colour information – see Television, Television Signal.

CIRCUIT-BREAKER is a switching device for interrupting an electrical circuit, most commonly found in electrical supply systems. The contacts are normally made but under fault conditions when the current would rise excessively, the contacts automatically break and isolate the circuit. Circuit-breakers connected in high voltage circuits require special arrangements to reduce arcing at the contacts. They are also used in domestic electrical systems instead of fuses. The graphical symbols are given in Figure C7.
(* Fuse, Switch, Residual Current Circuit Breaker >> Arc)

CIRCULATOR A ferrite device with several ports. Microwave energy entering one port has its polarization changed so that it is able to leave the device only via a certain other port. As an example, a circulator may be used to couple a microwave antenna to its transmitter and receiver.
(* Ceramic, Ferrite >> Electromagnetic Wave, Microwave)

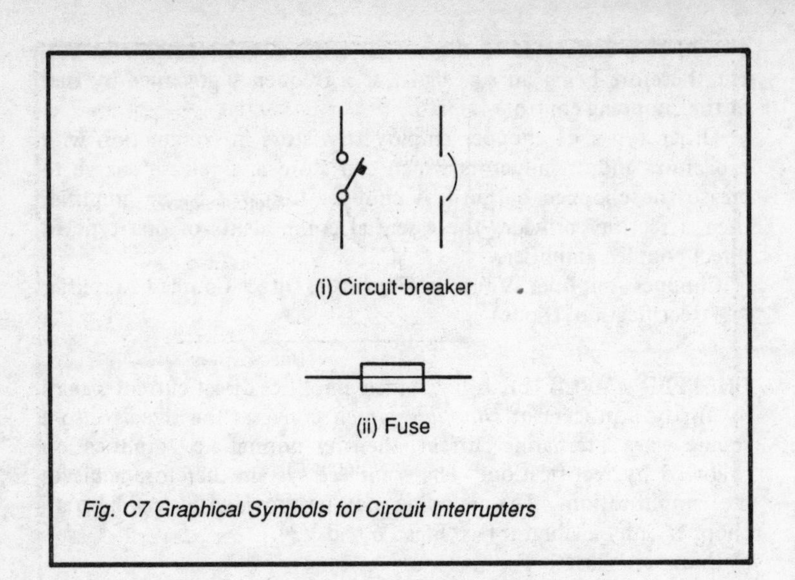

Fig. C7 Graphical Symbols for Circuit Interrupters

CLASS A AMPLIFIER Class A is one of the modes of operation of a transistor or thermionic valve in which the device is biased approximately to the centre point of the straight portion of its transfer characteristic (e.g. for a transistor, collector current/base current). A *quiescent* collector current flows when there is no input signal and the amplitude of the signal is limited so that the collector does not swing into non-linear parts of the characteristic. The fact that collector current flows continually throughout the cycle, i.e. the *angle of flow* is 360°, distinguishes the mode as Class A. The operating conditions are illustrated in Figure C8(i).

A Class A amplifying stage is relatively uncomplicated and reasonably distortion free. It is invariably used when d.c. power consumption is of minor consequence. Efficiency when expressed as the ratio between a.c. power output and power supply input can be shown to be around 25%, which compared with other modes such as Class AB and Class B, is low.

Class A is used mostly in small-signal amplifiers. Because of its low efficiency and likelihood of distortion if driven onto the non-linear parts of the transfer characteristic, its use for power output stages is limited.
(* Class AB, Class B, Class C Amplifier >> Characteristic, Amplifier, Distortion)

CLASS AB AMPLIFIER As its name implies, this is an amplifier biased so that its mode of operation is between that of Class A and

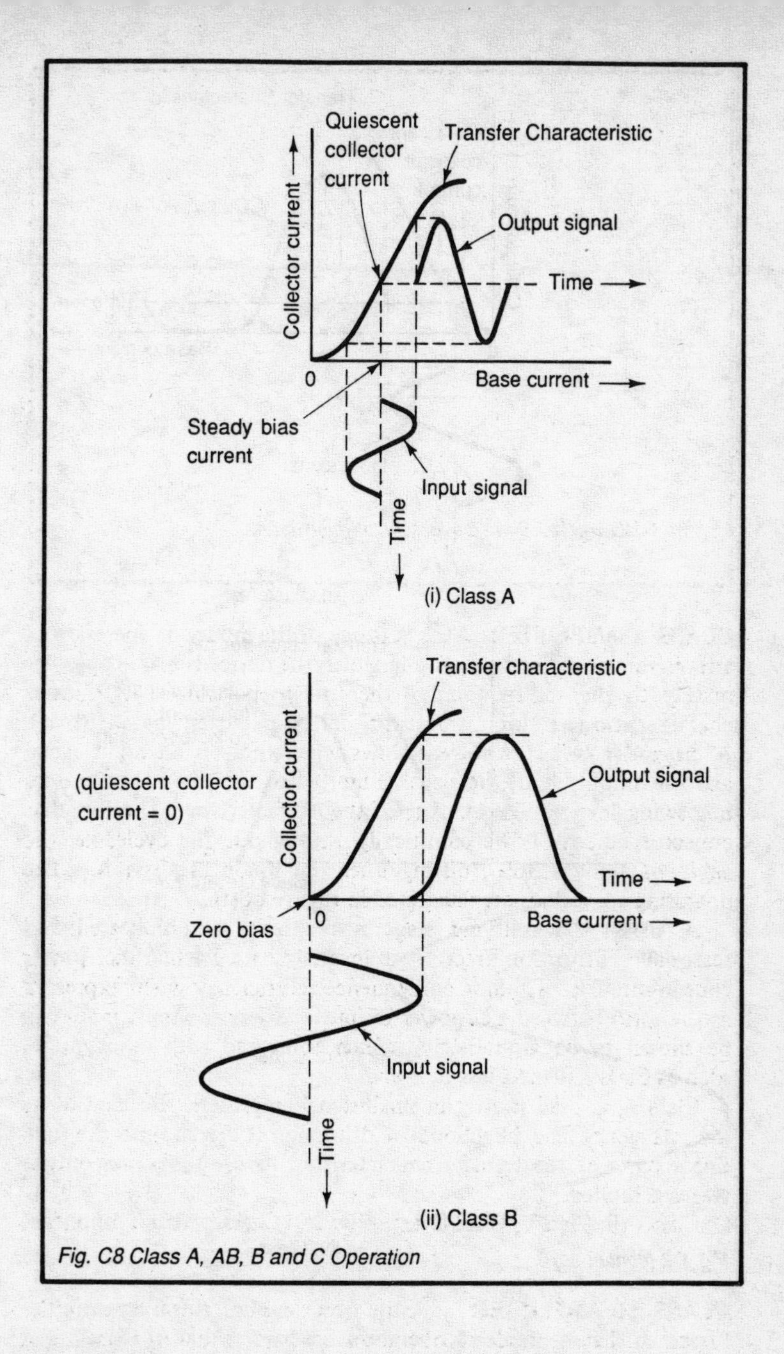

Fig. C8 Class A, AB, B and C Operation

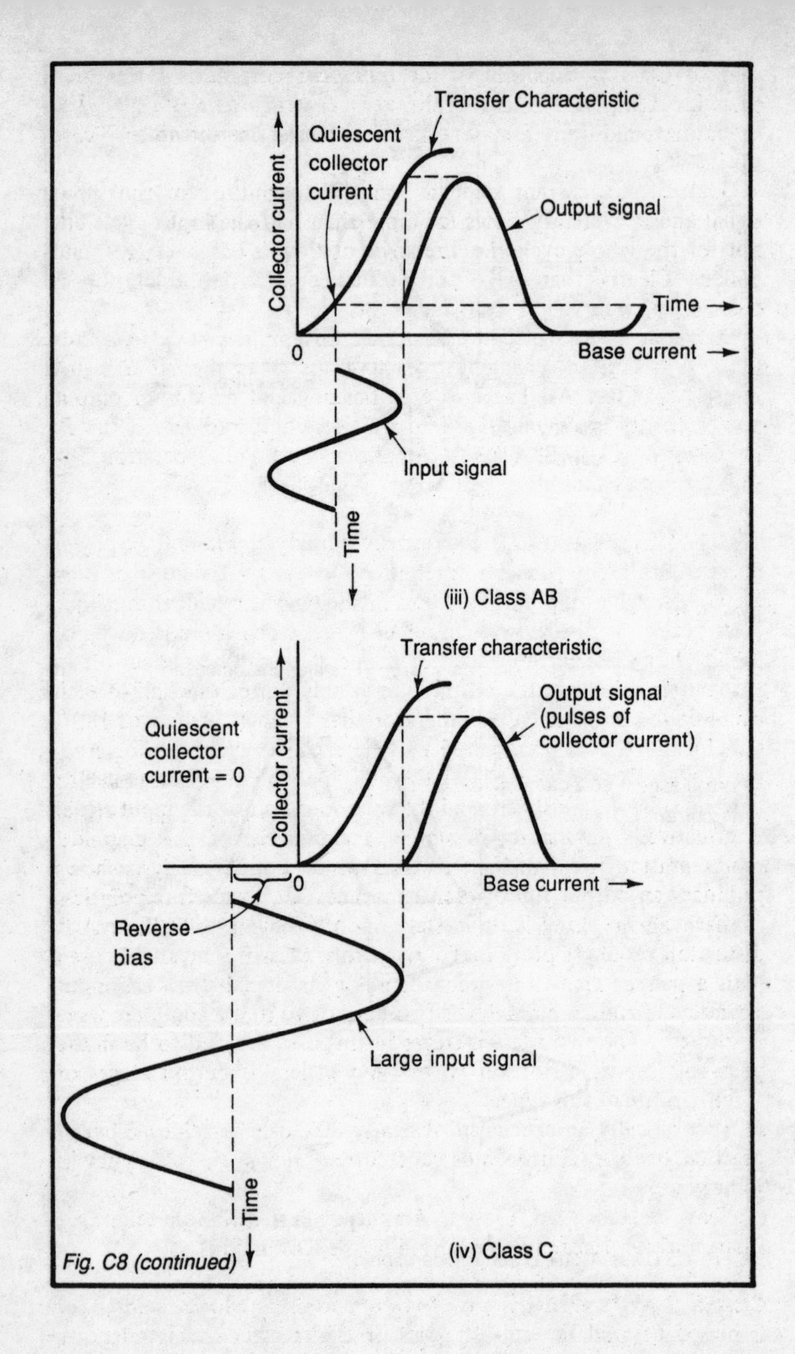

Fig. C8 (continued)

that of Class B, accordingly the *quiescent* current is lower than that for Class A but above the zero current for Class B. The operating conditions for a transistor so biased are shown in Figure C8(iii).

The output current depends on the magnitude of the input signal and it evidently flows for more than half the input cycle but not for the whole cycle, i.e. the angle of flow is between 180° and 360°. Clearly there is distortion hence push-pull operation is frequently employed as for Class B.

At small input signal levels a Class AB amplifier tends towards Class A operation, changing over to Class B as the input signal increases. Class AB has greater efficiency and maximum output power than Class A and lower distortion compared with Class B. (* Class A, Class B, Class C Amplifier, Push-Pull Operation >> Characteristic, Amplifier, Distortion)

CLASS B AMPLIFIER is one usually employed where high power output with high efficiency is required. In Class A the angle of flow is 360° showing that current flows in the output circuit throughout each cycle. It also flows continually even when there is no signal input. For Class B, the transistor is operated with bias at cut-off so that current flows in the output circuit only during one half of each cycle of the input signal. It therefore has an angle of flow of 180°. Graphically this is represented in Figure C8(ii) which can be compared with Class A [Fig.C8(i)] to show that the quiescent collector current is now almost zero and that only one half of the input signal is effective. As Figure C8 stands, a circuit having this graphical representation is a half-wave rectifier which Fourier analysis shows produces an output full of even harmonics. It is therefore pointless to have an amplifier output stage more efficient than Class A if distortion products prevail. To avoid this, Class B is invariably used with a pair of transistors, each handling its own half of the input signal cycle and combining the two outputs so that a complete wave is formed. The two Class B stages in this case are said to be in the push-pull mode, distortion is low and generally output stages of amplifiers are of this type.

Theoretically an efficiency of nearly 80% can be achieved but in practice because a little quiescent current flows, the efficiency is somewhat lower.
(* Class A, Class AB, Class C Amplifier, Push-Pull Operation >> Characteristic, Harmonic, Fourier Analysis, Distortion)

CLASS C AMPLIFIER is a mode of operation in which an amplifier is biased beyond the cut-off point on the transfer characteristic as

shown in Figure C8(iv). Output is in the form of pulses occurring for only a small fraction of the input cycle, the angle of flow therefore being less than 180°. Efficiency can be high (over 90%) but because the amplifier is non-linear it cannot be used directly for linear amplification as for Class A or for Class B in push-pull. On the other hand it is especially useful for radio frequency power amplification stages to add pulses of energy to a tuned output circuit. The latter rejects harmonics from the Class C amplifier and so oscillates sinusoidally at its resonance frequency.
(* Class A, Class AB, Class B Amplifier, Push-Pull Operation >> Characteristic, Distortion, Resonance, Tuned Circuit)

CLIPPING is a name for what occurs when a *limiter* is in action – see Limiter.

CLOCK is an oscillator which delivers pulses for use in control of timing and synchronization in the operation of computer and logic circuits. The oscillator frequency is known as the *clock frequency* (usually in the MHz range) and it can be sub-divided as required.
(* Computer, Digital Logic >> Oscillator, Pulse)

CLOCK PULSE is a single pulse delivered by an electronic clock – see Clock.

CLOSED-LOOP CONTROL SYSTEM is a system in which feedback from the system output is used to control the output. Systems of this type control a multitude of industrial operations from operation of machine tools and robots to filling bottles. A schematic diagram of the basic system is shown in Figure C9.

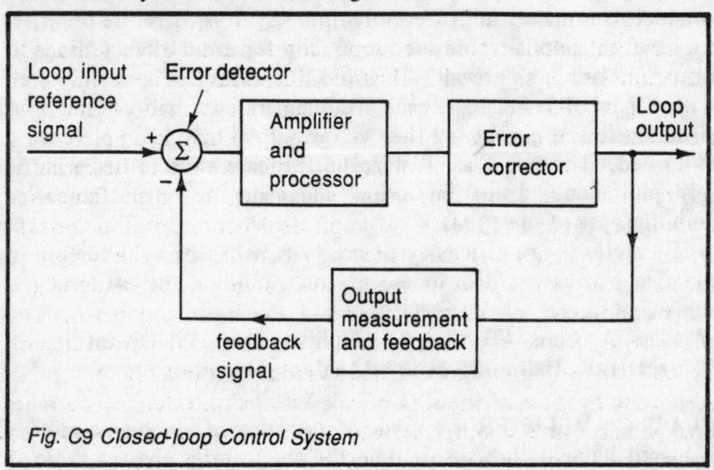

Fig. C9 Closed-loop Control System

The output measuring device is a transducer (e.g. a proximity detector, photocell) which examines the output and transforms it into an electrical signal which is processed to become the loop feedback signal, this is applied to the error detector. The detector generates an error signal proportional to the difference between the previously determined loop input reference signal and the feedback signal. The greater the error signal therefore, the greater is the amount of control provided by the error corrector. This unit supplies the power required to change the output and thereby reduce the error. The error signal rapidly tends to zero but a small error inevitably remains.

Most of the many different types of transducer are to be found in closed-loop control systems and when the controlled variable is a mechanical device such as a robot, drilling machine or vehicle, the system is known as a *servomechanism*.

(* Transducer >> Feedback, Photocell)

CMOS is an abbreviation of Complementary Metal-Oxide-Semiconductor – see this term.

COAXIAL CABLE is a transmission line specially constructed for carrying high frequency signals. The cable conductors consist of a flexible copper tube or braiding through the centre of which runs a single copper wire, the tube and central wire are therefore *coaxial*. In the larger cables the wire is held in position by polyethylene support discs but for small cables for t.v. etc. which have to be more flexible, the wire is held by a continuous cellular (containing cavities) polythene filling. In both cases the insulation between the two conductors is mainly air.

A typical coaxial cable used especially for antenna downleads to television sets is sketched in Figure C10. This one has an overall diameter of about 7 mm, generally diameters run from some 3–4 mm to 20 cm or more.

Compared with a straightforward pair of wires this rather peculiar construction has some important advantages for high frequency working, say, above 10 MHz. A simple explanation involves the *skin effect* which forces high frequency signals to flow on the surface of a conductor, in the case of the coaxial cable, on the inside of the outer conductor and on the outside of the inner conductor. The electric and magnetic fields generated by the signal therefore terminate on the inner surface of the tube so radiation is mainly prevented. Also again because of the skin effect, external interference currents flow mainly on the outer surface of the outer conductor and so cause little disturbance of the signal current on the inner surface (of

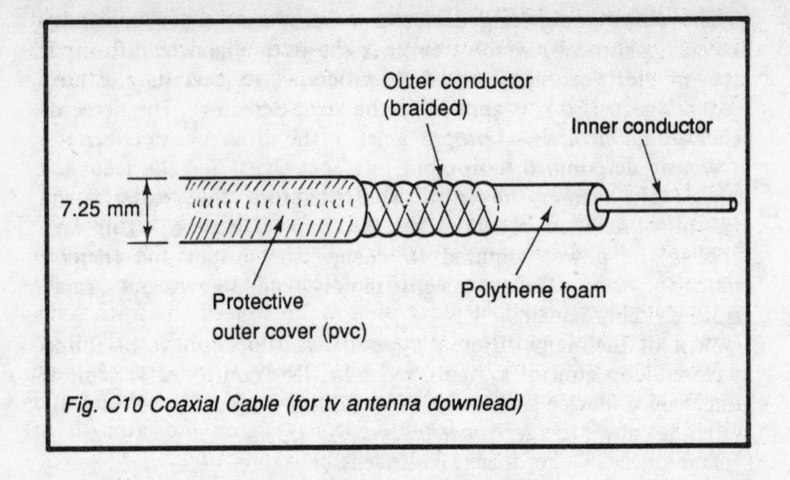

Fig. C10 Coaxial Cable (for tv antenna downlead)

the outer conductor). In fact this benefit increases with frequency because there is a greater separation of signal and interference currents. These features give us a cable which is virtually non-radiating and interference free. In addition, compared with many pair-type cables, the coaxial cable capacitance is lower, hence attenuation is less.

Because at the high frequencies at which coaxial cables are employed, $\omega L >> R$ and $\omega C >> G$, with tongue in cheek the formula for the characteristic impedance, Z_0 can be reduced to $\sqrt{L/C}$, which makes Z_0 independent of frequency since there is no ω in the formula. Taking a practical television coaxial cable as an example with $L = 0.3$ mH per km and $C = 0.05$ μF per km:

$$Z_0 = \sqrt{L/C} = 77\ \Omega.$$

Generally Z_0 for coaxial cables lies between 50 and 100 Ω. In most cases matching terminations are required not only for maximum power transfer but also to minimize reflection, the latter is especially important with television signals.

The attenuation can be shown to be approximately proportional to the square root of the frequency and inversely proportional to the cable dimensions, hence large diameter cables are employed when low attenuation is essential. Typically a television antenna downlead has an attenuation of 7.5 dB per 100 m at 100 MHz. (* Matching, Skin Effect, Multiplex System, Television Signal >> Transmission Line, Electromagnetic Radiation, Characteristic Impedance)

COINCIDENCE CIRCUIT is one with two or more inputs and which produces an output pulse when and only when all inputs receive pulses simultaneously or within a specified time interval. The circuit is also known as a *coincidence gate.*
(* Digital Logic, Logic Gate)

COLD CATHODE is one which emits electrons at ambient temperatures, i.e. it is not heated. For emission a sufficiently high voltage gradient must exist at the surface. Light can have the effect of releasing those electrons from a cold cathode which receive sufficient energy from incident photons to exceed the work function. Electronic emission is also possible from a cold cathode in a gas-filled tube for example, with neon at moderately low pressure. The normal space charge surrounds the cathode and electrons may be drawn from it depending on the strength of the electric field existing between the anode and cathode.

Cold cathodes are preferably of, or coated with, materials of low work function.
(>> Space Charge, Work Function, Photoelectric Effect, Photoemission, Gas Discharge)

COLOUR BURST is part of the television signal for one line of the picture. It corrects a reference oscillator in the colour section of a television receiver – see Television Signal and/or Figure T5(ii).

COLOUR CELL is the smallest area on a colour picture tube screen which contains one of each of the primary colour phosphors – see Colour Picture Tube.

COLOUR CODE is a system used for marking small components such as resistors and capacitors with their values, tolerances, ratings, etc. by colours rather than by printing directly. Components so marked are more easily distinguished and sorted, furthermore tiny printed numbers are more liable to become disfigured and unreadable. The basic colour code allocates a different colour for each of the numbers 0 to 9, i.e.:

0 black	2 red	4 yellow	6 blue	8 grey
1 brown	3 orange	5 green	7 violet	9 white

From 2 to 7 are the colours of the rainbow minus indigo which may be difficult to distinguish from blue and violet. Before and after this group are 4 non-rainbow colours, getting paler as the number increases. The method generally accepted assumes that any

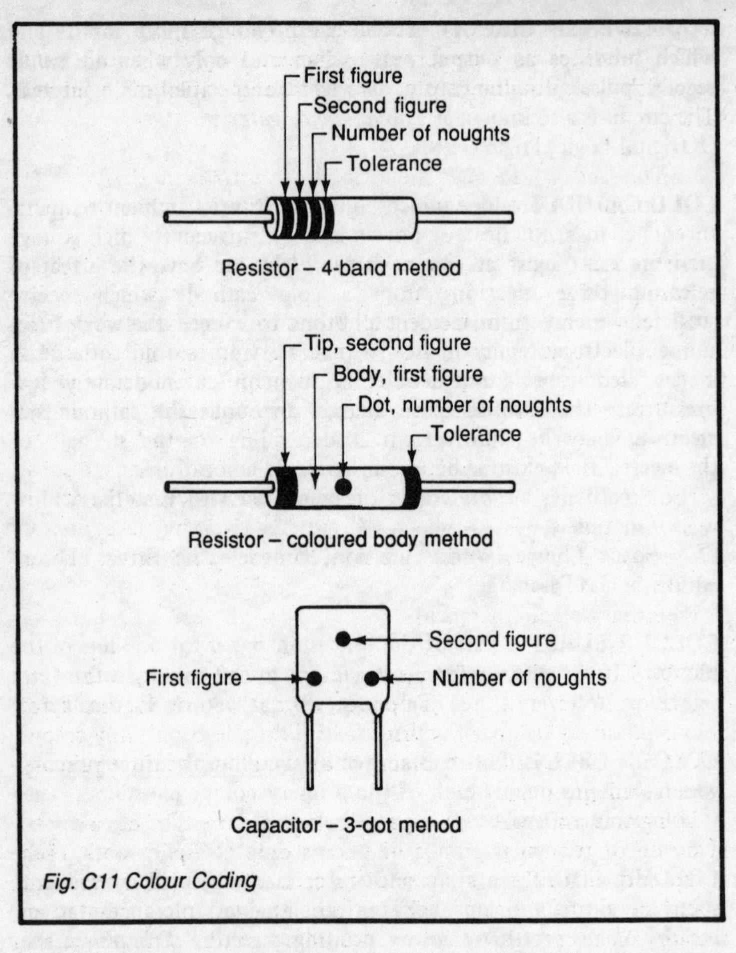

Fig. C11 Colour Coding

value has two digits followed by none or a number of noughts, e.g. a value of 47 000 can be colour coded but one of 47 300 cannot. This is a workable arrangement because the latter value is unlikely to be available generally, only the nearest *preferred value*.

To indicate the value of a resistor or capacitor the colour code may be printed on the case in one of a number of ways. Resistors are invariably colour coded and for them one generally accepted arrangement is as shown in Figure C11, i.e. with 4 colour bands. The first band indicates the first digit, the second band the second digit and the third band the number of noughts following these two digits. As an example, if the first three bands are yellow, violet, orange, the value is 47 000 Ω but yellow, violet, brown is 470 Ω and yellow, violet, black is 47 Ω (black = no noughts).

The tolerance as a percentage is indicated by the fourth band for which we enlist the help of two additional "colours", gold and silver:

Tolerance	± 1%	± 2%	± 5%	± 10%	± 20%
Colour	brown	red	gold	silver	none

These are the tolerances in general use, there are others which may be introduced as required.

So far we have accounted for all values which are integers (whole numbers). Occasionally it may be necessary to indicate a decimal fraction so again gold and silver come to the rescue but now in the third band. If this is gold then the first two figures of the number are multiplied by 0.1, if silver, by 0.01.

Figure C11 also shows another method of colour coding a resistor and at the bottom is just one of the many ways of using the colour code with a capacitor for which the number given by the code is in *picofarads*, e.g. brown, black, green is decoded as 1 000 000 pF, i.e. 1.0 μF.
(* Preferred Value, Tolerance)

COLOUR PICTURE TUBE is basically a cathode-ray tube (see Fig.C2) with the additional components and structures for display of colour pictures, mainly of course, for colour television. Any colour can be obtained by additive mixing of any or all of the three primary colours, red, green and blue.

Using this principle, one type of colour picture tube has a screen made up of triangular groups of microscopic phosphor dots, each group containing three dots, one for each of the primary colours. When an electron beam strikes a dot, the latter contributes an amount of its particular colour according to the strength of the beam. What the eye sees is the net colour output of the group, not the individual dots. This is illustrated by the sketch in Figure C12 which shows how the phosphor dots might be arranged on the glass screen (nothing is to scale in this figure). The figure shows that three electron guns are required compared with one only for black and white (see Fig.C2). The electrons are accelerated and deflected as for a black and white tube. In the colour tube the guns are usually arranged in triangular form.

The incoming television signal is processed so that each of the colour components is directed to the appropriate electron gun. At any instant the electron beams pass through a perforated *shadow mask* very close to the screen and impinge on a group of phosphor

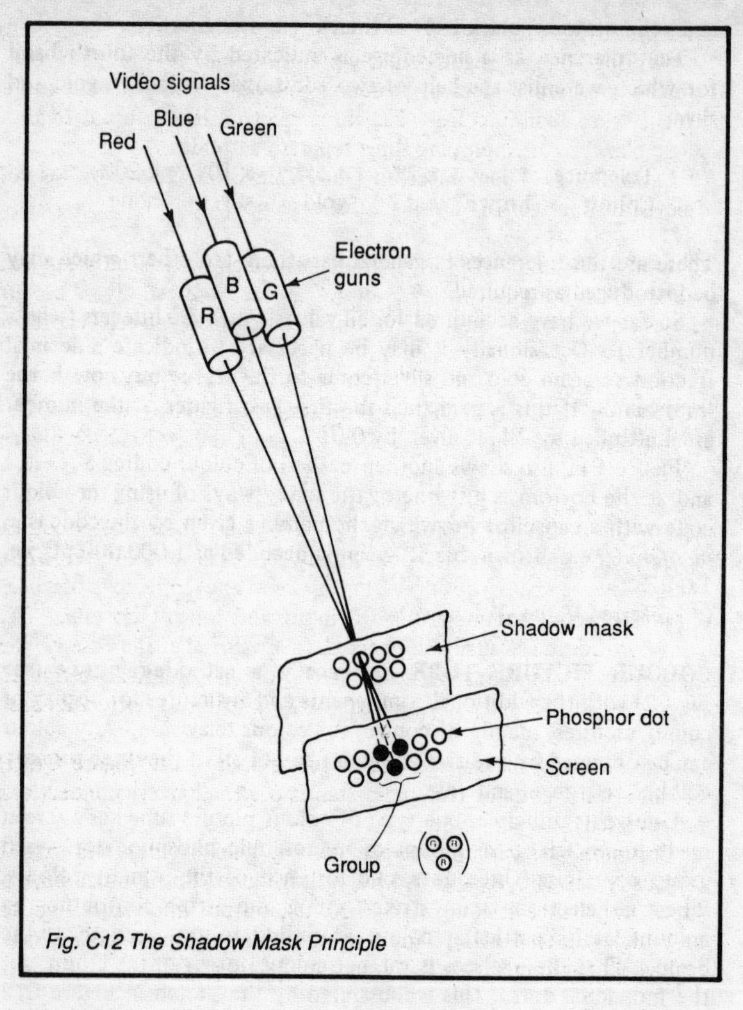

Fig. C12 The Shadow Mask Principle

dots. There is one hole in the mask per group of dots so that each electron beam can only strike its appointed dot and is "shadowed" from the other two. Thus the beam from say, the red electron gun can only strike red phosphot dots, similarly for green and blue. The mask also acts as a barrier to the electron beams while they shift from one group of dots to the next, hence preventing the excitation of wrong phosphors.

An alternative system, but still based on the shadow mask has narrow vertical slit openings in the mask and the phosphors are arranged in narrow vertical lines. The electron guns are fitted horizontally.

Working on a slightly different principle is the *Trinitron*, capable of sharper pictures than the shadow mask type but more expensive to manufacture. The three electron beams are used in a single gun system employing three separate cathodes.
(* Cathode-Ray Tube, Electron Gun, Television, Television Signal, Television Receiver >> Colour, Luminescence)

COLOUR TELEVISION is a system through which pictures and sound resembling the original scene are reproduced by a colour television receiver – see Television, Television Receiver, Television Signal.

COLPITTS OSCILLATOR is a sinusoidal oscillator with its frequency controlled by a tuned circuit – see Oscillator and/or Figure O3(ii).

COMMON-BASE CONNECTION – a bipolar transistor circuit in which the input signal is applied between base and emitter while the output signal is developed from base and collector, the base therefore being common to both input and output circuits. The common point is usually connected to *chassis*, i.e. the case of the equipment, sometimes even to earth (or in American terms to *ground*, hence the alternative description, *grounded-base connection*).

The essential features of the circuit are shown in Figure C13(i) for an n-p-n transistor (for p-n-p transistors the battery connections are reversed).

Common-base circuits have a current gain slightly less than 1 (typically about 0.98 – 0.99) but voltage gain can be much higher. Input impedance is low (30 – 100 Ω), output impedance high to very high (up to 1 MΩ). The output and input signals are in phase.
(* Hybrid Parameters >> P-N Junction, Transistor)

COMMON-COLLECTOR CONNECTION – a bipolar transistor circuit in which the input signal is applied between collector and base while the output signal is developed from collector and emitter, the collector therefore being common to both input and output circuits. The essential features of the circuit are shown in Figure C13(v) for an n-p-n transistor (for p-n-p transistors the battery connections are reversed). The common point for both input and output is the positive supply line but note that the power supply is normally of very low impedance hence to a.c. the positive and

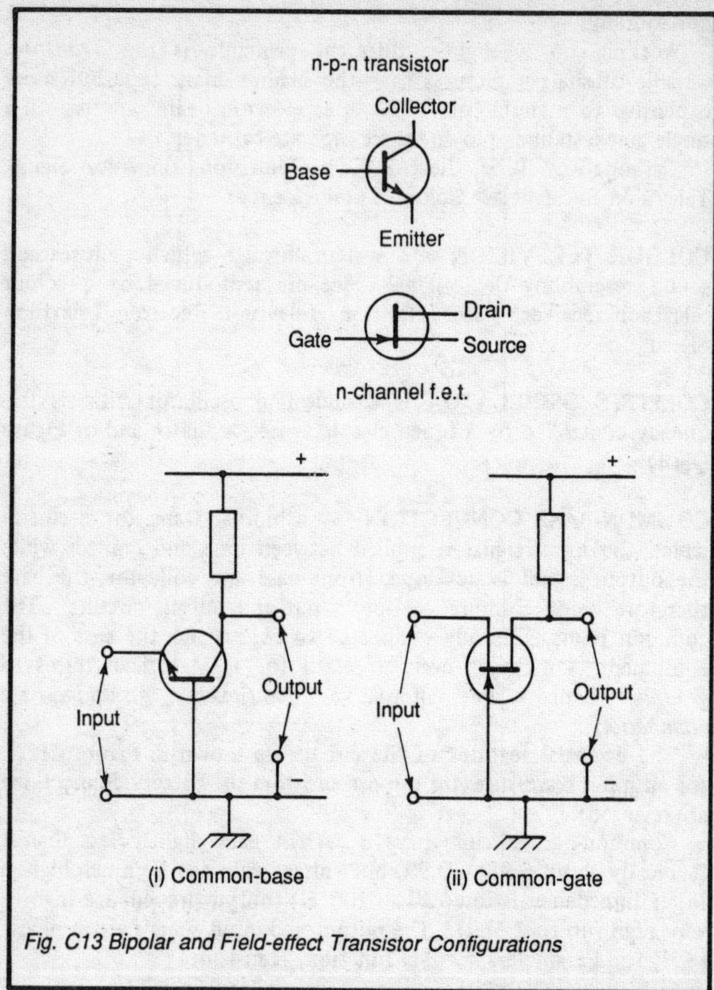

Fig. C13 Bipolar and Field-effect Transistor Configurations

negative supply lines may be considered to be at the same potential.

The negative line is usually connected to *chassis*, sometimes even to earth or in American terms to *ground*, hence the alternative description, *grounded-collector connection.*

Common-collector circuits have a voltage gain of approximately unity. For this reason the circuit is also known as an *emitter follower.* Current gain can be high. Input impedance is high (5 – 500 kΩ), output impedance is low (below 1 kΩ). The output and input signals are in phase.

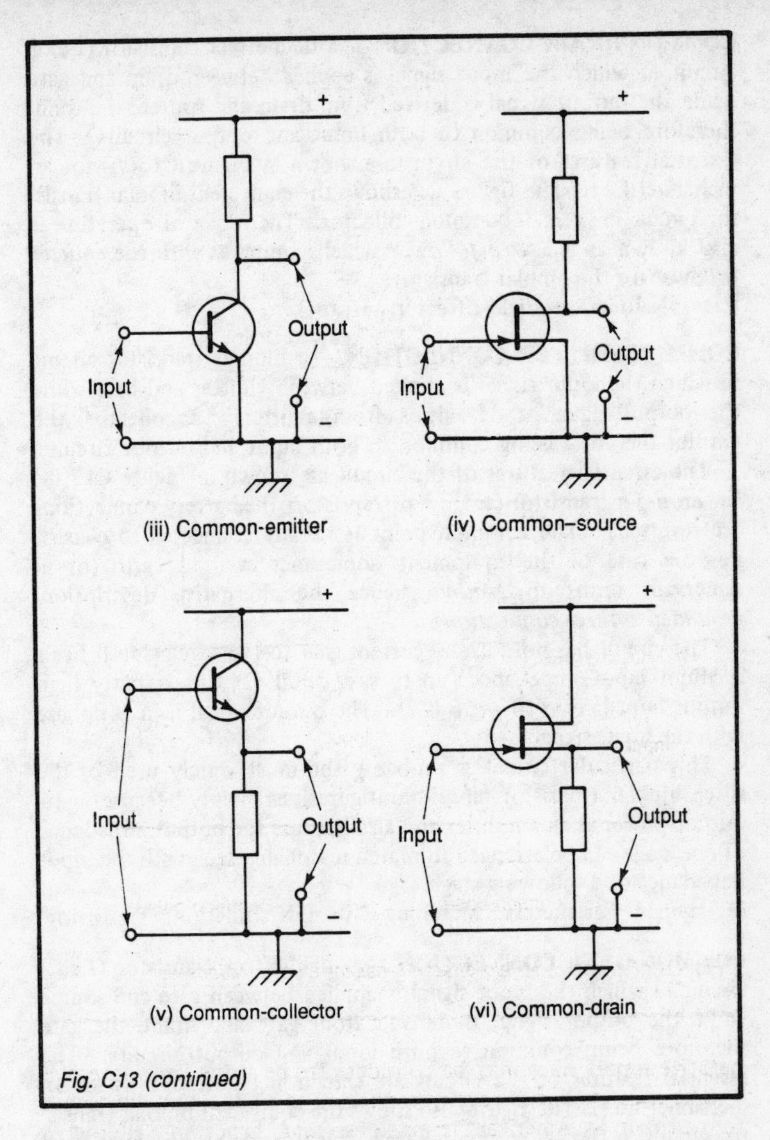

Fig. C13 (continued)

A common use for this circuit is as an impedance transformer because it can be connected between a high impedance source and low impedance load.
(* Hybrid Parameters, Matching >> P-N Junction, Transistor)

COMMON-DRAIN CONNECTION – a field-effect transistor (f.e.t.) circuit in which the input signal is applied between drain and gate while the output signal is derived from drain and source, the drain therefore being common to both input and output circuits. The essential features of the circuit are shown in Figure C13(vi) for an n-channel f.e.t. The figure also shows the equivalent bipolar transistor circuit in (v), i.e. common-collector. The mode of operation is also known as a *source follower* which compares with the *emitter follower* for the bipolar transistor.
(>> P-N Junction, Field-Effect Transistor)

COMMON-EMITTER CONNECTION – a bipolar transistor circuit in which the input signal is applied between emitter and base while the output signal is developed from emitter and collector, the emitter therefore being common to both input and output circuits.

The essential features of the circuit are shown in Figure C13(iii) for an n-p-n transistor (for p-n-p transistors the battery connections are reversed). The common point is usually connected to *chassis*, i.e. the case of the equipment, sometimes even to earth (or in American terms to *ground*, hence the alternative description, *grounded-emitter connection*).

The circuit has both useful current gain and voltage gain. It has a medium input impedance (up to say, 5000 Ω) with a fairly high output impedance (10 – 50 kΩ). The output signal is in antiphase with the input signal.

This particular circuit is probably the most widely used of the three bipolar transistor circuit configurations mainly because of its output power as an amplifier and also because the output impedance of one stage can be arranged to match reasonably well with the input impedance of a following stage.
(* Hybrid Parameters, Matching >> P-N Junction, Transistor)

COMMON-GATE CONNECTION – a field-effect transistor (f.e.t.) circuit in which the input signal is applied between gate and source while the output signal is derived from gate and drain, the gate therefore being common to both input and output circuits. The essential features of the circuit are shown in Figure C13(ii) for an n-channel f.e.t. The figure also shows the equivalent bipolar transistor circuit in (i), i.e. common-base. This is probably the least used of the three f.e.t. configurations.
(>> P-N Junction, Field-Effect Transistor)

COMMON-MODE REJECTION RATIO is a measure of the degree to which a differential amplifier produces a zero output for equal inputs – see Differential Amplifier.

COMMON-SOURCE CONNECTION – a field-effect transistor (f.e.t.) circuit in which the input signal is applied between source and gate while the output signal is derived from source and drain, the source therefore being common to both input and output circuits. The essential features of the circuit are shown in Figure C13(iv) for an n-channel f.e.t. The figure also shows the equivalent bipolar transistor circuit in (iii), i.e. common-emitter.

This is the normal mode of operation of an f.e.t. It has a high input impedance and develops a large voltage gain.
(>> P-N Junction, Field-Effect Transistor)

COMMUNICATIONS SATELLITE is an earth-bound artificial satellite which acts as a repeater for high capacity long distance microwave telephony, television and data links. These satellites are almost invariably in a geostationary orbit – see Satellite.

COMMUTATOR is that part of an electrical machine which connects the windings on the rotating shaft with the power supply in the case of an electric motor or with the load for a generator.
(* Electric Motor, Generator)

COMPACT DISC (CD) – audio signals are recorded in digital form on a small, high capacity disc – see Disc Recording.

COMPANDING is a technique used for the improvement of signal-to-noise ratio over audio frequency or multiplex circuits. A complete companding system comprises (i) a *volume compressor* at the transmitting end of the channel which gives more gain to low amplitude signals than to high amplitude ones and (ii) a *volume expander* at the receiving end which does the opposite and so restores the signal to its original range of amplitudes. The dynamic range of the signals transmitted over the channel is reduced and low level input signals are less affected by noise on the channel because of their increased amplitudes. Compressor and expander together give us the description *compandor.*

The operation of a compressor can be understood from the elementary circuit given in Figure C14(i). The signal is first amplified then it meets two diodes shunting the transmission path. Both diodes are reverse-biased but one conducts and reduces the overall amplification on positive-going signals while the other does the same on negative-going signals. Clearly the higher the level of the signal, the greater is the shunting effect of the diodes. The type of input–output characteristic obtainable with such a circuit is also shown. Typically an input variation of 20 dB might be reduced to an output variation of 5 dB.

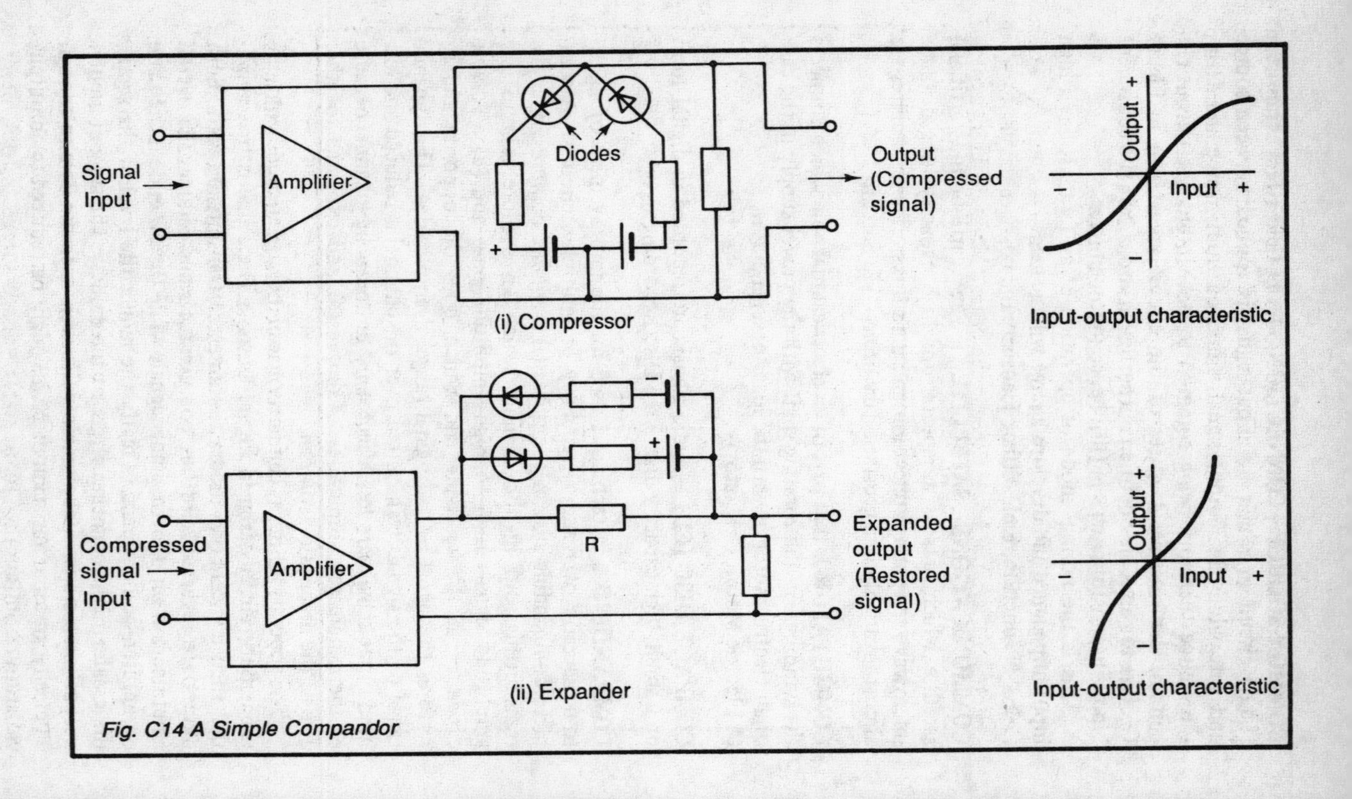

Fig. C14 A Simple Compandor

An expander may similarly use diodes but in this case they shunt a series resistor (R) and therefore reduce its attenuation on the higher level signals. The circuit is shown in (ii) of the figure with an idea of the input–output characteristic. To match the characteristics of the compressor described above, an input variation of 5 dB to the expander should result in an output variation of 20 dB.
(* Multiplex System, Signal-to-Noise Ratio, Limiter)

COMPARATOR – an active circuit which compares two input levels (one of which may be a reference level) and changes its output when either of the input levels exceeds the other. Many different types of circuit are available for example, employing a differential or

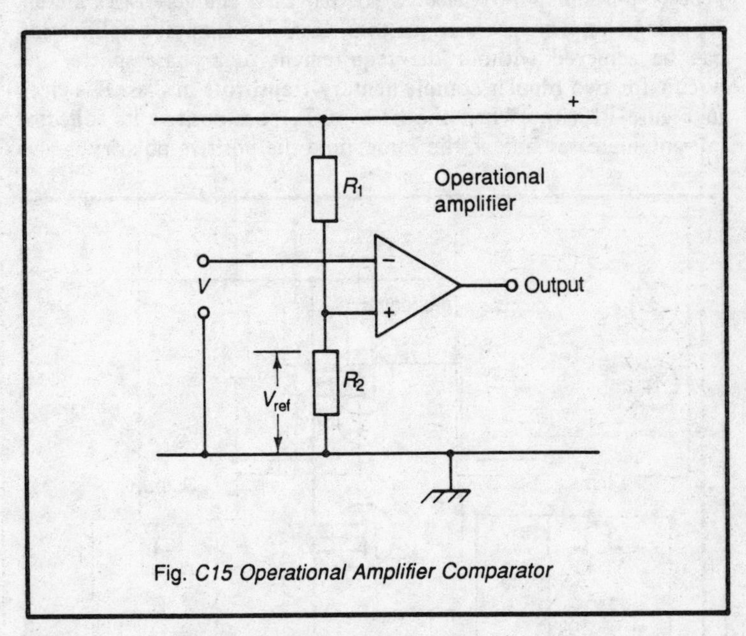

Fig. *C15 Operational Amplifier Comparator*

operational amplifier. The latter has certain advantages and in fact may be specially designed for this purpose.

Figure C15 shows the basic elements of an operational amplifier comparator in which V is compared with a reference level, V_{ref}, obtained from the resistance chain R_1R_2. When $V < V_{ref}$ the amplifier output remains high at several volts (positive saturation) but when V increases and just exceeds V_{ref}, the output switches rapidly to a low value (negative saturation). Switching time can be as low as a few nanoseconds. V_{ref} can of course be derived directly from another more stable voltage source instead. This is

an analogue comparator, digital ones are also used, for example, employing logic circuits which compare two binary numbers.
(* Differential Amplifier, Operational Amplifier, Binary, Binary Code, Digital Logic)

COMPLEMENTARY METAL-OXIDE-SEMICONDUCTOR (CMOS) – a pair of insulated gate field-effect transistors used in integrated circuits, one p-type matching with one n-type. They are especially useful in digital logic circuits because the input impedance is very high and current drain very low – see Complementary Transistors.

COMPLEMENTARY TRANSISTORS – two transistors of opposite type (n-p-n and p-n-p) selected so that their characteristics match. By using complementary transistors, Class B push-pull amplification can be achieved without the requirement of a phase splitter. A circuit for two bipolar complementary transistors in Class B is given in Figure P13(ii). When the base of T_1 goes positive its collector current increases but at the same time the positive polarity is also

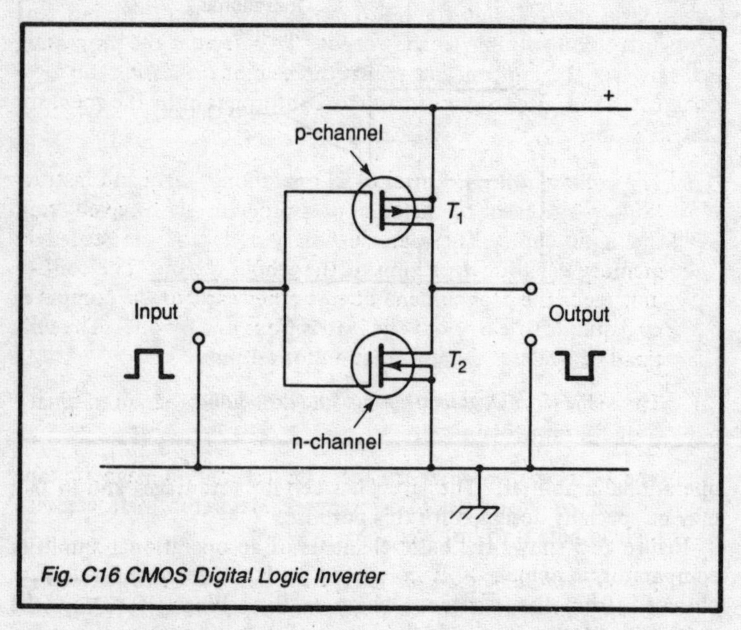

Fig. C16 CMOS Digital Logic Inverter

applied to T_2, the collector current of which falls and vice versa. Hence the two transistors effectively work together in push-pull.

Complementary metal-oxide-semiconductors (CMOS) are also used especially for integrated logic circuits. They have low power

dissipation and a simple example of their use is as an inverter (a NOT gate). The basic circuit is shown in Figure C16. When the input is low (around 0 V), T_1 conducts hence the output terminal voltage rises towards that of the positive line. Conversely when the input is high (around 5 V), T_2 conducts and the output terminal voltage falls, the output is therefore an inversion of the input. CMOS transistors are similarly employed in integrated circuits for NAND and NOR gates.
(* Push-Pull Operation, Class B Amplifier, Digital Logic, Logic Gate, Phase Splitter >> Transistor, Field-Effect Transistor)

COMPRESSOR – short for Volume Compressor – see Companding.

COMPUTER is an electronic device for controlling operations and/or performing calculations according to instructions supplied to it. In a few words, it processes information. Nearly all computers are *digital*, i.e. all information is processed in the form of binary digits (bits). Figure C17 shows a typical digital computer layout. As suggested in the drawing, the information flows from the input unit through the control unit to the output. To carry out the processing task however the control unit enlists the help of the *arithmetic logic unit* (ALU) and also may need to store information in the memory backing store.

(1) The *control unit* is central to all operations. Data and instructions in the form of the computer program are received from the input unit. These are in binary code and are stored in memory cells for operation of the whole system. The control unit reads the program and directs other parts of the computer as required to carry out the instructions one by one. The unit finally correlates the information for output.

(2) The *main store memory* retains the data and program in binary code for immediate use.

(3) The *backing store memory* keeps data stored on magnetic tape or disc for future use in a program. Main store data can also be held here if to be saved.

(4) The *arithmetic logic unit* handles arithmetical calculations (it is similar to an electronic calculator), sorts data (e.g. into alphabetical or numerical order) and performs logical operations.

When the program is completed, the result is sent to the output unit for transmission to a visual display unit (VDU), printer, etc.

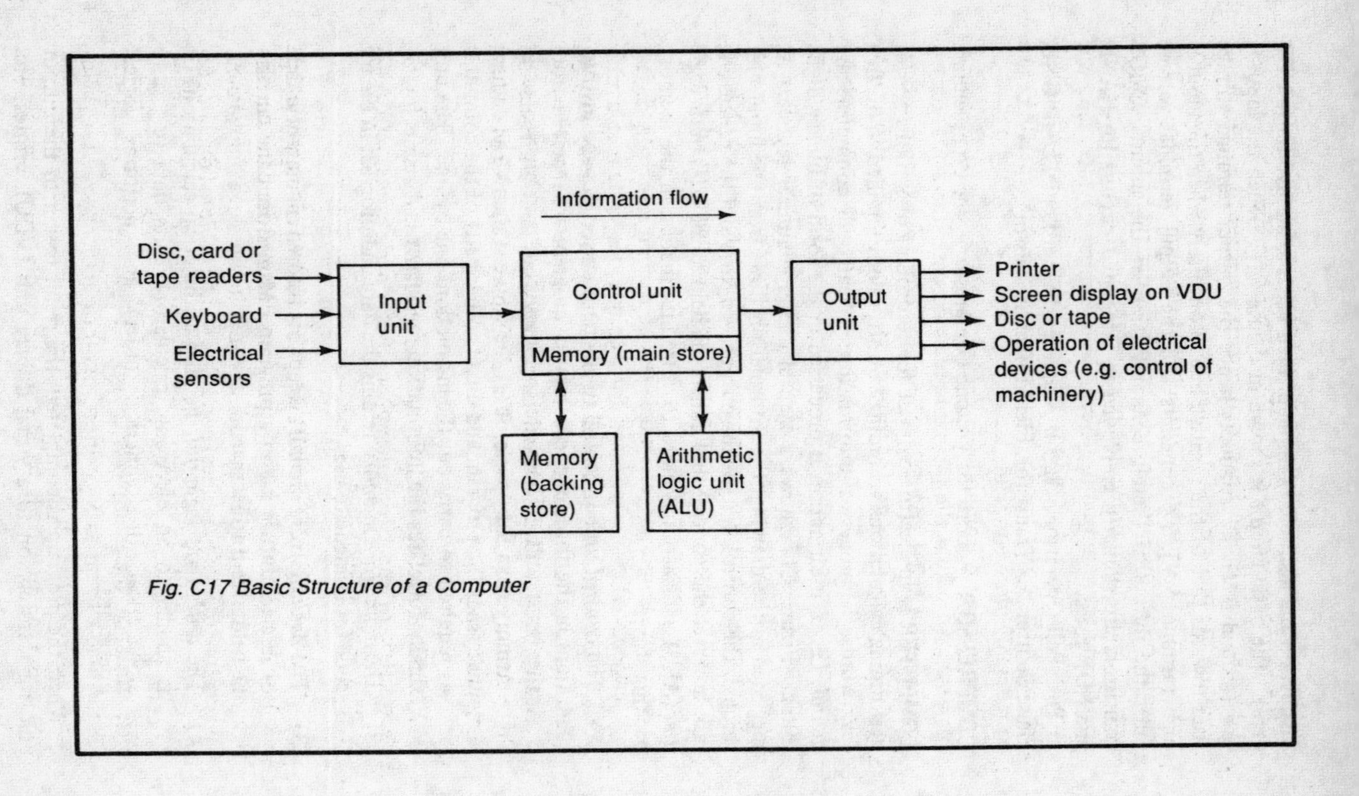

Fig. C17 Basic Structure of a Computer

Generally the control unit and ALU are combined, then known as the *central processing unit* (CPU). Other functions may be added and when in a single integrated circuit, because most computer functions are now catered for, the unit is known as a *microprocessor* and in fact a modern one is virtually a "computer on a chip". The microprocessor operates only on groups of binary digits, known as *words.* Many microprocessors use an 8-bit word but there are also 16, 32 and more bit words. Naturally a computer which can only operate with 32 bits at a time is more complicated and expensive than an 8-bit model but its processing and general capabilities are considerably more powerful.

Programming a computer is carried out in a special computer *language.* Of course the programmer could enter the actual binary digits (the 0's and 1's) which represent a letter, number or instruction and this is done by the experts in a shorthand way, but not generally. To avoid the programmer getting lost in a sea of digits an abbreviated form of the English language is used instead according to the particular use of the computer (e.g. home, finance, etc.). A built-in *interpreter* then accepts the special program instructions and translates them into the one or more word instructions required by the microprocessor. A commonly used language is known as BASIC.

Analogue computers are much less used compared with digital but have advantages when used for example, for certain scientific work or in industrial control of robots where continuously varying quantities have to be monitored.
(* Binary, Binary Code, Digital Logic, Memory, Central Processing Unit, Arithmetic Logic Unit, Visual Display Unit, Word, Chip, Microprocessor)

CONDENSER MICROPHONE An old-fashioned name for an electrostatic or capacitor microphone but a name which refuses to go away – see Microphone.

CONSTANT CURRENT SOURCE This is a current supply which ideally has an infinitely high output impedance so that the current remains constant irrespective of changes in the load impedance. The extent to which the ideal condition can be achieved depends on the type of circuit employed. The earliest and simplest but most wasteful of power uses a high voltage supply operating through a high resistance, for example as shown in Figure C18(i). The figures for the load current as R_L varies from 0 to 200 Ω speak for themselves, the reduction in current is only 0.02%. What can be achieved with this type of circuit is determined simply from Ohm's Law.

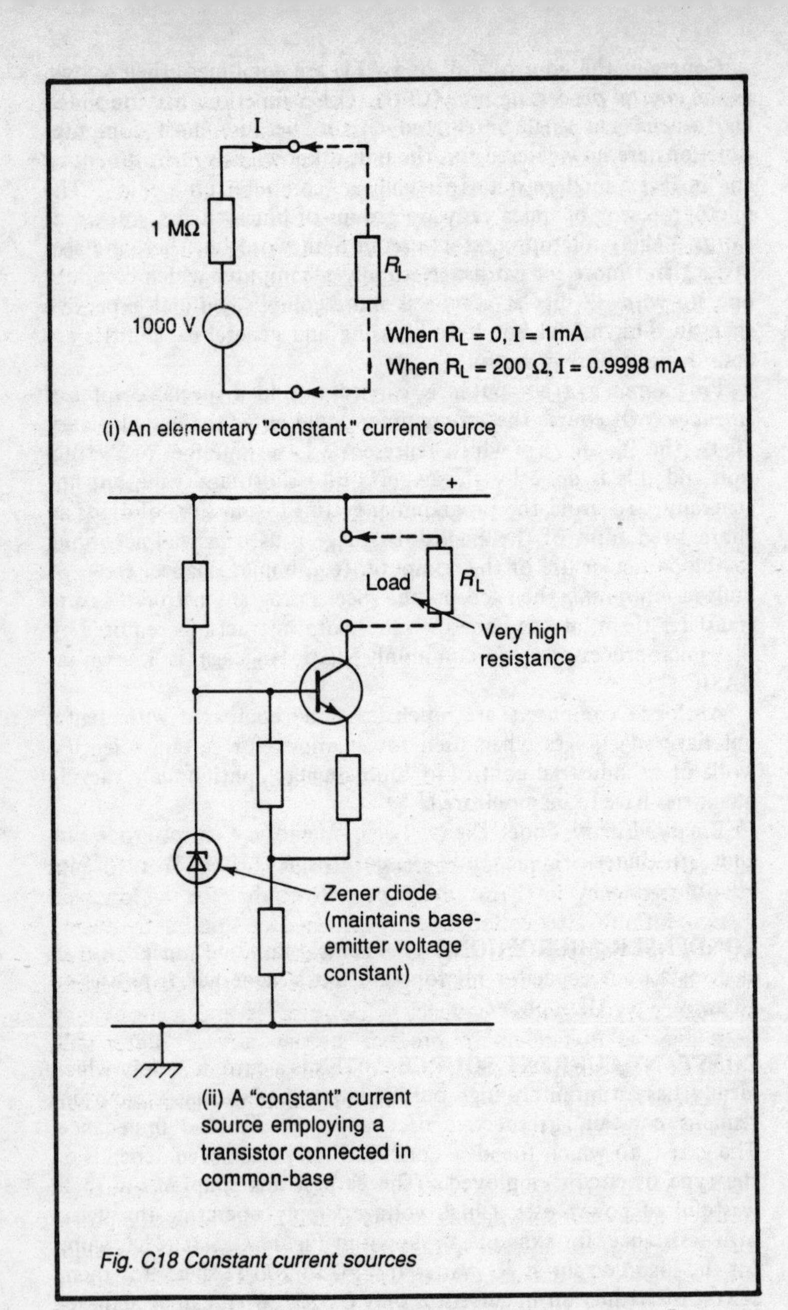

Fig. C18 Constant current sources

Sources employing active components provide reasonably constant current more efficiently. For example a transistor connected in common-base has a very high output resistance which can be kept constant by maintaining a constant emitter-base voltage. In (ii) of the figure the essential features of such a circuit are shown. The performance of a single transistor circuit can easily exceed that of the elementary circuit shown in (i). Circuits embodying field effect transistors or operational amplifiers are also used.
(* Load, Operational Amplifier >> Transistor, Field-Effect Transistor, Zener Diode)

CONSTANT-k FILTER is a type of filter comprising series and shunt reactances of opposite sign as shown for low and high pass sections in Figure C19. Inductive reactance is directly proportional to frequency, capacitive reactance is inversely proportional hence their product is independent of frequency because $j\omega L \times -j/\omega C = L/C$. In design of the filter a *design impedance* R_0 is chosen such that $R_0^2 = L/C$ and L and C can then be calculated. The cut-off frequency becomes:

$$f_c = \frac{1}{\pi\sqrt{LC}} \text{ for the low pass and}$$

$$f_c = \frac{1}{4\pi\sqrt{LC}} \text{ for the high pass}$$

with attenuation/frequency characteristics as shown for a 10 kHz cut-off frequency in (ii) of the figure. Note that for the low pass section infinite attenuation is only attained at infinite frequency and for the high pass it is only at zero frequency. These characteristics do not seem particularly good, moreover the characteristic impedance varies with frequency. However several sections may be connected in tandem to produce steeper curves. Better still, although more complicated, is the m-derived section.
(* m-Derived Filter >> Filter, Network, Complex Notation, Characteristic Impedance)

CONSTANT VOLTAGE SOURCE This is a facility frequently required in electronics which is usually found in the form of a power supply having an output voltage which is substantially constant irrespective of the current drawn. Here we look at the most elementary arrangement to understand why no circuit, however complicated, can produce a truly constant voltage although many modern

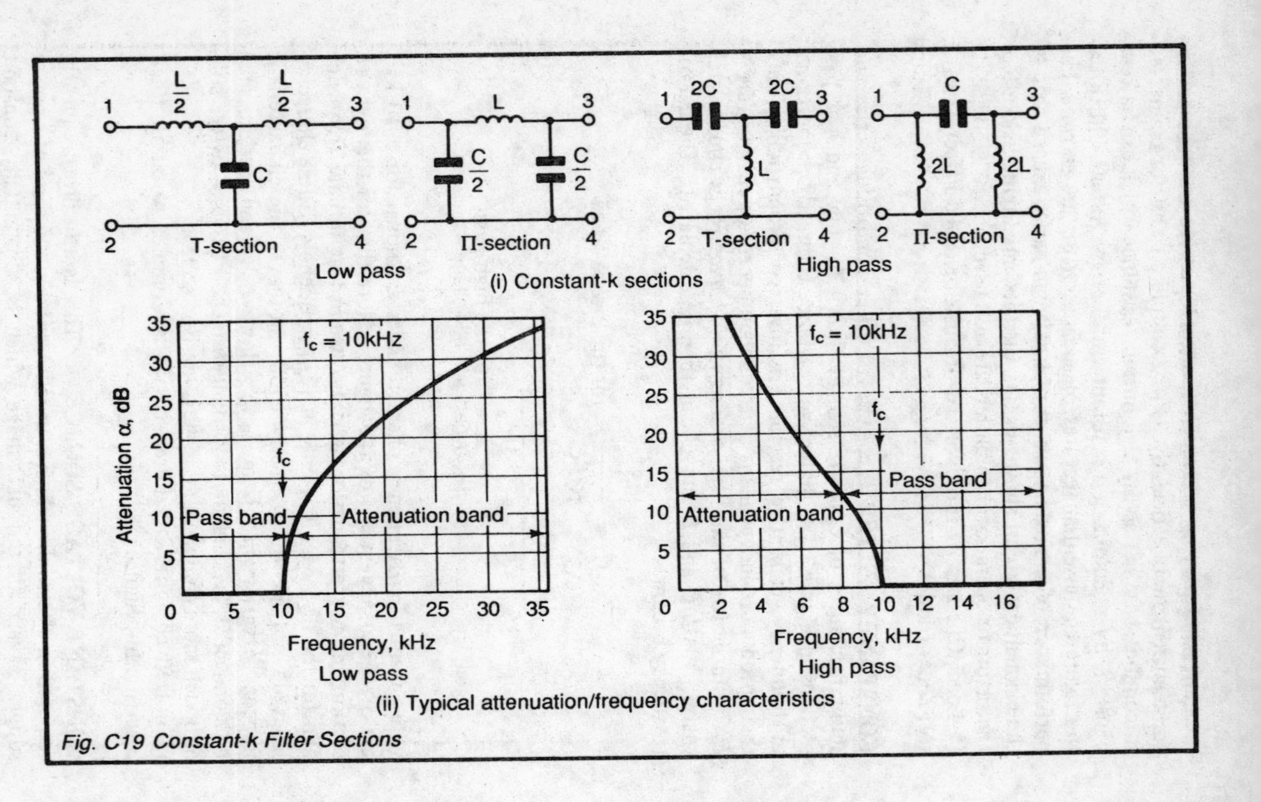

Fig. C19 Constant-k Filter Sections

circuits employing semiconductor technology have a voltage stability which leaves little to be desired.

In Figure C20(i) a 10 V generator supplies a load of resistance R_L. The generator internal resistance is 10 Ω. Simple Ohm's Law calculations show that if R_L changes from 20 to 200 Ω, the voltage across it rises from 6.667 V to 9.523 V, i.e. a rise of nearly 43%. Clearly there is nothing "constant voltage" about this. In (ii) of the figure the generator is shunted by a 1 Ω resistance and with this arrangement the output voltage for the same change in R_L is reduced to 4.1%, still not very good regulation but the simple figures

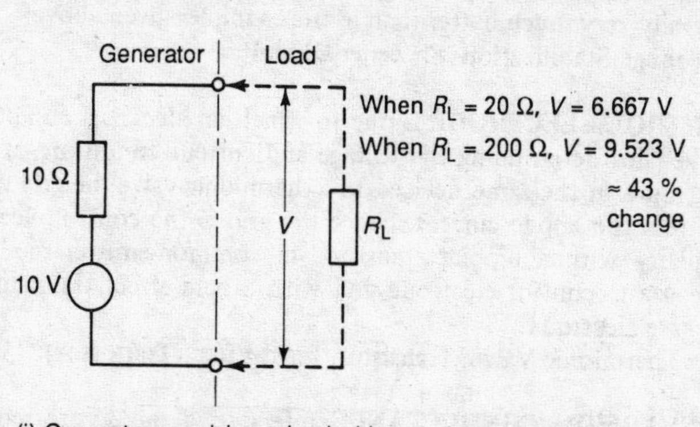

(i) Generator supplying a load with no voltage regulation

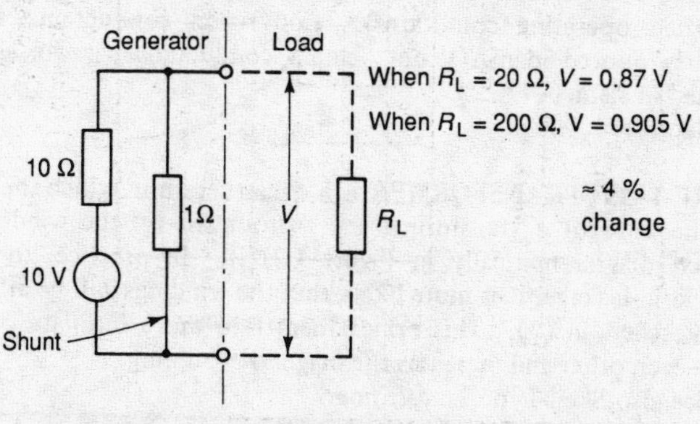

(ii) Generator shunted to provide voltage regulation

Fig. C20 Constant Voltage Source

show what is happening. Changes in R_L have less effect when the generator resistance is low. The price to be paid is in the higher current required from the generator. Every voltage source has some internal resistance, accordingly perfection can never quite be achieved.

An everyday example of a constant voltage source is given by the electricity mains from which we can draw heavy currents with little effect on the voltage. That the source resistance is low is obvious if we pause to consider the enormous number of low resistance devices connected in parallel across the generator output.

Most constant voltage sources now rely on semiconductor technology with results depending on the complexity of the circuit but generally very much better than in the examples given above.
(* Voltage Stabilization >> Zener Diode)

CONTROL ELECTRODE is one to which an electrical condition is applied for determining the voltage and current conditions at other electrodes in the same device. In a thermionic valve the grid voltage controls the anode current, hence the grid is the control electrode. Similarly with a bipolar transistor in common-emitter mode, the base is the control electrode and with a field-effect transistor it is the gate electrode.
(>> Thermionic Valve, Transistor, Field-Effect Transistor)

CONVERSION CONDUCTANCE refers to a mixer or frequency changer. It is the ratio between a small change in the output current and the small change in signal input voltage which causes it (under specified operating conditions). Conversion conductance is frequently quoted in mA/V but being a conductance, it can also be quoted in siemens (A/V).
(* Mixer >> Siemens)

CORE-TYPE TRANSFORMER is a construction in which the limbs of the core of a transformer are surrounded by the windings as shown diagrammatically in Figure C21(i). In practice, to avoid magnetic leakage, it is more likely that the windings will be arranged as sketched in (ii). This brings them into more intimate contact with each other and increases the magnetic coupling.

See also Shell-Type Transformer.
(* Lamination >> Transformer, Core, Magnetic Circuit)

COUNTER is the name most frequently used to describe a laboratory instrument capable of operating in several different counting modes. Some of the tasks it can perform are (i) frequency

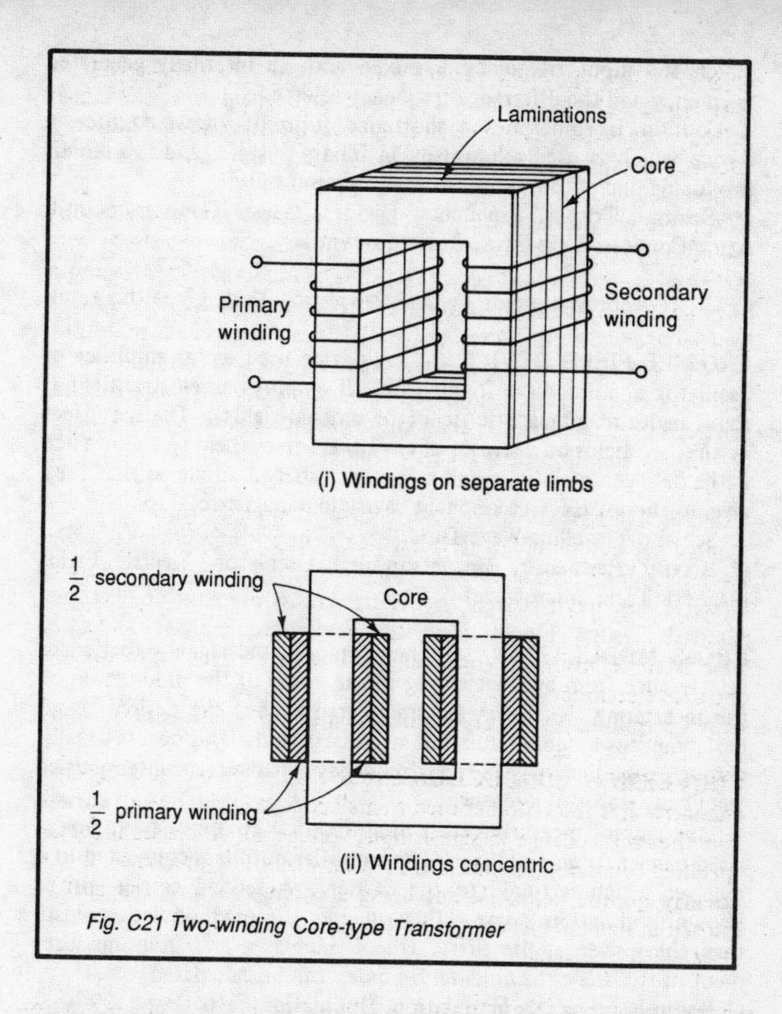

Fig. C21 Two-winding Core-type Transformer

measurement including frequencies in the gigahertz range, (ii) frequency comparison, (iii) totalising i.e. adding the number of pulses received over a given period and displaying the total, (iv) time measurement, (v) finding the ratios between two input signals.

Because input signals may be of any form and amplitude, they are first amplified if necessary and then shaped by using for example, a Schmitt trigger to produce square pulses for operation of the counting circuits. A stable internal crystal-controlled oscillator is employed to generate a measurement time base. For the measurement of very high frequencies the input frequency is first divided down, alternatively the heterodyne principle may be employed in which the input frequency is mixed with an internally generated frequency and the difference frequency selected.

Counter is sometimes a shortened form of *digital counter*, a device which is used extensively in binary systems and is a circuit producing one output pulse for every *n* input pulses.
(* Schmitt Trigger, Frequency Divider, Geiger Counter, Scintillation Counter, Time Base >> Heterodyne)

CPU Abbreviation of Central Processing Unit – see this term.

CROSSED-FIELD DEVICE A device used as an amplifier or oscillator at microwave frequencies. It employs an electric field at right angles to a magnetic field (the crossed fields). The net effect of the two fields on a stream of electrons forces them to follow such paths between a cathode and a specially shaped anode so that they give up energy, e.g. to a resonant cavity in a magnetron.

See also Travelling-Wave Tube.
(* Cavity Resonator, Magnetron >> Oscillator, Electric Field, Magnetic Field, Microwave)

CROSS MODULATION When a modulated signal experiences interference from another strong signal, some of the modulation of the interfering signal may be transferred. Thus the desired signal has some unwanted modulation impressed on it. This occurs usually through non-linearity in the frequency changer or intermediate frequency stages of a receiver.

One way of measuring cross modulation is to apply an unmodulated carrier to an amplifier. The amplifier output is connected to a receiver which is tuned to the carrier. A second carrier with a known modulation factor is then added. If cross modulation exists then the power of the first carrier is increased and from measurement of this the *cross modulation index* can be calculated.
(* Radio Receiver >> Modulation, Modulation Factor)

CROSSOVER DISTORTION arises in Class B push-pull transistor amplifiers due to curvature of the transfer characteristic (collector current v base-emitter voltage or base current) at the lower end. Similar conditions apply to the same type of thermionic valve amplifiers. In push-pull working each of the two transistors handles its own half of the input cycle, their characteristics can therefore be drawn together as shown in Figure C22. If the transistors are biased to cut-off for the greatest efficiency, then the output current waveform will not be a pure sine wave but will exhibit distortion where the wave crosses the axis as shown. This is known as *crossover*

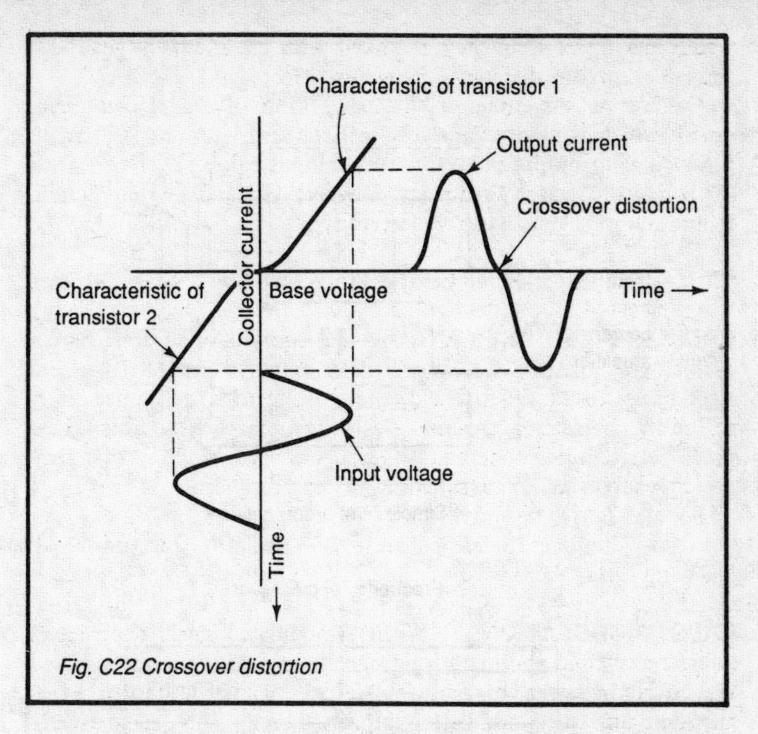

Fig. C22 Crossover distortion

distortion and it can be reduced by biasing the transistors slightly so that a small quiescent (no signal) current flows. The transistors then operate over less of the bottom bend of the characteristic and distortion is less.
(* Class B Amplifier, Push-Pull Operation >> Distortion)

CROSSOVER NETWORK is a special filtering system used with two or more loudspeakers which divides the input frequency range into the appropriate bands for each speaker. It is also known as a *dividing network.* With 2-speaker systems the network separates the bass and treble frequency bands. The network has a *crossover frequency* below which all frequencies are directed to the bass (l.f.) unit and above which to the treble (h.f.) unit. The simplest type of network but one which demonstrates the principle, is shown in Figure C23(i). It consists solely of an inductor which passes low frequencies to the l.f. loudspeaker in parallel with a capacitor feeding the h.f. unit.

Crossover networks are classified according to their rate of change of attenuation with frequency in the crossover region. They are known as *first*, *second* or *third order* networks and have 6, 12 or

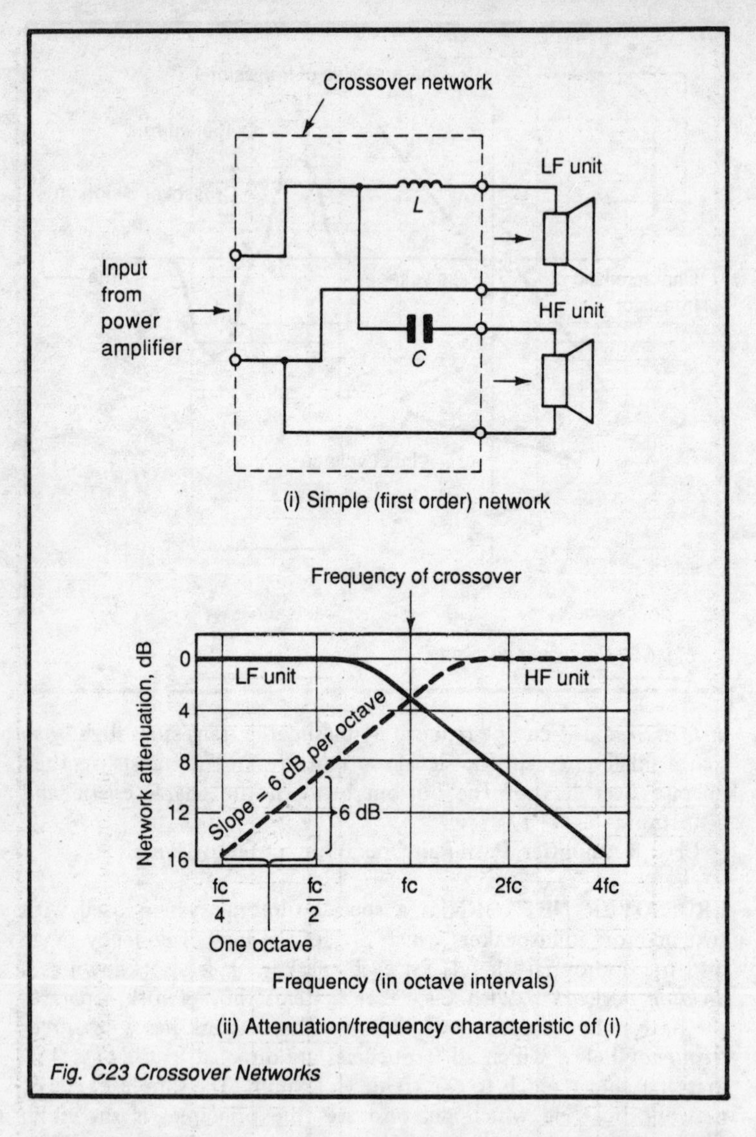

Fig. C23 Crossover Networks

18 dB attenuation per octave respectively. The network shown in (i) is first order and the type of frequency characteristic obtainable is shown in (ii). Second and third order networks have sharper cut-off characteristics but require extra components.

The complete story of a crossover network being used to combine an l.f. unit having little response above 10 kHz with an h.f. unit

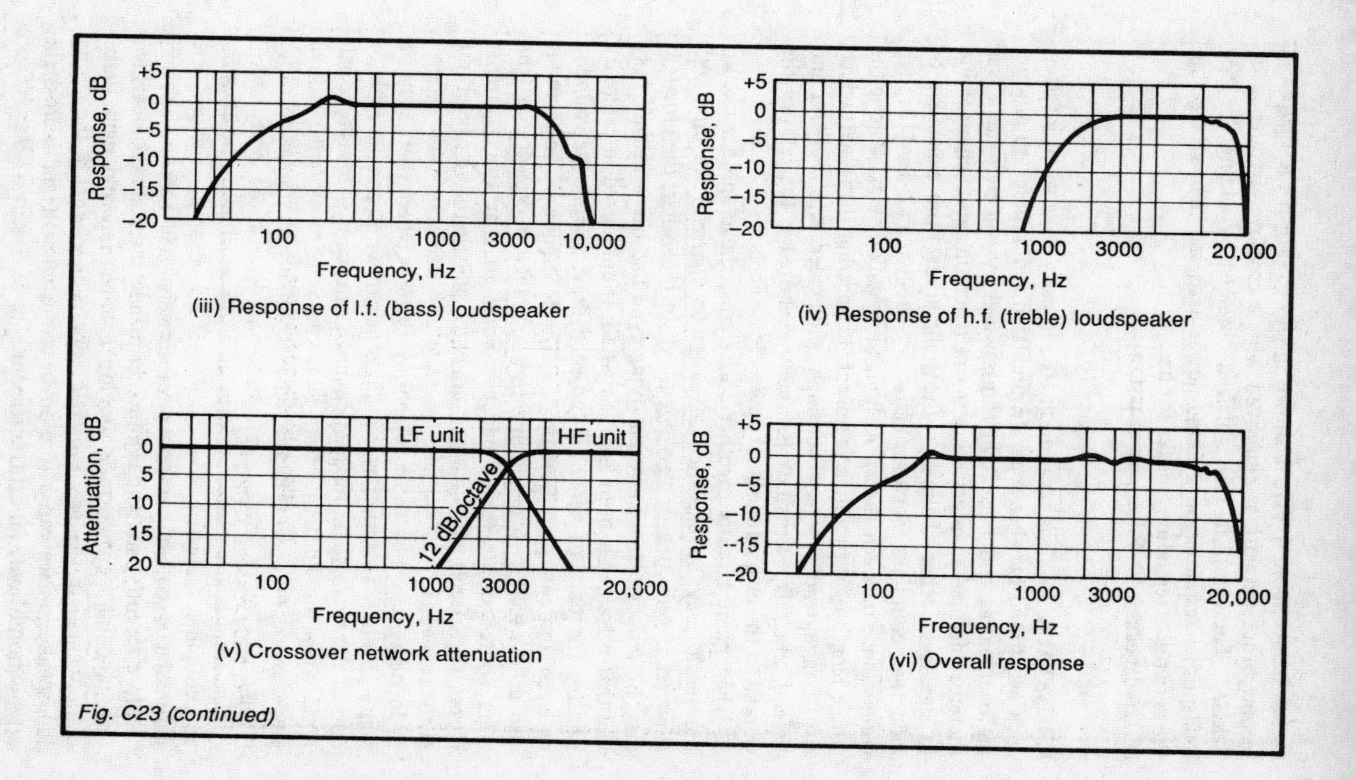

Fig. C23 (continued)

useless below about 1 kHz is shown in (iii) to (vi) of the figure. A second order network is employed with a crossover frequency of 3 kHz. The result in (vi) which is obtained by adding the two loudspeaker responses on a sound power basis and then subtracting the network attenuation, speaks for itself.
(* Loudspeaker >> Filter, Attenuation)

CROSSTALK This term originated in early days when interference was found between separate circuits in audio cables, so producing overhearing and noise. In transmission by cable crosstalk was therefore defined as interference in one communication channel due to signals in other channels. Crosstalk arises from capacitive or inductive couplings between adjacent circuits and also through conductance between them. Although crosstalk may exist along the whole length of a circuit, it is only that appearing at the ends which is of consequence. It is accordingly subdivided into *near-end* and *far-end* crosstalk. Crosstalk is usually measured as the ratio of the wanted to the unwanted signal powers in decibels.

When many circuits together create crosstalk in another circuit, the result may be classified as noise or *unintelligible* crosstalk. However if only one or two circuits disturb another, the crosstalk may be *intelligible*, a more annoying type because a listener may feel that privacy has been lost. Crosstalk is minimized in cables by rotating the pairs of wires around each other so that the coupling between any two pairs is reduced. The technique of *balancing* is also used which involves adding tiny amounts of capacitance (the main source of crosstalk) between wires so that stray currents picked up in each wire of a pair are equal and therefore cancel out at the two ends.

In high frequency cable telephony systems where there may be many channels operating over a single pair of wires, coaxial cable or optical fibre, crosstalk between channels can occur. This is especially so when non-linearity exists somewhere in the system for then any channel may develop frequency components proper to other channels. High crosstalk separation of 80 dB or more is necessary.

The term is also used in television, again referring to the unwanted coupling between two circuits, for example, when the chrominance (colour) component of the signal is affected.

More recently, stereo has joined in with its crosstalk problems for unwanted interference may develop between left and right signal components. In this case crosstalk appears as a signal in the wrong loudspeaker so we can afford to be more tolerant and a crosstalk attenuation of only 30 dB is sufficient.

(* Channel, Telecommunication System, Television Signal, Stereophonic System >> Non-Linearity)

CRYOTRON is a switching device used at very low temperatures where superconductivity is possible. The idea behind it is to be able to switch a material either into its superconductive state or out of it. Materials which can become superconductive, do so at a certain critical low temperature but if an applied magnetic flux has a value above a certain level, the superconductivity is destroyed. Hence if two strips of superconductive material (such as tin and lead) cross, but are insulated from each other on a thin-film circuit, the magnetic field arising from the presence of a current in one of the strips can change the superconductivity of the other strip. Accordingly the current carrying strip acts as a switch.
(* Hybrid Integrated Circuit >> Magnetic Flux, Superconductivity)

CRYSTAL FILTER A quartz crystal behaves as an electrical resonant circuit hence for certain applications it can replace the normal LC circuit. It follows therefore that crystals may be employed as the frequency determining elements in filters. Owing to the high Q-factor of quartz crystals their use is usually limited to filters of the narrow band-pass type.
(>> Quartz Crystal, Piezoelectric Effect, Filter, Q-Factor)

CRYSTAL MICROPHONE A type of microphone which functions by varying pressure on a piezoelectric crystal – see Microphone.

CRYSTAL OSCILLATOR Oscillators controlled by the piezoelectric effect in a crystal have the considerable advantage of high stability, hence their use in high precision frequency control and in time keeping. For this quartz probably has pride of place and so is used extensively. If a specially cut plate from a crystal of quartz has an oscillatory voltage applied to a pair of electrodes on opposite sides of the plate, the latter will vibrate at the frequency of the applied voltage. When this frequency coincides with the mechanical resonance of the plate, the mechanical vibration increases greatly and the voltage developed across the plate is maximum. A crystal under these conditions behaves as an electrical resonant circuit and in fact can be shown to have an equivalent circuit of inductance, L, capacitances, C and C_0 and resistance, R as shown in Figure C24. It is evident that a crystal can replace the resonant circuit of most oscillators with the attendant advantages of high frequency stability and high Q-factor. That Q can be very high can be judged from the

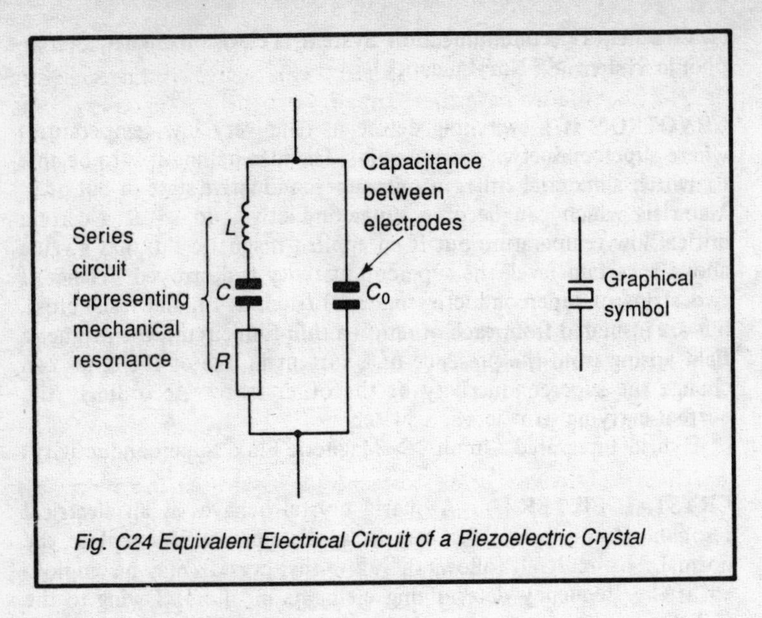

Fig. C24 Equivalent Electrical Circuit of a Piezoelectric Crystal

following set of typical values:

$$L = 15\ \text{H} \qquad C = 0.08\ \text{pF} \qquad R = 200\ \Omega\,.$$

The series resonance frequency is about 145 kHz with Q at around 68 000. C_0 which is a parallel capacitance, represents that between the electrodes and as the circuit indicates, there must also be a parallel resonance frequency. This is normally quite close to the series resonance frequency and in fact either can be used.

An example of an oscillator which shows how a crystal can be inserted in the feedback path of an amplifier is given in Figure O3(iv). On the same diagram are the Colpitts and Hartley oscillators, both are easily adapted for crystal control. In the Colpitts for example, it is the inductor which is replaced by a crystal. Alternatively in the Hartley the crystal may be added to the resonant circuit by connecting it across the capacitor, *C*. Both the electrical and crystal resonances are of the same order of frequency but in this case the crystal "pulls in" the frequency to its own resonance and hence adds its frequency stability to the circuit. This is an example of a *crystal controlled oscillator*, i.e. one in which the crystal is an added refinement, not the main source of resonance.

Typically crystal oscillators have a frequency stability of some 1 in 10^6 when operated under the variations of "room temperature". By operating the crystal in a temperature-controlled oven, stabilities up to 1 in 10^{10} are possible.

For an example of the widespread use of quartz crystal oscillators in everyday life we have the quartz crystal clock. The crystal runs at some 2–5 MHz and in fact acts like a high speed pendulum. Such clocks have a high degree of accuracy, the omnipresent home clock is usually accurate to less than a minute per year, some even down to a few seconds.
(* Oscillator >> Quartz Crystal, Piezoelectric Effect, Resonance, Q-Factor)

CURRENT FEEDBACK is one of the methods of applying negative feedback to an amplifier. A fraction of the current output to the load is diverted back to the input.
(>> Feedback)

CURRENT TRANSFORMER is generally used in an instrument for measuring heavy alternating currents. Its purpose is to carry most of the circuit current to avoid it flowing through the instrument. The circuit current flows through a heavy duty primary winding of low resistance. The secondary has a small current induced into it (according to the turns ratio of the transformer) which operates the measuring instrument. Such a transformer is also known as an *instrument transformer.*
(>> Transformer, Ammeter)

CYCLOTRON is a particle accelerator used for nuclear physics investigations. A beam of high-energy particles is accelerated between semicircular electrodes by a radio frequency field. The particles are forced to travel in an open spiral by a magnetic field applied at right angles to the plane of the electrodes – see Accelerator.

DARK CURRENT The current which flows in a photosensitive material when there is no illumination.
(>> Photodiode)

DARLINGTON PAIR refers to a pair of transistors connected to operate effectively as a single transistor having a high current gain (forward-current transfer ratio). The basic features of a circuit are shown in Figure D1. In this particular circuit there is evidently a

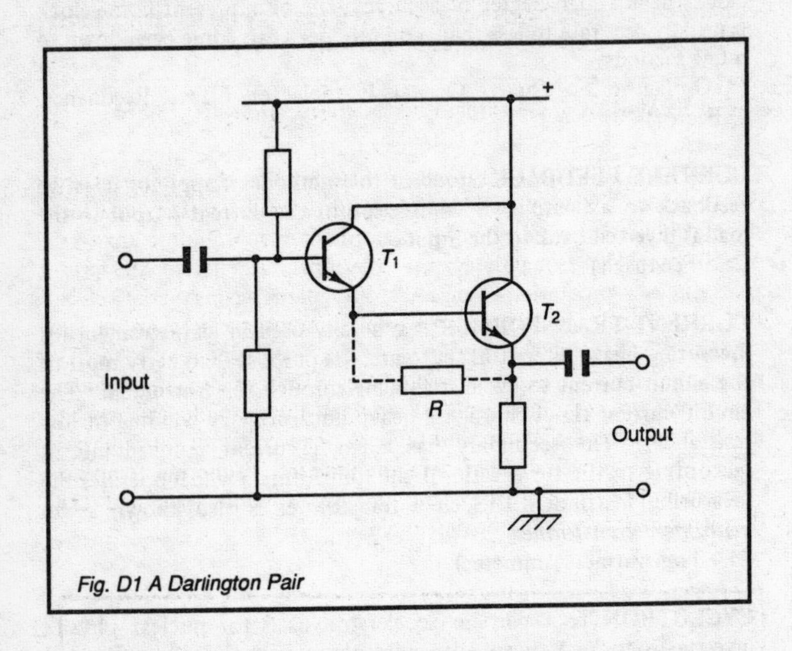

Fig. D1 A Darlington Pair

relationship with the emitter-follower since both collectors are connected directly to the supply line. Darlington pairs may also be connected in common-emitter. Note that in the figure the emitter current of T_1 supplies the base current of T_2. If however the emitter current of T_1 is too small (it can only be the tiny base current of T_2), then the resistor, R, may be added. R must be carefully chosen because too high a value does not increase T_1 emitter current sufficiently while too low a value diverts current away from T_2 base.

It can be shown that such a circuit has approximately unity voltage gain and a current gain theoretically the sum of the two individual current gains, but in practice somewhat less. The input impedance is very high, the output impedance, very low. Darlington pairs may be formed from discrete components or alternatively may be available within single encapsulations.
(* Emitter Follower, Common Emitter Connection, Hybrid Parameters)

D.C. AMPLIFIER Abbreviated form of Direct-Coupled Amplifier – see this term.

D.C. COUPLING refers to interstage coupling within an amplifier. For the coupling to be effective at zero frequency no reactance must be present – see Direct-Coupled Amplifier.

D.C. RESTORER – see Direct Current Restoration.

D.C. STABILIZATION is a means of ensuring that the d.c. operating conditions of a device such as a transistor are substantially unaffected by the various conditions which normally would impose changes. Stabilization guards mainly against variations in the device characteristics due to temperature changes. It also guards against variations in circuit performance when for example a transistor is changed for unless specially selected, transistors of the same type may in reality have appreciably different characteristics. There is also the problem of *thermal runaway* in transistors in which for example, an increase in temperature of the junction increases the collector current and therefore the power dissipated in the junction. Junction temperature therefore rises further, the process is cumulative and the transistor may eventually be destroyed.

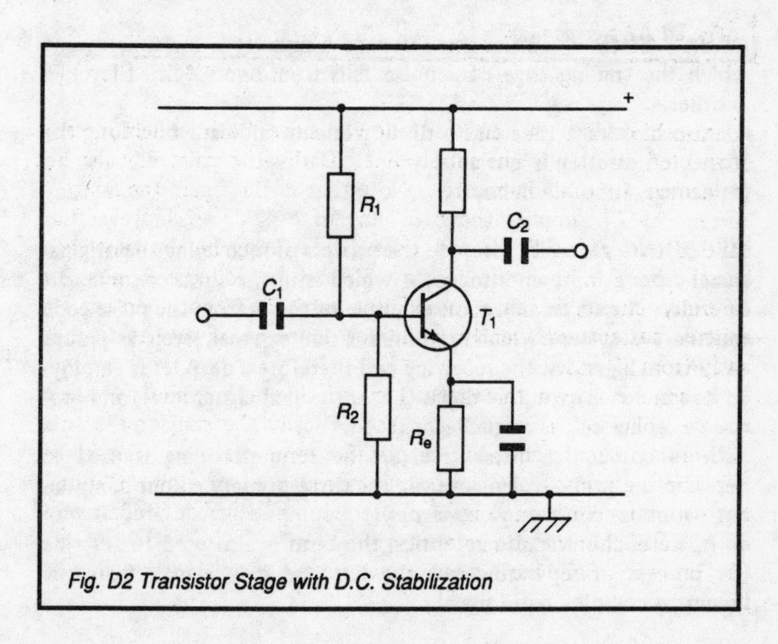

Fig. D2 Transistor Stage with D.C. Stabilization

The classic circuit used to demonstrate d.c. stabilization is given in Figure D2. It is a straightforward amplification stage built around an n-p-n transistor T_1. The potential divider R_1R_2 holds the base of the transistor slightly positive. The emitter is also held positive by the voltage developed across R_e. The emitter-base potential is therefore the difference between these two potentials, this is chosen so that the transistor is forward biased to the degree required.

Assume that there is an increase in base current and/or temperature in the collector-base junction. The collector current increases but so does the emitter current. This gives rise to an increase in the voltage developed across R_e which reduces the forward bias and so reduces the base current, i.e. there is automatic compensation for the original change. With such an arrangement it is clear that the transistor cannot destroy itself by thermal runaway. Also replacement of the transistor by another of the same type will affect the circuit performance less than without stabilization.

(* Stabilization >> P-N Junction)

DEBUNCHING arises in an electron beam for example, as emitted by an electron gun. Electrons, being all equal negative charges, repel each other therefore a beam will tend to spread. The degree of spread is measured by the *divergence angle.*

(* Electron Gun >> Charge)

DECAY TIME When this refers to a pulse it is the time during which the trailing edge of a pulse falls from one specified level to another.

Also a storage tube has a decay time to indicate how long the stored information is available.

(* Storage Tube >> Pulse)

DECODING generally refers to the process of recovering the original signal from a representation of it which is in the form of some sort of code. A particularly good example of this is from the pulse code modulation system which transmits discrete signal levels as groups of binary digits. At the receiving end therefore a decoder is employed to take each group of digits (i.e. the coded signal level) and produce a replica of the original signal.

In a colour television receiver the term decoding is used to describe the process of recovering the three primary colour components from the complex video signal.

In stereophonic radio reception the term is also used to describe the process of separating out the left and right signals from the incoming complex radio signal.

(* Pulse Code Modulation, Binary Code, Television Receiver, Television Signal, Stereophonic Broadcasting)

DECOUPLING is the technique of preventing signals in one path of a main circuit from causing interference in other parts. Figure D3 shows two well established methods of decoupling as examples.

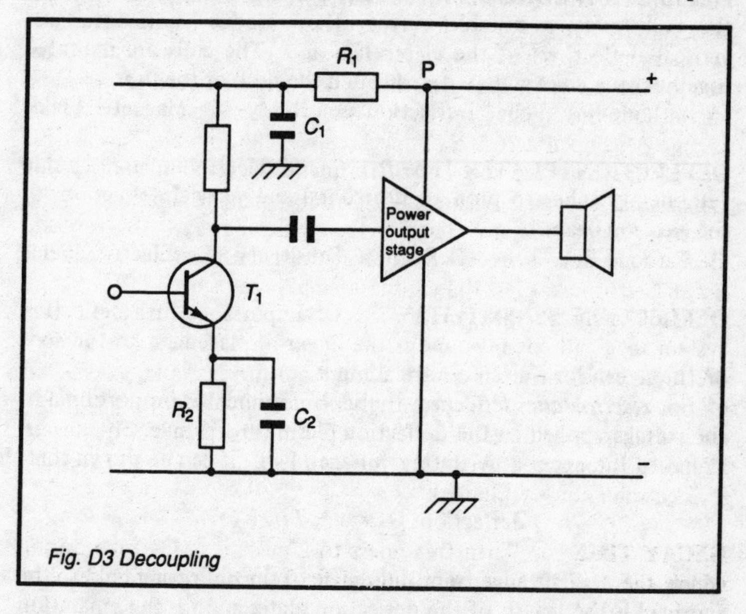

Fig. D3 Decoupling

R_1C_1 acts as a simple filter and decouples the positive line supply to the amplifier stage of T_1 (and earlier stages, if any). This minimizes the effect of signal voltages set up at point P by the power output stage (not shown in detail). It is essential that these voltages should not reach T_1 and so be amplified otherwise instability may arise. The reactance of C_1 is made small at the lowest frequency to be amplified hence on a potential divider basis, most of the signal voltage arising at P is dropped across R_1, accordingly it does not enter the T_1 stage.

C_2 is also a decoupling capacitor. R_2 is an emitter bias resistor used in the d.c. stabilization of T_1, it provides a measure of d.c. feedback. Without C_2 therefore, R_2 also provides a.c. feedback which may not be required. Accordingly C_2 decouples R_2, i.e. it provides a low reactance path for the signal currents. Generally the reactance of C_2 should be at least one-tenth of the resistance of R_2 at the lowest operating frequency for satisfactory decoupling. (* D.C. Stabilization >> Transistor, Reactance)

DE-EMPHASIS is part of a *pre-emphasis* technique for the improvement of signal-to-noise ratio at the higher frequencies on audio signals. Subjectively the effect of noise is reduced – see Pre-Emphasis.

DEFLECTION COILS are those used with cathode-ray tubes. When the coils carry a suitable current they produce horizontal and vertical deflections of the electron beam. The coils are mounted together on a *yoke* and are fixed round the neck of the tube.
(* Cathode-Ray Tube, Deflection Sensitivity >> Magnetic Field)

DEFLECTION PLATES are flat metal electrodes used inside cathode-ray tubes to produce horizontal and vertical deflections of the electron beam.
(* Cathode-Ray Tube, Deflection Sensitivity >> Electric Field)

DEFLECTION SENSITIVITY Of importance in a deflection system in a cathode-ray tube is the linear displacement of the spot on the screen for a given electrical input.

For *electrostatic deflection* the spot movement is proportional to the voltage applied to the deflection plates (v) and inversely proportional to the beam accelerating voltage (V_A). It can be shown that:

$$\text{deflection}, D \propto v \times Ll/2V_A s$$

where L is the distance from the centre of the deflecting field to the screen, l is the length of the deflection plates and s is the separation between the plates.

For a given system therefore D varies only with v hence the deflection sensitivity may be quoted for example in millimetres of spot movement per volt applied to the plates.

For *electromagnetic deflection* the deflection is proportional to the flux density in the coil (and therefore to the current) and inversely proportional to the square root of the beam accelerating voltage:

$$D \propto I \times Ll/\sqrt{V_A}$$

where I is the coil current, L and V_A are as above and l is now the length of the deflecting field.

For a given system therefore D varies only with I hence the deflection sensitivity may be quoted for example as millimetres of spot movement per milliampere of current in the windings.

For both electrostatic and electromagnetic systems the deflection sensitivity is linear up to the frequency at which the phase of the deflecting voltage or current begins to reverse before an electron has passed out of its influence. This frequency is higher for the electrostatic because it has not the limitations imposed by coil inductance. (* Cathode-Ray Tube, Electron Gun >> Electric Field, Magnetic Flux Density)

DEGASSING is a process employed in the manufacture of thermionic valves, cathode-ray tubes, etc. with glass envelopes to remove the last traces of occluded (retained) gases from the metal electrodes. While the device is still connected to the vacuum pump a coil carrying a large radio frequency current is placed around it. Eddy currents induced in the metal parts within the glass envelope heat up the metal to a high temperature, any remaining gases are therefore driven off and removed by the pump. After this the envelope is sealed.

The process usually includes the use of a *getter*. This is for example, a magnesium or barium pellet placed inside the envelope. It is vapourised by eddy current heating to remove any further traces of gas chemically.
(* Cathode-Ray Tube >> Eddy Current, Thermionic Valve)

DEKATRON is a cold-cathode gas-filled tube containing a central anode with 10 cathodes arranged in a circle around it with *transfer electrodes* between them. When a suitable voltage is applied between the anode and any cathode a glow discharge is set up between them. If a voltage pulse is applied to the transfer electrodes, the glow discharge moves from one cathode to the next. The tube is therefore capable of counting the voltage pulses received since the glow discharge moves round the circle in 10 steps. Several tubes in cascade make a complete decimal counter.
(>> Cold Cathode, Gas Discharge)

DELAY EQUALIZER is a network which compensates for the effects of delay distortion. It generally consists of a filter with the appropriate attenuation/frequency characteristic in conjunction with a phase correcting section which provides a level delay response over the filter pass band.
(* Equalization >> Delay Distortion, Filter, Phase)

DELAY LINE is a circuit which increases the delay in the transmission of a signal over a system. The term "line" is used because a length of cable was one of the devices originally used. However relatively long delay times using for example, coaxial cable are hardly practical because electromagnetic waves propagate in coaxial cables at a speed approaching that of light hence the cable is long and bulky and its attenuation is high. In place of the cable, artificial transmission lines may be used consisting of lumped capacitors and inductors.

Longer time delays are achieved using acoustic delay lines in which the signal is converted into an acoustic wave first through the piezoelectric effect. Such waves are comparatively slow in moving and are transmitted through a liquid or solid before reconversion. Charge-coupled devices are also used, they have the distinct advantage of extremely small size.
(* Acoustic Wave Device, Charge-Coupled Device >> Transmission Line)

DETECTOR is a circuit or device used in any transmission system involving a carrier wave to regain the original modulating signal. The process is also known as *demodulation.* One of the earliest detectors used was the *crystal* which in conjunction with its *cat's whisker* acted simply as a rectifier. Nowadays a tiny diode does the same job only better. Detectors can be *linear*, i.e. the output is proportional to the modulated signal amplitude or *square law*, giving an output proportional to the square of the modulated signal.
(>> Modulation, Carrier Wave, Demodulation)

DICHROIC MIRROR The word comes from the Greek, meaning two colours and in this type of mirror doubly refracting crystals *reflect* the visible frequency band required but *transmit* all other frequencies. Such mirrors are used in television cameras, flying-spot scanners, etc. for separating out the red, green and blue components from white light.
(* Television Camera, Flying-Spot Scanner >> Light, Visible Spectrum)

DIELECTRIC HEATING is electrical heating of insulating or dielectric materials. The technique can be considered as founded on a two plate capacitor having a dielectric which is the material to be heated, with a high frequency alternating voltage applied to the plates. The alternating electric field creates an alternating electric polarization within the dielectric which therefore heats up. The power generated within the dielectric is proportional to the permittivity and the dielectric power factor. The power factor is quite low at low frequencies, hence considerably higher frequency voltages are used, in fact in the MHz and low GHz range. The heating is also proportional to the square of the voltage applied, hence the voltage is limited to a value below that which would cause breakdown.

(>> Dielectric, Electric Polarization, Permittivity, Dielectric Phase Angle, Breakdown)

DIELECTRIC ISOLATION is a technique used in integrated circuit manufacture to insulate elements from each other – see Isolation.

DIFFERENTIAL AMPLIFIER is a direct coupled amplifier with two inputs but only one output. The output signal is proportional to the *difference* between the two inputs and is therefore zero when the input signals are equal. How such an amplifier functions is probably best understood by considering an elementary circuit as in Figure D4(i). In this circuit the two emitters are directly connected with a common emitter resistor R_E. Both transistors are forward biased by the same amount by the resistor chains R_1, R_2 in conjunction with R_E, hence equal collector currents flow in the load resistors R_L and no difference of potential exists across the output terminals. Temperature changes affect both transistors equally, hence the zero output condition remains.

When a signal is applied to the input terminals, the collector voltages swing in opposite directions and the output voltage is the difference between them hence the name *differential* or *difference* amplifier. This makes the circuit suitable for use as a phase-splitter. For obvious reasons the circuit is also known as an *emitter-coupled pair* or *long-tailed pair*, the latter term referring to the common emitter resistor. This on a circuit diagram, by a small stretch of the imagination, might be looked upon as a tail, the length (in resistance terms) determining how nearly it becomes a constant current source.

In a practical amplifier zero output for no input signals may be difficult to achieve so there may be a small residual voltage at the output. How good an amplifier is in this respect is indicated by its *common-mode rejection ratio*, that is, the extent to which common-mode signals at the input produce no output. It is defined by the ratio between the signal voltages v_1 and v_2 where v_1 is that which when applied to both input terminals will produce the same output as v_2 applied to one terminal only – see (i) of the figure.

Many types of differential amplifier are derived from operational amplifiers which conveniently have the two inputs and one output. A very simplified arrangement is given in (ii) of the figure especially to show a method of introducing the input voltages.
(* Direct-Coupled Amplifier, Operational Amplifier >> Transistor, Amplifier)

DIFFERENTIAL GALVANOMETER A special type of galvanometer which produces a deflection according to the difference

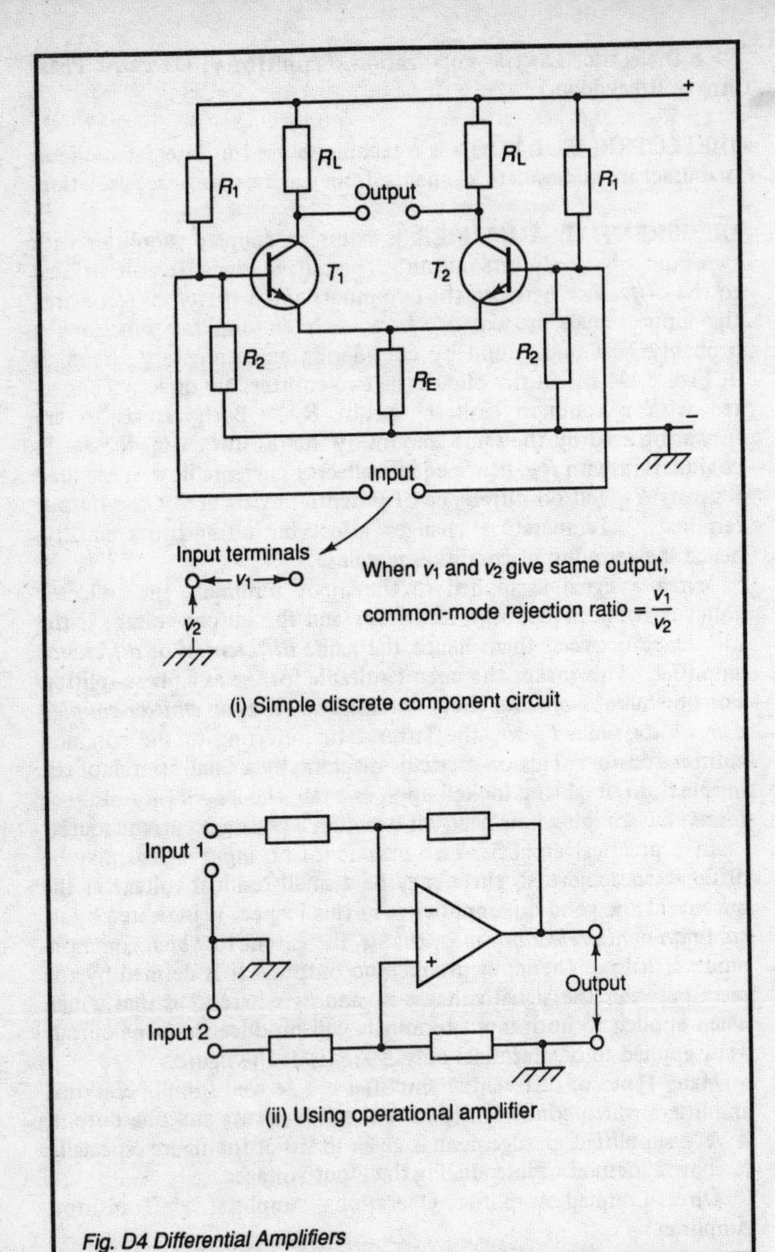

(i) Simple discrete component circuit

(ii) Using operational amplifier

Fig. D4 Differential Amplifiers

between two input currents. The currents flow in opposite directions through two separate identical coils so that the deflection is proportional to their difference. Equal currents therefore produce no deflection.
(>> Galvanometer)

DIFFERENTIAL RESISTANCE is the ratio between a small change in voltage drop across a component and the small change in current it produces, i.e. $\delta V/\delta I$. It can be calculated from the V/I characteristic or alternatively measured under "small signal" conditions.
(>> Resistance)

DIFFERENTIAL WINDING comprises two windings on a relay or coil so wound that when carrying the same current their magnetomotive forces cancel.
(* Relay >> Magnetomotive Force)

DIFFERENTIATING CIRCUIT is one which provides the electrical equivalent of mathematical differentiation, i.e. it has an output which is approximately proportional to the rate of change of the input signal. A simple differentiating circuit or *differentiator* is the resistance–capacitance arrangement shown in Figure D5(i). C and R are such that their time constant CR is small compared with the periodic time (T) of the input voltage.

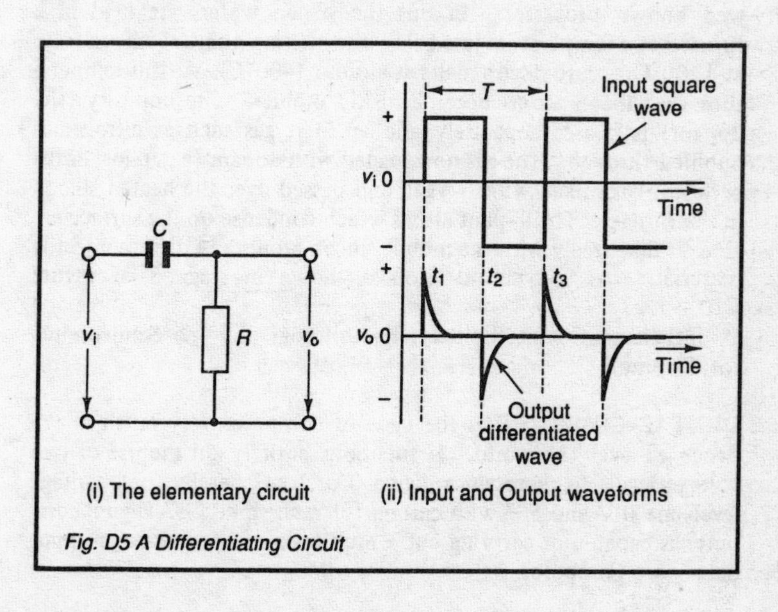

Fig. D5 A Differentiating Circuit

A graphical example of the differentiation of a square wave is given in (ii) of the figure. At time t_1 the rate of change of v_i is maximum, accordingly v_o rises to its positive maximum. From t_1 to t_2, v_i is constant, i.e. its rate of change is zero. v_o should therefore fall to zero immediately but with the simple circuit as shown in (i) the capacitor C needs time to discharge, hence the shape of the fall depends on the time constant. At t_2 v_i rapidly changes direction hence v_o falls to its negative maximum. Between t_2 and t_3 v_o again reaches zero.

Circuits providing more accurate differentiation are usually based on the operational amplifier.

(* Operational Amplifier >> Integration, Integrating Circuit, Time Constant)

DIFFUSION This is a process whereby controlled amounts of impurities are injected into a semiconductor material. It is widely used, mainly because it lends itself readily to mass production of semiconductor components and integrated circuits. Several silicon wafers can be processed together and therefore all receive the same exacting treatment. The aim of the technique is to enable the atoms of the required dopant to propagate through the crystal lattice of the material and take their appointed places.

We can move on from stage 11 of Figure P3 or stage 4 of Figure E10 and gain an understanding of the technique from one of the well known processes. In this the silicon wafers are held in a furnace at a temperature just below the melting point of silicon (say, at 1200°C – pure silicon melts at around 1400°C). At this temperature the silicon atoms become highly mobile. The impurity (the dopant) is heated separately and an inert gas such as nitrogen is bubbled through. The gas now loaded with dopant (e.g. phosphorus or boron) is mixed with oxygen and passed over the heated silicon in the furnace. The dopant atoms which condense on the surface are able to mix freely with the mobile silicon atoms and diffuse into the material. An n-type diffusion is shown in stage 5 of Figure E10.

(* Integrated Circuit, Epitaxy, Photolithography >> Semiconductor, Doping)

DIGITAL COMPUTER is the type of computer very much in evidence all over the world. It functions entirely on the use of two voltage levels to represent a digital 0 or 1. Generally these voltage levels are 0 V and 5 V with certain tolerance limits. A digital computer is capable of carrying out a multitude of operations on input data – see Computer.

DIGITAL LOGIC This embraces discrete signals switched "on" or "off" (the binary system) and the original digital logic device was the electromagnetic relay. This is now superseded in data processing by the semiconductor "gate", thousands of which can be accommodated within a single integrated circuit. How the word "logic" gets into the term may perhaps be appreciated by looking at the simple switch systems between points X and Y in Figure D6(i) and (ii). Without realising it, we use logic (i.e. our ability in reasoning) to say that in (i) X reaches Y electrically only when both A *and* B are closed yet in (ii) logic tells us that X reaches Y when either A *or* B is closed. These are called logic functions and it was George Boole (an English mathematician) who first considered this kind of logic mathematically and was able to produce what is now called *Boolean Algebra.*

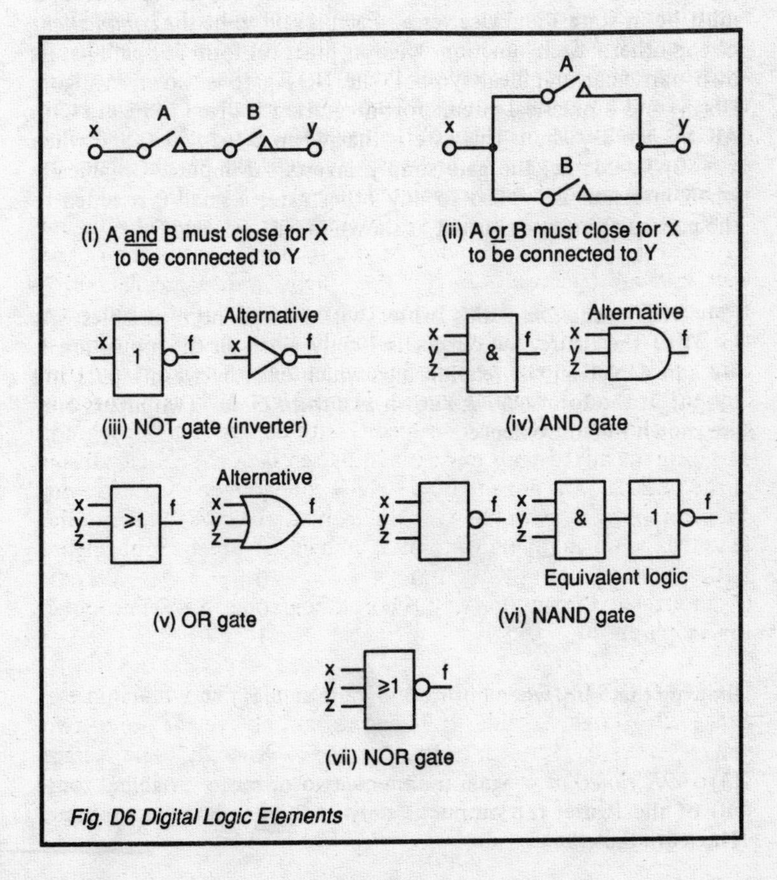

Fig. D6 Digital Logic Elements

The two binary states "on" and "off" may also be described by "high" and "low", "true" and "false", etc., but generally in digital logic considerations we use "logic 1" and "logic 0", generally abbreviated even more to "1" and "0".

Digital logic is not as complicated as it might at first seem for it is all founded on the simple principle that a digital logic element can only exist in one of the two possible states "on" or "off" which we now described as 1 or 0. A digital logic unit or *gate* is normally considered as a "black box" with its graphical symbol in the same form on the basis that it is only the input and output conditions which matter (for a typical *circuit* see Logic Gate). There are only three basic functions:

(1) *NOT function* – if a digital logic circuit is not in state 0, it must be in state 1 and vice versa. Each is said to be the *complement* of the other. Each function when in practical form as a gate has its own particular graphical symbol, the NOT gate is shown in Figure D6(iii) and a practical circuit for integration is given in Figure C16. All we can say about this gate is that when $x = 1, f = 0$ and when $x = 0, f = 1$, i.e. the gate simply inverts the input. Graphically when inversion is applied to any other gate, a small 0 is added to the particular input or output as shown in (iii), (vi) and (vii).

(2) *AND function* – this is used with two or more variables. As in (i) of the figure, the output is 1 only when all the inputs are 1. We can depict all the relationships which exist between inputs and output in the form below, known as a *truth table*. Two inputs only are shown for convenience.

x	y	=	f
0	0		0
1	0		0
0	1		0
1	1		1

showing that only when both x *and* y are at 1, is f at 1.

(3) *OR function* – again used with two or more variables. As in (ii) of the figure, the output is only at 0 when both inputs are 0. The truth table is:

x	y	=	f
0	0		0
1	0		1
0	1		1
1	1		1

On the NOT, AND and OR functions, all others are derived, for example:

NAND (= NOT AND) is equivalent to an AND function followed by a NOT function, in gate form as shown in (vi) of the figure. The truth table is that for the AND but with f reversed.

NOR (= NOT OR) – an OR function followed by a NOT as shown in (vii).

There are other derived functions, slightly more complex than those above, two of which are of great importance in computer technology. These are known as EXCLUSIVE – OR and EXCLUSIVE – NOR.

Boolean algebra provides us with a means of analysing any switching requirement and subsequently determining the mixture of gates required. As an example, in a manufacturing process the inputs may arise from sensors indicating pressure, temperature, liquid level, etc. with the logic system arranged to sound an alarm (when f changes from 0 to 1) only when certain input combinations occur.
(* Integrated Circuit, Relay, Binary, Black Box, Logic Gate, Logic Level, Boolean Algebra, Diode-Transistor Logic, Transistor-Transistor Logic, Integrated Injection Logic)

DIGITAL-TO-ANALOGUE (D/A) CONVERSION Frequently the output of a digital system has to be converted into an analogue form, e.g. any digital transmission system carrying speech or music must involve a final d/a conversion for the eventual output of sound by earphone or loudspeaker. Generally d/a conversion is simpler to achieve than its opposite, a/d. Here we look at one of the methods although only with regard to a 4-bit system, nevertheless the principles are the same as for higher bit systems.

Consider the much simplified circuit of Figure D7(i). What we are looking for is a current which is proportional to the numerical content of a string of 4 bits, b_3 to b_0. If a current I_0 represents b_0, then $2I_0$ is needed to represent b_1, $4I_0$ for b_2 etc. since b_2 is twice the value of b_1, 4 times the value of b_0 (note that in a 4-bit binary code the digits are labelled from left to right as b_3 to b_0). It

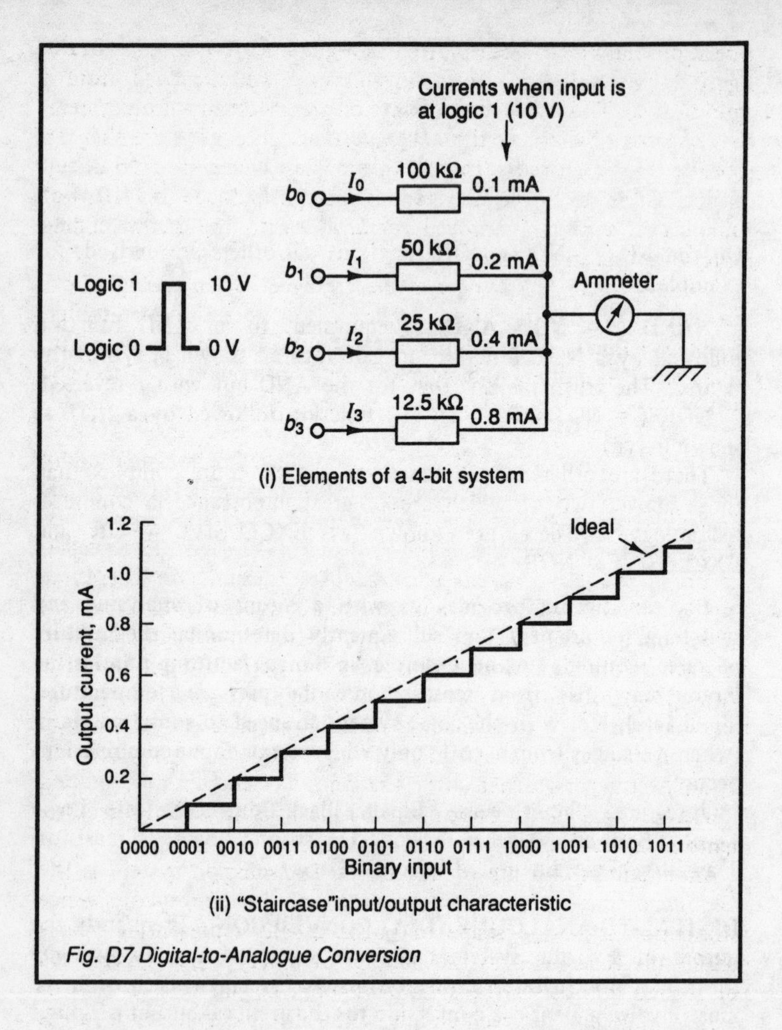

Fig. D7 Digital-to-Analogue Conversion

is therefore simply a matter of reducing the value of the resistor in each branch to one half each time we move one digit to the left. If a binary 0 has a level of 0 V and a binary 1 a level of 10 V then the total current flow is easily calculated, so for example:

a binary input 0 0 0 0 results in a current of 0 mA
a binary input 0 0 0 1 results in a current of 0.1 mA
a binary input 0 0 1 0 results in a current of 0.2 mA
a binary input 0 0 1 1 results in a current of (0.2 + 0.1) = 0.3 mA
a binary input 1 0 1 1 results in a current of (0.8 + 0.2 + 0.1) = 1.1 mA

a relationship which when plotted as a graph as shown in (ii) of the figure is of "staircase" form, in this case well removed from a smooth line. This is because we have only considered a 4-bit system, it is capable of dividing the analogue range into no more than 16 separate output currents, that is, the smallest change is 1/16 of full output. Given say, a 10-bit system each step is reduced to 1/1024 of full output, a much improved *resolution* with the graph tending more towards a straight line.

A converter of this type may be arranged for an analogue output voltage instead of current by use of an operational amplifier. (* Binary, Binary Code, Bit, Digital Logic, Digital Transmission, Operational Amplifier, Analogue-to-Digital Conversion >> Analogue Signal)

DIGITAL TRANSMISSION is a means of conveying information by a series of pulses and for long circuits it has the significant advantage of using regenerative repeaters (regenerators) which accept a relatively poor digital signal and transmit onwards a signal identical to the original. This contrasts with analogue transmission where line amplifiers have no choice but to amplify noise and distortions picked up by the signal on its way. After several amplification stages therefore an analogue signal may be quite different from the original but the digital is "as new". The digital transmission system therefore provides a transmission quality independent of distance. Other advantages are that different types of data (e.g. speech and facsimile) can be carried over the same system without mutual interference and that it happens to be ideally suited to the requirements of optical fibres.

An important feature of any digital transmission system is the maximum rate at which information can be conveyed. Since information is in the shape of pulses usually representing binary codes, this is assessed as the number of binary digits transmitted per second, known as the *system bit rate*, i.e. in bit/s, k bit/s or M bit/s. The link between circuit bandwidth and system bit rate is not easily determined even though we have information theory to help because many factors such as error rate (important for computers but less so for speech), noise, etc. must be considered. Theoretically to be transmitted unscathed a pulse needs fast rise and decay times which implies infinite bandwidth because any restriction of harmonics rounds off and spreads a square wave. In the limit of course, with no harmonics transmitted, a pulse emerges as a sine wave. The practical bandwidth therefore is that which ensures that any two adjacent pulses are clearly distinguishable.

See also Frequency Shift Keying.

(* Analogue-to-Digital Conversion, Digital-to-Analogue Conversion, Pulse Code Modulation, Facsimile Transmission, Binary, Binary Code, Bit >> Digital Signal, Pulse, Information Theory, Harmonic)

DIGITAL VOLTMETER A voltmeter which does not use a pointer moving over a scale but displays the value of voltage directly as a number. If the voltage being measured varies the voltmeter will repetitively sample the input and display the result with a predetermined response time.
(* Voltmeter, Analogue-to-Digital Conversion)

DIGITRON is a cold-cathode gas-filled tube containing 10 cathodes so placed that glow discharges at the cathodes illuminate the numerals 0 – 9. The display is initiated by a voltage between an anode and the appropriate cathodes.
(>> Cold-Cathode, Gas-Discharge)

DIODE DETECTOR is a particular form of amplitude modulation demodulator based on the rectifying characteristics of a diode. In an amplitude modulated wave the modulating frequency is impressed on both the positive and negative swings of the carrier wave. Only one of these is required for recovery of the information hence all positive or all negative half-cycles are first discarded usually by means of a semiconductor diode. This results in a waveform typically as shown in Figure D8(i). Detector circuits use the diode in parallel or in series on the transmission path, (ii) in the figure shows an example of the latter. In this particular circuit the diode is followed by a capacitor C shunted by resistor R.

On each half-cycle C charges but in a rather complex way because R drains some of the current away during the charging periods and in between them. The result of this process is shown by the curve marked "detector output" in (iii). This now has some resemblance to the modulating frequency although it clearly contains a d.c. component as one would expect from rectification; this is blocked by the capacitor C_b. The smoothness of the modulating frequency output is obtained by the filter combination $R_f C_f$ which removes what is left of the carrier frequency.
(>> Amplitude Modulation, Demodulation, D.C. Component, Filter)

DIODE ISOLATION Isolation of a semiconductor zone from the substrate of an integrated circuit by the creation of a reverse-biased junction diode between them – see Isolation.

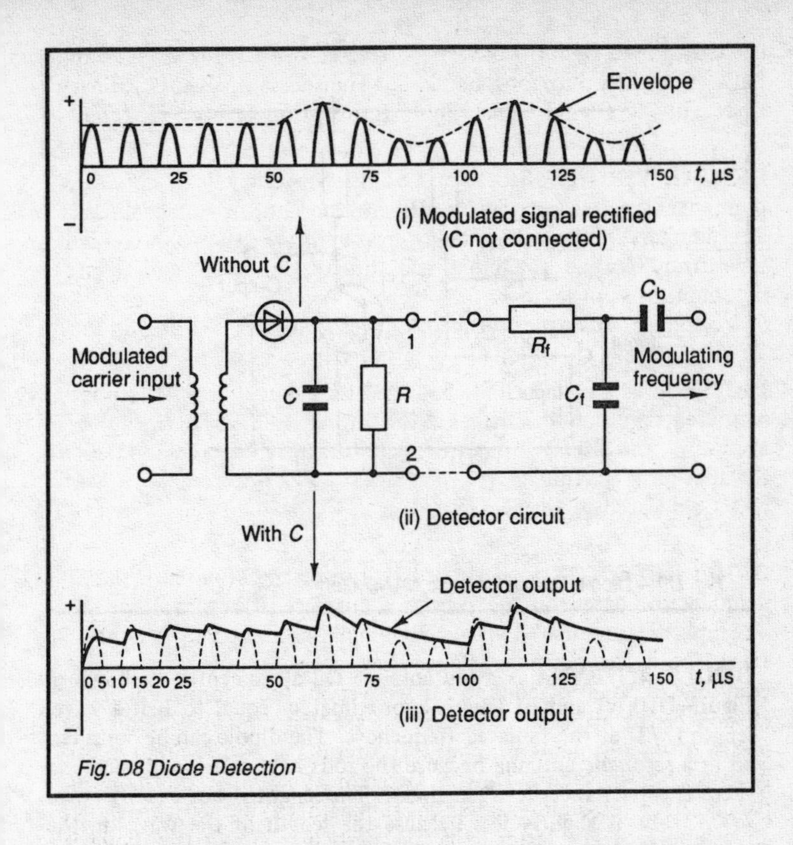

Fig. D8 Diode Detection

DIODE-TRANSISTOR LOGIC (DTL) is one of the several families of integrated logic circuits. As its name implies the inputs are connected to diodes which are followed by a single transistor. Many different arrangements based on this format are used, Figure D9 shows an elementary one but sufficient to demonstrate the principle. Note the two diodes D_1 and D_2 followed by the transistor, T_1. The circuit is that of an AND gate followed by a NOT gate, therefore classified as NAND.

With no input or when both are at logic 1, the transistor is held ON by the bias current through R_b; the output is therefore at logic 0. If a logic 0 is connected to one or both of the inputs the transistor is held OFF and the output then switches to logic 1. Additional inputs simply require extra diodes connected to T_1 base. NOR gates are also available in DTL.

(* Digital Logic, Logic Gate, Transistor-Transistor Logic >> Diode, Transistor)

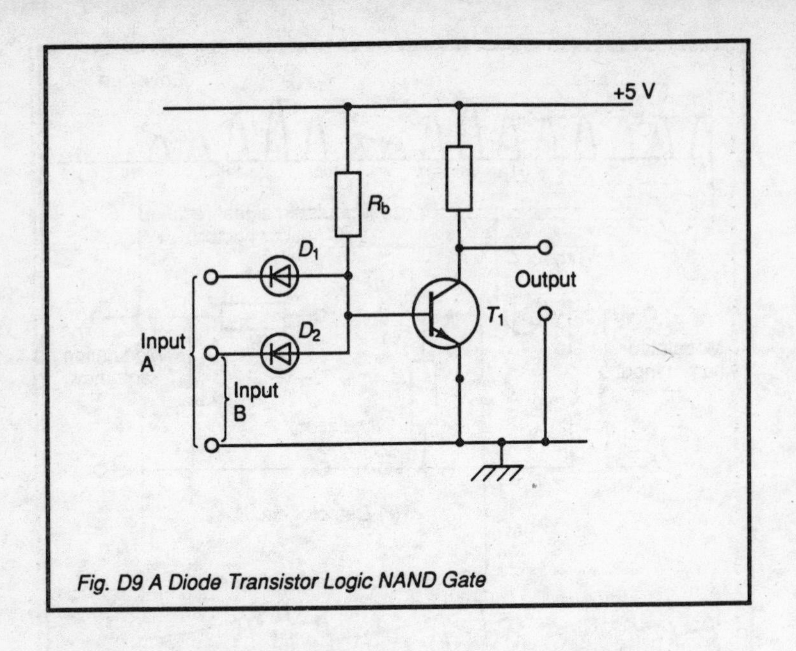

Fig. D9 A Diode Transistor Logic NAND Gate

DIPOLE ANTENNA is a rod antenna fed at its centre as shown in Figure D10(iv) and of length approximately equal to half a wavelength ($\lambda/2$) at the radiated frequency. The dipole can be considered as a *resonant* antenna because the rods have self inductance and there is capacitance between them. The length is not exactly equal to $\lambda/2$ but is slightly less because the length of the wave on the antenna is shorter than it is in free space since the velocity of propagation is lower.

The dipole antenna can be imagined as evolving from the quarter-wavelength transmission line. Figure D10(i) shows such a ($\lambda/4$) line fed by a generator of the appropriate frequency. The line is open-circuited at the end remote from the generator hence has voltage and current standing waves as shown. At the open circuit the current must be zero, the voltage is therefore maximum. At the generator the opposite conditions hold, i.e. maximum current, zero voltage. The transmission line wires are close together and parallel hence each wire creates a field which is cancelled by that from the other and there is no radiation.

Next in (ii) we consider the line to be opened up. Some energy will be radiated as indicated by the arrow because there is now incomplete cancellation of the two fields especially at the open ends of the wires. In (iii) the line has developed into a dipole antenna by opening up the two $\lambda/4$ wires fully as shown. There is now maximum

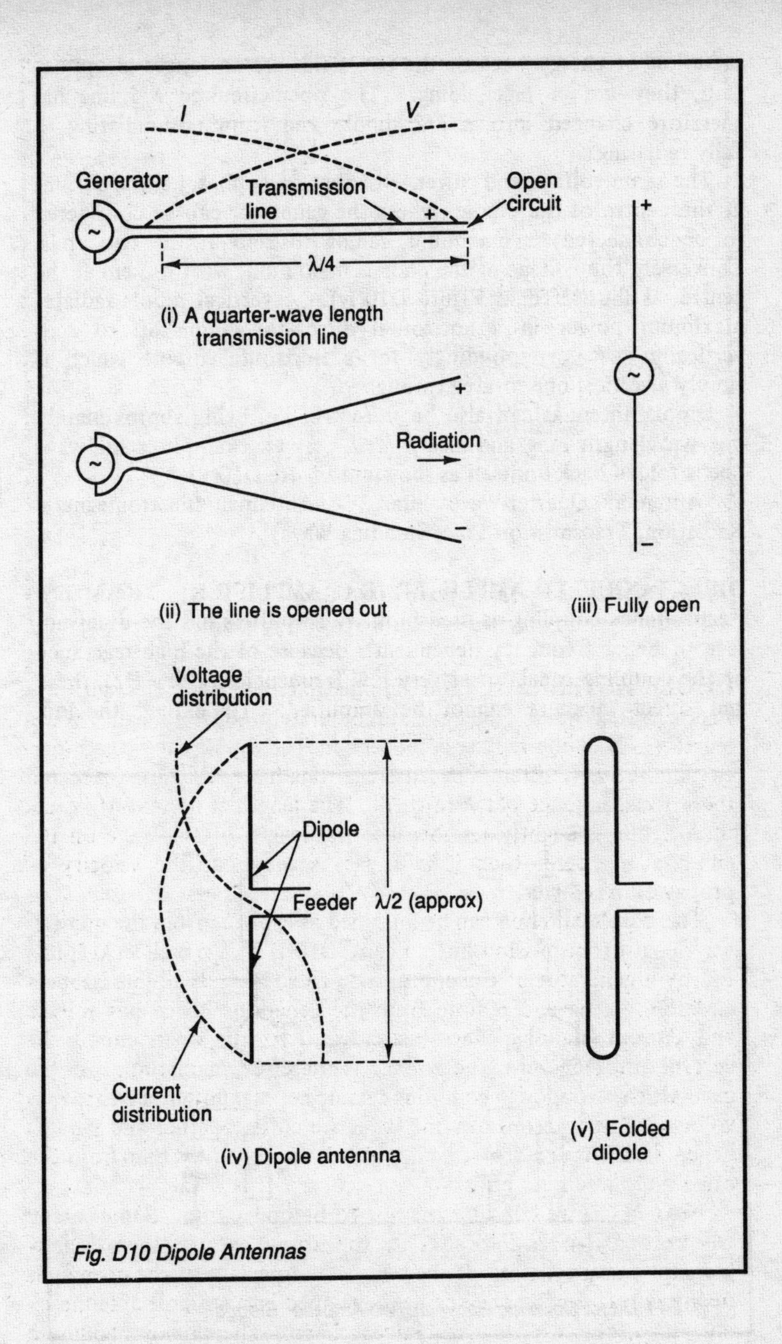

Fig. D10 Dipole Antennas

radiation of energy because the two fields are no longer in opposition, they are in fact aiding. The open-circuited λ/4 line has therefore changed into a λ/2 dipole and from non-radiating to fully radiating.

The same voltage and current distribution applies, i.e. the current at the centre of the dipole (where the generator can be considered to be connected) is maximum, falling to zero at the two ends. Conversely the voltage at the ends is maximum, with its zero at the centre, as illustrated in Figure D10(iv). A vertical dipole radiates maximum power in a horizontal direction, tailing off to zero vertically and correspondingly for a horizontal dipole which is simply a vertical one rotated through 90°.

Dipole antennas can also be *full-wave*, i.e. being approximately one wavelength long and also *folded*. As an example, a full-wave one is folded back on itself as shown in Figure D10(v).

(* Antenna, Quarter-Wave Line >> Antenna, Electromagnetic Radiation, Transmission Line, Standing Wave)

DIRECT-COUPLED AMPLIFIER (D.C. AMPLIFIER) Resistance–capacitance coupling as used in many amplifiers has the disadvantage of being frequency dependent. Because of the high reactance of the coupling capacitor at very low frequencies (a few Hz), these and direct currents cannot be amplified. To extend the low

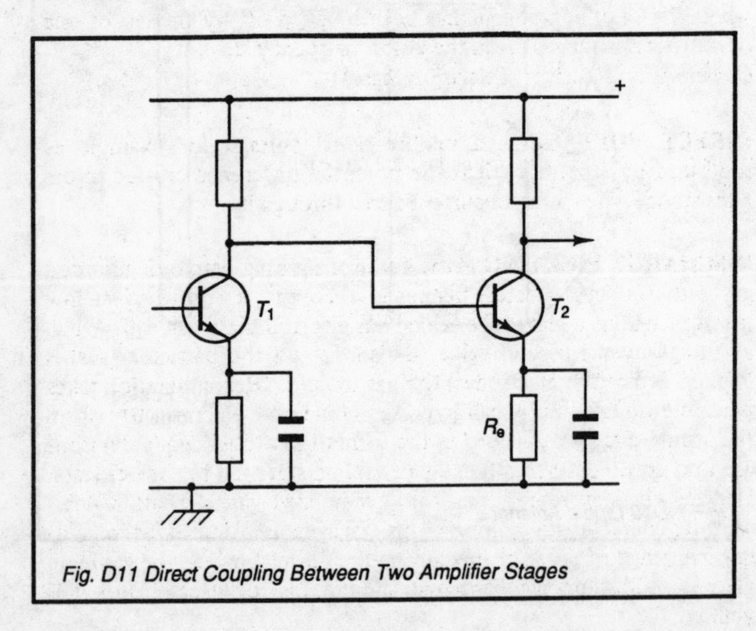

Fig. D11 Direct Coupling Between Two Amplifier Stages

frequency range of an amplifier down to zero frequency, the capacitor must therefore be eliminated. When this is done the amplifier is said to be *direct coupled.* Figure D11 shows two transistor stages with direct coupling, i.e. the collector of T_1 is connected directly to the base of T_2. With no capacitor to block the d.c. voltage at T_1 collector from T_2 base it is evident that for example, the emitter potential of T_2 must be adjusted so that the correct base/emitter voltage is obtained. This is done by suitable choice of R_e. Many other arrangements are available for maintaining correct biasing.

D.C. amplifiers abound in operational amplifiers which usually have frequency responses from zero upwards.
(* Operational Amplifier, Resistance–Capacitance Coupling >> Transistor)

DIRECT COUPLING is a non-reactive coupling between two circuits, hence the coupling circuit is not frequency dependent. It is mainly found as interstage coupling in transistor amplifiers – see Direct-Coupled Amplifier.

DIRECT CURRENT RESTORATION The technique of replacing the d.c. or low frequency component of a signal. The component may have been lost during transmission of the signal or may have been deliberately removed. A common use is in television receivers where the d.c. component has been blocked off by the use of one or more series capacitors in the vision frequency stages.
(* Television Receiver, Television Signal)

DIRECT VOLTAGE is a unidirectional voltage for example as produced by a battery. It is the potential difference created across a resistance when a direct current flows through it.

DISCHARGE LIGHTING is the form of lighting employing ionized gas rather than a heated filament. The gas is contained at low pressure within a glass tube which has electrodes at each end. When a voltage over a certain value (depending on the particular gas) is applied across the electrodes, the gas ionizes. Recombination takes place continually and when ions recombine with electrons to reform the atoms, energy is released in the form of photons (light). Photons are also emitted when atoms in an excited state fall to a lower state. Hence, when current passes through ionized gas, the latter glows with its characteristic colour. This effect is used in *discharge lighting.* A range of gases or metal vapours is available, e.g. the gas neon gives a reddish-orange light and sodium (as for street lighting) is yellow.

Fluorescent lighting is a discharge type. The gas in the tube is a mixture of argon and mercury vapour. Special arrangements are required for starting the gas discharge but once it commences, it is self sustaining. The ionized mercury vapour emits energy at around 1.18×10^{15} Hz which is in the ultraviolet range. This is not visible light so it is used to excite phosphors coated on the inside of the tube which then emit their own characteristic colours. Various colours and grades of "white" light are obtained by choice of phosphor.

Fluorescent lamps are available either as hot or cold-cathode types. In *preheat* lamps the electrodes are heated for a few seconds before ionization of the gas is induced. *Instant-start* lamps are started by applying a sufficiently high voltage across the electrodes while *rapid-start* lamps combine electrode heating with a lower voltage. Once the mercury vapour discharge is established, a series inductor ensures that the lamp operates over the normal discharge range.

Sodium vapour lamps have no phosphor coating, the light is that directly emitted from the vapour atoms as they decay from the excited states.

(>> Ionization, Excitation, Gas Discharge, Energy Levels, Quantum Theory, Photon, Phosphor)

DISC RECORDING A system which captures sound wave pressures and stores their message in the walls of a disc *groove*. The gramophone disc subsequently reproduces the recorded sound through vibrations of a stylus running in the groove which on the single side of a large disc may be more than half a kilometre long. Most discs cater for stereophonic reproduction.

The two separate (stereo) channels are recorded on the master disc by cutting into each groove wall an amount corresponding to the frequency and amplitude of the signal being recorded. The inner wall (nearer the disc centre) carries the L channel and the outer wall the R channel. The cutting stylus is heated and is shaped like a pointed chisel, it is of very hard material such as sapphire or diamond. Most cutter heads are of the electromagnetic type for which the cutter velocity is proportional to the input voltage while the degree of lateral movement is inversely proportional to the input signal frequency. A typical disc recording system layout is given in Figure D12(i).

The fact that the lateral movement of the recording cutter is inversely proportional to frequency means that without special arrangements a groove might run into an adjacent one. This is avoided by (i) making the width of the *land* (i.e. the disc surface

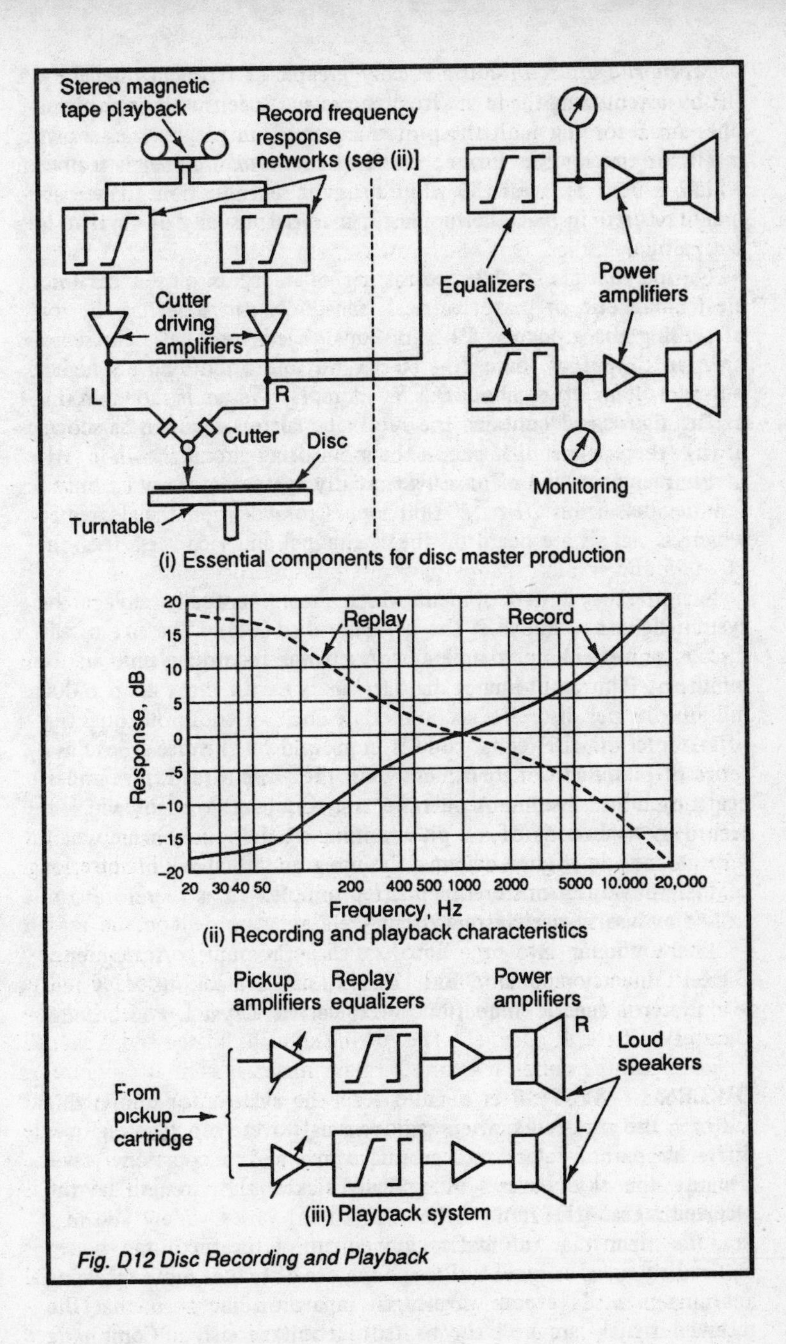

Fig. D12 Disc Recording and Playback

between the grooves) automatically greater as frequency falls and (ii) by attenuating the lower frequencies and accentuating the higher ones on recording with the process reversed on playback as shown in (ii) of the figure. From the cut disc a *metal stamper* is formed which is used to press the vinyl discs for reproduction. These are manufactured from a thermoplastic material, usually of vinyl resin with a filler.

On playback a *pickup* consisting of a stylus plus a ceramic, electromagnetic or piezoelectrical transducer *cartridge* has the job of sensing the groove width variations. Electromagnetic cartridges have an output of some 5 – 10 mV but piezo units have a higher output voltage up to about 0.5 V. A replay system is shown in (iii) of the figure and contains the replay equalizers required as shown in (ii) [there is a similar pair in the monitoring circuit shown in (i)].

Frequency response for a high quality system can vary by only a few decibels from 20 to 20 000 Hz. Crosstalk, i.e. the degree to which L signals are heard on the R channel and vice versa is about 20 – 35 dB.

A more recent development which must eventually replace the system described above is the *compact* disc (CD). The size of the disc is a mere 12cm diameter for a total recording time of 74 minutes. The recording is digital (binary) with more than 6,000 million bits per disc. To accommodate such an enormous quantity of information, the digital code is impressed on the disc groove as a series of pits, each a mere 0.5 μm wide. The disc is read from underneath by a laser beam. A pit reflects a tiny beam of light which is sensed by a photodiode, no pit resulting in a defocused beam which returns considerably less light. Tracking and focusing of the laser beam is obviously more than a little complex, it is therefore controlled by a servomechanism system.
(* Stereophonic System, Equalization, Crosstalk, Analogue-to-Digital Conversion, Binary, Bit, Laser, Closed-Loop Control System >> Electromagnetic Induction, Piezoelectric Crystal, Photodiode, Decibel)

DIVERSITY SYSTEM is a radio receiving system for minimizing fading. Fading occurs when radio waves travel to a receiver over different paths, e.g. via a ground wave and also a sky wave. Because the sky wave is notoriously fickle, the strength of the received signal (the sum of the two waves) varies widely and in a random manner. Automatic gain control is useful but a better method of signal control is through the use of two or more receiving antennas spaced several wavelengths apart on the basis that the received signals are unlikely to fade simultaneously. Combining

the outputs of the antennas therefore ensures that there will always be some signal available.
(* Ionosphere, Fading, Ground Wave, Sky Wave, Antenna, Radio Receiver)

DIVIDING NETWORK Used to couple high and low frequency loudspeakers together – see Crossover Network.

DMOS is an abbreviation of Double-Diffused Metal-Oxide Semiconductor – see this term.

DOPPLER EFFECT We notice this as the apparent change in pitch of a sound wave from a moving body as it passes by. The effect is not limited to sound waves but occurs similarly with radio waves and it was discovered by Christian Doppler, an Austrian physicist.

For a stationary observer, the apparent frequency is equal to the radiated frequency divided by $(1 - v/c)$ where v is the speed of approach of the source and c is the velocity of the wave. When the source is travelling away from the observer, v is negative.

In radar, by measuring the change in frequency between the directly transmitted wave and the echo received, it is possible to determine the velocity of the target (the object causing the reflection). The Doppler effect is also used by astronomers to measure the speeds of stars and galaxies.
(* Radar >> Acoustic Wave, Electromagnetic Wave)

DOUBLE-BALANCED MODULATOR A bridge-type circuit designed to suppress both carrier and modulating signal so that its output consists of lower and upper sidebands only – see Ring Modulator.

DOUBLE-BASE DIODE is a special type of transistor with a single emitter, two bases but no collector. It is generally known as a *unijunction transistor* but because it has two bases it is sometimes given this name. The characteristic exhibits negative resistance. (>> Unijunction Transistor)

DOUBLE-DIFFUSED METAL-OXIDE SEMICONDUCTOR (DMOS) belongs to the planar insulated-gate field-effect transistor family but has special diffusions to produce a very short channel for high speed operation and low resistance, hence it is especially useful at microwave frequencies. Figure D13 shows the structure of a DMOS transistor. The channel length is considerably reduced compared with that of a "normal" n-channel enhancement metal-oxide semi-

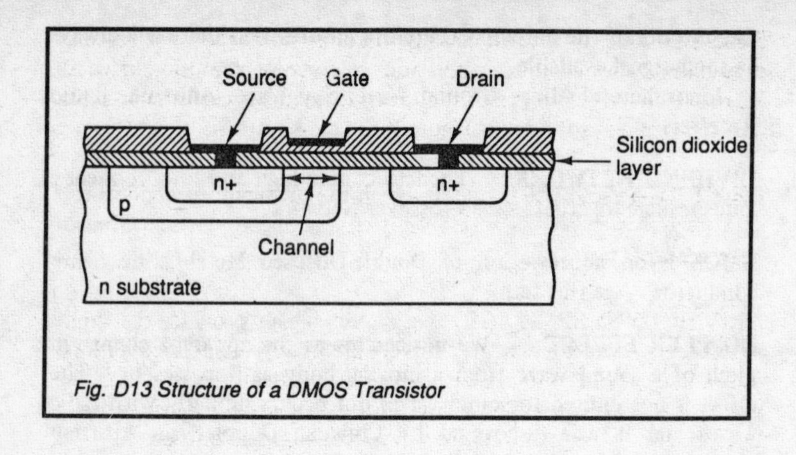

Fig. D13 Structure of a DMOS Transistor

conductor field-effect transistor (MOSFET). This is accomplished by diffusing the two types of impurity successively through the same opening in the silicon dioxide layer.
(* Planar Process, Diffusion >> Field-Effect Transistor, Doping)

DOUBLE-SIDEBAND TRANSMISSION Apart from sometimes referring to the normal system of amplitude modulation in which lower and upper sidebands plus the carrier are transmitted, this term usually refers specifically to the same system but minus the carrier, it has the only advantage of reduced power to transmit the same information. In this form it is known as double-sideband suppressed-carrier (d.s.b.s.c.). One of its disadvantages is that the carrier must be introduced in correct frequency and phase at the receiving end for demodulation. Generally therefore the system is superseded by the single-sideband method which utilizes less bandwidth and overcomes the carrier reinsertion difficulty by sending a low-level *pilot* carrier with the main transmission.
(* Single-Sideband Transmission >> Carrier Wave, Amplitude Modulation)

DOUBLE SUPERHETERODYNE RECEPTION is basically two superheterodyne units in tandem for producing an enhanced receiver selectivity and better performance on weak signals. The incoming signal is first mixed with the output of a local oscillator and the intermediate frequency (i.f.) so generated is amplified. This first i.f. is then mixed with the output of a second local oscillator to generate the second i.f. which also is amplified.
(>> Superheterodyne Reception, Intermediate Frequency)

DRIFT SPACE is a term usually used in reference to a velocity modulated tube such as a klystron, microwave amplifier or oscillator. In the klystron the drift space is located between the buncher and the catcher as shown in Figure K1 – see Klystron.

DRIFT TRANSISTOR is one in which the base impurity concentration decreases in the direction emitter to collector – see Graded-Base Transistor.

DRIVER (DRIVER STAGE) is a circuit which provides the input signal for a succeeding stage. Drivers are usually associated with (i) power output stages or (ii) in digital logic assemblies in which the driver is a stage providing a low impedance drive for use when a large number of logic inputs are driven from a single output.
(* Digital Logic >> Amplifier)

DROPPING RESISTOR (DROPPER) is a resistor connected in series with a circuit to provide a "voltage drop" and hence reduce the voltage applied to that circuit. As an example, suppose a device requires a 5 V supply and at this voltage passes 20 mA. The supply however is at 8 V.

From Ohm's Law, resistance of device is equal to:

$$E/I = 5/0.02 = 250\ \Omega\ .$$

The dropping resistor, R_d to be connected in series must therefore account for 8 – 5 = 3 V, i.e. $R_d = 3/0.02 = 150\ \Omega$. The 20 mA device current flowing through R_d therefore drops the 3 V required.
(>> Resistance, Ohm's Law)

DRY CELL There are several types of this primary cell, all based on the Leclanché principle and usually with an electrolyte in the form of a moist paste contained within an outer zinc case as shown typically in Figure D14. Three different types are in everyday use:

(i) the zinc-carbon with the electrolyte in jelly form;
(ii) the zinc chloride which is generally superior to (i); and
(iii) the alkaline, superior to both (i) and (ii) and more expensive.

Several dry cells may be connected together in series and used as a single unit, this is the standard dry battery used in hand torches, portable radios, remote control, quartz clocks, etc.
(>> Primary Cell, Leclanché Cell, Electrolyte)

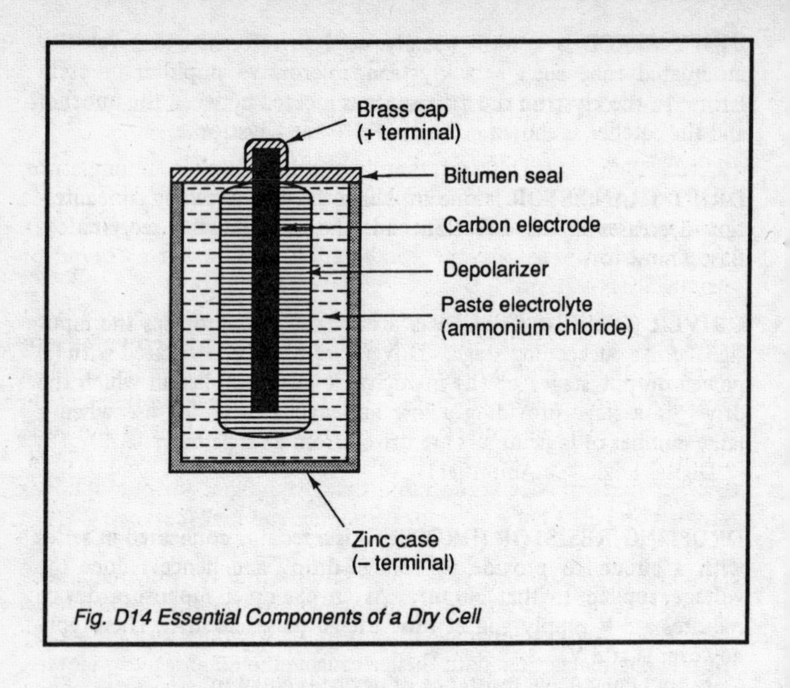

Fig. D14 Essential Components of a Dry Cell

DUMMY ANTENNA A network with the electrical characteristics of a real antenna but one which does not radiate – see Artificial Antenna.

DUST CORE is a magnetic core especially suitable for working at high frequencies because of its high resistance to eddy currents. These cores are usually made from powdered ferrite which is compressed into the shape required and then fired – see Ferrite.

DYNAMO is a machine for converting mechanical energy into electrical energy by rotating conductors in a magnetic field – see Generator.

DYNAMOMETER WATTMETER is an instrument for measuring the power consumed by a load – see Electrodynamometer.

DYNODE is the name given to an electrode specially manufactured for its secondary emission properties.
(* Electron Multiplier >> Secondary Emission)

E

EARPHONE This is rather like a loudspeaker in miniature, designed for use at the ear. Earphones exist singly when for example used in telephones or hearing aids and in pairs when coupled by a headband in which case the combination is known as a *headset* or pair of *headphones.*

Apart from being smaller, earphones differ in basic design from loudspeakers especially in that whereas the loudspeaker works into open air, the earphone is coupled to a very small volume of air via a very peculiarly shaped entrance. There are four basic principles on which earphones in general work. For an appreciation of the basic constructions it is possible to use either a microphone or a loudspeaker diagram, bearing in mind that diaphragms for microphones are thin and light but not so for earphones and loudspeakers.

(1) *Variable reluctance* – the sketch of a variable reluctance microphone in Figure M10(iv) also shows how this type of earphone functions. Audio frequency currents in the windings vary the steady flux in the magnetic circuit, hence causing the diaphragm to vibrate. This type has a response suitable only for telephony (up to about 4 kHz).

(2) *Moving coil* – the principle can be seen from the sketch of a moving coil loudspeaker in Figure L8(i). The better quality earphones of this type cover the full audio range, e.g. from 20 Hz to 20 kHz. Less expensive ones still have a good response, e.g. 30 Hz to 15 kHz.

(3) *Piezoelectric* – see Figure M10(v). This is for a microphone but as an earphone the principle is reversed for then a p.d. applied across the crystal causes it to distort and drive the diaphragm.

(4) *Electrostatic* – the basic principle is identical with that of the loudspeaker, however Figure M10(vi) for the microphone may be used to give an idea of the construction. The electret principle which embodies a self-polarized diaphragm may be used to avoid the inconvenience of a d.c. polarizing supply. These earphones also cover the entire audio frequency range.

(* Loudspeaker, Microphone, Electret >> Electromagnetic Induction, Piezoelectric Effect)

EARTH is that on which we stand so it needs no introduction. Its importance in the electronics world however should not be underestimated. From early days it has been known that the earth is a good conductor of electricity which may be surprising considering that sand and rock for example are insulators. Nevertheless provided that a good connection can be made far enough down by for example, water pipes, buried plates or spikes, an earth circuit of considerable length can have as low a resistance as 2 – 3 ohms (but as high as say, 300 ohms in sandy soil) although a few extra ohms must be allowed for the earth connection itself.

To wires and cables laid in the ground each wire-earth circuit is in the form of a transmission line with its own four primary coefficients and therefore propagation coefficient. Because the earth carries a multitude of currents from other systems, interference currents are therefore able to enter such a transmission line especially at radio frequencies. The earth also has an appreciable effect on ground wave propagation of radio waves.

We frequently use the earth as a reference of zero potential, especially in systems which have earth connections. The electricity mains provides an example for the *neutral* wire is earthed and so is labelled 0 V. Accordingly a *live* wire potential of 240 V means that it is at 240 V with respect to the neutral or earth. Electronic equipment has its own zero potential reference, often referred to as "frame" or "chassis" although it may no longer consist of a metal frame. This point may or may not be connected directly to earth although at the higher frequencies it has a capacitance to earth and therefore may be regarded as being at earth potential.

In some countries "earth" is known as "ground".
(* Polyphase System >> Transmission Line, Primary Coefficient, Propagation Coefficient)

EARTH LEAKAGE CIRCUIT-BREAKER A device for protection against electric shock – see Residual Current Circuit Breaker.

EARTH RETURN refers to a transmission line in which the earth is used as one of the conductors – see Earth.

ECHO In everyday life this refers to the repetition of sound by the reflection of sound waves. However, echoes are also said to occur with audio frequency and radio waves. On long distance audio telephony circuits for example, an echo arises from an unmatched termination at the receiving end. The echo is transmitted back to the sender and given sufficient magnitude and delay, it can be disturbing. Accordingly *echo suppressors* are fitted into each circuit, these provide attenuation in one direction while the other direction carries speech and so the echo is reduced.

Echoes become visible in t.v. reception when two signals are received together, the first having travelled directly, the second via a reflection from a building, tower, etc., and therefore having travelled over a longer path. This second signal gives rise to a "ghost" picture on the screen, i.e. a second, faint picture removed slightly from the main one. Echo is also the term used in radar systems for the wave reflected back from the target.
(* Matching, Television Receiver, Radar >> Transmission Line, Reflection)

EDDY CURRENT HEATING A method of heating a metal workpiece by deliberately inducing eddy currents in it – see Induction Heating.

EFFECTIVE HEIGHT (EFFECTIVE LENGTH) of a receiving antenna is a term used in assessment of how well the antenna extracts energy from a radio wave. If the electric field strength of the wave is quoted in volts per metre e and h is the effective height of the antenna, then the open circuit voltage delivered by the antenna is $e \times h$. For example, with a surrounding field strength at a certain frequency of 250 μV/m, an antenna of effective height 4 metres will deliver a signal voltage of 250 μV/m × 4 m = 1 mV. Effective height (or length) can be applied to any antenna irrespective of its shape or size.
(* Antenna >> Antenna, Electromagnetic Radiation, Electric Field Strength)

EHF is an abbreviation of *Extremely High Frequency*. This refers to the band of frequencies extending from 30 to 300 GHz (millimetric waves).
(>> Frequency Band)

EHT An abbreviation of *extra high tension*, i.e. a very high voltage. As an example, cathode-ray tubes are said to have an e.h.t. supply.
(* Cathode-Ray Tube)

ELECTRET When a material comprising molecules which have permanent dipole moments is heated and then cooled slowly in an intense electric field, the field direction becomes permanently established. The material is then known as an electret, it has an electric polarization in the same way that a permanent magnet has magnetic polarization. Certain fluorocarbons and polycarbonates are especially suited to this process.

An example of the use of an electret is given by the electret microphone. The electrostatic microphone from which this is developed requires a high d.c. polarizing voltage, the electret microphone diaphragm is already polarized and therefore requires no such d.c. supply. The electret microphone is therefore suitable for telephones whereas the electrostatic type is not. It is suggested that the polarization could last over 100 years.
(* Microphone >> Dipole, Electric Field, Electric Polarization)

ELECTRET MICROPHONE A type of microphone which functions by changing its capacitance – see Microphone and Electret.

ELECTRIC LAMP has a chequered but fascinating history starting as far ago as in 1809 when Sir Humphry Davy demonstrated an electric arc between two electrodes of carbon. Then followed the troublesome days of carbon filaments and poor vacuums until the arrival of the tungsten filament and argon filling in 1911 when the modern light bulb was truly born. Since then many different types have been developed.

Incandescent Lamps – the ubiquitous electric light bulb. This has a filament of tungsten heated to a high temperature by the passage of an electric current. The filament is contained within a gas-filled glass bulb. The lamp is relatively inefficient because most of the power is wasted as heat. As an example a 100 watt lamp has a luminous efficiency of about 16 lumens per watt (lm/W) which when compared with the two types of lamp below is poor.

Gas Discharge or Vapour Lamps – these contain a gas which radiates light when an electric current flows through it. The colour of the light emitted depends on the gas, for example, reddish for neon, yellow for sodium vapour. They are more efficient compared with the incandescent type since little energy is wasted as heat. A 100 W mercury vapour lamp for example might have an efficiency of 36 lm/W.

Fluorescent Lamps – each of these consists of a glass tube containing a mixture of mercury vapour and an inert gas such as argon. Current passing through the gas produces ultraviolet radiation which excites a phosphor coated on the inside of the tube, the phosphor then emits visible light. Very little heat is produced so this type is very efficient, e.g. a 100 W lamp might have an efficiency of 55 lm/W.

(A light-emitting diode is a form of lamp but its use is more as an indicator rather than for illumination.)
(>> Lumen, Luminescence, Gas Discharge)

ELECTRIC MOTOR is an electrically driven machine which supplies motive power, usually by turning a shaft. In practice motors range from the heavy duty ones for driving trains and cranes down to the simple one turning the hands of a clock. The basic action of the electric motor arises from the fact that if a wire carrying a current is placed within a magnetic field, it will move. Here we look at the main types in general use.

Electric motors consist basically of two components, a slotted iron core known as the *armature* or *rotor* in which are embedded coils so as to form electromagnets around the shaft. The latter is free to rotate. The armature or rotor rotates within the other component, the *stator* [see Fig.E1(i)] which comprises fixed electromagnets. Energising the rotor and stator electromagnets from a source of electricity causes their magnetic fields to interact and the shaft to turn as shown in (ii). However when for example, two unlike poles come together as in (iii), torque on the shaft ceases so arrangements are made for the polarity of the rotor poles to be reversed. Like poles now drive apart so the shaft continues to rotate (iv). The trick is to change over the electromagnet pole polarities at the right time. This is accomplished by (i) use of a commutator [see Fig.G1(iii)] so that the rotor polarities are continually reversed (*brush motors*) or (ii) drive by alternating current for then the supply current itself continually reverses.

A special type of a.c. motor in common use is the *induction motor*. Alternating current is supplied to the stator only and the magnetic field set up induces e.m.f.'s into rotor windings which are closed loops. The currents created around the loops themselves set up a magnetic rotor flux. Interaction between the stator and rotor fluxes produces the torque on the shaft. The induction motor is cheaper and more robust than the brush-type, however the latter have certain desirable characteristics of their own such as high starting torque. They can also be used on an a.c. supply.

When a.c. electric motors need to be started this can be accomplished by use of an auxiliary stator winding which in fact creates a rotating magnetic field which the rotor follows. As the rotor reaches normal running speed, the additional winding may be switched out of circuit.

The *linear induction motor* is based on the same principles as the rotating induction motor except that the stator magnetic field travels in a straight line instead of a circular path. On a locomotive for example, current is fed from a shoe on an electric rail to stator coils attached to and running along the train. The "rotor" closed loops are a metal strip running along the track. Current in the stator coils induces e.m.f.'s in the strip which give rise to a magnetic

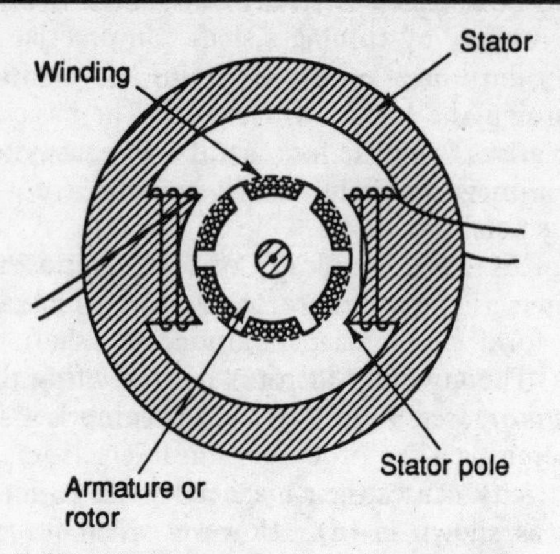

(i) Simplified arrangement of rotor and stator

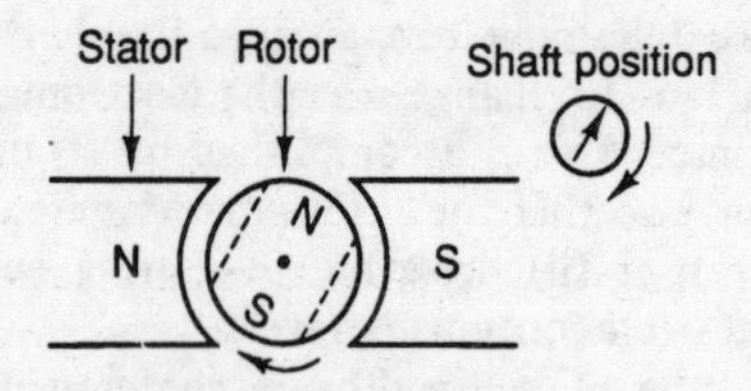

(ii) Rotation by attraction

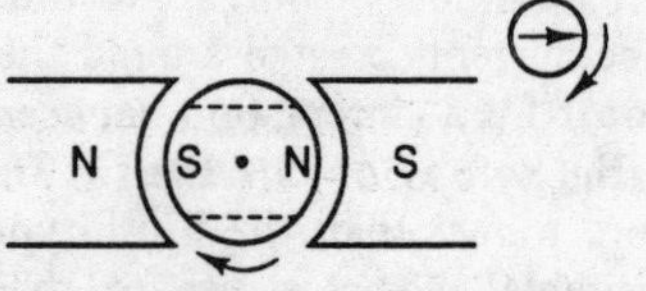

(iii) No torque exerted, therefore change over rotor poles

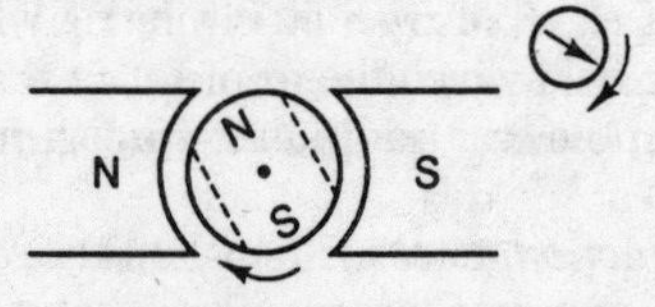

(iv) Rotation by repulsion

Fig. E1 Electric Motor and Commutation

field. Interaction between the stator and strip fields propels the train along the track.

Direction of rotation of an electric motor can be determined by use of Fleming's Rules.
(* Generator, Synchronous Motor >> Electromagnetic Motor Action, Electromagnetic Induction, Fleming's Rules)

ELECTRIC SCREENING (ELECTROSTATIC SCREENING) Aims at preventing interference from electric fields – see Screening.

ELECTROACOUSTIC TRANSDUCER The technical term embracing mainly microphones and loudspeakers – see Transducer.

ELECTROCARDIOGRAM (e.c.g.) is a plot on a base of time of the electrical signals generated by the heart. Voltage (and current) waveforms are sensed by surface electrodes attached to the patient's skin, peak signals being of the order of a few millivolts. During the measurement process the safety of the patient is paramount accordingly no more than about 10 μA is allowed to pass through the body.

ELECTRODE A.C. RESISTANCE is the ratio between a small change in electrode voltage and the small change in electrode current it produces. The electrode is usually the anode of a thermionic valve.
(>> Thermionic Valve)

ELECTRODYNAMIC WATTMETER is an instrument for measuring the power consumed by a load – see Electrodynamometer.

ELECTRODYNAMOMETER is a measuring instrument based on the magnetic interaction between two coils one of which is fixed, the other rotatable and coupled to the instrument scale. A sketch of a typical coil system is given in Figure E2(i). The coils are connected in series and because the magnetic field strength of each coil is directly proportional to the current then the deflection is proportional to the current squared.

When used as a wattmeter a circuit as in (ii) of the figure applies. The fixed coils carry the main circuit current I_1 (the current coils), the moving coil is wound to a high resistance so that only a small current I_2 flows through it. The supply voltage is dropped across it hence it is known as the voltage or potential coil. The two magnetic fields react according to $I_1 \times I_2$ and because I_2 is proportional to the supply voltage V_s, the instrument deflection is proportional to $V_s I_1$,

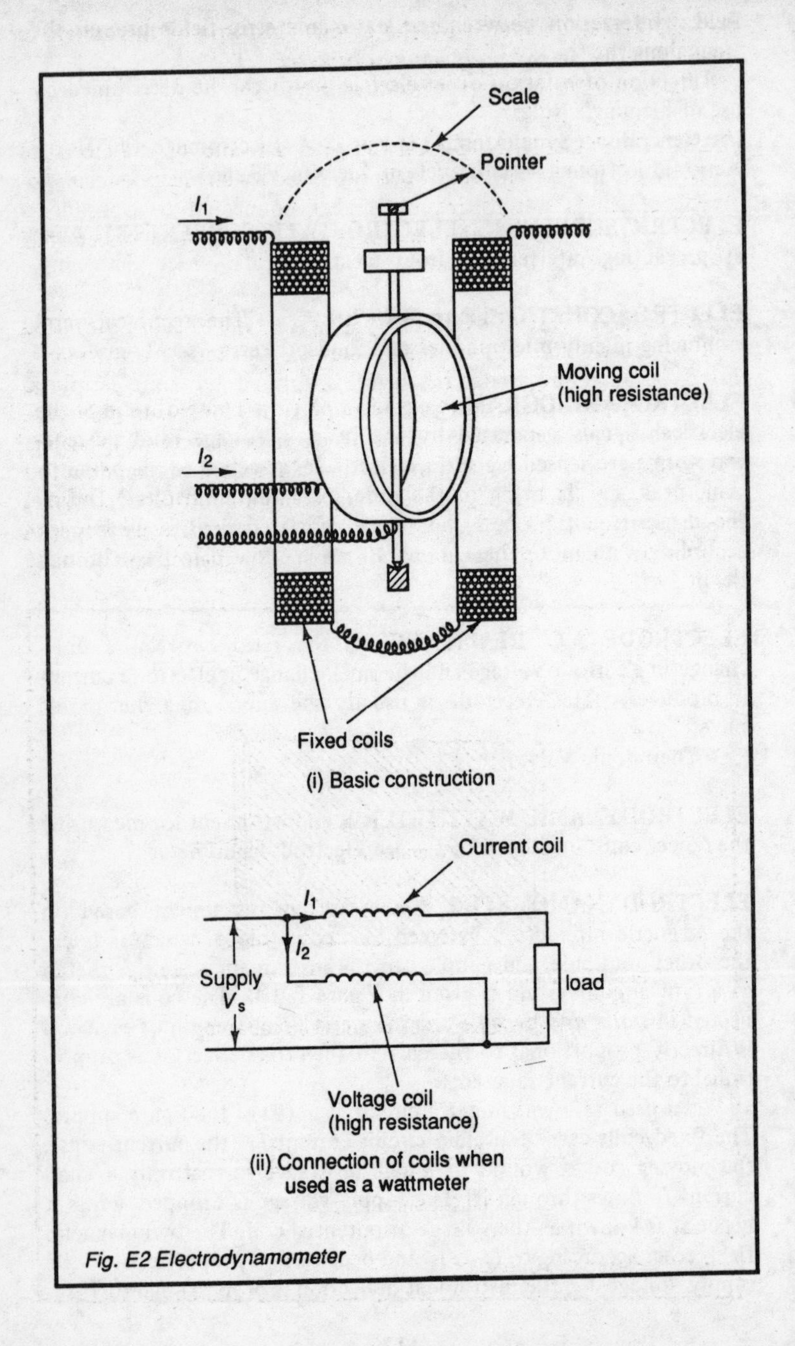

Fig. E2 Electrodynamometer

i.e. the power dissipated by the load. This type of instrument is also known as an *electrodynamic wattmeter.*
(* Wattmeter >> Magnetic Field Strength)

ELECTROENCEPHALOGRAM (e.e.g) is a record of the electrical activity of the human brain. It is produced by an *electroencephalograph* which is a sensitive instrument connected to transducers attached to the body for recording the tiny voltage waveforms. (* Transducer >> Waveform)

ELECTROLYTIC CAPACITOR This is a type of capacitor noted for high capacitance in a small volume. The term *electrolytic* is used because the dielectric layer is formed by an electrolytic method. Typically capacitances of 0.1 μF for a sub-miniature component up to 47 000 μF for a 10 cm tall can-type are available. These capacitors are usually made from aluminium or tantalum foil plates with a semi-liquid conducting compound (the electrolyte) between them as sketched in Figure E3(i). Alternatively a special impregnated paper or gauze may be used. The dielectric is actually

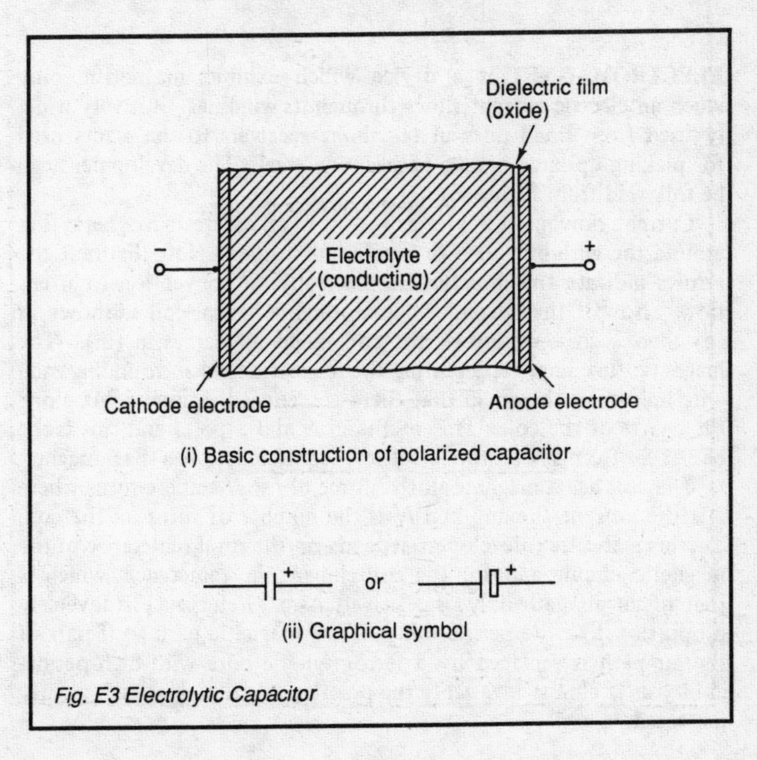

Fig. E3 Electrolytic Capacitor

a thin insulating layer of oxide which is formed on one of the foils when a polarizing voltage is applied. As shown in the figure, the foil with the oxide film is the positive plate, the electrolyte acts as the negative plate.

The extremely thin dielectric has a relative permittivity of about 8 for aluminium but as high as 28 for tantalum. Tantalum electrolytic capacitors are therefore smaller than their aluminium counterparts. In both types the high capacitance is offset by comparatively low working voltages and high leakage current. Because the dielectric film is formed by electrolysis the capacitor is said to be polarized. In use the voltage across the terminals must have the correct polarity otherwise the dielectric film is destroyed. The graphical symbol for a polarized electrolytic capacitor is shown in (ii) of the figure.

Their high capacitance makes them especially suitable for decoupling and smoothing circuits and fortunately in these a polarizing voltage is present. However non-polarized electrolytic capacitors are also available but are more expensive.

(* Decoupling >> Capacitance, Dielectric, Electrolyte)

ELECTROMAGNET is a device which exhibits magnetism only when an electric current flows through its windings. It is very widely used from small ones in telephone receivers to the giants used for picking up large masses of iron and steel. The development can be followed from Figure E4.

Current flowing in a wire as shown in (i) creates a magnetic flux around the wire but no N or S poles are formed. Note that here the arrows indicate the direction of electron, not conventional current flow. Now if the current flows through a helical coil as shown in (ii) then a cross-section of the coil might appear as in (iii). The magnetic flux lines representing the magnetic field surrounding each wire link up as shown so that there is a concentration of flux along the centre of the coil. This results in N and S poles and this is the basic electromagnet, the electrical equivalent of a bar magnet.

The coil has a magnetomotive force of $I \times N$ ampere-turns where I is the current flowing and N is the number of turns on the coil. The magnetic flux developed depends on the total reluctance of the magnetic circuit and for the coil shown, the reluctance, which is that of an air path only, is relatively high. Reluctance is inversely proportional to the permeability of the magnetic path so if part of the air path is replaced by a ferromagnetic core with high permeability as is almost invariably the practice, the flux density is greatly increased.

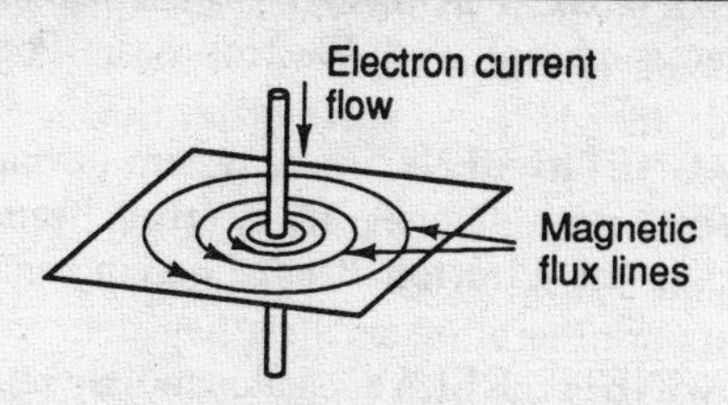

(i) Pictorial representation of magnetic field surrounding a wire

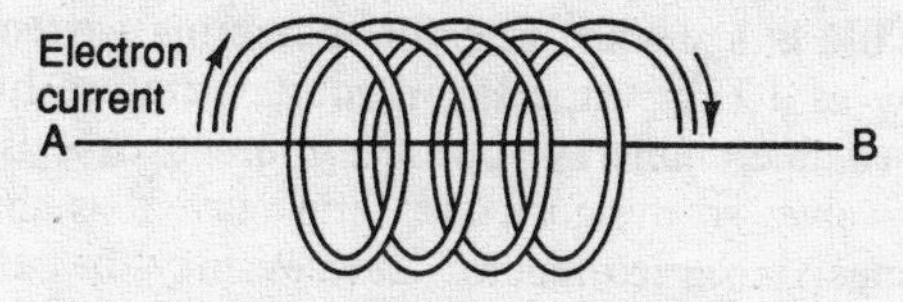

(ii) Coil of wire carrying a current

Looking down on section of (ii) cut across plane AB

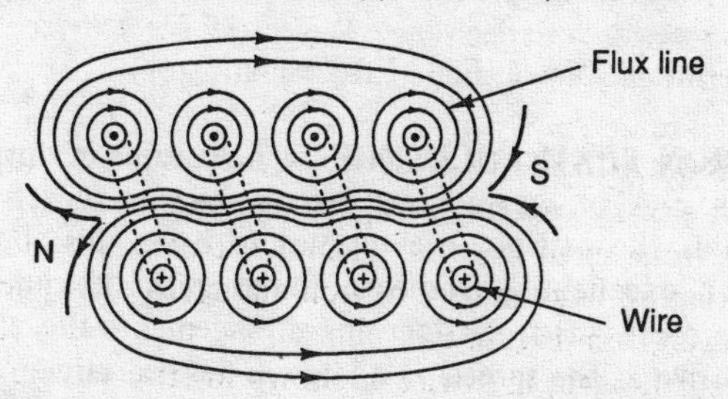

(iii) Circles of flux round wires adding up to produce field within coil

Fig. E4 Electromagnet

Electromagnets are fundamental to electric motors and generators and in these they are excited by *field coils.*
(>> Magnetomotive Force, Reluctance, Permeability)

ELECTROMAGNETIC DEFLECTION (also known as *magnetic deflection*) is the deflection of the electron beam in a cathode-ray tube by circular coils positioned outside the neck of the tube. When a current flows in the coils a magnetic field is set up. An electron beam passing through a coil is therefore deflected by the action of the field on the electrons. Usually the beam can be deflected both horizontally and vertically.
(* Cathode-Ray Tube, Deflection Sensitivity >> Electromagnetic Motor Action)

ELECTROMAGNETIC FOCUSING The use of a magnetic field to focus an electron beam – see Electron Beam Focusing.

ELECTROMAGNETIC LENS A system having similarities with an optical lens which focuses an electron beam by means of a magnetic field – see Electron Beam Focusing and/or Figure E5(i).

ELECTROMAGNETIC RELAY A remotely controlled switching device – see Relay.

ELECTROMETER is a device used for measuring extremely small currents (as low as 10^{-15} amperes), it must therefore have a very high input impedance. One type of *electrometer tube* is based on the thermionic valve, so designed that grid current is almost zero. Alternatively special semiconductor devices may be used which have high input impedances e.g. metal-oxide semiconductor field-effect transistors. Such devices also provide amplification of the input signal for measurement on for example, a standard moving-coil instrument.
(>> Thermionic Valve, Field-Effect Transistor)

ELECTRON BEAM FOCUSING A *focus* as in optics is a point at which rays or waves meet after refraction or reflection hence focusing is the technique employed to bring this about. We can use as an excellent example of focusing the ubiquitous cathode-ray tube for without its focusing arrangements the electron beam would arrive at the screen as a large ill-defined circle of light rather than the bright spot required. Focusing is necessary because when a stream of electrons leaves an electron gun, *debunching*, i.e. the mutual repulsion of electrons within the stream, tends to make the electrons spread out. Many different methods are employed to focus the beam in a cathode-ray tube, the general principles are given below:

Electromagnetic Focusing – the *electromagnetic lens* employed follows the electron gun and consists of a specially constructed focus coil with a large number of turns of fine wire. The coil is wound on a bobbin which is fitted around the neck of the tube. The essential features are shown in Figure E5(i). The direction of the field is along the axis of the tube and electrons which are travelling exactly along the line of the axis are unaffected. Those electrons which are on a path at an angle to the tube axis have a component of velocity across the field and it can be shown that the force imposed on them imparts a helical motion which results in the electrons crossing the axis at *focus points* along its path. By adjustment of the coil, coil

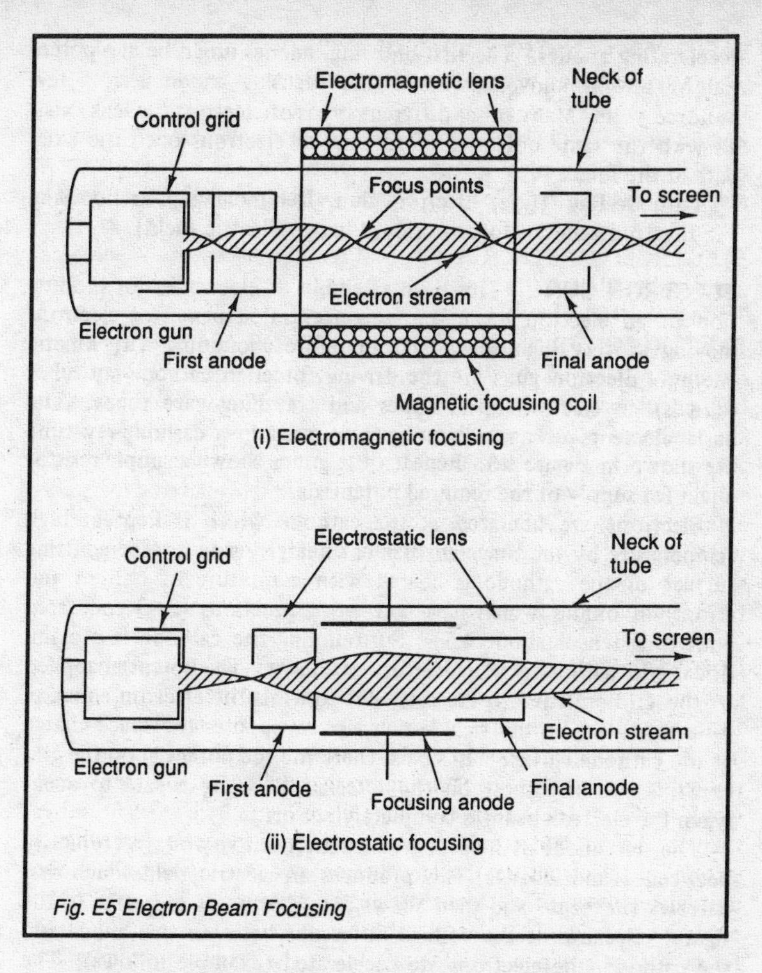

Fig. E5 Electron Beam Focusing

current and accelerating electric field, a focus point can be made to coincide with the screen.

Electrostatic Focusing – employs an *electrostatic lens* which in its simplest form is a cylindrical electrode (the focusing anode) fitted concentrically with the electron stream as it travels through the accelerating anodes as suggested in (ii) of the figure. The cylindrical electrode may contain one or more disc apertures and is maintained at a lower positive potential than the first and final anodes. This potential is adjusted so that its effect is to repel electrons which stray from the axial path and force them to converge back onto the axis as they reach the screen. The electrode potential is of course negative relative to the potentials of the

accelerating anodes. The first and final anodes might be at a potential of several kilovolts whereas the focusing anode is at a few hundred volts. Many other different types of electrostatic lens exist, all with the same objective of forcing all electrons onto the axial path at the focus.
(* Cathode-Ray Tube, Electron Gun, Debunching, Gas Focusing >> Electromagnetic Motor Action, Charge, Electric Field)

ELECTRON GUN This is an assembly of electrodes for production of an electron beam, i.e. a concentrated pencil of electrons moving at very high speed and therefore abounding with kinetic energy. Electron guns are the driving forces in cathode-ray tubes (c.r.t.'s), in electron microscopes and travelling-wave tubes. The basic elements of an electron gun as used in a cathode-ray tube are shown in Figure E6. Beneath the gun is shown a simple resistor chain for supply of the required potentials.

Electrons are liberated at the cathode which is kept at high temperature by the tungsten filament heater inside it. The emitting surface of the cathode is coated with a mixture of barium and strontium oxides which have low work functions (2–3 compared with tungsten at about 4.5). Surrounding the cathode is a cylindrical grid with a circular aperture as shown. The potential applied to the grid (relative to the cathode) controls the electron emission by creating an electric field which aids or opposes the space charge at the cathode surface. In a c.r.t. therefore the potential on the grid controls the brightness on the screen. *Blanking* is said to occur when the electron beam is completely cut off.

The 1st anode is held at a constant positive voltage (typically between 1 and 2 kV). This produces an electric field which first narrows the beam and then allows it to diverge as suggested in the figure. Because of the voltage difference between this anode and the cathode, the electrons are accelerated (example follows). The beam passes through the aperture in the 1st anode, some electrons hit the anode at its edges and form a small 1st anode current.

The purpose of the 2nd anode which is positive but to a lower voltage than for anode 1, is to focus the beam so that it converges to a small spot on the screen. Finally the 3rd anode accelerates the electrons further by its high positive potential, probably of several thousand volts. Each electron ultimately hitting the screen therefore has relatively high (kinetic) energy which it gives up as heat and causes the screen to glow.

A useful exercise which helps to bring the energy/motion equations into perspective is to calculate the velocity of an electron as it hits the screen. To do this we must assume that the velocity of

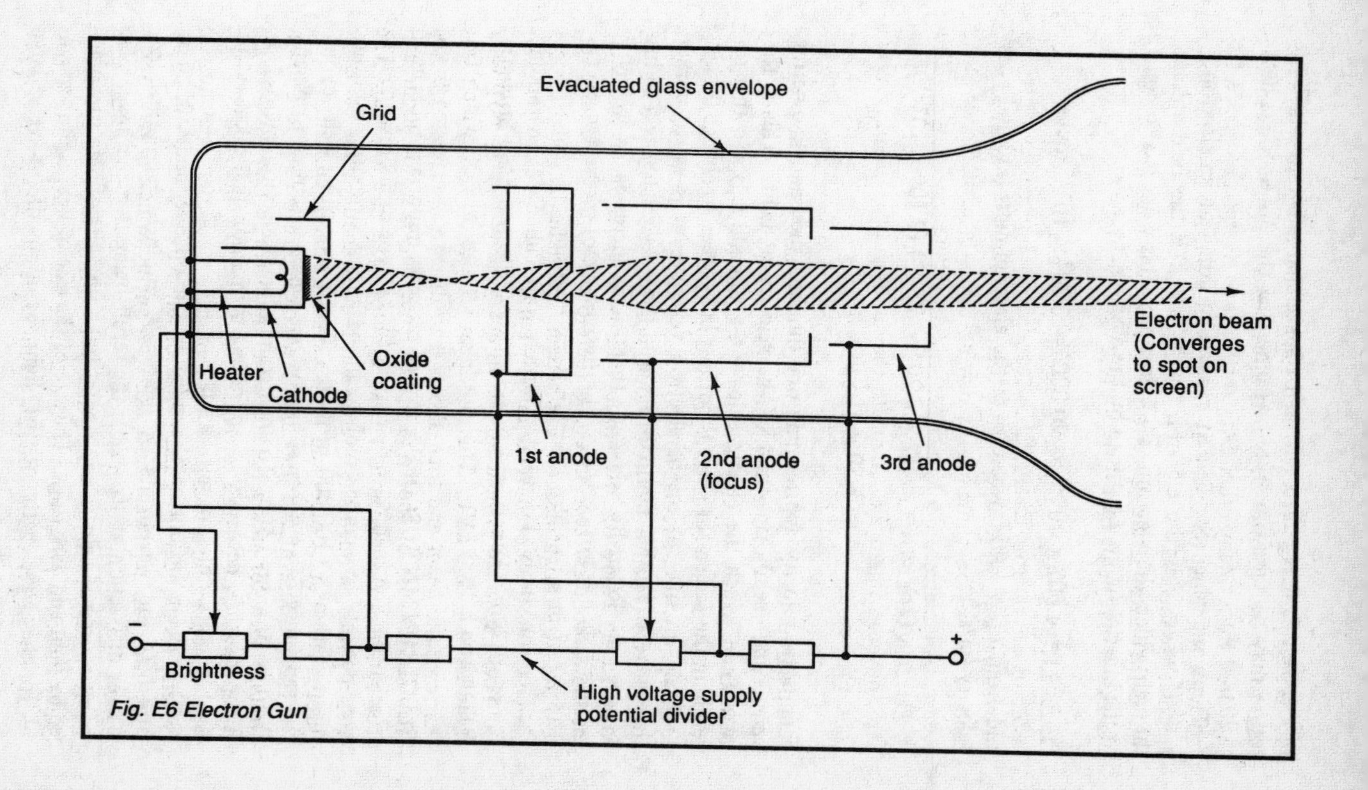

Fig. E6 Electron Gun

an electron as it is pulled out of the space charge is zero which of course may be far from true. Assume that the 3rd anode is held at 20 000 V.

The work which the field is capable of doing on an electron = $e \times V$ where e is the electron charge and V is the field voltage through which the electron is accelerated. This work is also equal to the kinetic energy, E_k gained by the electron, i.e.:

$$E_k = 1.602 \times 10^{-19} \times 20\,000 = 3.204 \times 10^{-15} \text{ joules}$$

and from $E_k = ½mv^2$ where m is the electron mass (kg) and v its velocity (m/s):

$$v = \sqrt{(2E_k/m)} = \sqrt{[(2 \times 3.204 \times 10^{-15})/(9.109 \times 10^{-31})]}$$

$$= 8.39 \times 10^7 \text{ m/s}$$

a fantastic velocity approaching one hundred thousand kilometres *per second*, nearly one-third of the velocity of light. This is the velocity at which the electrons leave the gun and it is also that on reaching the screen for there is nothing in between to change things.

While on this subject of electron velocities, it is worth noting that there is another approximation in the answer. Einstein in his Theory of Relativity showed that mass increases as velocity increases, so v is in fact lower. In this case a more correct answer is 8.15×10^7 m/s. See also Electron Beam Focusing.
(* Electron Beam Focusing, Cathode-Ray Tube >> Thermionic Emission, Work Function, Kinetic Energy, Electric Field Strength, Relativistic Effect)

ELECTRON MICROSCOPE is one of the most important tools used in scientific and medical research. With this type of microscope it is even possible to examine molecular and atomic structures by using magnifications of 100 000 or more. This is something well beyond the capability of any optical microscope which is limited to magnifications of around 500. To understand why the electron microscope is superior it is necessary to appreciate *diffraction* first because this is what limits useful magnification.

Diffraction occurs at the edge of an opaque body when it obstructs the wavefronts of light. Accordingly an optical lens causes diffraction at its edges, the result being that the image of a point source of light is not a point but a tiny disc of light surrounded by light and dark rings. The size of the disc of light is proportional to the wavelength of the light being used. A very large lens therefore produces less diffraction than a small one. This infers that very small detail in the object being examined cannot be *resolved* (distinguished apart) no matter how high the magnification employed because the individual images overlap. Reducing the wavelength of the light (e.g. ultraviolet) improves the resolving power but not significantly.

This is where the electron comes in. As de Broglie has shown, particles have a wavelike behaviour and moving electrons have an associated wavelength which in fact decreases as the electron energy increases. As an example, an electron with a velocity of 10^7 m/s has a wavelength of 7.3×10^{-11} m (0.073 nm – compare with ultraviolet light at 200 nm). Hence high energy electrons can be used instead of light rays by projecting them through a very thin specimen. Resolutions of some 0.1 nm (approximately the diameter of an atom) are obtained in practice, some 1–2000 times better than for the optical microscope.

In the practical electron microscope magnetic lenses replace optical ones. These lenses are current carrying coils which focus an electron beam as would an optical lens. A sketch of the system is given in Figure E7. A diverging beam of electrons leaves the electron gun, the beam is then made parallel by the magnetic condenser. Electrons falling on the thin specimen are partially transmitted according to its structure. Those electrons passing through are brought into focus by varying the magnetic fields of the various magnetic lenses. The image is finally developed on a fluorescent screen or photographic plate.

(* Electron Gun >> de Broglie Waves, Charge, Electromagnetic Motor Action, Diffraction)

ELECTRON MULTIPLIER This is a device for producing current amplification through secondary emission. It is particularly useful in light-sensitive devices where the number of electrons released from a cathode when light falls upon it is relatively small. Such a very weak current can easily be swamped by noise currents so it is amplified immediately as shown in the simplified sketch of Figure E8. In this drawing it is assumed that the secondary emission ratio (δ) of each of the *dynodes* is 2. The drawing demonstrates how a single electron when released at the cathode is attracted by the positive potential on dynode 1 where it releases 2 secondary electrons which are then attracted to dynode 2. The process repeats to the anode where for every electron released at the cathode, at least 8 are ultimately collected at the anode.

The multiplication at each dynode is likely to be greater than 2, in fact up to about 10. If, for example, each of 10 dynodes has a

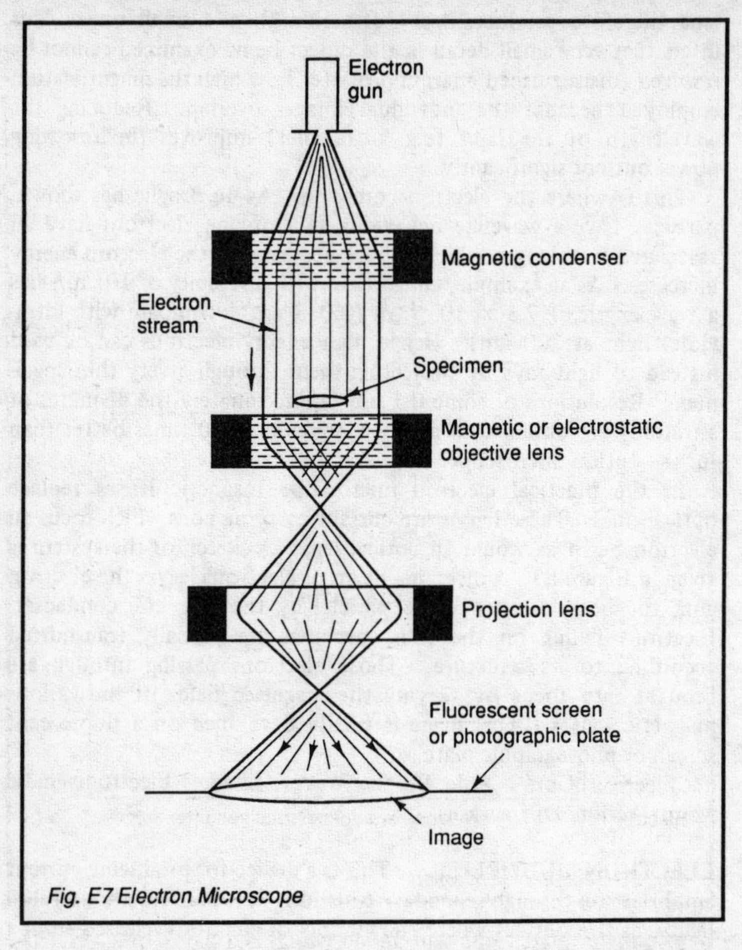

Fig. E7 Electron Microscope

secondary emission ratio of 4, there is an overall multiplication of 4^{10}, hence for each electron emitted at the cathode over one million are collected. This is in no way the best which can be achieved.

In practical multiplier systems the dynodes are more likely to be curved in shape.

(* Photomultiplier >> Secondary Emission, Secondary Emission Ratio)

ELECTROPLATING is the process of coating an object with a metal such as silver, copper or chromium by electrolysis. Silver plating can be used as one of the more straightforward examples. In an electrolyte of silver nitrate are immersed the cathode which is the

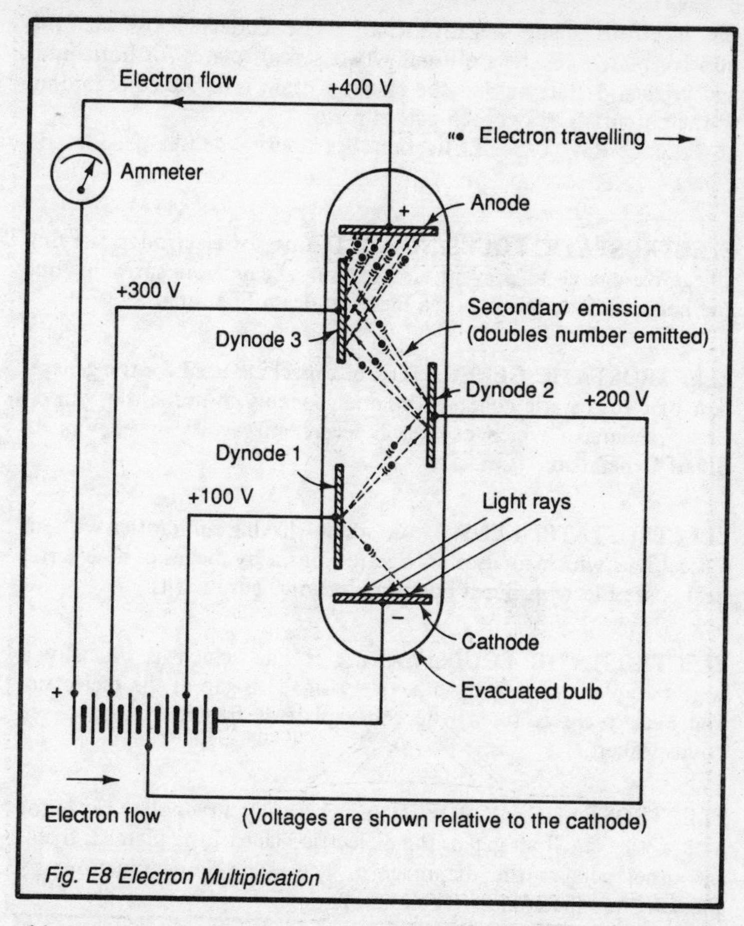

Fig. E8 Electron Multiplication

object to be plated and the anode which is a block of silver. The anode is maintained at a positive potential relative to the cathode. The chemical composition of silver nitrate is expressed as $AgNO_3$ and it dissociates into two ions, Ag^+ and NO_3^-. The Ag^+ ions (silver) are attracted to the cathode and deposit silver on it. A continuous supply of these ions is available from the silver anode. (>> Electrolysis, Electrolyte, Ionization)

ELECTROSTATIC DEFLECTION is the deflection of an electron beam in a cathode-ray tube by charged metal deflection plates assembled within the neck of the tube. When a potential is applied across the plates an electrostatic field is set up between them. An electron beam passing between the plates is therefore deflected, the

the electrons being negative charges are deflected towards the positive plate. There are usually two sets of plates for horizontal and vertical deflection and the electron beam is deflected according to the potentials across each pair of plates.
(* Cathode-Ray Tube, Deflection Sensitivity >> Charge, Electric Field)

ELECTROSTATIC FOCUSING The use of electrodes carrying a negative charge to prevent electrons in a beam from spreading out and hence to focus them – see Electron Beam Focusing.

ELECTROSTATIC GENERATOR is a machine used for the generation of electrostatic charges, the one generally in use is the Van de Graaff generator which can reach several megavolts – see Van de Graaff Generator.

ELECTROSTATIC LENS A system having similarities with an optical lens which focuses an electron beam by means of an electric field – see Electron Beam Focusing and/or Figure E5(ii).

ELECTROSTATIC LOUDSPEAKER is one which is basically a large two-plate capacitor with a very small air-gap as the dielectric. The back plate is fixed, the other plate is free to vibrate – see Loudspeaker.

ELECTROSTATIC MICROPHONE is basically a two-plate capacitor with a very small air-gap as the dielectric. One of the plates is fixed, the other acts as the diaphragm. The microphone functions by changing its capacitance – see Microphone.

ELECTROSTATIC VOLTMETER is an instrument used for measuring high direct voltages and is one which after an initial charging current, takes no power from the source of voltage being measured. The voltmeter is constructed around a set of small metal vanes which rotate within a fixed set against the returning force of a hairspring. The mechanism resembles that of a multiplate, air-dielectric tuning capacitor. When a voltage is applied across the two sets of plates the resulting attraction of the opposite charges turns the movable set through an angle depending on the voltage. This can be read directly as voltage on a scale. This type of meter works over a full-scale deflection of some 1000 – 10 000 volts.
(* Voltmeter >> Capacitor, Charge)

EMITTER-COUPLED LOGIC (ECL) is a non-saturating logic circuit in which certain transistors are coupled by their emitters. When transistors are normally operated as switches they change between a very low collector current and the higher saturation current as shown in Figure S16. The change from saturation to cut-off takes time because of carrier storage. Computers are often required to complete thousands of operations per second so they expect their logic circuits to work even faster. Accordingly a circuit which does not saturate its transistors and thereby can operate much more quickly has much to recommend it; such is the emitter-coupled logic circuit. It is the fastest type of logic circuit available commercially for in most ECL gate circuits arrangements are made to keep the transistors from saturation by limiting the total current through them. Typically an OR/NOR ECL gate has an operating time of 1 – 2 nanoseconds, less than one-quarter of the time for a high speed TTL circuit. The output impedance is low hence the gate can provide a high current drive and rapidly charges and discharges external circuit capacitances.
(* Digital Logic, Switching Transistor, Logic Gate, Transistor–Transistor Logic >> Carrier Storage)

EMITTER FOLLOWER is a type of amplifier comprising a bipolar transistor connected in common-collector as shown in Figure E9.

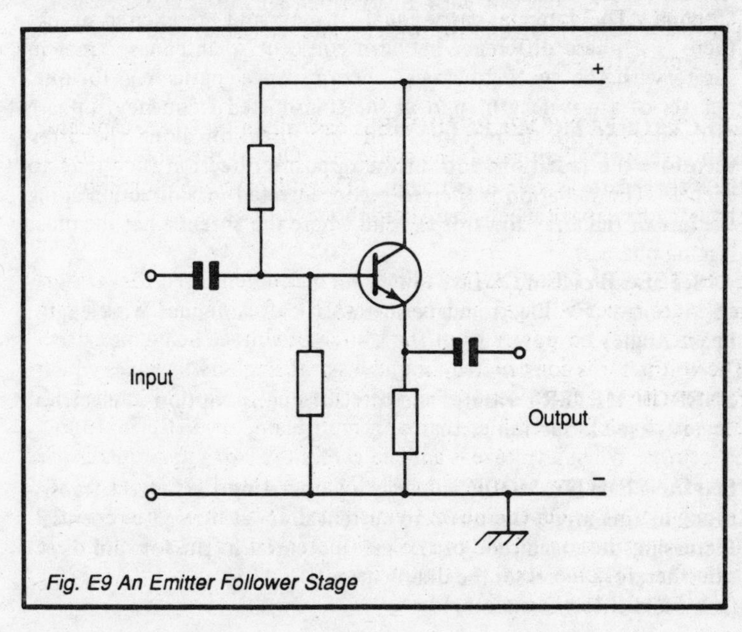

Fig. E9 An Emitter Follower Stage

Although the collector is not connected directly to the common line, it is effectively so as far as the signal is concerned because the power supply impedance is low. The output voltage tends to follow the input voltage so closely that the voltage gain is approximately unity. There is however a current gain because a small base current controls a much larger emitter current. The collector-base junction is reverse-biased, therefore the input resistance is high; the base-emitter junction is forward biased so the output resistance is low. This confirms the absence of voltage gain because although there is a current gain, it operates in a low resistance output circuit and can only give rise to a low voltage.

The emitter follower is frequently used for impedance matching, for example from a high impedance source to a low impedance load; when so used it avoids the power loss of resistive or transformer matching.

See also Common-Collector Connection.
(* Common Collector Connection, Matching >> Transistor)

ENCRYPTION is the process used in audio or television systems to prevent unauthorized listening or viewing – see Scrambling.

END-FIRE ARRAY consists of a series of antennas arranged in a line for enhanced directional characteristics compared with a single antenna. The antennas carry equal currents and are excited so that there is a phase difference between consecutive antennas commensurate with the spacing between them in wavelengths, e.g. for one-quarter of a wavelength apart at the transmitted frequency, a phase difference of 90° is required. In one direction along the array therefore the radiations add, in the opposite direction they tend to cancel. The radiation is therefore concentrated in a direction along the line of the array towards the end where the antenna has the most lagging phase.

See also Broadside Array.
(* Antenna >> Electromagnetic Radiation, Antenna, Wavelength, Phase Angle)

ENERGY METER measures and totals the consumption of electrical energy – see Induction Meter.

ENHANCEMENT MODE is a way of operating field-effect transistors. In this mode there is zero current drain at zero gate potential. Increasing the magnitude of the gate potential in the forward direction therefore increases the drain current.
(>> Field-Effect Transistor)

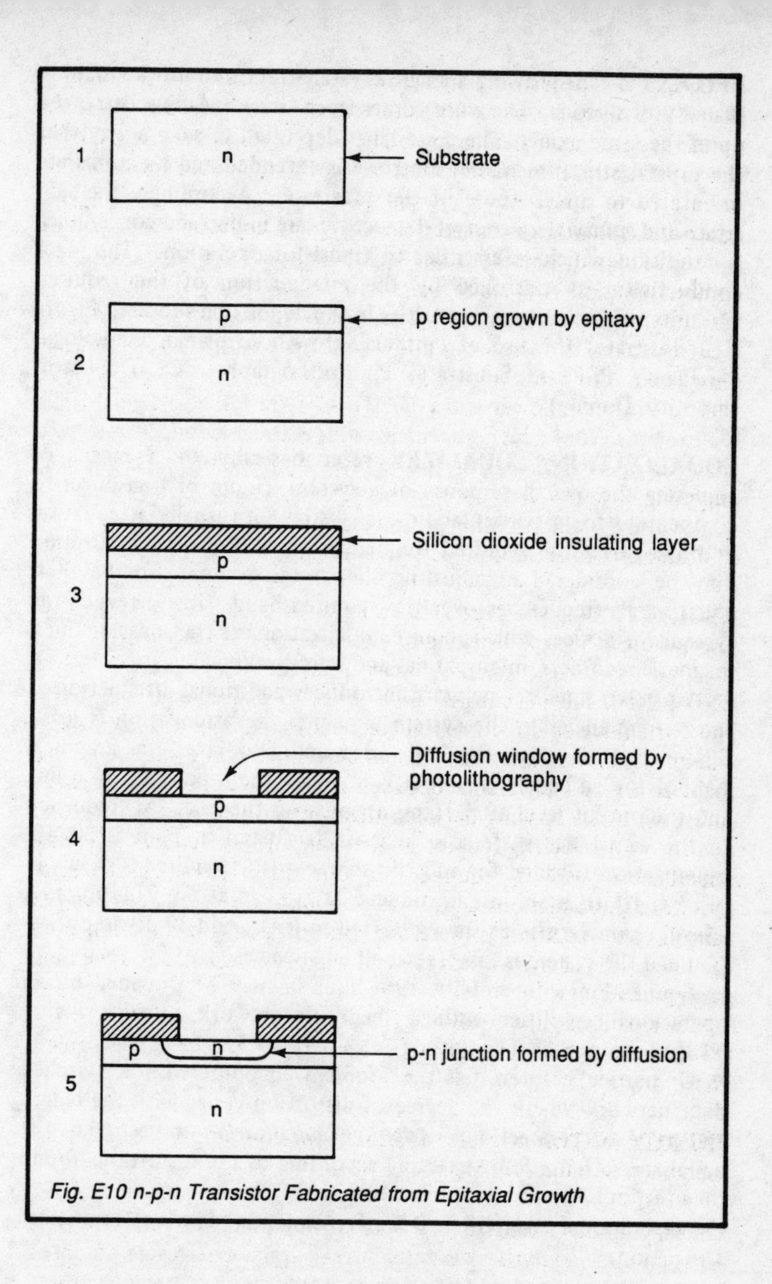

Fig. E10 n-p-n Transistor Fabricated from Epitaxial Growth

EPITAXY means growing a single crystal structure onto a substrate (usually of silicon). The word comes from Greek meaning "arranged upon the same axis". The material is deposited in such a way that the crystal structure of the substrate is extended and its atoms are orientated to match those of the substrate. Accordingly the substrate and *epitaxial layer* crystal structures are in-line and continuous, a condition which is essential to transistor operation. The layer conductivity is controlled by the introduction of the required amounts of p- or n-type impurities in the deposition process. Figure E10 illustrates the use of epitaxial growth in planar technology. (* Planar Process, Substrate, Photolithography >> Transistor, Impurity, Doping)

EQUALIZATION, EQUALIZER refer basically to a means of adjusting the overall response of a system, circuit or transducer to compensate for a particular type of distortion (usually attenuation or phase) over the required frequency band. Equally equalization may be considered as adjusting the overall response so that it is equal at all frequencies over the required band. Just a few of the systems or devices which require equalization are transmission lines, magnetic recorders, microphones and loudspeakers.

A passive equalizer network introduces additional attenuation at those frequencies in the system at which the attenuation is least. Figure E11 develops the basic idea and also gives the graphical symbol for an equalizer. At (i) are shown the input level to a line and the output level after transmission over the line. At frequency f_1 the signal has suffered a loss of 20 dB but at f_2 it is 30 dB. Equalization is called for and the characteristic required is shown in (ii), i.e. 10 dB more loss introduced at f_1 than at f_2. This provides a level characteristic as shown dotted in (iii). Add 30 dB amplification and the system is loss-free at all frequencies f_1 to f_2.

Equlization with amplification built in may be provided by an operational amplifier with a feedback network to suit. Figure T13(iv) shows such a circuit.

Of particular interest is the problem encountered in a switched data network where the degree of distortion varies with the length and type of connection. *Adaptive equalization* is used, i.e. the equalizer sets itself for example according to the distortions found on a test pulse transmitted over the circuit.
(* Operational Amplifier >> Transmission Line, Attenuation, Distortion)

EQUIVALENT CIRCUIT This is used in analysis of circuit action, design and in teaching electronics. An equivalent circuit

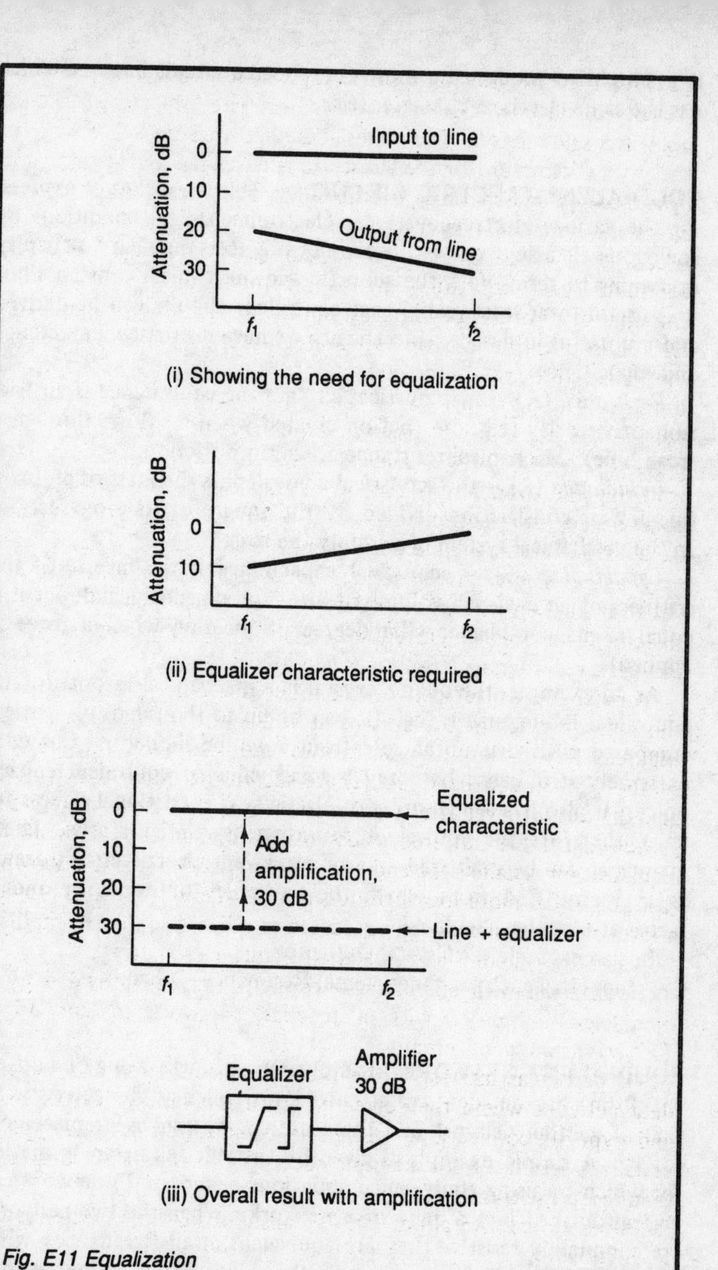

(i) Showing the need for equalization

(ii) Equalizer characteristic required

(iii) Overall result with amplification

Fig. E11 Equalization

is a simplified model of a more complicated circuit but one which has the same electrical characteristics.

EQUIVALENT ELECTRIC CIRCUIT This is a means of expressing the various electroacoustic or electromechanical conditions by analogous electric circuits. Electronics engineers may have difficulty in coming to terms with the acoustic and mechanical constants but it is useful to at least realise that equivalent circuits can be derived and are useful in design. Electrically we have resistance, inductance and capacitance:

Resistance (R) – in acoustical circuits the equivalence is air friction or viscosity (e.g. the friction created when air flows through a small hole). Mechanical resistance arises from friction.

Inductance (L) – the acoustical equivalent is the mass of air in an opening or constriction divided by the square of its cross-section. In the mechanical system it is simply the mass.

Capacitance (C) – acoustical capacitance is the inverse of the stiffness of an enclosed volume of air. For a mechanical device it is equal to its compliance (the degree of yielding when a force is applied).

As an example, the quartz crystal is a mechanical resonator. Its equivalent inductance is high (it can be up to thousands of henries) compared with that obtainable from a wound inductor. Quartz is extremely stiff hence has only a small value of equivalent capacitance. It also has a high order of elasticity (i.e. frictional effects are low), therefore the equivalent resistance is relatively low. These quantities can be evaluated and an equivalent electric circuit drawn as in Figure C24 from which the frequency of resonance and Q factor etc. can be calculated.

For an example see Crystal Oscillator.
(>> Inductance, Capacitance, Mass, Resonance, Q Factor)

EQUIVALENT NETWORK is one which although being of a different form, has an identical attenuation/frequency characteristic to that of another network and therefore can be used as a replacement for it. A simple example is given by the star-delta transformation for which by using equivalence equations a star (or T) network can be transformed into a delta or π network. When the two networks are completely resistive they are equivalent at all frequencies, when however reactances are present the equivalence arises at one particular frequency only.
(* Star-Delta Transformation >> Network)

EXCITATION is a term used in several different spheres of electronics. In general excitation induces activity in a device, for example:

(1) the current which flows in an electromagnet is known as the *excitation* current;
(2) the current which flows in the field coils of a d.c. motor is usually known as the field current but also as the *excitation* current;
(3) alternators (a.c. power generators) require current for the magnetic field system. This is usually provided by a small d.c. generator known as an *exciter*;
(4) it is the application of a voltage to a crystal to start it oscillating or maintain it in oscillation also the application of periodic pulses to a radio frequency tuned circuit to maintain oscillations (e.g. from a Class C amplifier);
(5) an antenna is said to be excited when radio frequency power is switched to it.

(* Generator, Electromagnet, Electric Motor, Alternator, Class C Amplifier, Antenna)

EXCLUSIVE-NOR GATE A logic gate with two inputs which has an output of logic 0 when one and only one of the inputs is at logic 1 – see Digital Logic.

EXCLUSIVE-OR GATE A logic gate with two inputs which has an output of logic 1 when one and only one of the inputs is at logic 1 – see Digital Logic.

EXPANDER Short for *volume expander* – see Companding.

FACSIMILE TRANSMISSION is the production at a distance of an exact copy of written, printed or photographic matter on paper, card, etc. There are many techniques employed in both the recording and the reproduction processes. Scanning is required in both again with a variety of techniques for example, electronic line scanning only with the picture or document rotating on a drum, flying-spot scanners, line or area scan using charge-coupled devices. Photocells are the most likely transducers to be found in use.

Transmission may be analogue or digital, often transmitted on a carrier wave. The bandwidth required naturally depends on the rate of transmission. At the receiver the incoming signals are demodulated, amplified and then used to modulate a light source which again is involved in some sort of scanning process to implant the image of the original onto photo-sensitive paper.
(* Scanning, Flying-Spot Scanner >> Photocell, Analogue Signal, Digital Signal, Bandwidth)

FADING commonly occurs in radio transmissions at broadcast and higher frequencies. It is a variation in received signal amplitude due to interference between waves which have travelled to the receiver along different routes. Mostly this occurs when a wave arriving on earth via the ionosphere interferes with the same transmission arriving by a ground wave. The ionosphere is notoriously fickle hence the reflected path varies in length and the received signal fades as the two waves move in and out of phase.

When all transmitted frequencies are attenuated equally, *amplitude fading* is said to occur, if however some frequencies are attenuated more than others, the term *selective fading* is used. (* Ionosphere >> Electromagnetic Wave, Phase)

FAILURE/FAILURE RATE *Failure* of a system or component is a detected cessation of its ability to perform a specified function within previously established limits. *Failure rate* is the number of failures of an item as a function of a specified length of time, number of operational cycles etc. It is usually determined from life tests and/or by observation of working equipment. Two commonly used measurements of failure are:

Mean time to failure (m.t.t.f.) – is the measured operating time of a single item of equipment divided by the total number of failures of that item during a given time. If several similar items are tested, each will have a different time to failure. The m.t.t.f. is then the sum of all the times for all the items divided by the number of items. The m.t.t.f. is especially useful with discrete components which are not repaired when they fail, many fall into this category, e.g. transistors, capacitors, resistors.

Mean time between (or before) failures (m.t.b.f.) – this is a very useful indicator of reliability and is of most use with repairable items or systems, the time in each case being simply that between two successive failures. The m.t.b.f. is given by the total operating time divided by the total number of failures:

$$\text{m.t.b.f.} = \frac{\text{number of items} \times \text{operating time}}{\text{total number of failures}}$$

The reciprocal of this gives the failure rate, λ, hence m.t.b.f. = $1/\lambda$.

Multiplying λ by 100 gives the *percentage failure rate* and from the failure rate the reliability can be estimated.
(* Reliability)

FALL TIME is synonymous with *decay time* which is a characteristic of a pulse. It is a measure of the rate of decrease in amplitude of a pulse.
(>> Pulse)

FARADAY CAGE, FARADAY SCREEN is an earthed cage-like arrangement of wires for the protection of items sensitive to strong electric fields. Where high tension equipment is in use a wire cage is also used as a protection for human operators. According to Gauss's theorem, equipment or components which themselves exhibit no charge and are contained within a closed metallic surface are shielded from external electric fields. However it is found that the metal screen need not be solid but is just as effective if in the form of open wires.

A Faraday screen is used when inductive coupling is required between two circuits but with any stray capacitance coupling between them eliminated. The screen consists of stiff wires connected together at one end only (rather like a comb) and earthed. Magnetic fields pass through because there is no continuous conducting surface for eddy currents but electric fields do not.
(* Screening >> Electric Field, Gauss's Theorem)

FAST-RECOVERY DIODE is a semiconductor diode in which carrier storage is very low. Because of this, storage time is short and the diode is therefore suitable for high speed operation. The diode would normally be manufactured from gallium arsenide in preference to silicon because the minority carrier lifetimes of gallium arsenide are shorter.
(>> Diode, Carrier Storage, Minority Carrier, Lifetime)

FEEDBACK CONTROL LOOP is an electronic control system for operation of mechanical, electrical, heating etc. devices in which the system output is measured, compared with a reference and then automatically corrected – see Closed-Loop Control System.

FEEDER A general name for a line carrying electrical power, e.g. from a power generating station to the distribution network, also for a transmission line carrying radio frequency power from a radio transmitter to an antenna.
(* Polyphase System, Antenna >> Transmission Line, Antenna)

FERRITE A ceramic is a type of pottery which is very hard and therefore brittle. A ferrite is a ceramic comprising certain oxides of iron fired with other metals such as zinc, nickel or cobalt. According to the mix, a large range of magnetic characteristics can be produced, both magnetically soft and hard. Generally ferrites have high permeability coupled with high electrical resistance which makes them especially suitable for magnetic cores working at high frequencies. Resistivities can be as high as 10^{14} Ωm hence eddy currents can be reduced considerably.

Ferrites are therefore useful as cores for radio frequency transformers and inductors and for the magnetic deflection units of cathode-ray tubes. They are widely used for microwave isolators and circulators. These ceramics are extremely hard so cutting or drilling is practically impossible, hence cores are produced and fired in the shape ultimately required.
(* Ceramic, Circulator >> Magnetic Hysteresis, Permeability, Eddy Current)

FERRITE-ROD ANTENNA is a ferrite rod typically some 1 cm diameter and 10–15 cm in length on which coils are wound for use in a portable radio receiver as a replacement for an external antenna. The coils are usually the resonant circuit inductors in the first stage tuning for reception from medium and long wave radio stations, hence they are connected directly to the tuning capacitor. The rod is of high permeability and concentrates the magnetic component of the incident wave through the coil. Although of much shorter length compared with an external antenna, the ferrite antenna has a higher Q factor (up to 200) so it can provide an equally good signal.

This type of antenna has "figure of 8" directional properties, hence there is a disadvantage in that the receiver may need to be rotated for maximum pick-up. On the other hand it has the advantage that by rotating the receiver it is possible to discriminate against unwanted radio stations and interference.
(* Antenna, Radio Receiver >> Ferrite, Antenna, Resonance, Q Factor)

FIBRE OPTIC TRANSMISSION is the transmission of information between two points by means of a cable made up of one or more *optical fibres.* Optical transmission directly through the atmosphere has long been feasible but for the majority of applications where security, reliability and low attenuation are required, light is now transmitted from source to receiver through flexible fibres. Fibre optic communication is especially used for telephone circuits and for links between computers and their peripheral equipment where freedom from electrical noise and other interference is paramount.

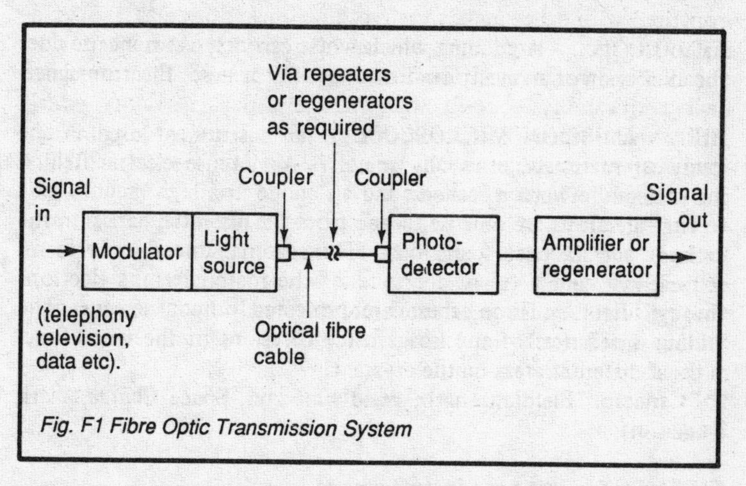

Fig. F1 Fibre Optic Transmission System

A fibre optic communication system consists essentially of a light source such as a laser or light emitting diode (l.e.d.) coupled to an optical fibre cable. At the distant end the cable is coupled to a photodetector such as an avalanche or p-i-n diode as shown in outline in Figure F1. Transmission is usually digital and certainly most of the available light sources and detectors function better this way. The light source must have adequate brightness and it must be capable of being modulated at sufficiently high rates, i.e. its response time must be short. The semiconductor diode laser is especially suitable and it can be modulated through the junction current up to several GHz. The l.e.d. is more limited but because of its relative simplicity of manufacture it is likely to be preferred for short range links (a few km).

Both avalanche and p-i-n diodes are fast operating photodetectors so are used for this type of application. They have the shortest response times of all photodetectors and can respond to modulation frequencies up to nearly 1 GHz, the avalanche having several decibels greater power sensitivity.

Fibre optic transmission systems have several advantages over electric cable systems: (i) fewer repeaters (or regenerators) are required on long circuits, (ii) they do not suffer from electrical interference, (iii) glass, even though when made ultra-pure, is cheaper than copper, and (iv) for a given total bandwidth optical fibre cables are very much smaller than the equivalent electrical ones.
(* Digital Transmission >> Optical Fibre, Laser, Light Emitting Diode, Photodiode, Modulation)

FIELD COIL A winding which when carrying a current provides the excitation of an electric motor or generator – see Electromagnet.

FIELD EMISSION MICROSCOPE is an instrument used in the study of materials, especially metals. An intense electric field is maintained between a cathode and an anode in a high vacuum tube so that electrons are able to escape from the potential barrier at the cathode surface (field emission). The material under study forms the cathode and a tip of a crystal of the material emits electrons through field emission, these are projected onto a screen. The various intensities of the image are indications of the work functions at different areas on the crystal tip.
(>> Electric Field Strength, Field Emission, Space Charge, Work Function)

FILAMENT is a fine conducting wire in:

(i) an electric lamp. The wire is heated to incandescence by a current through it, it is not easily fusible under normal operating conditions. The resistance of the filament when cold is very different from its value when working because of the positive temperature coefficient of resistance, typically a 240 V, 100 W lamp might have a resistance of 45 Ω cold rising to over 550 Ω when the full voltage is applied.

(ii) a thermionic valve either as a directly heated cathode, usually coated with metal oxides to increase the emission or as the heating wire in an indirectly heated cathode.
(>> Temperature Coefficient of Resistance, Thermionic Valve)

FILM RESISTOR is a fixed resistor using a thin film of monocrystalline carbon, boron-carbon, metal or metal oxide deposited onto an insulating substrate. This type of resistor is capable of providing a stable resistance to within 1 or 2 % and is a good alternative to wire resistors being both smaller and less expensive – see Resistor.

FLASHOVER is the making of an electric circuit by arcing or sparking across a gap between two conductors or between one conductor and earth caused by excessive voltage or insulation breakdown. The voltage at which flashover just occurs is the *flashover voltage.*
(* Spark >> Breakdown, Arc)

FLIP-FLOP A computer term for a bistable multivibrator used as a memory cell – see Multivibrator.

FLOATING describes the condition of a circuit or component which is not connected to any source of potential. The term is used especially with thermionic valves, if the grid electrode is disconnected, the valve is aid to be floating (i.e. not going anywhere).

The term is also used in secondary cell charging, when the cells are being charged at the same time as they are discharging, the battery is said to be floating.
(>> Thermionic Valve, Secondary Cell)

FLOATING-CARRIER MODULATION is an advanced method of amplitude modulation (a.m.) developed for lower transmission of power compared with conventional a.m. The technique is to generate a control signal from the amplitude of the modulating wave continually averaged over a short period of time. This control signal is then used to adjust the carrier level so that it is only just sufficient to accommodate the modulating wave, accordingly the modulation depth approaches 100% irrespective of the modulating signal amplitude. Carrier power is therefore reduced especially when the modulating signal is at low amplitude.
(>> Modulation, Carrier, Amplitude Modulation)

FLOOD GUN is a special electron gun mounted within a storage cathode-ray tube to provide energy for maintaining the display – see Storage Tube and/or Figure S14.

FLUORESCENT LAMP A gas discharge lamp containing mercury vapour which generates light by fluorescence – see Discharge Lighting.

FLUTTER is a term which applies in sound reproduction systems. It is used for unwanted rapid deviations in frequency (at say, above 10 Hz) from the original frequency. It usually arises from rhythmic speed variations in the disc or tape motor drive and may be perceived as a slight harshness in the reproduced sound quality. The term is frequently associated with *wow* which is concerned with lower frequencies than above.
(* Disc Recording, Magnetic Recording, Wow)

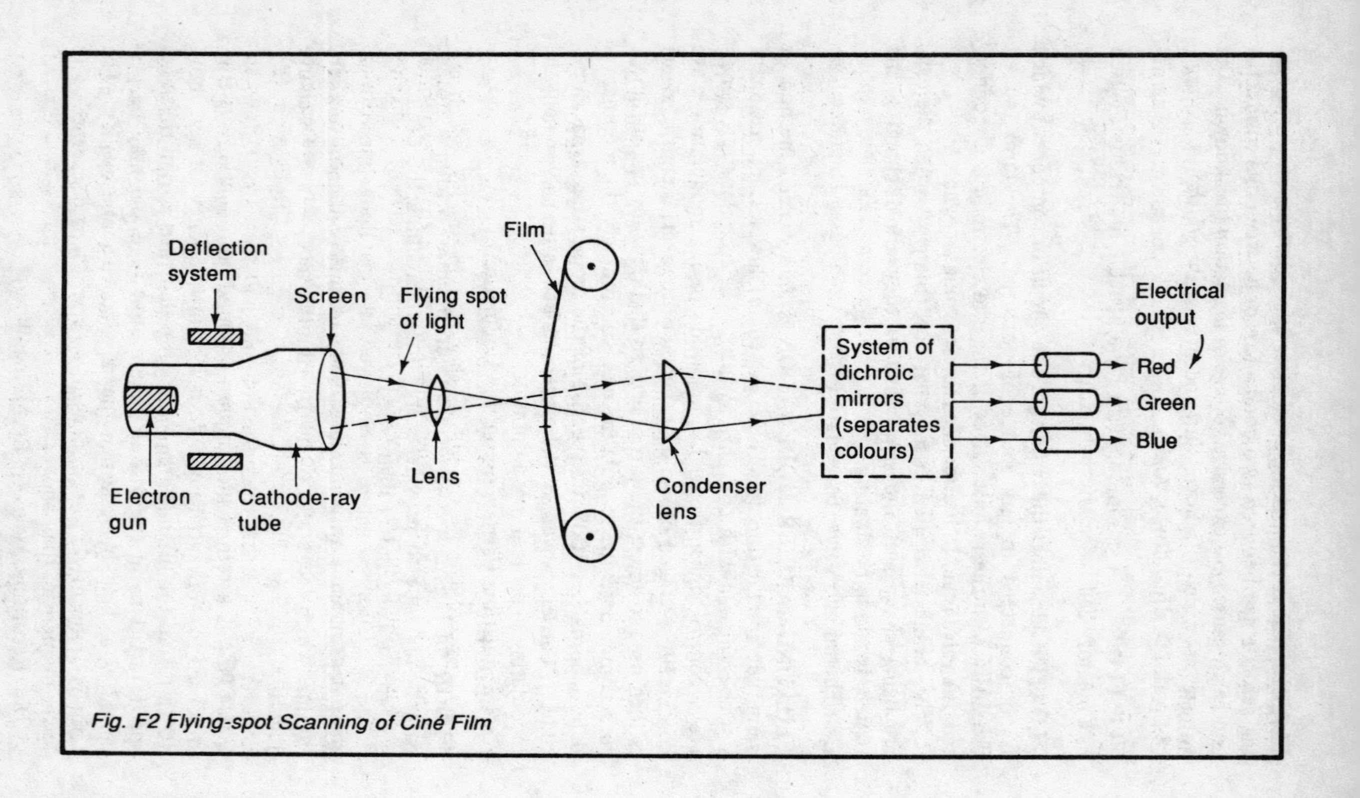

Fig. F2 Flying-spot Scanning of Ciné Film

FLUXMETER is an instrument for the measurement of magnetic flux. Several different types are available, perhaps one of the more reliable is the *Hall-effect fluxmeter.* A constant current is passed through a small slab of semiconductor material. When no magnetic field is present the voltage between upper and lower surfaces is zero. When the field is applied the (Hall) voltage is measured, it is proportional to the magnitude of the field and the instrument can be so calibrated.
(>> Magnetic Field, Hall Effect)

FLYBACK – see Time Base.

FLYING-SPOT SCANNER is a device which scans an object such as a frame of a ciné film to produce a video signal. A typical arrangement is shown in Figure F2. A high brightness cathode-ray tube with its spot controlled by line and frame time bases generates the "flying spot" which is focused onto the film. The light passes through the film and is then fed via a system of *dichroic* mirrors which separate out the primary colours (red, green and blue). Each colour is directed to the appropriate photocell or photomultiplier, the output of which constitutes the video signal.

Mechanical scanning is sometimes employed. The light spot is produced by a high intensity lamp and scanning is accomplished by means of an oscillating concave mirror.
(* Cathode-Ray Tube, Time Base, Scanning, Dichroic Mirror >> Photocell, Photomultiplier)

FOLDED DIPOLE ANTENNA is basically a half-wave dipole antenna split down the middle as shown in Figure F3. Such an antenna is used when a higher input impedance than the normal 70 Ω is required for example, when a transmitting feeder is long and a 300 Ω transmission line is employed. A matching transformer could do the same job but it is likely to reduce the bandwidth. The antenna is basically two half-wave dipoles closely spaced and connected at their outer ends as shown in (iii). The figure at (ii) shows that by splitting the normal dipole, half the current flows in each wire but so far nothing is gained since the impedance is still V/I.

Joining the ends of the antenna as shown in (iii) and doubling the applied voltage to $2V$ now produces the same antenna current but the input impedance is increased 4 times. Alternatively we may understand this better by considering the folded dipole as a full-wave wire folded into a half-wave. If the current maxima are considered [see Fig.D10(i)] it will be found that folding has reversed the current

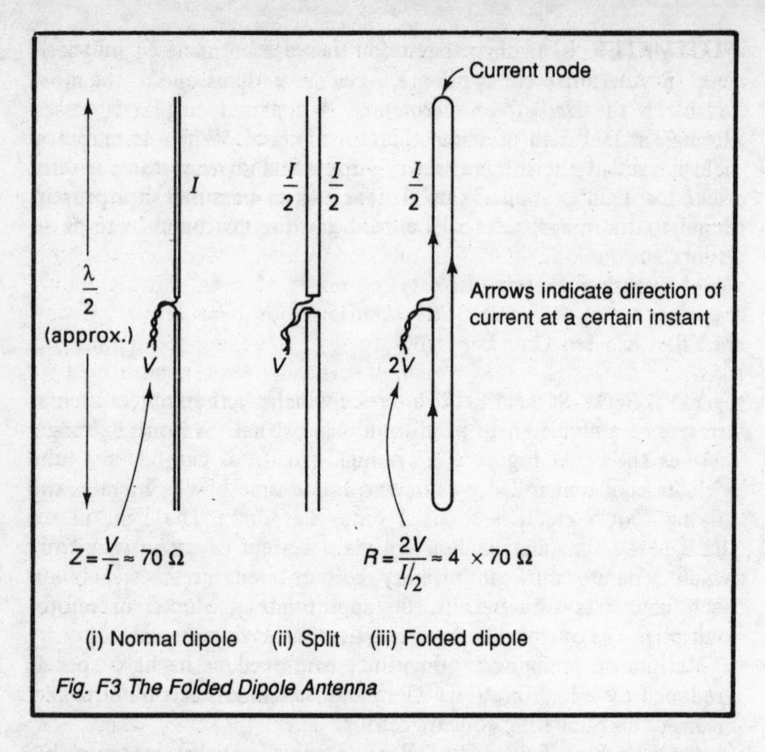

Fig. F3 The Folded Dipole Antenna

in the right hand wire as shown hence all arrows in the diagram point the same way so the folded dipole is equivalent to two single-wire dipoles in parallel.

A folded dipole is the main element in a Yagi antenna, in this case generally used as a receiving antenna.
(* Antenna, Dipole Antenna, Yagi Antenna, Matching >> Antenna, Dipole, Electromagnetic Radiation)

FOUR-LAYER DIODE a pnpn device usually used as a controlled diode – see Thyristor.

FOUR-WIRE CIRCUIT a telephony circuit (usually long distance) which has 2 wires for each direction of transmission, i.e. one pair of wires in the send (or go) direction and a second pair for the receive (or return) direction. Amplifiers are inserted in the circuit as required. The two pairs of wires are combined at the end of the circuit by *terminating sets* which link both send and receive channels to the 2-wire line – see Figure T6(i).
(* Telecommunication System, Terminating Set >> Transmission Line)

FRAME ANTENNA a type of antenna used for direction finding – see Loop Antenna.

FREE-FIELD a field in which there is no obstruction. The term is used particularly with acoustic measurements so that comparisons can be made under the same conditions. As an example, the acoustic response of a microphone will differ according to the reflections of objects surrounding it. Thus the response will be different if the measurement is first made in a laboratory then in a living room. Free space provides free-field conditions but because this is not normally available, in the laboratory a free-field room may be constructed; this is one in which all surfaces are sound absorbent so that no reflections occur. Of interest perhaps is the fact that early attempts to provide free-field conditions involved carrying out tests at the top of a tower or pole in open air.
(>> Field, Free Space, Acoustic Wave)

FREE SPACE PATH LOSS a term used mainly in space communication. It is a measure of the signal attenuation between two isotropic antennas (sometimes dipole antennas are used instead of isotropic). If the distance between them is d metres and one transmits with a power P_t watts, then the power flux density at the other is $P_t/4\pi d^2$ (see Fig.I14). The effective absorbing area of an isotropic receiving antenna can be shown to be equal to $\lambda^2/4\pi$ where λ is the transmission wavelength. Hence the available power from the receiving antenna is:

$$P_r = \frac{P_t}{4\pi d^2} \times \frac{\lambda^2}{4\pi}$$

so that:

$$\text{transmission loss, } L_{fs} = \frac{P_t}{P_r} = \frac{(4\pi d)^2}{\lambda^2}$$

and in decibels this becomes:

$$L_{fs} = 20 \log 4\pi d - 20 \log \lambda \text{ dB},$$

stated also as:

$$L_{fs} = 92.44 + 20 \log f + 20 \log d \text{ dB}$$

where f, the transmission frequency, is in gigahertz and d is in kilometres. This is the *free space path loss.*

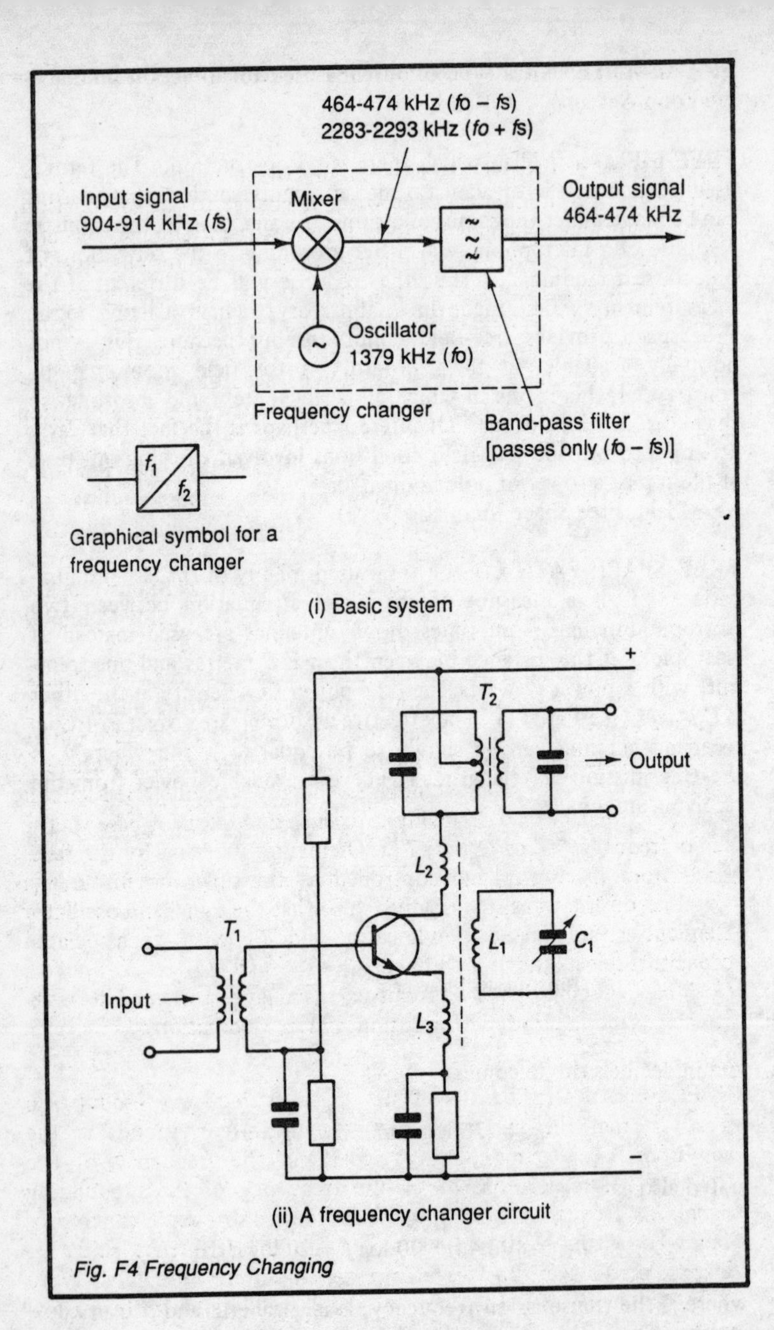

Fig. F4 Frequency Changing

(* Antenna, Isotropic Antenna >> Attenuation, Decibel, Free Space, Power Flux Density)

FREQUENCY CHANGER is a circuit which changes the carrier frequency of a modulated wave without change to the modulation. Most frequency changing is to a lower carrier frequency because lower frequencies are easier to handle. In superheterodyne receivers the frequency changer transfers the modulation of all incoming signals to a lower intermediate frequency. In a broadcasting satellite it is essential that the signals arriving from the ground station do not interfere with those going back down, accordingly a frequency changer is employed to make the change but with the modulation still intact.

The basic system is illustrated in Figure F4(i). The frequency changer is shown here as consisting of three separate units: the mixer, oscillator and band-pass filter. The mixer contains the non-linear device to which both the incoming signal and the local oscillator frequencies are applied. Its output contains several components but only the one required [$(f_o - f_s)$ in this example] is selected by the band-pass filter.

Frequency changers normally require active devices (e.g. transistors) to generate the oscillation frequency and for the mixer. It is possible for one transistor to do both jobs as shown in Figure F4(ii). This particular circuit which seems to have inductors everywhere is shown for ease of understanding, generally an integrated circuit would be used instead. The input reaches the transistor base via the radio frequency transformer, T_1. Oscillation is set up by the feedback from L_2 to L_3 and controlled by the tuned circuit, L_1C_1. The bias on the transistor is adjusted so that the signal and oscillator frequencies are mixed non-linearily and T_2 with its associated capacitors selects the desired band.
(* Mixer, Oscillator >> Frequency Changing, Intermediate Frequency, Superheterodyne Reception, Filter, Modulation)

FREQUENCY DISCRIMINATOR In a frequency modulation (f.m.) system the maximum frequency shift corresponds to the amplitude of the modulating signal and the frequency of the frequency shift corresponds to the frequency of the modulating signal. A frequency discriminator is a device or circuit which produces an output voltage proportional to the frequency shift. It first converts the f.m. wave into an amplitude modulated wave (a.m.) following which the a.m. wave is demodulated in the normal way.

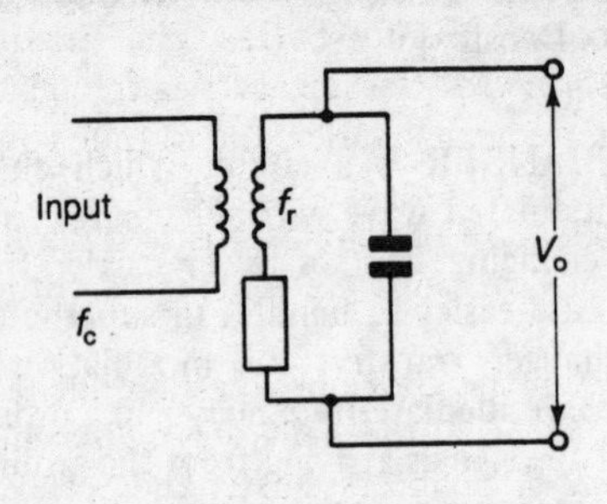

(i) Basic parallel tuned circuit

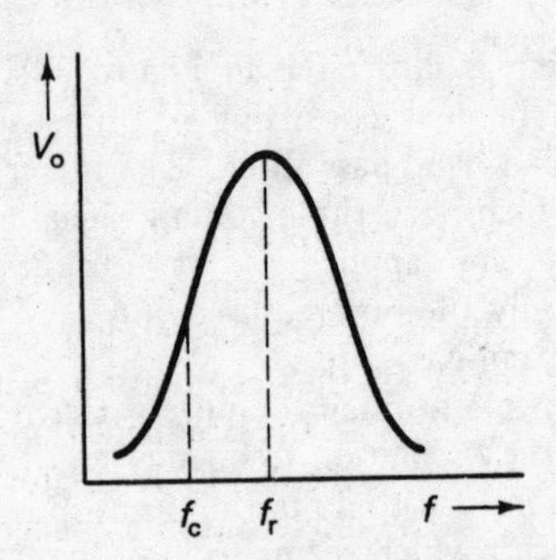

(ii) Output/frequency characteristic of (i)

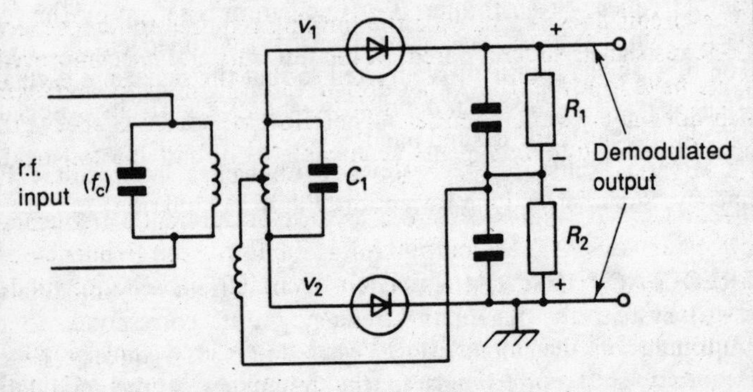

(iii) Elements of the Foster-Seeley circuit

Fig. F5 Frequency Discriminator

An elementary frequency discriminator is based on the parallel tuned circuit as shown in Figure F5(i). The circuit is tuned to a frequency f_r above or below the f.m. carrier frequency f_c as shown so that as the input frequency varies, the output voltage amplitude "slides" up and down the steep slope of the characteristic, for example as in (ii). Because the characteristic is non-linear however, only small frequency deviations are acceptable without noticeable distortion.

A popular version of the above basic arrangement is given in (iii) of the figure, it is the basis of the well-known discriminator developed by the two American engineers, Foster and Seeley. The design is such that one of the diodes conducts more with increases in frequency, the other with decreases. Note that the secondary winding of the transformer is tuned by the capacitor C_1 and that a sample of the primary voltage is injected into a centre-tap. The primary and secondary voltages are in quadrature at the resonance frequency of the secondary. At higher frequencies the secondary voltage lags on the quadrature condition according to the degree of frequency deviation, at frequencies below resonance the secondary voltage leads the quadrature condition. Since a sample of the primary voltage exists at the centre of the secondary it can be shown that the voltages v_1 and v_2 vary as the frequency moves above and below resonance, e.g. above resonance, v_1 is greater than v_2, below resonance, v_2 is greater. The diode outputs change accordingly so producing a demodulated output. The polarities shown across the load resistors R_1 and R_2 show that at resonance, when $v_1 = v_2$, the output is zero.

The circuit does not provide the limiting required to remove any extraneous signals superimposed on the f.m. carrier, hence improved circuits have followed the earlier design, resulting in a *ratio detector* which does not require a limiter. The effort of course is always to design for as many components as possible to be suitable for inclusion in an integrated circuit.

Frequency discriminators are also used in automatic frequency control circuits where the output voltage controls the frequency of a tuned circuit, e.g. by its action on a variable capacitance diode (varactor).

(* Automatic Frequency Control, Varactor >> Frequency Modulation, Amplitude Modulation, Demodulation, Tuned Circuit, Resonance, Quadrature)

FREQUENCY DIVIDER is a circuit which accepts an input frequency f and delivers an output at a frequency f/n where n is an integer, i.e. the output frequency is a submultiple of the input frequency. Many different types of circuit can be employed, one commonly found is the binary divider which lends itself well to integration, it divides the frequency by 2. For greater division several of these circuits may be used in cascade. The circuit is a special arrangement of a bistable multivibrator.

Alternatively a blocking oscillator will divide for example, by 2 if its natural frequency is made slightly less than one half of the frequency of synchronizing pulses generated by the incoming signal. In this case the oscillator is triggered into oscillation by every second synchronizing pulse and so it runs at precisely half the incoming frequency. Equally such a circuit can be designed to run at other sub-multiples of the incoming frequency.
(* Multivibrator, Blocking Oscillator)

FREQUENCY DIVISION MULTIPLEX is a multiplex system in which each incoming signal is assigned a different frequency band hence two or more (up to many thousand) signals can be transmitted over a single transmission path together – see Multiplex System.

FREQUENCY METER a device for measuring the frequency of a waveform. The type and operation naturally depends on the frequency range over which the meter is to be used and the accuracy required. There are several methods of doing the job:

(i) using a *calibrated resonant circuit*. An example is given by the *absorption wavemeter*, used for measurement of the frequency of a radio wave. Power is collected from the wave in a coil which is tuned by a variable capacitor with a scale calibrated in kHz, MHz, etc. Maximum response of the circuit to the wave is indicated by a sensitive meter or lamp. A calibrated radio receiver works equally well but requires mains or battery power. The method is satisfactory for many purposes but has no claim to accuracy because simple *LC* circuits are not sufficiently stable with temperature. For high accuracy at the higher frequencies a cavity resonator may be employed.

(ii) by comparing the unknown frequency with a known frequency. Quite simply any frequency can be measured on a cathode-ray oscilloscope if the frequency of the time base is known, e.g. if the time base is sweeping at 1000 times per second (one sweep per millisecond), a stationary trace of one cycle on the screen must be due to a frequency of 1000 Hz. For two full cycles on the screen the frequency must be 2000 Hz etc. Other methods are either by Lissajous patterns on an oscilloscope or by heterodyning the two frequencies together for zero beat. The accuracy naturally depends on that of the known frequency.

(iii) by counting the number of cycles over a known time interval, say 1 up to 10 seconds. An accurate time interval may be derived from a quartz crystal oscillator. The result is displayed in digital form and the method is capable of high accuracy.

(iv) by balancing a frequency sensitive bridge such as a Wien bridge.

(* Cavity Resonator, Lissajous Figures, Crystal Oscillator >> Electromagnetic Wave, Resonant Circuit, Beat Frequency, Wien Bridge)

FREQUENCY MULTIPLIER is a circuit which has an output at a frequency which is an exact multiple of the input frequency. There are several ways of doing this, for example:

(i) using a non-linear amplifier with a tuned output circuit. The resonance frequency, f_r of the tuned circuit is that required and the circuit can be kept in oscillation by regular pulses of current fed from a Class C amplifier at a sub-multiple of f_r. In other words the output circuit resonates to a harmonic of the input frequency.

(ii) an impulse generator employing a step-recovery diode has an output which is rich in harmonics, the desired harmonic can be selected by a filter. Useful frequency multiplication is possible up to about 10 times.

(iii) the varactor diode can also be used as a harmonic generator. Typically one or more might be used for multiplying up from an oscillator working at a few hundred MHz to the GHz range.

(* Impulse Generator, Class C Amplifier, Multivibrator, Varactor >> Tuned Circuit, Harmonic, Filter)

FREQUENCY RESPONSE CHARACTERISTIC is a graph linking the transmission loss or gain or any other parameter of a system, circuit or device against frequency. Typical examples are given by the characteristics in Figure C23(ii) to (vi).

(>> Characteristic, Decibel)

FREQUENCY SHIFT KEYING (FREQUENCY SHIFT MODULATION) is a method of transmitting digital data over audio frequency (e.g. telephone) lines. Although codes of more than two digits can be transmitted, binary is almost exclusively used. For this, two audio frequencies are transmitted, for example for a logic 1, 1300 Hz and for a logic 0, 1700 Hz. Generally at the transmitting end a type of frequency modulation is employed in which a single oscillator is switched between the two frequencies (although of course separate oscillators could be used). At the receiving end the decoder locks to each input frequency and produces a high level output pulse for a 1300 Hz input or a low level output for 1700 Hz.

With such a system as described above a bit rate of 600 – 750 bits per second is normal. Higher bit rates up to about 1200 bits per second can be achieved over audio frequency lines but generally higher rates require lines of greater bandwidth.
(* Digital Transmission, Binary, Binary Code, Bit, Logic Level, Oscillator >> Digital Signal, Frequency Modulation, Pulse, Bandwidth)

FRYING is a descriptive term for the audio outcome of certain types of electrical noise, especially noticeable in disc reproduction where it arises from a lack of smoothness in the groove. The noise is a sputtering sound or sizzle as in frying.
(* Disc Recording >> Noise)

FULL-SCALE DEFLECTION (f.s.d.) is the maximum value on the scale of a measuring instrument.
(* Meter)

FUEL CELL This is basically a primary cell in that it has positive and negative electrodes separated by an electrolyte. It is potentially very efficient and is especially applicable to electric power generation for vehicles, hence the cell is the subject of considerable research. Figure F6 shows the original conception, i.e. two porous electrodes through which gases permeate, separated by the electrolyte. In use the potassium hydroxide ionizes and produces negative hydroxide ions. These react with the hydrogen at the negative electrode with the result that electrons are released and water is formed as a by-product. Oxygen fed to the positive plate takes on electrons and water to replenish the negative hydroxide ions.

To provide the gases as above in their pure state is hardly a practical arrangement hence the aim is to use chemicals instead which can serve the same purpose.
(>> Primary Cell, Electrolyte)

FUSE is a short length of wire inserted in a circuit which heats sufficiently to melt when the current through it exceeds a predetermined value, so disconnecting the circuit under fault conditions. The fuse wire may be held between two screw terminals in a porcelain holder or alternatively held within a glass tube, soldered to the two end caps which make the connection. After operating the fuse is replaced, either by renewing the piece of wire or by replacing the complete tube.

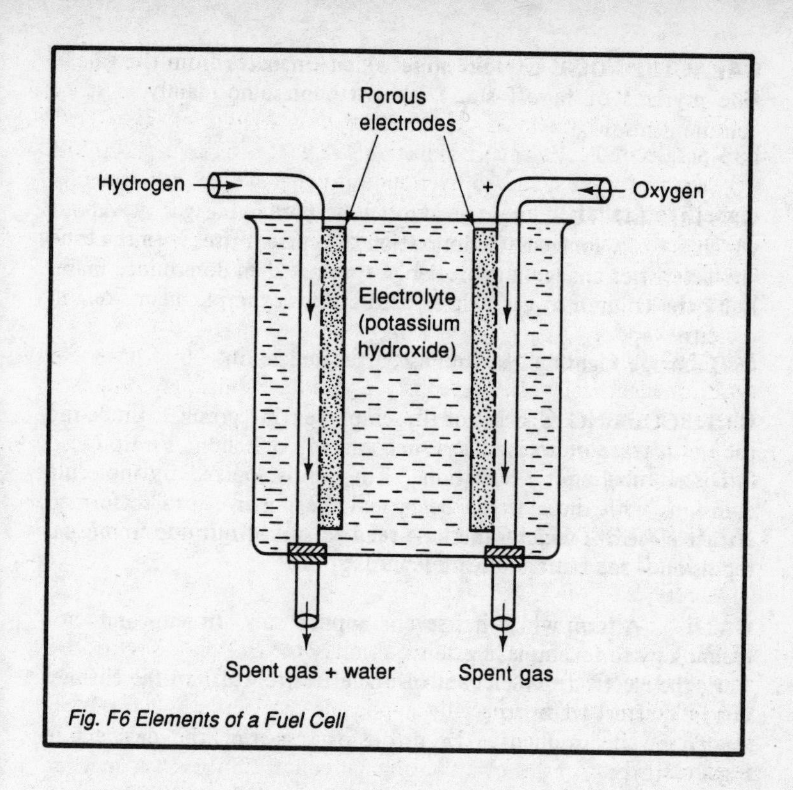

Fig. F6 Elements of a Fuel Cell

As a rough guide the fusing current is double the maximum operating current, e.g. a 15 A fuse will normally "blow" at around 30 A.

The graphical symbol is given in Figure C7(ii).
(* Circuit-Breaker)

G

GAIN CONTROL, also known as a *volume control*, this is a circuit or device (usually a resistive potentiometer) which varies the output of an amplifying system.
(>> Amplifier, Gain)

GALACTIC NOISE is radio noise which emanates from the galaxy (the myriads of far-off stars). It is troublesome mainly in space communications.
(>> Noise)

GAS-FILLED TUBE is an electron tube containing gas or vapour which is easily ionized. On ionization the current rises with the tube characteristics changing appreciably, they are then determined mainly by the column of gas. Gases used are for example, neon, xenon, mercury vapour.
(* Discharge Lighting >> Gas Discharge, Ionization)

GAS FOCUSING is occasionally employed in certain cathode-ray tubes. A trace of an inert gas such as argon or helium is introduced into the tube after evacuation. The gas is ionized by molecule collisions with the electron beam and the positive ions so formed attract electrons which otherwise tend to spread out due to mutual repulsion – see Electron Beam Focusing.

GATE A term which has several applications. In semiconductor technology for example, a gate is:

(i) the electrode which controls the effective width of the channel in a field-effect transistor;

(ii) the electrode of a thyristor for triggering the device [see Fig.T11(iii)] ;

(iii) the electrode of a silicon controlled switch, again for triggering [see Fig.S7(i)] ;

(iv) an electrode on a charge-coupled device which accepts clock pulses for initiation of a charge shift (see Fig.C4).

In digital logic circuits gates are individual units which have one or more inputs but only one output. The gate is opened or closed according to the binary conditions on the inputs.

The term is frequently found in other spheres, generally used with reference to the opening or closing of a circuit.
(* Thyristor, Silicon Controlled Switch, Digital Logic, Logic Gate, Trigger >> Field-Effect Transistor)

GEIGER COUNTER (Geiger-Müller tube or counter) This is a form of *proportional counter*. It consists of an ionization chamber of similar construction to that shown in Figure I12. As the battery voltage is increased the field strength between cathode and anode also increases. Electrons freed by ionization caused by incoming high velocity particles then gain sufficient additional energy from the field to be able to create ionizations of their own. The effect is cumulative, resulting in a very high multiplication of charge. However the density of the gas and the voltage applied can be so arranged that the *overall* ionization remains low and avalanche conditions are avoided. Under these conditions the final charge generated by the incoming radiation is proportional to the number of ion pairs originally released (the primary ion pairs).

The Geiger counter works similarly except that the multiplication is greater and results in an avalanche. For this the gas is at low pressure. When a single high velocity particle enters the tube, free electrons resulting from ionization are accelerated by the electric field between the electrodes and themselves produce further ionization by collision. The gas breaks down, its resistance falls dramatically and a pulse of current flows in the external circuit. Although only of the order of one microampere, the pulse is ample for operation of an electronic counter or for amplification to operate a loudspeaker and so produce the click so well known.

Special arrangements, especially in choice of battery voltage, are required to avoid the pulse length being too great, hence preventing the counting of particles arriving in quick succession.

(* Ionization Chamber >> Charge, Collision, Ionization, Electric Field, Avalanche)

GENERATOR Electric generators are devices which change one form of energy into electrical energy. Their range of achievement is exceedingly great, from the mighty power station machines with outputs of megawatts down to the thermocouple with its microwatts. Under this term however we concern ourselves mainly with those generators which are excited mechanically, i.e. with the a.c. or d.c. generator or *dynamo*.

The basis of a mechanical generator is *electromagnetic induction*. More practically and in all simplicity, current flow arises in a conductor as it moves in a magnetic field as shown in Figure G1(i). Making the conductor into a loop gives a closer approximation to an actual generator as shown in (ii). The sides of the loop cut the flux as the loop rotates, so producing electromotive forces (e.m.f.'s) in series-aiding. Larger e.m.f.'s simply require more turns on the loop. Current is taken from the generator via the *slip rings* S_1 and S_2 on which rub the *carbon brushes*. This produces an alternating current but if direct current is required, a *commutator* is employed, fitted to the end of the shaft carrying the loop as illustrated in (iii). As the loop changes from downward flux cutting to upward so the commutator segments change over to the alternate brushes, hence the load current is unidirectional. Practical d.c. generators employ

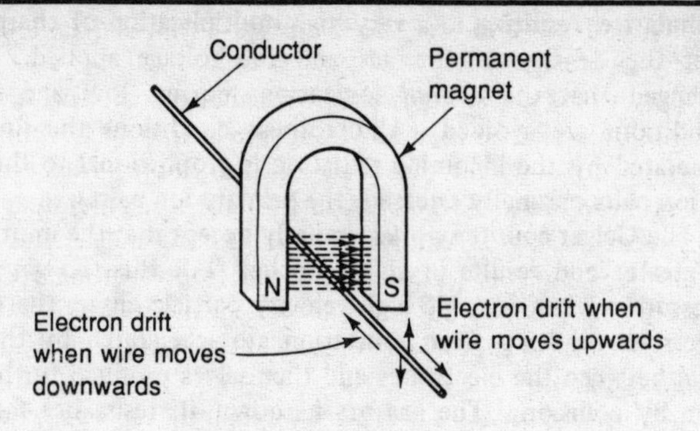

(i) An elementary generator

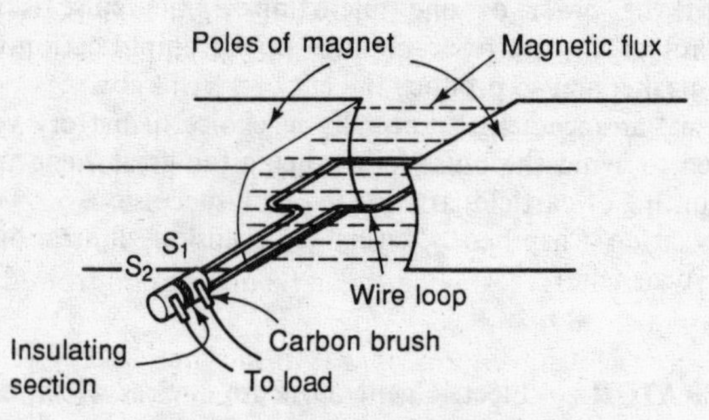

(ii) Single loop rotating in a magnetic field

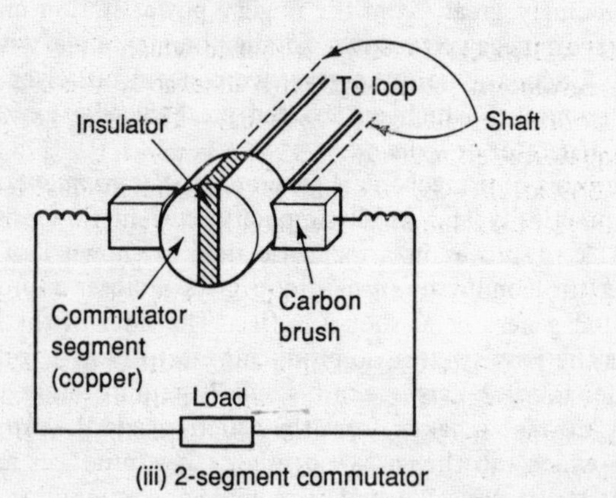

(iii) 2-segment commutator

Fig. G1 The Generator

many coils wound on the *armature* hence its commutator has many segments.

Heavy duty slip rings and commutators on the big machines leave much to be desired from the maintenance point of view because not only do they wear but the carbon brushes rubbing on them wear also. Accordingly most large a.c. generators have fixed coils on the *stator* energised by a rotating magnetic field on the *rotor* [see Fig.P8(i)], usually derived from rotating coils fed with d.c. The shaft may be driven by an engine, steam or water turbine, even an electric motor, each provides the energy input subsequently collected as electricity.

Two other types of mechanical generator are worthy of mention, (i) friction, because rubbing certain things together (e.g. a plastic ruler and a piece of flannel) generates static electricity and (ii) the microphone. In this the energy comes from the sound wave which moves a diaphragm.

Non-mechanical generators include (i) electronic oscillators in which a d.c. power supply emerges as a waveform of some predetermined frequency, (ii) chemical, from batteries, (ii) heat via a thermocouple and (iv) light via a photovoltaic cell. How each of these functions as a generator can be understood from the appropriate term named below.
(* Electric Motor, Alternator, Electromagnet, Microphone, Thermocouple, Oscillator >> Electromagnetic Induction, Static Electricity, Photovoltaic Cell)

GEOSTATIONARY ORBIT is that in which a satellite completes a single revolution round the earth in exactly the same time as the earth rotates once (86 164 seconds). The orbit lies directly above the equator at an altitude of 35 786 km with the satellites travelling at 11 069 km/hr. To an observer on earth a satellite in such an orbit appears to be stationary – see Satellite.

GETTER Used in evacuation processes – see Degassing.

GLOW DISCHARGE arises in a cold-cathode gas-filled tube at low pressure. Glow discharge tubes are mainly used for luminous signs and as lamps, the colour of the glow depending on the gas used, for example neon for its characteristic red glow.
(* Gas-Filled Tube >> Gas Discharge)

GONIOMETER is an instrument for measuring angles (from Greek, *gonia* = angle). In radio direction finding it is used to avoid the necessity of mechanically rotating a loop antenna. Two fixed

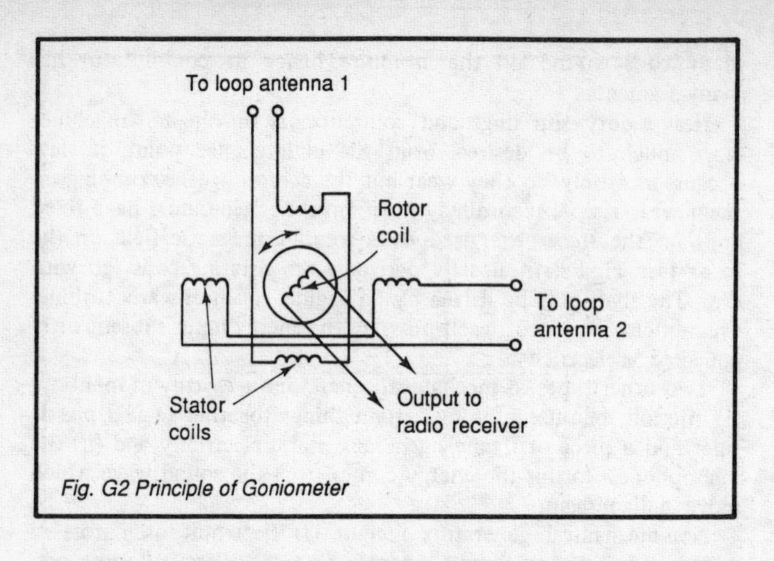

Fig. G2 Principle of Goniometer

antennas are used at right angles to each other and their outputs are combined in the goniometer. No antenna rotation is required. Connections of the antennas to the goniometer are shown in Figure G2. The antennas are connected to 4 stator coils and the rotor coil which is coupled to all four delivers a signal to a radio receiver. It can be shown that for any position of the rotor coil the directional characteristic of the two-loop system is identical with the directional characteristic of a single loop.
(* Antenna, Loop Antenna, Radio Receiver)

GRADED-BASE TRANSISTOR (also known as a Drift Transistor) is a planar junction transistor manufactured so that the base impurity concentration is not uniformly distributed but decreases in the direction emitter to collector. An idea of the doping levels in this type of n-p-n transistor can be gained from Figure G3. The abrupt transition in doping level between emitter and base arises from the heavy emitter doping. The potential distribution through the transistor leads to the development of an electric field within the base in such a direction that electrons are accelerated from emitter to collector. This not only improves the high frequency response but also reduces the base recombination current.
(* Planar Process >> Transistor, Doping, P-N Junction)

GRID is the term used to describe the main electricity distribution system. Distribution is at high voltage, e.g. 132, 275 or 400 kilovolts, 3-phase. High voltages are used despite the cost of insulation

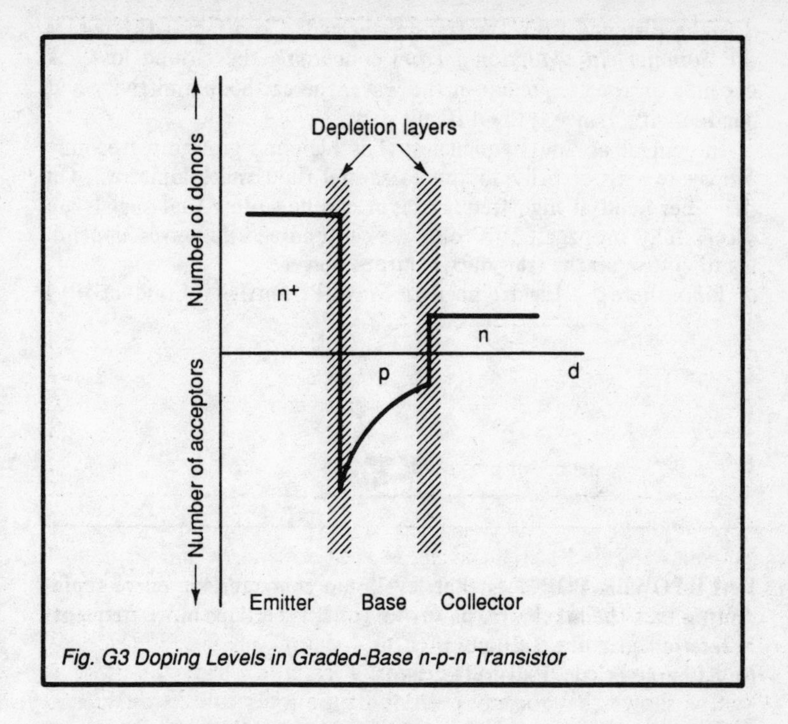

Fig. G3 Doping Levels in Graded-Base n-p-n Transistor

because if power is so transmitted, the current is correspondingly small, accordingly both voltage drop and power loss in the transmission lines are less.
(* Polyphase System >> Grid)

GROUND WAVE The energy radiated from a transmitting antenna located on the earth's surface consists of a ground wave which travels along the surface of the earth and also a sky wave which is propagated via the atmosphere. As the ground wave travels away from the radio transmitter it becomes progressively weaker through spreading and the absorption of energy by the earth. The latter effect arises from the fact that the wave induces charges in the earth and because these travel along with the wave they represent a current flowing in the resistance of the earth and therefore a power loss. Prediction of wave field strength at any particular location is beset with difficulties but as a start:

$$\text{ground wave field strength} = (k/d) \times A$$

where k represents the strength of the field radiated horizontally, *d* is the distance from the transmitter and *A* is a factor (known as the *Sommerfeld reduction factor*) concerning the ground loss. *A* depends on the frequency of the wave, the earth's permittivity and conductivity, hence is the difficult part.

In general at low frequencies, *A* is high and ground waves may propagate satisfactorily for up to several thousand kilometres. On the other hand at high frequencies *A* can be so low that signals are successfully propagated for only a few hundred kilometres, depending of course on the transmitter output power.
(* Ionosphere >> Electromagnetic Wave, Permittivity, Conductivity)

H

HALF-POWER POINT is that level on a characteristic curve representing half the maximum power value. It is perhaps more frequently referred to as the 3 dB point.
(>> Characteristic, Power, Decibel)

HALL PROBE Since the conductivity of a Hall-effect device is proportional to the applied magnetic field, it is possible to construct a probe for measuring magnetic flux density from a tiny piece of semiconductor which has high electron mobility [e.g. indium arsenide (InAs) or indium antimonide (InSb)]. The Hall voltage developed across the material has a good linear relationship with the magnetic flux density being measured.
(>> Hall Effect, Semiconductor, Magnetic Flux Density, Mobility)

HARDWARE The bits and pieces which make up a computer, i.e. the objects we can see such as the equipment and components.
See also Software.
(* Computer)

HARMONIC DISTORTION arises from non-linearity of the input–output characteristic of a component, network or system. This results in the production of harmonics which are not present in the input waveform. It is expressed by the ratio of the root mean square (r.m.s.) voltage of the total harmonics in the output to the total r.m.s. voltage at the output.

(* Harmonic Distortion Analyser >> Non-Linearity, Distortion, Harmonic, Root Mean Square)

HARMONIC DISTORTION ANALYSER can take many forms, the simplest of which is the analyser designed for measuring the total harmonic distortion developed by an amplifier. Figure H1 shows the essential features of the measurement technique. The sine wave

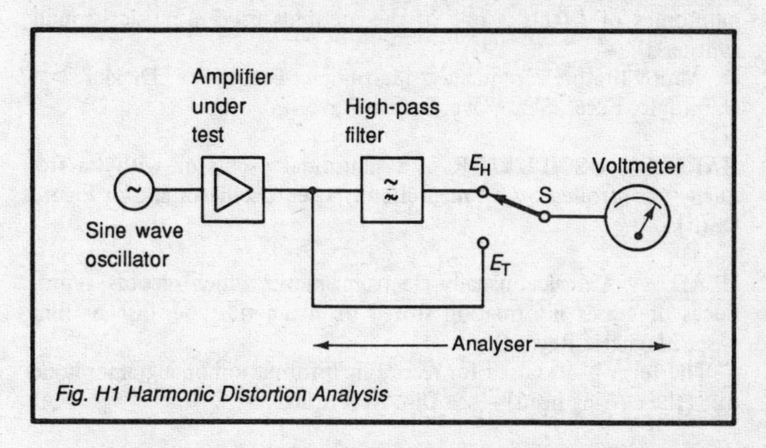

Fig. H1 Harmonic Distortion Analysis

oscillator has very low distortion and is set at the test frequency. It feeds into the input terminals of the amplifier under test. The output of the amplifier contains added harmonics and the total of fundamental plus harmonics, E_T is measured as an a.c. root mean square (r.m.s.) voltage on the voltmeter. For this the switch S is in the lower position. The output from the amplifier is also fed into the tunable high-pass filter which rejects the fundamental frequency but passes all frequencies above (the harmonics). With S in the upper position, the harmonic r.m.s. voltage, E_H is then measured and:

$$\text{percentage harmonic distortion} = (E_H/E_T) \times 100 .$$

(* Harmonic Distortion >> Harmonic, Filter, Root Mean Square)

HARMONIC GENERATOR is a device which produces harmonics of a given fundamental frequency. As an example, since musical notes are based on the particular harmonics they contain, harmonic generators are important in music synthesizers.

Many methods can be envisaged for producing one or more harmonics from a fundamental frequency, f. Since a square wave

theoretically contains all the odd harmonics to infinity, the simplest perhaps is to generate such a wave at frequency *f* (e.g. by an astable multivibrator) and select the harmonics required by band pass filters. This caters for odd harmonics. For both odd and even harmonics it is possible to generate *f* as a sine wave and connect this to the input of a *frequency multiplier.* Alternatively a sine wave of frequency n*f* might be generated with a *frequency divider* used to produce the harmonics of *f* (this is one of the methods used in musical sound synthesis).
(* Multivibrator, Frequency Multiplier, Frequency Divider >> Harmonic, Filter, Sine Wave, Square Wave)

HARTLEY OSCILLATOR is a sinusoidal oscillator with its frequency controlled by a tuned circuit – see Oscillator and/or Figure O3(ii).

HEAD A device, usually electromagnetic, which records, reproduces or erases information stored on magnetic tape, disc or film – see Magnetic Recording.

The term is also used for recording information on a gramophone disc (the cutting head) – see Disc Recording.

HEAD GAP refers to the gap in a magnetic recording or playback head, it is only a few micrometres in length. It inserts a high reluctance path in the magnetic circuit of the head to force the magnetic flux to flow via the tape in which the head is in contact, rather than via the head gap – see Magnetic Recording and/or Figure M2(ii).

HEARING AID is a device which compensates for poor hearing. To so many people therefore this is a device of untold benefit. In the early nineteen hundreds the acoustic amplification of the ear trumpet gave way to electronics and now size is such that a complete sound reproduction system is accommodated within a "behind the ear" (BTE) aid, within a "button in the ear" (ITE) aid or even within the frames of spectacles.

Figure H2 shows a BTE type. It consists of a minute crystal or electret microphone followed by an integrated circuit containing the main amplifier, frequency control circuits, automatic volume control etc. The amplifier delivers power to the receiver (e.g. an electromagnetic type) and the sound output is fed into the ear via the plastic tubing. With an ITE aid the receiver is already in the ear canal. Power is usually supplied to the amplifier by a mercury or zinc-air cell at 1.4 V. Typical maximum acoustic amplifications are 60 – 80 dB over a frequency range generally from about 100 Hz to

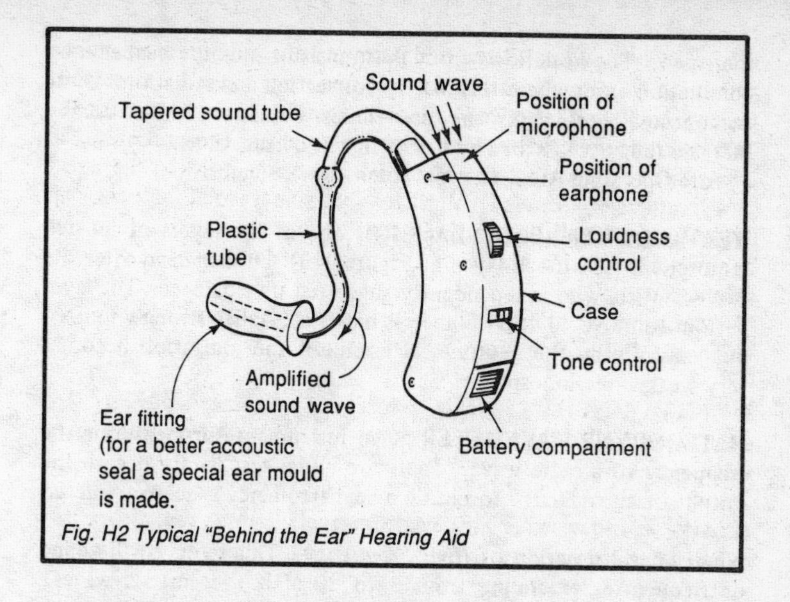

Fig. H2 Typical "Behind the Ear" Hearing Aid

5000 Hz. With high gain, instability in the form of an audible whistle may arise due to positive acoustic feedback if sound escapes from the ear canal and reaches the microphone.

Should the user have a hearing defect such that the above types of aid are of no use, sound can be injected directly into the *mastoid bone* (just behind the ear). For this a special *bone conduction receiver* is used. Typically such a receiver works on the variable reluctance principle and in a way "hammers" on the mastoid bone instead of vibrating a diaphragm.
(* Microphone, Earphone, Audiometer, Integrated Circuit >> Amplifier, Feedback, Decibel)

HEATER is a device which supplies heat by current flowing through a resistive element. In particular the term applies to the resistance wire which heats a cathode to produce thermionic emission, e.g. in a thermionic valve or in an electron gun (see Fig.E11).
(* Electron Gun >> Resistance, Joule, Thermionic Valve)

HEAT SINK is a metal strip or structure coupled physically to a component such as a power transistor to improve heat dissipation and therefore prevent an excessive rise in component temperature. Power transistors are usually constructed with the collector terminal connected to the metal case. By bolting the case onto a sheet of metal or a metal chassis the area from which the heat is removed is

increased. The heat flows from the transistor into the heat sink by conduction from where it is lost by convection and radiation. Quite complicated heat sinks are sometimes necessary, these usually increase the heat loss area by use of fins or corrugations.
(* Safe Operating Area, Thermal Runaway >> Transistor)

HEAVISIDE-KENNELLY LAYER is one of the layers of ionized atmosphere (see the E-layer in Figure I13). It is named after the two scientists who independently suggested its existence. The layer is from some 90 to 150 kilometres high. It is fairly strongly ionized but only during the daytime, after sunset the ionization becomes very weak – see Ionosphere.

HETERODYNE WAVEMETER is an instrument for measuring the frequency of a radio wave. The wave under test is mixed with the output of an oscillator to obtain a beat frequency – see Wavemeter.

HF is an abbreviation of *High Frequency*. This refers to the band of frequencies extending from 3 to 30 MHz (decametric waves).
(>> Frequency Band)

H-NETWORK is a 4-terminal network containing 5 elements. It is more generally known as a *balanced-T network*.
(>> Network)

HORIZONTAL POLARIZATION is a property of an electromagnetic wave which has a horizontal electric field vector. The term is also used in conjunction with antennas arranged for the reception of of horizontally polarized waves.
(* Antenna >> Electromagnetic Wave)

HORN LOUDSPEAKER consists of a horn coupled to a small vibrating diaphragm; the energy conversion efficiency is relatively high – see Loudspeaker.

HOT-WIRE AMMETER is basically a very simple current measuring instrument. The current flows through a metallic strip or wire which has a large coefficient of thermal expansion. This heats up and expands and the expansion is measured directly by a pointer coupled to the strip and moving over a scale. The meter is suitable for measuring both d.c. and a.c. and with the latter, root mean square values are automatically given. Measurements are possible up to very high frequencies.
(>> Ammeter, Root Mean Square)

***h*-PARAMETER** abbreviated form of Hybrid Parameter – see this term.

HUM is an unwanted low frequency sound originating from equipment powered by the electricity mains. It is at the mains supply frequency plus harmonics of it. Hum frequently arises directly as sound from vibrations in mains transformer laminations, it is also heard as a result of ripple on the direct current supply to an amplifier driving a loudspeaker or earphone.
(* Ripple Filter >> Transformer)

HYBRID INTEGRATED CIRCUITS The two predominating classes of integrated circuit are the *monolithic* in which everything is manufactured on a single chip and the *hybrid* which, as its name implies, is a mixture embodying different techniques of component construction and wiring. The hybrid circuits comprise *thick* or *thin* film techniques plus added monolithic circuits as required. The thick and thin films are a means of producing components and "wiring them up" by use of a film of material deposited on a substrate. The difference between thick and thin is not clearly definable as one type may encroach upon the other but it is suggested that films exceeding some 10 micrometres (μm) in thickness are rated as thick, those of less than 1 μm up to a few μm are thin. Apart from the film thickness the two types differ mainly in the manufacturing process. Resistors and capacitors lend themselves readily to the technology but naturally inductors do not except at very high frequencies when any inductance required is low. Substrates in both cases are usually of glass, ceramic or glazed alumina.

Thin film circuits are built up on the substrate by evaporating the metal onto it by one of three processes, vacuum evaporation, sputtering or ion plating which effectively is a mixture of the two preceding ones. The deposition pattern may be obtained using a photoresist technique or metal masking. For conductor tracks gold reigns supreme although aluminium is also used because of its lower cost. Resistors are generally limited to the range 20 Ω to 50 kΩ if nichrome is used (80% nickel, 20% chromium). For higher resistance values, cermets may be employed. Tantalum gives high stability. Capacitors are frequently of MOS type but tantalum or alumina types with the substrate as the lower plate are also available.

Thick film circuits use printed thick film inks containing finely divided metal (conducting) or metal oxide (resistive) particles together with binding agents. The inks are applied to the substrate by stencil, by masking or written in by a computer controlled stylus. When deposition of the ink is finished, the substrate is dried and then fired. Resistors are available over a large range of values but tolerances in production may be high hence for accurate values, trimming of the fired ink may be necessary, either by an abrasive or laser technique. Accuracies down to 0.1% are attainable.

Both thin and thick film circuits may be extended by wiring in silicon chips containing active devices or components not realizable by the film techniques. The completed hybrid circuit is then packaged.

(* Integrated Circuit, Substrate, Vacuum Evaporation, Photolithography, Sputtering, Cermet, MOS Capacitor, Chip)

HYBRID PARAMETERS (*h*-PARAMETERS) These are basically the electrical characteristics of a 4-terminal network using the "black box" technique as shown in Figure H3(i). Whatever is in the box is expected to respond to the external input circuit and deliver power to the external load. From the input and output values of current and voltage only, much useful design information can be gained, for example, input and output characteristics, input and output impedances and the transfer characteristic (I_o versus I_i). There is a generally accepted convention that I_i and I_o are positive when they flow into terminals 1 and 3 as shown in the figure.

As an "electronic system", the transistor is especially suited to this type of analysis. The technique is valid even though a transistor has only 3 terminals because in fact one of the terminals is common to both input and output. As an example, we open the black box as in (ii) of the figure to disclose the equivalent circuit of a bipolar transistor, specially drawn and labelled for use as a small-signal amplifier (for field-effect transistors *y-parameters* are more suitable). Note that capital letters for the quantity symbols change to lower case to indicate the small-signal application. The equivalent circuit shown is effectively in two parts (i) an input circuit containing a voltage generator representing the voltage feedback of the transistor (the output current also flows in the input circuit) and (ii) a current generator representing the transistor action operating with a parallel output resistance which for convenience in these calculations is expressed as a conductance. Theoretically the *h*-parameter approach requires that the system being analysed is linear, it is seldom so, but in most cases the small discrepancies can be tolerated.

There are 4 *h*-parameters used to characterize a circuit such as in (ii) of the figure. Each is given the symbol *h* with subscripts as shown below and when required there is an additional subscript to indicate the transistor configuration (e, b or c for common-emitter, base or collector). Two of the parameters are simply ratios and are therefore dimensionless, the other two differ, hence the description

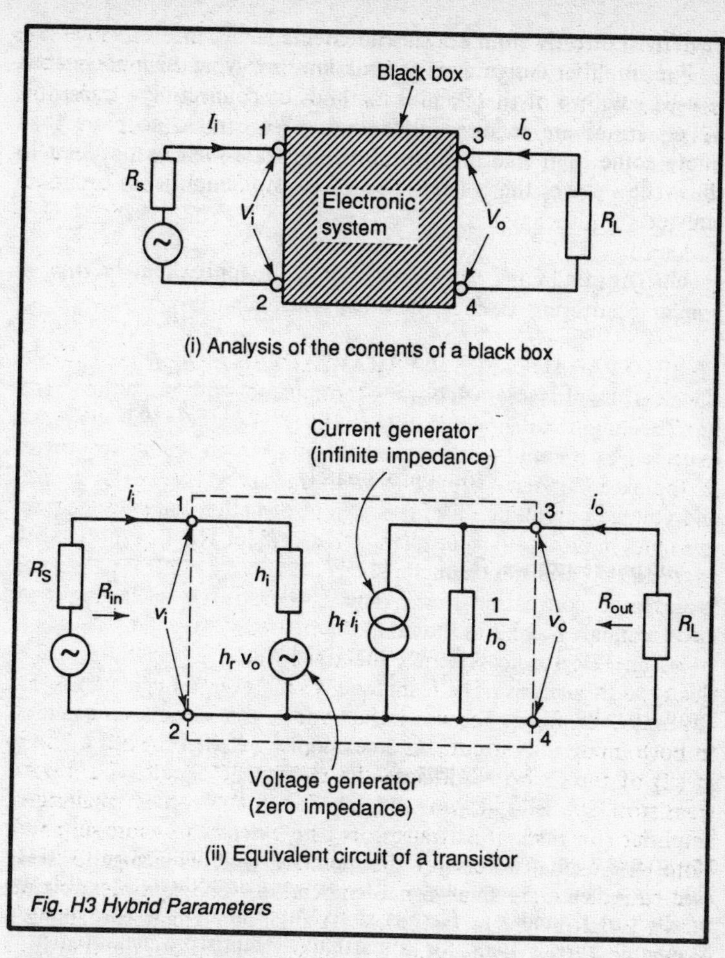

Fig. H3 Hybrid Parameters

"hybrid". See Figure H3(ii):

h_i is the input impedance, measured with terminals 3 and 4 short-circuited to a.c. so that $v_o = 0$. Hence $h_i = v_i/i_i$ ohms.

h_f is the current gain or forward current transfer ratio, measured as above. Hence $h_f = i_o/i_i$.

h_o is the output conductance, measured with $i_i = 0$. Hence $h_o = i_o/v_o$ siemens.

h_r is the voltage feedback ratio or reverse voltage transfer ratio, measured with $i_i = 0$. Hence $h_r = v_i/v_o$.

Manufacturers' data frequently includes curves of each of these at various values of collector current. Alternatively the parameters may be calculated from the transistor static characteristics or may be derived directly from a.c. measurements.

For amplifier design a set of equations involving the *h*-parameters is used. With 4 of these and 3 methods of connecting a transistor, 12 equations are required altogether. We can do no more than quote some of the formulae and demonstrate their use, at least to show the value of the system. For a transistor amplifier in common-emitter:

$$\text{current gain}, K_i = \frac{i_o}{i_i} = \frac{h_{fe}}{1 + h_{oe}R_L} \quad \text{or approximately}, h_{fe}$$

$$\text{input resistance}, R_{in} = \frac{v_i}{i_i} = h_{ie} - \frac{h_{fe}h_{re}R_L}{1 + h_{oe}R_L}$$

$$\text{or approximately}, h_{ie}$$

$$\text{output resistance}, R_{out} = \frac{v_o}{i_o} = \frac{h_{ie} + R_S}{h_{oe}(h_{ie} + R_s) - h_{fe}h_{re}}$$

$$\text{or approximately}, 1/h_{oe}\ .$$

From the above:

$$\text{voltage gain}, K_v = \frac{v_o}{v_i} = \frac{-K_i R_L}{R_{in}}$$

the minus sign as a reminder that through a common-emitter stage there is a 180° phase change. The power gain follows since it is the product of K_i and K_v. Here is an example of their use taken from a manufacturer's data for a particular transistor, measured at a collector current of 2 mA and collector-emitter voltage of 5 V:

$$h_{ie} = 4.5\ \text{k}\Omega \qquad h_{fe} = 330 \qquad h_{oe} = 30\ \mu\text{S}$$

$$h_{re} = 2.0 \times 10^{-4}\ (h_{fe} \text{ and } h_{re} \text{ are dimensionless})$$

Let $R_S = 1000\ \Omega$ and $R_L = 3.3\ \text{k}\Omega$.

In common-emitter and using the formulae above (the approximate answers are also given to show the degree of approximation):

current gain, $K_i = 300\ \Omega$ (approx. $= 330\ \Omega$)

input resistance, R_{in} = 4302 Ω (approx. = 4500 Ω)

output resistance, R_{out} = 55.6 kΩ (approx. = 33.3 kΩ)

voltage gain, K_v = −230 (approx. = −242)

Usually only *h*-parameters for common-emitter are available from manufacturers' data. This presents no problem because conversion equations are used for changing from common-emitter to common-base or common-collector as required.

See also *y*-parameters.
(* Black Box, Equivalent Circuit >> Transistor, Amplifier, Conductance)

HYBRID TRANSFORMER is the basis of a *terminating set*. It has 3 windings, all mutually coupled with 4 pairs of terminals as shown in Figure H4(v). The underlying theory is more easily demonstrated by considering an equivalent Wheatstone bridge resistive network first as in Figure H4(i). The important feature is that if a generator is connected in place of any one of the six impedances, the current in any other impedance can be made zero by suitable arrangement of the values of the other four. This develops as in (ii) and (iii) of the figure and for the network to act as a terminating set to a four-wire line, it must provide a signal path:

(1) Receive to 2-wire (but with no transmission Receive to Send)

(2) 2-wire to Send.

In (ii) of the figure, assuming that the bridge is balanced, it can be seen that condition (1) is obtained. Next the circuit can be redrawn to be electrically the same as is done in (iii) and this shows that condition (2) also applies. Note that in this case power is delivered to both Send and Receive terminals, but that to Receive serves no purpose and in fact it is normally connected to and lost in the output of an amplifier. Because power is also lost in an impedance other than the one intended, there is a transmission loss of just over 3 dB in both directions.

Referring again to (ii) of the figure, if for example, $Z_2 = Z_4$, then for balance Z_1 must be equal to the impedance of the 2-wire line. The impedances of 2-wire lines vary widely hence the circuit seldom provides very high attenuation between Receive and Send, but usually sufficient. Z_1 is known as the *balance* and is usually a single resistor but may be a resistance–capacitance network.

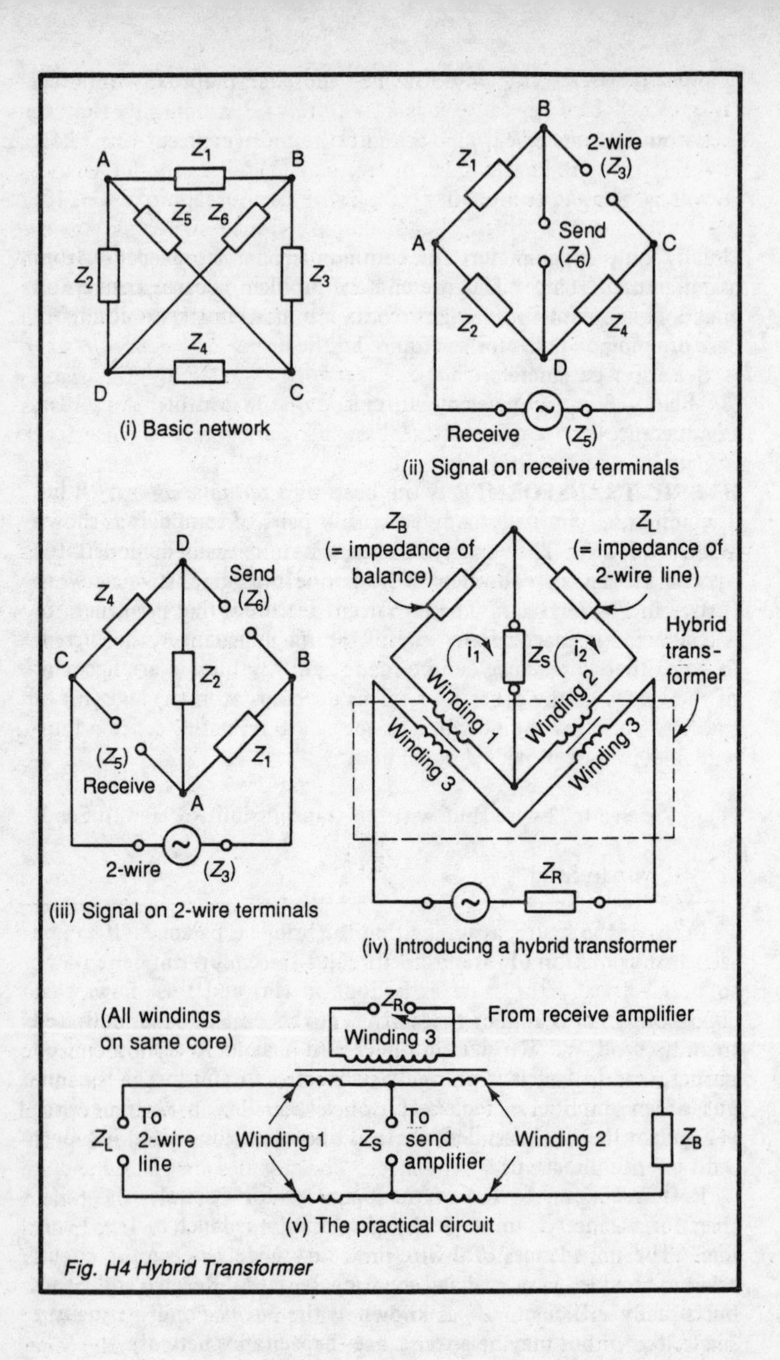

Fig. H4 Hybrid Transformer

Resistances absorb power, hence the change to a hybrid transformer ("hybrid" because it is a mixture of 3 windings). How the resistive network of (ii) changes into the more efficient one using a hybrid transformer is shown in (iv) and (v) where the impedances now have subscripts more in keeping with their use.

Telephone sets which do not employ speech switching also use hybrid transformers. In this case the microphone replaces the Send amplifier in (v) of the figure and the receiver or earphone replaces the Receive amplifier. This provides the attenuation required from microphone to receiver depending on the degree of balance between the 2-wire line and the balancing network Z_B. Microphone signals reaching the receiver are known as *sidetone*, if too high this creates discomfort for the user and causes a lowering of the voice level.

See also Terminating Set.

(>> Wheatstone Bridge, Network, Impedance, Transformer)

HYDROPHONE is a transducer used in sonar systems which produces an electrical output in response to sound waves (usually ultrasonic) propagated through water. Most hydrophones are based on the piezoelectric crystal although electrodynamic types are also used – see Sonar.

I

IC Abbreviation of Integrated Circuit – see this term.

ICONOSCOPE is one of the early types of camera tube, developed mainly by V. W. Zworykin in the U.S.A. It contains a photoemissive target scanned by a high velocity electron beam. The essential features are shown in Figure I1. The camera lens focuses an optical image of the scene onto a mosaic of photoemissive globules deposited over the surface of a mica sheet. The globules are minute and are insulated from each other. The reverse side of the mica sheet has a metal coating to form a conductive plate which is the *signal electrode.* The optical image projected onto the mosaic releases electrons from each globule according to the intensity of light at that point. Each globule can be considered as one plate of a minute capacitor with a mica dielectric and the signal electrode as the other

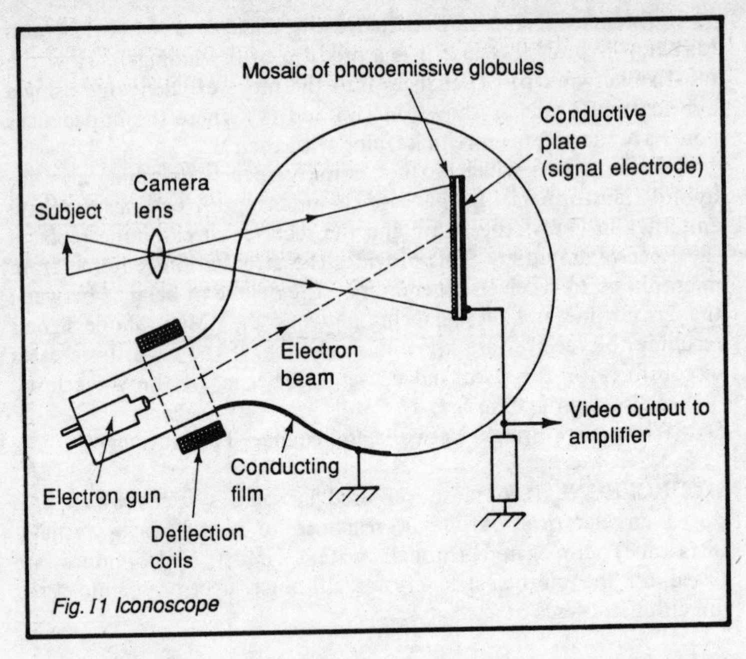

Fig. I1 Iconoscope

plate. The globules therefore become positively charged relative to the signal electrode and the charges build up at a rate governed by the light intensity.

An electron beam generated by the electron gun and passing through the magnetic field of the deflection coils, scans the mosaic. As the beam strikes each globule it replaces the electrons lost by photoemission, i.e. the globule is discharged. When this happens the resulting voltage change is transferred to the signal electrode via the capacitance.

The orthicon camera tube is similarly based on photoemission but the electron beam has lower velocity than is required for the iconoscope.

(* Camera Tube, Electron Gun, Scanning >> Photoemission, Capacitance, Charge)

IGNITER is an electrode in a mercury cathode gas-discharge tube which is constantly in contact with the mercury at its surface. Current passing through the igniter creates local heating to allow the mercury arc to strike – see Ignitron and/or Figure I2.

IGNITION COIL As generally used in motor vehicles this is a transformer with a very high step-up ratio in which a collapsing magnetic field creates a very high voltage sufficient to cause a spark to jump across the points of a sparking plug in an internal combustion engine. The sparks are used to ignite an inflammable gas – see Induction Coil (1).

IGNITRON is an advanced type of *mercury arc rectifier*. This is a gas-discharge device with a mercury cathode which, as an ignitron has an additional electrode known as an *igniter*. With this electrode a mercury arc rectifier requires a lower voltage between anode and cathode to initiate the arc. A basic construction is shown in Figure I2.

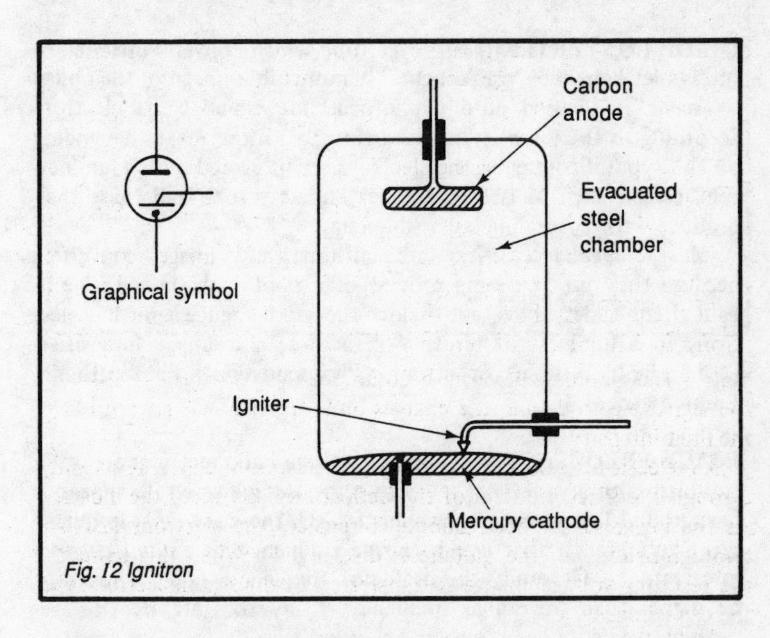

Fig. I2 Ignitron

The steel container is evacuated and has a pool of mercury as a cathode. If the working potential is applied between anode and cathode, no current flows because the gas vapour does not ionize. Ionization is initiated by the igniter which is a cone of silicon or boron carbide just touching the surface of the mercury. Application of a voltage between the igniter and the mercury cathode even for only a few microseconds, causes local heating or even sparking to occur at the igniter point of contact. The surrounding mercury vapour then ionizes and the main arc strikes to the anode.

While the ignitron is in the conducting state, the igniter serves no purpose because the arc produces a hot-spot on the cathode and this sustains ionization. The main discharge only ceases when the

anode–cathode voltage falls below a certain level. As a rectifier, a positive voltage is applied to the igniter at the beginning of each cycle of the applied alternating voltage, this causes the ignitron to conduct during the incoming positive half cycle but not during the negative.
(* Mercury Arc Rectifier, Spark >> Gas Discharge, Ionization, Rectifier)

IIL (I^2L) Abbreviation for Integrated Injection Logic – see this term.

IMAGE CONVERTER is an image tube which converts infra-red or ultraviolet light into visible light. A non-visible image of the object or scene is focused onto a photocathode which emits electrons according to the intensity of the light. By various means depending on the type of converter, the electrons are projected onto a luminescent screen such as is used in a cathode-ray tube and there they produce a corresponding but visible image.

Most *image intensifiers* are automatically image converters because they use the same process of a photocathode sensitive to light frequencies above and below the visible range emitting electrons to a luminescent screen – hence see also Image Intensifier.
(>> Light, Visible Spectrum, Photoemission, Photocathode, Luminescence)

IMAGE FREQUENCY Superheterodyne radio receivers are often troubled with a variety of spurious responses which either appear as background interference or as whistles. Of these the most frequently encountered is that due to image frequency or *second channel* interference. Generally the oscillator frequency, f_o is adjusted to be higher than the signal frequency, f_s by the intermediate frequency, f_{if}, i.e.:

$$f_o - f_s = f_{if}\,.$$

However, if while the receiver is tuned to f_s, a second frequency higher than f_o by an equal amount (i.e. by f_{if}) manages to get through, then this also produces an intermediate frequency signal, i.e.:

$$f_{im} - f_o = f_{if}$$

where f_{im} is the second, image frequency. Adding these two equations gives:

$$f_{im} = 2f_{if} + f_s$$

In other words, the image frequency is equal to twice the intermediate frequency plus the signal frequency.

It is unlikely that a second signal being received will be exactly on the image frequency. Suppose it differs by 1 kHz, then two intermediate frequency signals are produced differing by this amount. The non-linear characteristic of the demodulator combines them to give sum and difference frequencies, it is the latter which can produce an audio signal, i.e. at 1 kHz. This is heard as a whistle, changing in note as the tuning control of the receiver is adjusted.

Image interference is minimized by using selective circuits tuned to the incoming signal before the mixing stage. By this means the (near) image frequency is rejected before it becomes entangled with the oscillator frequency.

(* Mixer, Radio Receiver, Frequency Changer >> Superheterodyne Reception, Frequency Changing, Selectivity)

IMAGE INTENSIFIER is an image tube which increases the intensity of a non-visible image (infra-red or ultraviolet) and at the same time makes it visible. Such devices are used for night vision, in gun sights, photography and infra-red and ultraviolet microscopes. They have paved the way for "seeing in the dark".

The simplest to understand is the *proximity tube* which consists of an evacuated tube containing a flat photocathode placed close to (about 1 mm) and parallel with a luminescent screen. The screen is held at a high positive potential relative to the photocathode of several thousand volts. Electrons released from the photocathode by the incident radiation therefore travel over the short distance in straight lines to the screen to produce a distortion free image. Although electrons are emitted with energies of only a few electron-volts, the electrostatic field of several kV gives them extremely high accelerations so that the image produced is of increased brightness.

More complicated image intensifiers employ electron lenses with electrostatic or electromagnetic focusing. A single stage intensifier might have a luminance gain of between 70 and 100. A multi-stage image intensifier consisting of 2 or 3 stages in cascade could have a luminance gain of as much as 50 000. Details of a typical basic structure are given in Figure I3. This employs a more complex arrangement than the proximity tube especially in that a cone-shaped accelerating electrode is employed in each stage. The screen of one stage is coupled to the photocathode of the next by a fibre-optic lens.

(* Electron Beam Focusing, Electrostatic Focusing, Electromagnetic

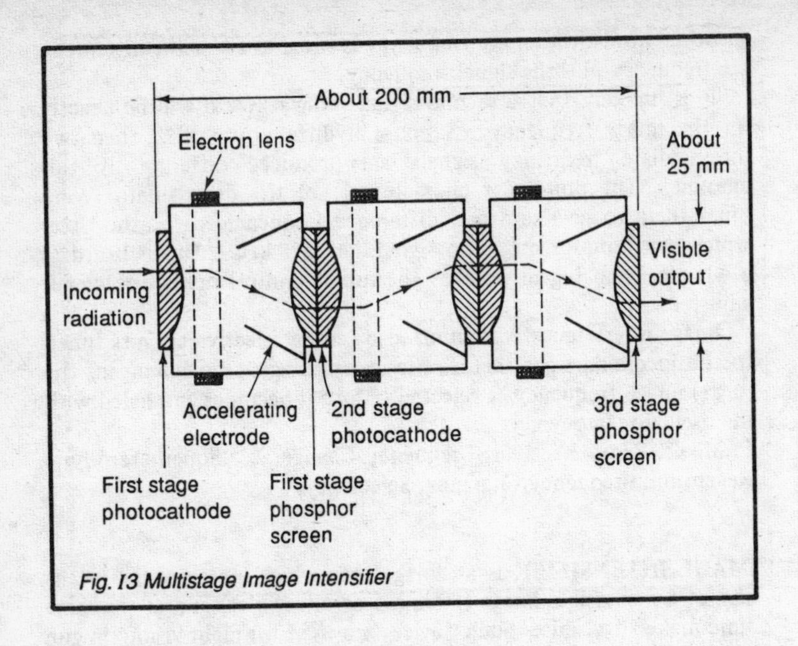

Fig. I3 Multistage Image Intensifier

Focusing, Luminance >> Light, Visible Spectrum, Photoemission, Photocathode, Luminescence, Optical Fibre)

IMAGE INTERFERENCE is encountered in superheterodyne radio receivers – see Image Frequency.

IMAGE ORTHICON is a device which contains the electronics section of a television camera. It employs an electron beam to scan a photosensitive surface on which an image of the scene is projected. The electron beam is modulated and the output is a video signal commensurate with the intensity of illumination over the scene – see Camera Tube.

IMAGE TUBE is an electron tube which converts an image which is not visible because it is in the infra-red or ultraviolet spectrum into a visible image, usually with an increase in intensity. If however its primary purpose is only to convert the spectral region of a non-visible image to visible, the tube is more likely to be called an *image converter*. If the purpose is only to intensify an image, it is an *image intensifier* – but note that most image intensifiers also act as converters – see Image Converter, Image Intensifier.

IMPATT DIODE The acronym IMPATT stands for IMPact ionization Avalanche Transit Time, almost a definition on its own. This is a

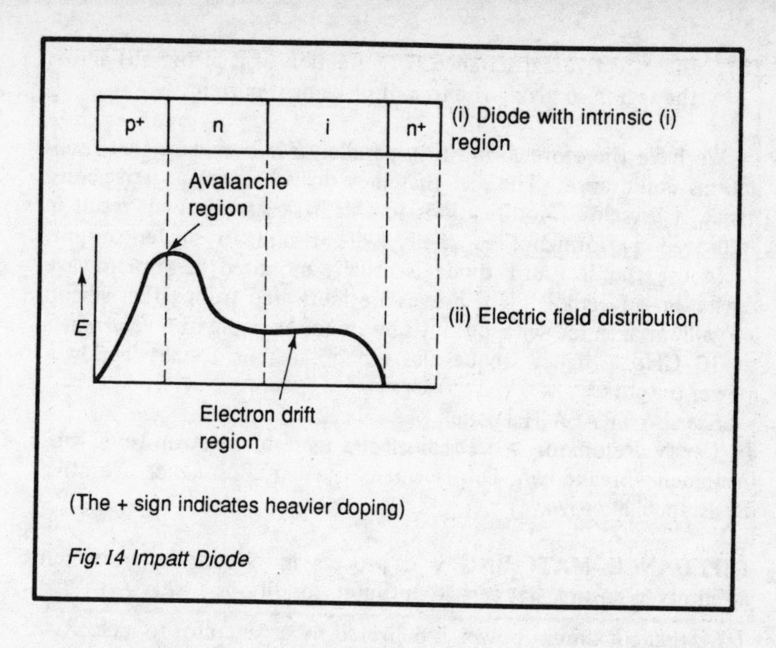

Fig. I4 Impatt Diode

type of microwave semiconductor device which by its construction is able to develop negative resistance. Details of it were originally published by W. T. Read in the U.S.A. in 1958 and its main use is in the generation of microwave power. The original proposal was for a p^+-n-i-n^+ structure as shown in Figure I4(i), the i-region having very few available charges in it. However it has been found possible to dispense with such an i-region hence practical diodes may be of the form p^+-n-n^+ or p^+-p-n-n^+.

Taking the original *Read diode* as an example, the device is reverse biased into avalanche breakdown. Negative resistance arises from a combination of the avalanche breakdown with the effects of electron transit time. The reverse bias creates an electric field distribution as shown in (ii). Breakdown occurs at the peak of the field and electron-hole pairs are generated. Electrons are accelerated into the i-region with constant velocity due to the high field strength.

What goes on in the avalanche region can be looked at from two different aspects:

(i) the avalanche current; the ionization process is a relatively slow process and reaches a maximum only after the field reaches its maximum. This is equivalent to an inductance L (a fraction of a nanohenry) since the current lags on the voltage;

(ii) the effective capacitance C (a fraction of a picofarad) across the region so giving rise to a displacement current.

We have therefore L and C in parallel so it is evident that oscillations could arise. The fact that they do is because negative resistance is present. Modifications to this basic arrangement result in improved performance especially with regard to power output.

In use the IMPATT diode is usually mounted in a microwave cavity or waveguide. The diodes are fabricated from either silicon or gallium arsenide with output powers for example of several watts at 10 GHz. Higher frequencies are obtainable, usually at lower power outputs.

See also TRAPATT Diode.

(* Cavity Resonator >> Diode, P-N Junction, Electron-Hole Pair, Avalanche Breakdown, Displacement Current, Resonance, Negative Resistance, Microwave)

IMPEDANCE MATCHING is a process in circuit design which attempts to ensure that certain optimum conditions arise:

(i) that maximum power is delivered by a generator to its load – in this case the load impedance must be the conjugate impedance of the generator;

(ii) that there is no reflection from the termination of a network or a transmission line – for this the termination impedance must be equal to the characteristic impedance of the line or the iterative impedance of the network.

(* Matching >> Impedance, Conjugate Impedance, Characteristic Impedance, Iterative Impedance, Transmission Line, Network)

IMPULSE This can be looked upon as a pulse of extremely short duration. An impulse voltage is therefore one which, from zero, rapidly attains its maximum value with a subsequent rapid decay. An impulse current is also unidirectional and changes similarly. Fourier analysis shows that the waveform theoretically contains frequency components up to infinity, i.e. it is "rich in harmonics".

Generally impulse voltages or *spikes* arise in systems where inductances are switched, for example, they occur on the electricity mains when motors and other inductive circuits are switched off. On the other hand, impulse voltages, because of their high harmonic content, may be deliberately generated for such purposes as frequency multiplication.

One type of impulse voltage which affects us all is the lightning stroke.

(* Impulse Generator, Frequency Multiplier >> Pulse, Fourier Analysis, Inductance)

IMPULSE GENERATOR This is a circuit capable of generating an impulse voltage, i.e. one which rises rapidly to its maximum value, then almost immediately falls to zero. Impulses may be required in electronic systems because they comprise many higher harmonics. Impulses can be generated through the charge and discharge of a capacitor but a circuit of perhaps greater interest utilizes the special characteristics of a step-recovery diode. A basic circuit of such a generator is given in Figure I5. With no input signal the d.c. supply reverse-biases the diode. When the signal input voltage exceeds this

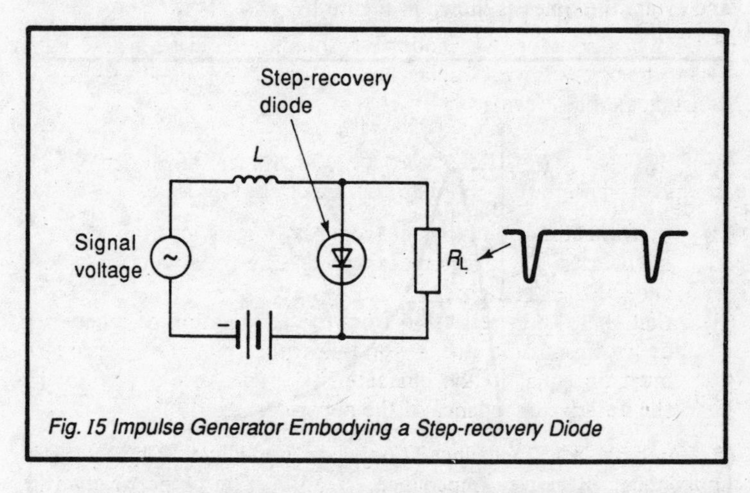

Fig. I5 Impulse Generator Embodying a Step-recovery Diode

d.c. voltage, the diode then becomes forward biased and so conducts with a charge being stored in the centre region. When reverse bias conditions return, conduction continues until the stored charge is removed. Changing the current in this way produces a voltage pulse across the inductor which is applied to the load resistor, R_L. The output voltage pulses are therefore generated according to the input signal voltage.

As an example of its use, an impulse generator of this type, when used with a filter to pick out a particular harmonic, becomes a *frequency multiplier.*

(* Step-Recovery Diode, Frequency Multiplier, Impulse >> Pulse, Fourier Analysis)

IMPULSE NOISE is a particular type of undesirable electrical signal which appears in electronic circuits. It is due to one or more irregular pulses of short duration and relatively high amplitude. Impulse noise can be generated by fault conditions in power systems and by switching surges. Lightning is an almost unrivalled impulse generator – see Impulse Voltage.

IMPULSE VOLTAGE is a unidirectional voltage of high amplitude and very short duration. As an example such voltages arise from fault conditions on power transmission lines or from the pick up of lightning discharges. Switching surges due to the breaking of inductive circuits also create impulses. To examine an impulse voltage waveform a storage cathode-ray tube may be employed and one way of describing a waveform is by the t_1/t_2 ratio where t_1 and t_2 are the times as shown in Figure I6.

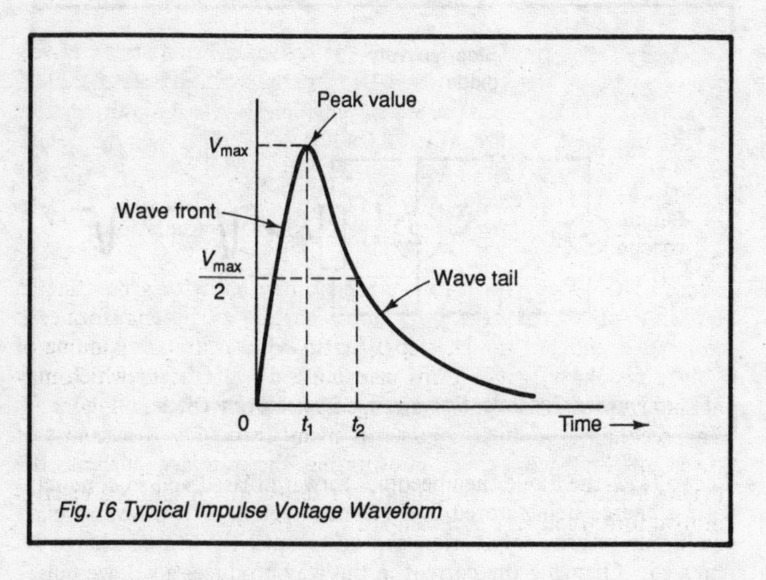

Fig. I6 Typical Impulse Voltage Waveform

A test impulse voltage to represent a lightning surge on a transmission line has a t_1/t_2 ratio of 1/50 which shows just how quickly the voltage rises compared with the time it takes to die away, mainly because of capacitance effects.

Semiconductors are very prone to damage by impulse voltages because p-n junctions are of very small size and therefore easily burnt out. They and other equipment can be protected by voltage-sensitive resistors, avalanche diodes and gas tubes, all devices which pass a high current when subjected to an overvoltage.

(* Storage Tube, Lightning, Voltage-Sensitive Resistor >> P-N Junction, Avalanche Breakdown, Gas Discharge)

INCANDESCENT LAMP is an electric lamp which produces light by the glowing of a white hot filament. It is the standard electric light bulb used everywhere – see Electric Lamp.

INDIRECTLY HEATED CATHODE Most cathodes, for example those in thermionic valves and cathode-ray tubes, require heat for the thermionic emission of electrons. An indirectly heated cathode is one which gains its heat from a separate heater inside it. The cathode is usually a nickel cylinder coated with a mixture of barium and strontium oxides to increase the emission. The heater is a tungsten resistance wire, looped or spiral, insulated from the cathode and heated by alternating current.
(* Electron Gun >> Thermionic Emission, Thermionic Valve)

INDIRECT WAVE (also known as the *reflected wave* or *sky wave*). Over a certain frequency range the energy radiated from a radio transmitter consists of a ground wave which travels along the surface of the earth and a wave which does not travel directly but is reflected back to earth by the ionosphere. This latter wave is appropriately known as the indirect wave.
(* Ground Wave, Ionosphere >> Electromagnetic Radiation)

INDUCTION COIL (1) is a transformer used for generating an intermittent high voltage from direct current. The transformer is iron-cored and has a high step-up ratio with a primary winding of only a few heavy-gauge turns carrying a direct current which may be interrupted. A typical arrangement is sketched in Figure I7. The secondary winding consists of many (probably thousands) of turns of fine wire. On interrupting the primary current, the magnetic flux set up falls rapidly to zero with an induced electromotive force (e.m.f.) e according to:

$$e = n \frac{d\varphi}{dt}$$

where $d\varphi/dt$ is the rate of change of flux and n is the number of turns on the secondary winding. Many thousands of volts can be so generated but at low current.

In the figure the battery energises the primary winding which therefore sets up a magnetic flux, enveloping the secondary winding and also attracting the armature thereby breaking the circuit. The flux collapses so generating the high voltage pulse and the armature moves back to remake the primary circuit. This action is repeated continuously.

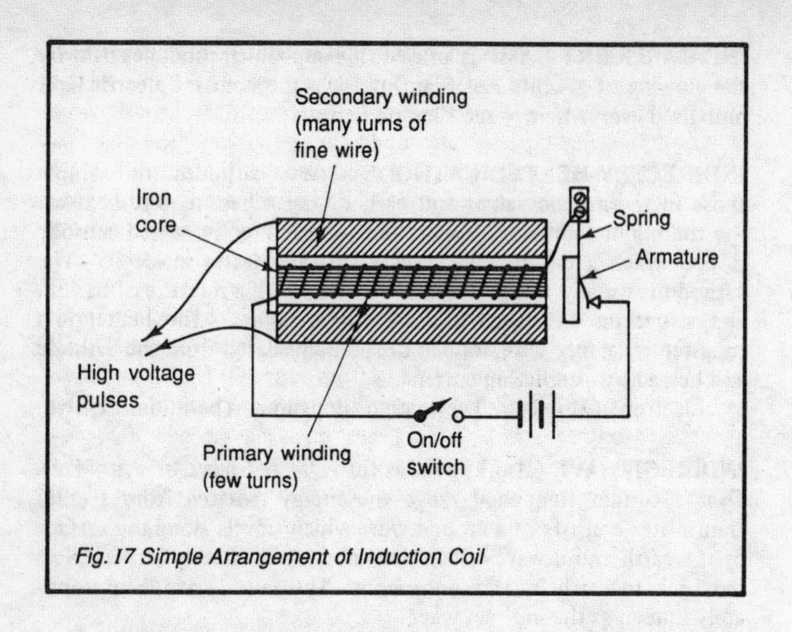

Fig. 17 Simple Arrangement of Induction Coil

Note that it is when the primary current is interrupted that the high voltage pulse is generated, not so much when the primary current is remade. This is because on break, the ratio L/R in the primary circuit is very low because R is extremely high (L is the primary circuit inductance, R its resistance). This means that the time constant of the circuit is short hence the rate of decrease of the flux is high so that the e.m.f. generated is high. On the other hand, immediately the primary circuit is remade, R falls to something low so L/R is much higher, the time constant rises and a smaller e.m.f. is generated.

Other methods of making and breaking the primary circuit are employed, even a mercury switch when large primary currents are involved. A well known application of the induction coil is the ignition coil in a motor vehicle.

(2) The term induction coil is sometimes used for the *hybrid transformer* of a telephone set. It has no relationship with the high voltage generation of (1) but simply couples the microphone and receiver of the set to the line while providing high attenuation between them.

(* Ignition Coil, Hybrid Transformer >> Electromagnetic Induction, Inductance, Transformer, Time Constant)

INDUCTION HEATING is an application in which eddy currents are used to heat both ferrous and non-ferrous metals. It provides a quick, efficient and easily controllable source of heat. A coil carrying an alternating current surrounds the metal to be heated (the workpiece) and the magnetic flux produced by the current in the coil induces a voltage in the metal. Eddy currents therefore flow through the resistance of the metal and power is disspated as heat. The use of the alternative term *eddy current heating* is understandable.

The heat generated in the metal is proportional to the square of the frequency of the coil current. The actual frequency used depends on the application, running from say, 500 Hz for an induction furnace to many kilohertz, even to a few megahertz. At these higher frequencies *skin effect* comes into play hence the eddy currents only flow near the surface of the metal. This is a useful facility when it is required to control the depth of penetration of the heat.
(* Skin Effect >> Eddy Current, Power, Frequency)

INDUCTION METER measures electrical energy consumption, usually in kilowatt-hours. Hence it is also known as an *energy meter* or as a *kilowatt-hour meter*. It is the type of meter which measures the energy consumed from the a.c. mains in homes and other premises. Figure I8 shows the basic features. An aluminium disc which is free to rotate and is coupled to a revolution counter is driven by the voltage and current coils. The voltage coil is connected across the supply and the current coil is in series between the supply and the load [see Fig.E2(ii)]. The effect of the magnetic field produced by the coils is to induce electromotive forces in the disc. By Lenz's Law their effect is in opposition to the magnetic field hence the disc rotates at a speed controlled by the current in the current coil. When this current ceases or falls suddenly the disc is brought rapidly to a stop by the permanent magnet brake which induces currents in the disc in such a direction that the rotation of the disc is damped.

This is an integrating type of meter since it provides a running total of the energy consumed by the load.
(* Electrodynamometer >> Energy, Power, Electromagnetic Induction, Lenz's Law)

INDUCTION MOTOR An alternating current electric motor which rotates due to the interaction between current supplied to the stator and that which it induces in the rotor – see Electric Motor.

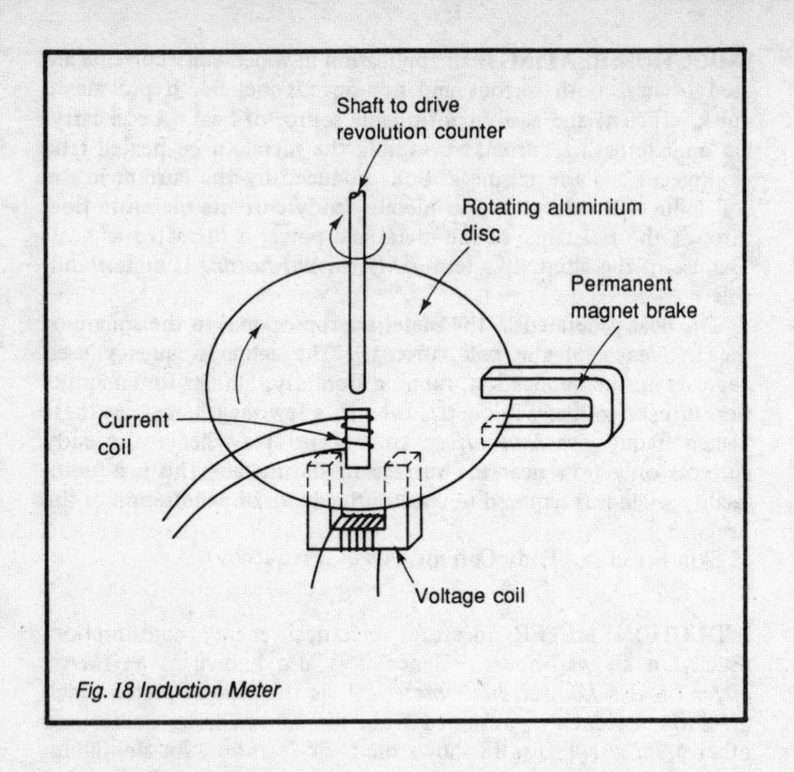

Fig. 18 Induction Meter

INDUCTIVE COUPLING is the term used when two circuits are coupled via a common inductor or by mutual inductance.
(>> Coupled Circuits)

INFRA-RED is the label used for electromagnetic waves having wavelengths just beyond the red end of the visible spectrum and extending to the microwave region. Infra-red radiation is emitted by a hot body at between about 100 and 200°C, the effect can be felt as radiant heat. Infra-red heating has many uses in industry, e.g. for drying paint and it has many uses in medical treatment since the rays penetrate body tissues.

The label is also used for any device which functions in this region of the electromagnetic spectrum, e.g. infra-red heating, infra-red camera. Infra-red sensors can detect temperature differences in the heat radiated by different objects, even between cloud cover and the earth below.
(>> Electromagnetic Radiation, Electromagnetic Spectrum)

INSERTION GAIN/LOSS is the gain (or loss) resulting from the insertion of a network somewhere between a generator and its load. It is usually expressed as the ratio of the power, voltage or current in the load before insertion of the network to that in the load after insertion. The result may be quoted in decibels. An increase in power in the load after insertion of the network indicates an insertion gain, a decrease in power is an insertion loss.
(* Generator, Load >> Network, Gain, Loss, Decibel, Attenuation)

INSTABILITY is a condition which occurs in systems containing amplification. The cause is usually unwanted capacitive or inductive couplings between parts of the circuit at different levels of gain, e.g. between the output and input circuits of a power amplifier. The result is oscillation which may be audible as a whistle or growl if the system works at audio frequency and includes a loudspeaker.

Instability at higher frequencies may be present in a system and cause power losses, incorrect functioning of the equipment and even interference through radiation.
(* Parasitic Oscillation >> Oscillation, Feedback, Nyquist Diagram)

INSTRUMENT TRANSFORMER "Instrument" here refers to a measuring instrument such as an a.c. voltmeter or ammeter. The transformer is employed to increase the range of the instrument:

(i) as a current transformer – the current to be measured flows through the primary winding and the secondary is connected to the ammeter. The transformer steps down the current by a known ratio, hence heavy currents in the main circuit do not flow through the meter;
(ii) as a voltage transformer – the high voltages to be measured are stepped down by a known ratio to a value which the voltmeter can handle. The instrument itself therefore does not need to cater for high and sometimes dangerous voltages.

(* Current Transformer, Voltmeter, Moving-Coil Meter >> Transformer, Ammeter)

INTEGRATED CIRCUIT is a component consisting essentially of a complete microelectronic circuit containing two or usually very many more interconnected circuit elements on a single substrate (integrate – from Latin "to make as a whole"). The technique is especially suited to low power applications (the standard power supply is at 5 V) using transistors, diodes, resistors and small capacitors. Large capacitors and inductors cannot be included so these are usually connected to the integrated circuit (IC) externally.

This may be avoidable when the required reactances can be simulated within the IC by special circuit techniques such as transistors with feedback. Basically there are two different types of IC:

(i) *hybrid integrated circuit* – this consists of two or more different components interconnected by wires or printed wiring on a ceramic substrate. Each of the components may be of monolithic form (see below) or thin or thick film construction;

(ii) *monolithic integrated circuit* – the description *monolithic* comes from the Greek, interpreted in this case as a "single block". All the circuit components plus interconnections are contained on the surface of a single chip of silicon or gallium arsenide. Silicon is more commonly used but gallium arsenide has a higher resistivity hence provides greater isolation between components formed on it.

Integrated circuit resistors are often obtained by using a length of the p type diffusion used for n-p-n transistor bases (emitter diffusions are usually too low in resistance, collector diffusions too high). Typically resistance values between some 100 up to several thousand ohms can be obtained by this method.

Integrated capacitors may be developed by using the capacitance of a reverse-biased p-n junction. This is voltage dependent so if a constant value is required care must be taken that in use the correct voltage is applied and maintained. Capacitances of only a few hundred picofarads can normally be realized. Alternatively in metal-oxide-silicon (MOS) technology a parallel plate capacitor can be formed. The top electrode is the aluminium metallization, the bottom electrode a heavily doped n-type diffusion with the normal silicon dioxide insulating layer acting as the dielectric. Again capacitances are in the picofarad range.

The chip itself is not just small, it is minute, being of the order of one to a few square millimetres in area. Connections to such a small device, and there may be many of them, are indeed fragile, hence such a chip cannot withstand the normal rigours of circuit construction and daily life so it is mounted in a protective case with external leads as sketched in Figure I9(i). This is an example of the commonly used DIL (dual-in-line) package. The leads may be inserted into special sockets (i.e. "plugged in") or soldered directly into printed wiring boards. A small IC with 8 leads only is shown, 16–20 is quite common while very complex IC's may require several times this number.

IC's are fabricated using both bipolar and MOS techniques. There are many variations in the processes used and these change with time as improved methods are developed. Accordingly we confine

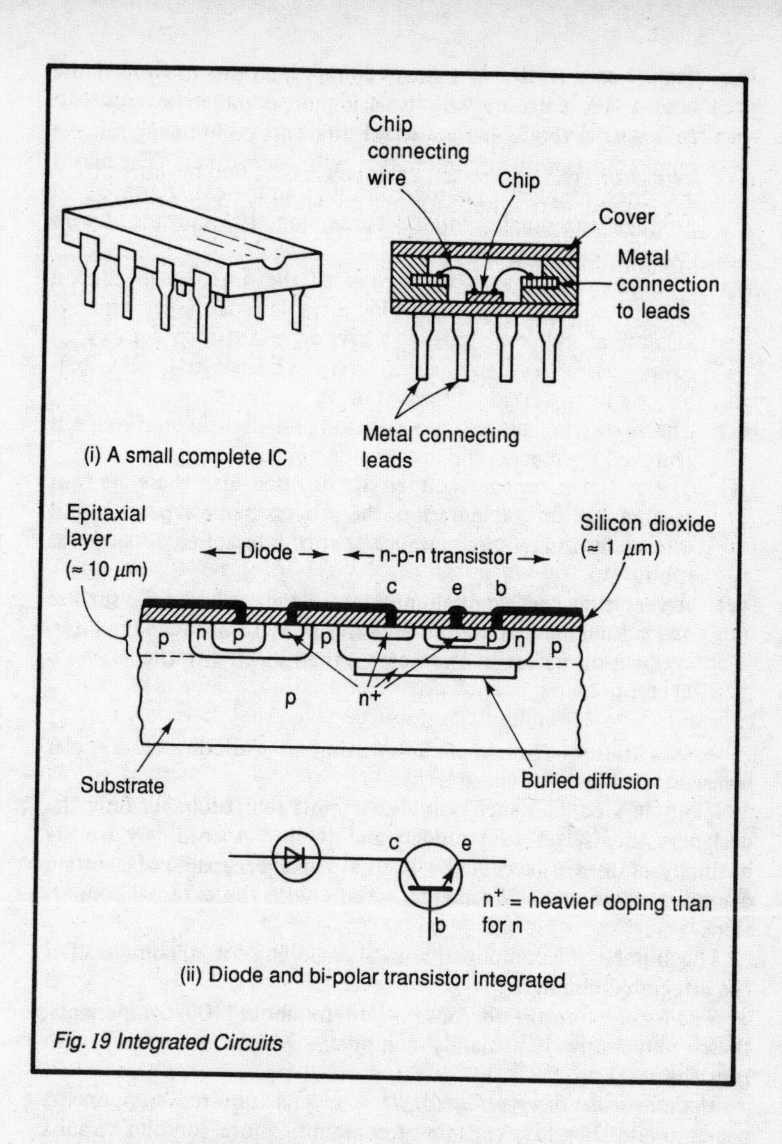

Fig. 19 Integrated Circuits

ourselves to uncomplicated explanations to understand how a seemingly impossible technique is carried out, with Figure C5 always at hand to remind us of the size of things. The depth of most layers is no more than a few micrometres (μm). If required, the complete process can be understood in greater depth by following the * terms below in the order given.

(i) The circuit is first designed, from which are developed the large mask patterns with isolation areas added as required. *Isolation* is the technique which prevents components on the same chip from being in contact with each other. The masks are then reduced photographically and next repeated to produce the smaller masks containing the multiple images covering a single wafer.

(ii) Of major importance in the use of the omnipresent silicon chip is its capability of growing a stable oxide layer which is insulating. Silicon happens to have a great affinity for oxygen so by passing oxygen or steam over the heated material a coating of silicon dioxide is formed on it.

(iii) The masks are placed into position and the silicon dioxide is removed from areas which are to be doped.

(iv) The p and n regions required are diffused into these areas or created by ion implantation, the process being repeated until eventually the required arrangement of interacting doped areas is built up.

(v) A very thin coating of aluminium is deposited over the surface and a final mask is used to etch this away to produce the interconnection pattern. The wafer is then sliced into the individual chips.

As illustration, the simple integration of a diode plus bi-polar transistor is shown in Figure I9(ii).

Many IC's contain such complex circuits that probably only the designers themselves fully understand them. Accordingly we are normally obliged to accept the IC as a package, capable of a certain overall performance. We merely wrestle with the external connections.

The number of components on a single chip of silicon classifies the integrated circuit as:

Small-scale integration (SSI) – up to about 100 components, these were early IC's mainly comprising bipolar transistors with resistors.

Medium-scale integration (MSI) – several hundred components per chip and therefore capable of containing more complex circuits than with SSI; generally with MOS transistors.

Large-scale integration (LSI) – at least 16 kilobits of memory or its equivalent. Such an IC can contain a complete microprocessor.

Very large-scale integration (VLSI) – refers to IC's containing up to one megabit of memory or its equivalent.

Extra large-scale integration (ELSI) – goes even further at more than one megabit of memory or its equivalent.

(* Substrate, Chip, Epitaxy, Photolithography, Diffusion, Isolation, Planar Process, MOS Capacitor, Hybrid Integrated Circuit, Memory >> Transistor, Doping, Ion Implantation)

INTEGRATED INJECTION LOGIC A type of integrated logic circuit with the significant advantage of high packing density. The name is abbreviated to IIL but is more popularly known as I^2L. The technique employs transistor switching only and a single gate embodies both a p-n-p and an n-p-n transistor. These can be merged together since no resistors or insulating regions are required, hence circuit density is high and very suitable for large scale integration. In addition I^2L works at smaller currents and voltages than equivalent TTL circuits. With low power disspation however, speed is slower but by trading one for the other, I^2L can be made faster than TTL and still have the advantage of higher packing density.

The benefits of I^2L can be gauged from Figure I10 which at (i) shows a typical gate circuit with its physical realization as an integrated circuit in (ii). The simplicity of the structure shows how circuit density can be high and that no resistors are required as with other bipolar arrangements. The supply voltage can up to some 15 V. At the higher voltages the current I increases accordingly and the gate speed improves with delay times down to around 2–5 nanoseconds.
(* Integrated Circuit, Logic Gate, Transistor–Transistor Logic, Digital Logic >> Transistor)

INTERELECTRODE CAPACITANCE is frequently troublesome but can also be used to good effect in semiconductors. It also occurs in thermionic valves in which it is mainly undesirable. The capacitance arises from the fact that two electrodes in close proximity behave as the plates of a capacitor. Instability can arise when some energy which should be moving forward in the device is instead fed back via the capacitance. The reactance of a capacitor falls with frequency hence interelectrode capacitances, even though of only a few picofarads have a significant effect at the higher frequencies. Anode and grid of a triode thermionic valve and base and emitter of a transistor are particularly affected.

Interelectrode capacitance can be used to advantage however, for example in the varactor diode in which the capacitance is variable. This makes the device suitable for use as a voltage controlled tuning capacitor.
(* Automatic Frequency Control, Varactor >> Thermionic Valve, Transistor, Capacitance, Feedback)

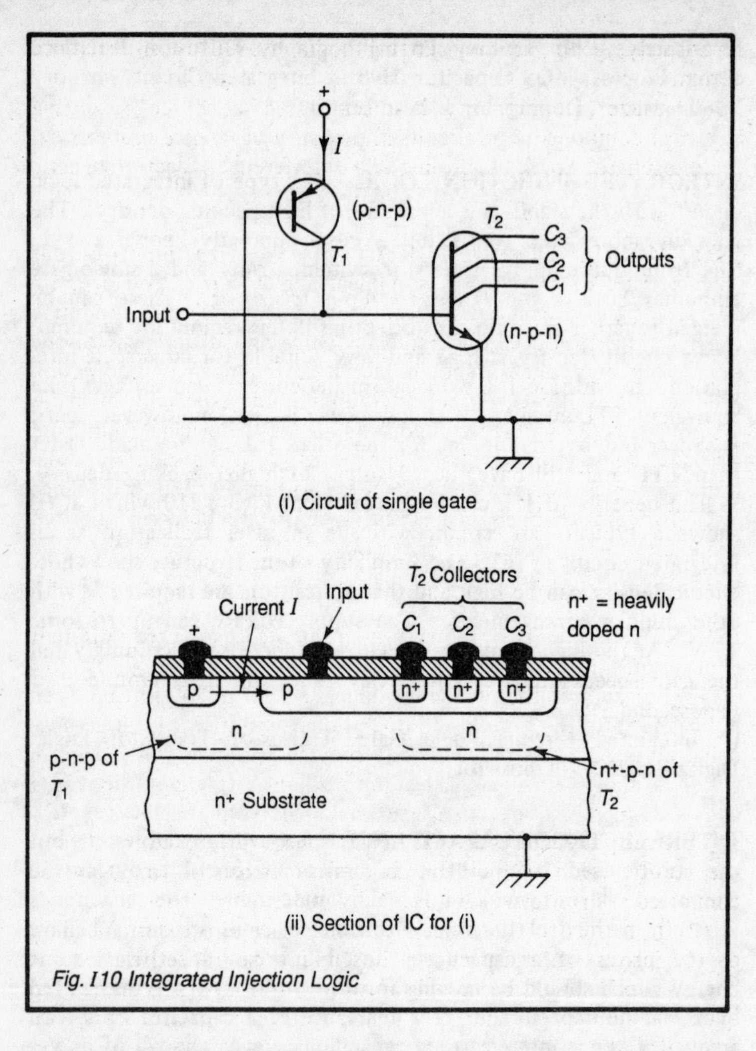

Fig. I10 Integrated Injection Logic

INTERFERENCE is the label given to any unwanted signal which causes disturbance in a communication system. Natural interference arises from lightning discharges or in radio transmission, with variations in the ionosphere. Man-made interference comes from many sources to disturb radio or television reception, for example (i) nearby frequency transmissions, (ii) the operation of electrical devices which interrupt current, (iii) anything which produces an electric spark for these are notorious for radiating electromagnetic energy over a wide bandwidth, (iv) the electricity mains are surprisingly good at transmitting radio frequency interference currents.

Man-made interference is best suppressed at source by fitting electrical components or circuits known as *interference suppressors.*
(* Ionosphere, Spark, Lightning >> Interference, Electromagnetic Wave)

INTERMODULATION DISTORTION When the input–output characteristic of a system is non-linear and it carries two or more complex signals, it is possible for some frequencies to modulate others. This produces the frequency sums and differences of the interacting components and in fact it is the normal modulation process. It is however frequently undesirable especially in audio systems where the added components distort the original sound and also for example, in telephony line systems. In these intermodulation components from one channel fall within the frequency range of a different channel, hence causing crosstalk between the two channels.
(* Crosstalk >> Distortion, Modulation)

INVERTER This term is used in at least three different applications:

(1) For an amplifier which introduces a 180° phase-shift between input and output. For this an operational amplifier is ideal because it has an inverting terminal already provided (marked –). A typical circuit is shown in Figure I11(i) (as a non-inverting amplifier the + and – connections are changed over). The voltage gain is R_1/R_2 and the output signal is inverted (180° phase difference) relative to the input. Both bipolar and field-effect transistors may also be connected as inverters.

(2) It relates to the process of converting direct current (d.c.) energy into an alternating form, i.e. the inverse of rectification. A typical application is the provision of power from a 12 V battery to operate a fluorescent lamp at a higher voltage a.c. There are several ways of doing this, for example by coupling a d.c. motor to an a.c. generator or by chopping the d.c. by means of a reversing contactor or switch; most however rely on the thyristor. The circuit of a basic bridge inverter which uses no mechanical switching is given in Figure I11(ii). The thyristor combinations T_1T_2 and T_3T_4 are fired alternately at a frequency determined by that required by the load. Many other arrangements of thyristors with and without transformer help are available depending on the application, e.g. load current and voltage, frequency and efficiency required.

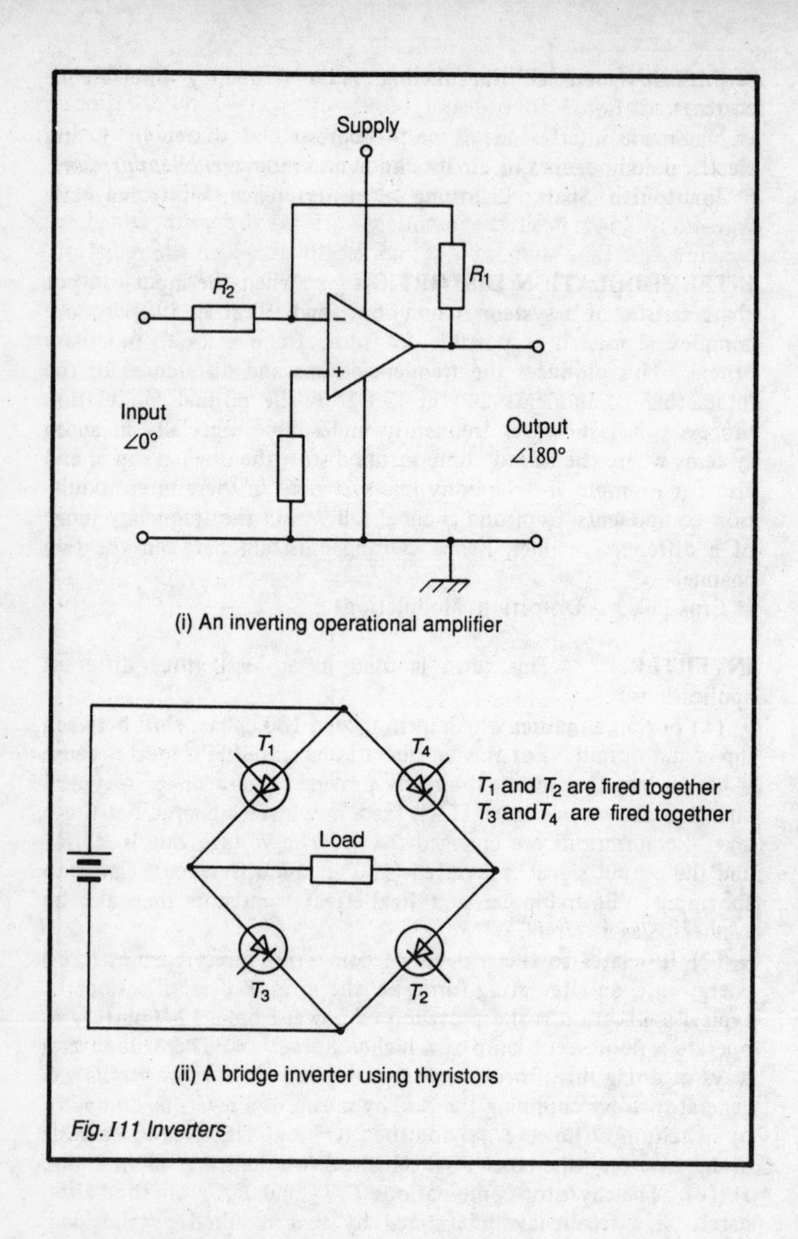

Fig. I11 Inverters

(3) The NOT logic gate which converts a logic 0 into a logic 1 and vice versa is also appropriately known as an inverter.
(* Operational Amplifier, Electric Motor, Generator, Thyristor, Digital Logic >> Amplifier, Phase Angle, Bridge)

IONIZATION CHAMBER This is used mainly in the detection of ionizing radiations. It consists typically of a metallic outer cylinder which acts as a cathode with a metal wire or rod inside, usually running axially and fixed at one end in an insulating collar as shown in Figure I12. The rod acts as an anode and is maintained at a moderately high positive potential. At the opposite end is a "window" of thin aluminium or mica through which the radiation enters. The chamber is filled with a gas or gas mixture. An alternative construction employs parallel plates within the chamber as cathode and anode.

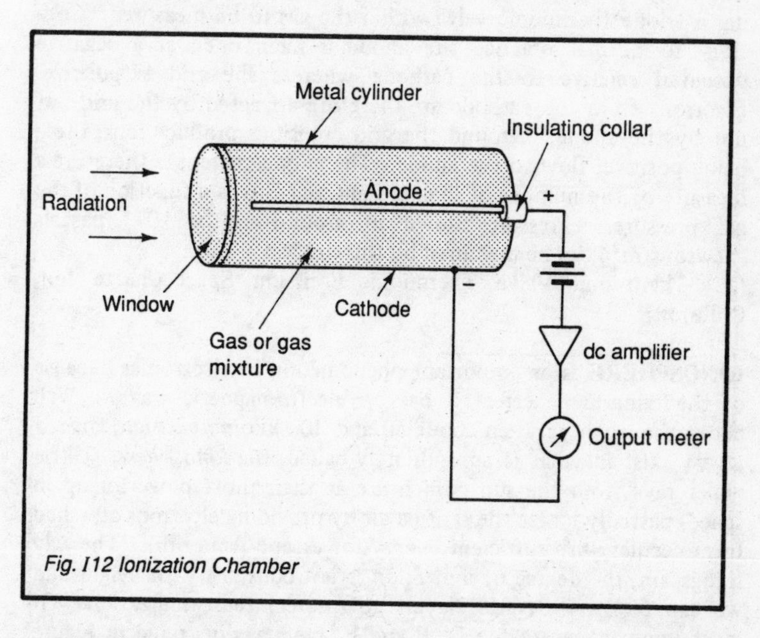

Fig. I12 Ionization Chamber

When a high velocity particle emitted from, say, a radioactive substance, bursts through the chamber, it can produce as many as 10^5 ion pairs (positive ion plus negative electron) before its energy is exhausted. Each ion carries a charge of 1.602×10^{-19} coulomb, each electron the same charge but negative. If the charges are kept separated by the electric field between anode and cathode, the positive will be collected by the cathode and the negative by the anode. A total charge of, say $2 \times 10^5 \times 1.602 \times 10^{-19} \simeq 3.2 \times 10^{-14}$ coulombs is therefore available. Now if this happens at a rate of only 100 per second, since one coulomb per second is equal to one ampere of current, then the current in the external circuit is about 3.2×10^{-12} amperes. This current is extremely small but can easily be handled by a d.c. amplifier for display on the output meter. The output current is therefore directly related to the intensity of the ionizing radiation.

The *Geiger Counter* is based on this principle but is designed for detection of single ionizing particles rather than a multitude of them. (* Geiger Counter >> Charge, Ionization, Impact Ionization, Electric Field, Collision)

IONIZATION PRESSURE GAUGE is a device used for measuring extremely low gas pressures. It can best be understood by considering a triode thermionic valve within the gas to be measured. Contrary to normal practice the anode is maintained at a negative potential relative to the cathode whereas the grid is positive. Electrons from the cathode are therefore attracted by the grid but not by the anode. Around the grid collisions produce ions, these being positive, flow to the anode. The anode current is therefore a measure of the number of ions present and this is a function of the gas pressure. Pressures down to around 1.3×10^{-6} pascals (newtons/m^2) can be measured by this process.
(>> Thermionic Valve, Thermionic Emission, Space Charge, Ion, Collision)

IONOSPHERE is an important phenomenon in electronics because of the remarkable effect it has on electromagnetic waves. Well above the earth between about 50 and 400 kilometres high, *ionized layers* exist in what is appropriately called, the *ionosphere.* Ultraviolet rays from the sun (which are at their most powerful up in space) partially ionize the rarified air by providing electrons attached to molecules with sufficient energy for escape from orbit. The way things are, the degree of ionization is not constant with height and we can pick out several "layers" of more intense ionization. Of most importance are the D, E and F layers as illustrated in Figure I13(i). Generally, the nearer to earth, the less powerful is the ultraviolet light, hence ionization in the lower layers is least. Obviously there is also an upper limit where the air becomes so rarified that there is little to ionize anyway.

An abbreviated explanation is that free electrons in the ionized layer receive energy from the wave and vibrate. Some of this energy is returned in a different phase, the effect on the wave being to bend it away from regions of high density to lower. As the wave penetrates the layer the *refraction* which is proportional to free electron density increases and pictorially the effect is as shown in Figure I13(ii). Although the bending of an electromagnetic wave is actually due to refraction, the term *reflection* is often used in a more general

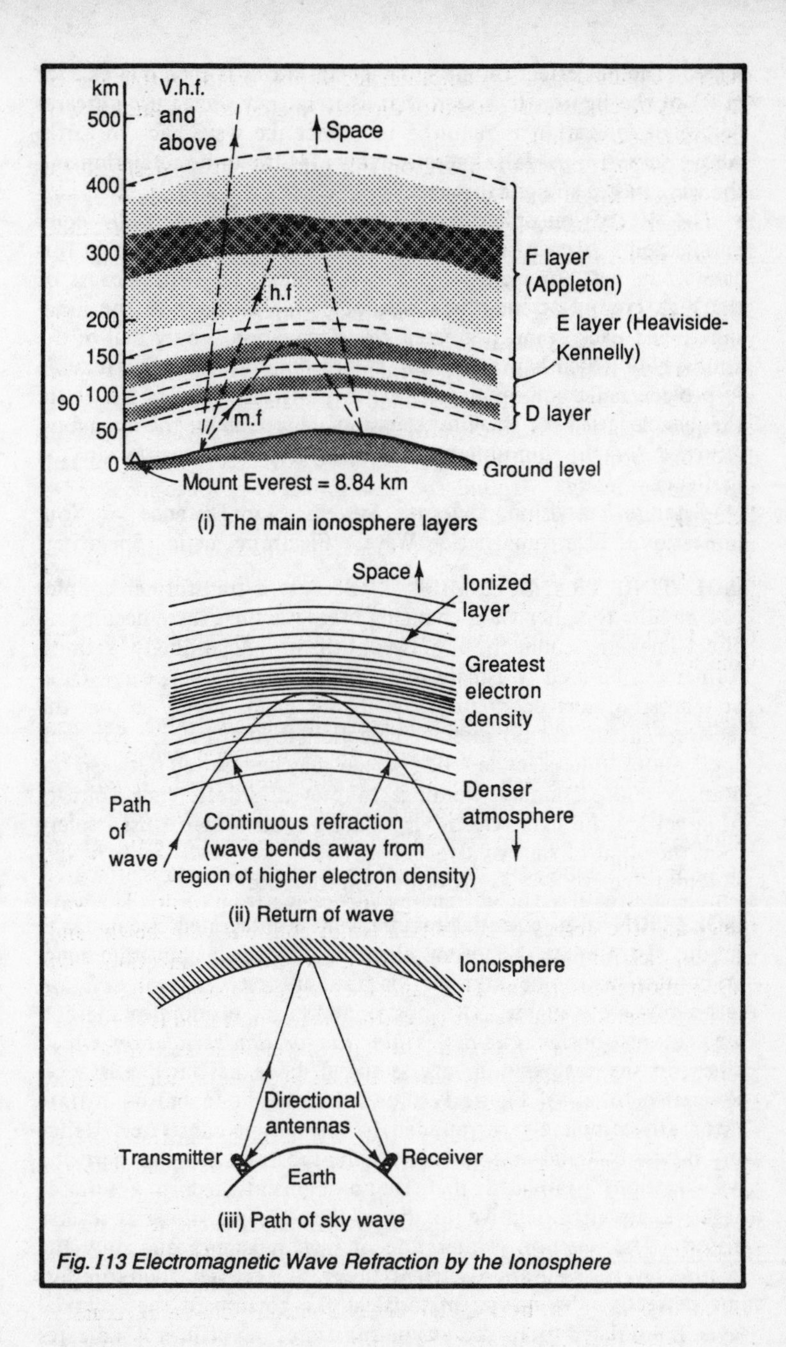

Fig. I13 Electromagnetic Wave Refraction by the Ionosphere

sense. The net effect on electromagnetic waves is shown in essence in (i) of the figure. It is seen that as frequency increases, a greater degree of ionization is required to reflect the wave back to earth. Above some 15–30 MHz therefore there is little or no reflection and the wave passes straight through.

The use of ionospheric reflection in long distance radio communication is shown in (iii) of the figure. A ground wave in this case would not survive a long journey around the earth because of the high ground attenuation. Although the distance to the ionosphere and back is much greater, the attenuation is only that of the atmosphere which is much lower. More than one "hop" is feasible to provide radio communication with the "other side" of the earth. Frequencies used for satellite television are well above the maximum returned by the ionosphere so we employ satellites to do the "reflecting" for us.

(* Satellite Television, Diversity System, Skip Distance >> Ion, Ionization, Electromagnetic Wave, Electromagnetic Spectrum)

ISOLATING TRANSFORMER Because a transformer couples two circuits together via a changing magnetic flux, there need be no direct metallic connection between them. Accordingly a transformer can be used to isolate one circuit from another, e.g. a radio or television receiver circuit from its a.c. mains supply so that the receiver circuit has no direct connection to the mains. For such applications a metal conducting screen may be inserted between the primary and secondary windings to prevent interference voltages from getting through. Often an isolating transformer is used solely from the point of view of safety.

(* Radio Receiver >> Transformer, Interference)

ISOLATION is an essential requirement in integrated circuit fabrication. To prevent the several elements on a single chip from being in contact with one another via the substrate, several *isolation* techniques are available. The most common and economical method used in monolithic circuits is *junction or diode isolation* which relies on the fact that a reverse-biased diode has high resistance. Reference to (ii) of Figure I9 shows that the diode and n-p-n transistor are completely surrounded by the p-type substrate. Hence any n-type material in contact with the substrate becomes part of a p-n junction. Provided that the p is maintained at a suitable negative potential relative to the n, then the p-n diode is reverse biased. The junction is therefore of high resistance and only the minute reverse saturation current flows. Effectively therefore but not perfectly, the n-type material at the bottom of the epitaxial layer is insulated from the p-type substrate. n^+ diffusion indicates a higher level of impurity diffusion than applies for the n-type epitaxial layer. Note that in the figure there is an n^+ diffusion buried in the substrate to isolate the normal n-type above it which is acting as the collector of the transistor.

The main disadvantage of the *diode isolation* technique explained above is the leakage current hence other methods have been developed which avoid this. As an example, *dielectric isolation* goes one step further and separates the particular regions by a dielectric layer of silicon dioxide. Insulation is good but some capacitance is present. Going even one better is *air isolation.* In this the individual components are separated from each other by isolation voids (air gaps). When the doping etc. has been completed on the upper surface of the wafer, this is turned over and by masking and etching, gaps are created in the substrate between the components as required. Because so doing weakens the substrate, thick metallic interconnections are used as support (*beam leads*). These provide structural support.
(* Integrated Circuit, Planar Process, Diffusion >> Semiconductor, P-N Junction, Doping, Diode)

ISOTROPIC ANTENNA A purely theoretical concept developed for assessment of the gain of practical antennas. "Isotropic" is derived from Greek meaning *equal in all directions*, and the antenna is considered to be a point source. If a transmitting isotropic antenna radiates a power of P_t watts, then at any distance d metres away, this power can be considered to be spread over the surface of an imaginary sphere of radius d. The surface area is $4\pi d^2$, hence the signal power flux density received per unit area:

$$P_r = \frac{P_t}{4\pi d^2} \text{ watts per square metre (W/m}^2\text{)}$$

This is developed pictorially in Figure I14. The isotropic antenna is an extremely useful concept. If at a certain distance and in a particular direction from a transmitting antenna, the power flux density is known, then the gain of the antenna *in that direction* is expressed by the number of times its radiated power is greater than that for an isotropic antenna, i.e.

$$\text{practical antenna gain, } G = \frac{\text{power radiated by the antenna}}{\text{power radiated by isotropic antenna}}$$

usually quoted in decibels.
(* Antenna >> Electromagnetic Radiation, Antenna, Power Flux Density, Decibel)

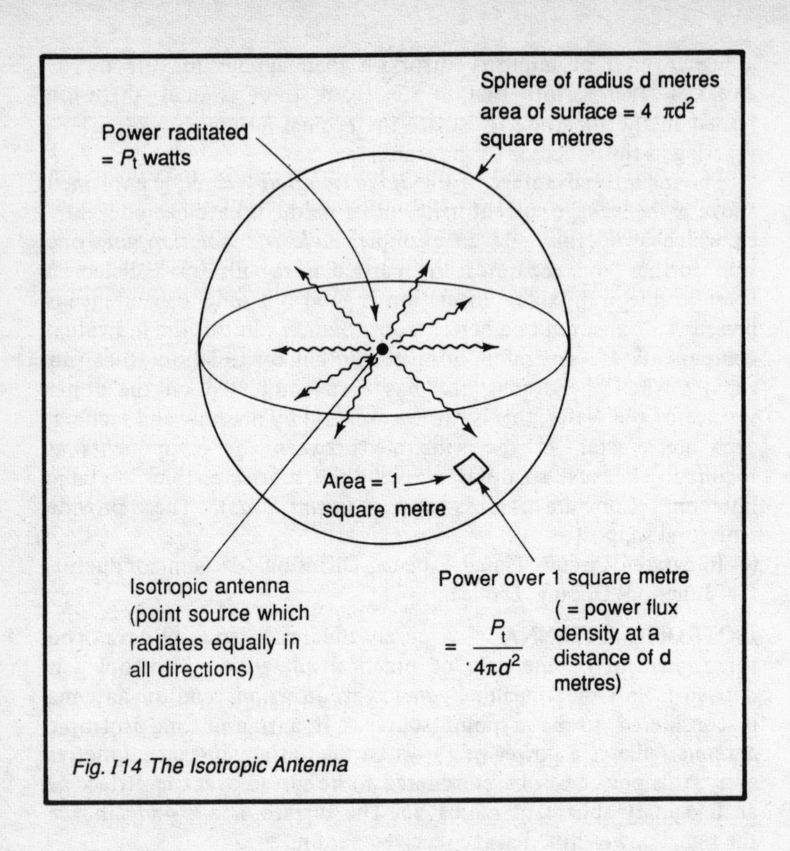

Fig. I14 The Isotropic Antenna

J

JITTER is a general term used in several electronics disciplines for unwanted short-term variations in the amplitude, phase or pulse duration of a signal. Examples are:

(i) certain types of magnetrons experience this variation in the starting time for oscillation, known as *leading-edge jitter*;
(ii) jitter can affect the image on a cathode-ray tube and incoming signal jitter can give rise to errors in synchronizing;
(iii) digital pulses transmitted over a line may suffer from variations in the pulse spacings, this is *pulse jitter*.

(* Magnetron, Cathode-Ray Tube, Digital Transmission)

K

KELL FACTOR is a term used in television reception to indicate the relationship between vertical and horizontal definition. It is a function of the number of lines per frame and the bandwidth allowed for the video signal; it is best explained through a typical example, here that for a 625-line system with an aspect ratio (picture width : height) of 4 : 3.

Not all lines are effective in building up the picture, say in this case 600 are used. The number of picture elements in a vertical direction is therefore fixed at 600. Ideally therefore there should be $600 \times 4/3 = 800$ picture elements per line. Suppose the duration of the visible part of a line is 52 microseconds (μs), then the ideal duration horizontally of a single picture element is 52/800 μs which leads to a picture element frequency of $800/52 \times 10^6$ Hz = 15.4 MHz.

On the assumption that the video frequency must be capable of displaying continuously alternating black and white picture elements, i.e. one half-cycle black, the next half-cycle white, then the video frequency should be half the frequency of the picture elements, i.e. 7.7 MHz. However to conserve bandwidth on the 625-line system, only 5.5 MHz is allowed (71% of the ideal) so because the vertical definition is fixed, this must result in a lower horizontal definition. The *Kell factor* in this case is 0.71 and this in fact provides a horizontal definition which is generally accepted by viewers as satisfactory.

In a way we can look at the effect of a low Kell factor as elongating the picture elements in the horizontal direction. The Kell factor may of course differ for other systems.
(* Television, Television Receiver, Television Signal, Picture Element, Scanning)

KENNELLY-HEAVISIDE LAYER Also known as the Heaviside-Kennelly Layer, is one of the ionized layers of the ionosphere – see the term under the alternative name or Ionosphere.

KILOWATT-HOUR is a unit of energy (or work) mainly used with electricity mains supply. It is given the symbol kWh and is the energy produced when a power of one kilowatt is expended for one hour. Since one joule is the energy produced when a power of one watt is expended for one second, then the kilowatt-hour is equal to $1000 \times 3600 = 3.6 \times 10^6$ joules.
(* Induction Meter >> Watt, Joule)

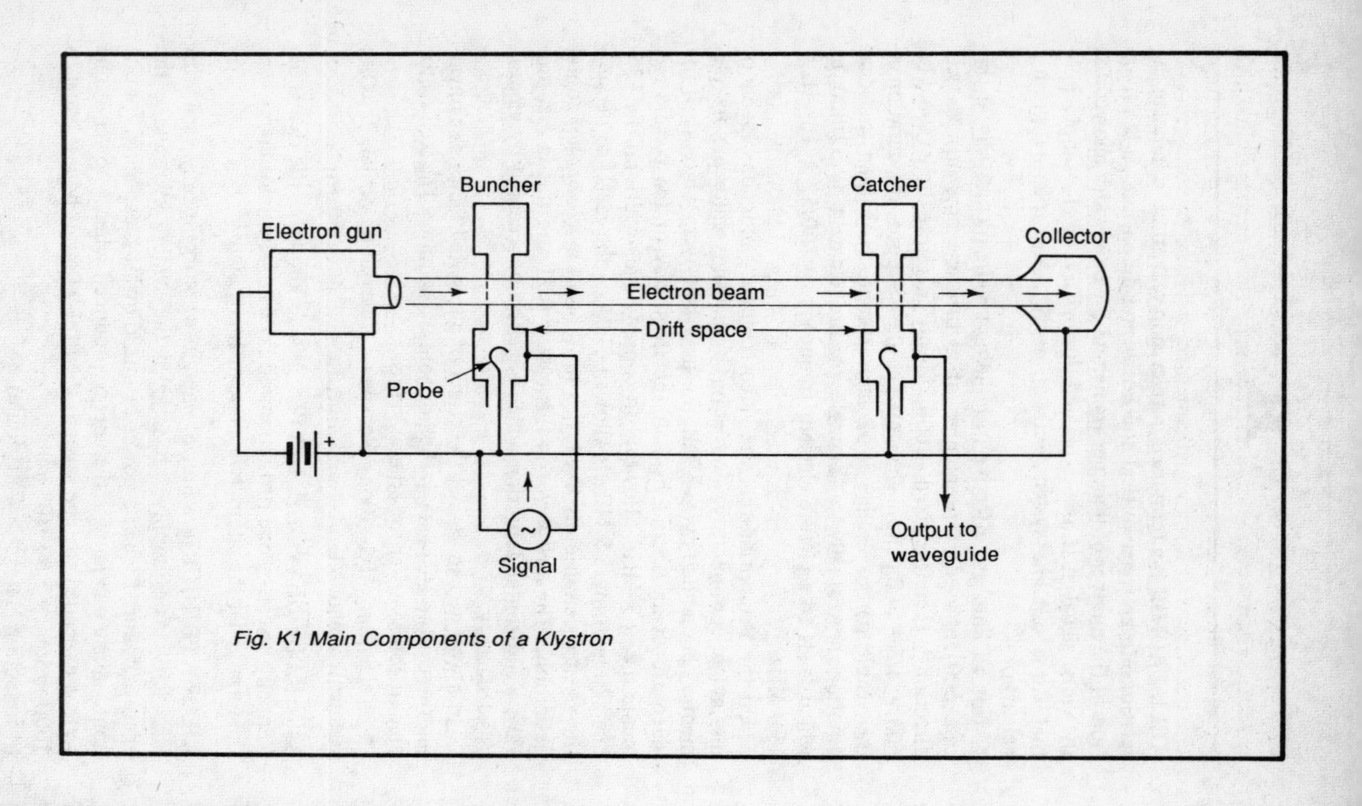

Fig. K1 Main Components of a Klystron

KLYSTRON is a microwave amplifier or oscillator which is constructed around an evacuated tube containing an electron gun from which a narrow beam of electrons is projected along the axis of the tube. The beam passes through small apertures inside cavity resonators. It is velocity modulated by the first resonator (the *buncher*) and energy is extracted from it by a second resonator known as the *catcher.* What is left of the beam continues until it is finally removed by a *collector* which is in a way similar to the anode in a thermionic valve. Figure K1 gives an idea of the structure of a klystron.

An electron gun (see Fig.E6) projects the stream of electrons along the tube firstly through a wire grid in the buncher resonant cavity. Here the signal velocity modulates the stream of electrons as they flow through the grid. The beam continues on into the *drift space* in which the faster moving electrons catch up with the slower ones resulting in alternate regions of high and low electron density as determined by the input signal. The beam is intercepted by a wire grid within the catcher resonant cavity and is fed into the output waveguide. Voltage amplification is possible because some of the d.c. energy of the beam is converted into radio frequency energy in the catcher. As an oscillator the output is connected back to the input, the phase relationships in the catcher and the construction of the tube combine to make the feedback positive.

Much in favour also is the *reflex klystron* which is used as a low-power microwave oscillator. This type has only one resonant cavity and has a reflector electrode mounted at the end of the tube remote from the electron gun. This electrode is maintained at a slightly negative potential with respect to the cathode. Velocity modulation creates bunching as above and the energy is reflected back into the single resonant cavity which now acts as both buncher and catcher. The distance of travel from the reflector and back again is such as to produce sustained oscillation.

(* Electron Gun, Cavity Resonator, Bunching, Oscillator >> Microwave, Velocity Modulation, Waveguide, Thermionic Valve, Phase, Feedback)

L

LAMINATION is a thin stamping of a ferromagnetic material such as iron or an iron alloy with a thin coating of insulation (e.g. a plastic film or coating of shellac) on one surface. Several laminations are laid up as required to produce a core for a transformer, choke, relay, etc. The insulating film reduces the flow of eddy currents. Transformer cores are illustrated in Figure C21(i) and Figure S6(i) in which the edges of the laminations can be seen. In practice the coils are wound on bobbins so each complete lamination must be in two halves for insertion in the bobbin. As an example, in Figure S6(i) the laminations would be a pair of E shapes or alternatively a pair consisting of an E and an I. Joints between them must be kept small otherwise unwanted air-gaps are created.
(* Core-Type Transformer, Shell-Type Transformer >> Core, Transformer, Eddy Current)

LARGE-SCALE INTEGRATION (LSI) – see Integrated Circuit.

LATCHING is in general the process by which a circuit (e.g. a multivibrator) is forced to rest in a particular condition until compelled to change by an external signal. The term *locking* is also used.

LAVALIER MICROPHONE A type of microphone specially designed for wearing on clothing – see Microphone.

LEAD-ACID CELL is a secondary cell which consists basically of "spongy lead" negative plates with composite lead positive plates containing lead dioxide. The two types of plates are connected alternately and are interleaved with porous separators to avoid short-circuits. The plates are immersed in an electrolyte of dilute sulphuric acid. The cell has an electromotive force of just over 2 volts when fully charged, falling to 2 V for most of the discharge period and then to 1.8 V when fully discharged. The internal resistance is low which ensures that the p.d. on load even with high discharge currents is only slightly less. During discharge the sulphuric acid becomes more diluted and so its specific gravity can be used as a measure of the state of charge. When it is necessary to avoid spillage the electrolyte may be in jelly form.

By passing a current through the cell in the opposite direction to that of the discharge current the chemical action which occurs on discharge is reversed and the cell can be fully restored to its charged condition.

A number of separate lead-acid cells connected in series and fitted into a single container constitutes the familiar car battery, usually of 6 cells to provide a 12 V supply. This type of cell is particularly suited to automobile applications because it can withstand the very high starter currents required without an excessive fall in p.d. Because the water in the electrolyte evaporates, the battery requires occasional "topping up".
(>> Cell, Electrolyte, Internal Resistance)

LEADING EDGE generally refers to a pulse, it is that part at which the amplitude first starts to increase.
(>> Pulse)

LEAKAGE CURRENT In general it is any current which flows (or leaks away) through an undesired path, usually a high resistance path through inferior or faulty insulation.

Leakage current is also another name for the reverse saturation current of a p-n junction.
(>> P-N Junction, Reverse Saturation Current)

LF is an abbreviation of *Low Frequency*. This refers to the band of frequencies extending from 30 to 300 kHz (kilometric waves).
(>> Frequency Band)

LIGHTNING is a visible electric discharge between clouds or between clouds and the ground. The air and the earth's surface become charged with electricity of opposite polarities and there is a constant interchange of charge while the air is moist. When the air is drier however the flow of charge becomes more difficult so that charges build up in the clouds. Lightning occurs when the potentials are sufficient to cause breakdown of the air. A *lightning flash* is a complete discharge over a single path.

The path to earth for a lightning flash is established by the *leader stroke*. This creates a highly ionized conducting path over which the main discharge takes place, known as the *return stroke* since it strikes in the opposite direction.

Lightning protection consists of by-passing a building, chimney, etc. by a single low resistance copper conductor terminating in a low resistance earth connection and capable of carrying a heavy lightning current.

Lightning discharges are notorious for their ability to insert crackles in radio reception.
(* Interference >> Charge, Ionization, Breakdown)

LIGHTNING CONDUCTOR is a heavy duty copper conductor running from the top of a tall building or chimney to an earth connection to provide a low resistance discharge path for lightning strokes – see Lightning.

LIMITER is any device which automatically adjusts the maximum output level of a signal irrespective of its amplitude at the input. Signals below a specified level pass through the limiter unchanged but for inputs above this level the limiter maintains either a constant (clipped) maximum level or a reduced one. Perhaps the simplest of all limiters is the diode connected in parallel with a headphone or telephone receiver to prevent acoustic shock from high level inputs. The diode characteristic is such that on high signal levels the diode conducts and therefore shunts the receiver, on low signals it is ineffective, hence the limiter prevents dangerously loud output. Crude but effective, although clearly distortion is introduced.

A limiter is almost essential in the reception of a frequency modulated signal. Amplitude variations above a certain level of the incoming signal must be removed to prevent noise picked up on the way from getting through. This is accomplished by clipping, i.e. all amplitudes above a predetermined level are cut off. In this case the waveform distortion introduced is immaterial because the system is not sensitive to amplitude distortions.

Limiters are also used to protect microwave amplifiers, mixers, demodulators etc. which may suffer breakdown from incoming high level transient pulses. For this purpose the p-i-n diode connected in parallel is suitable because a fast switching time is required. At microwave frequencies this type of diode acts as a resistive attenuator. When the radio frequency signal is below the design level the diode resistance is high, above this level the resistance falls resulting in an almost constant output level.
(>> Diode, Distortion, Frequency Modulation, P-I-N Diode, Breakdown)

LINEAR ACCELERATOR is a device for accelerating electrons or protons to high energies. Taking the electron linear accelerator first, a long evacuated chamber is employed as sketched in Figure L1. The chamber contains a system of tubes arranged in a straight line (hence the description, "linear"). Note the radio frequency (r.f.)

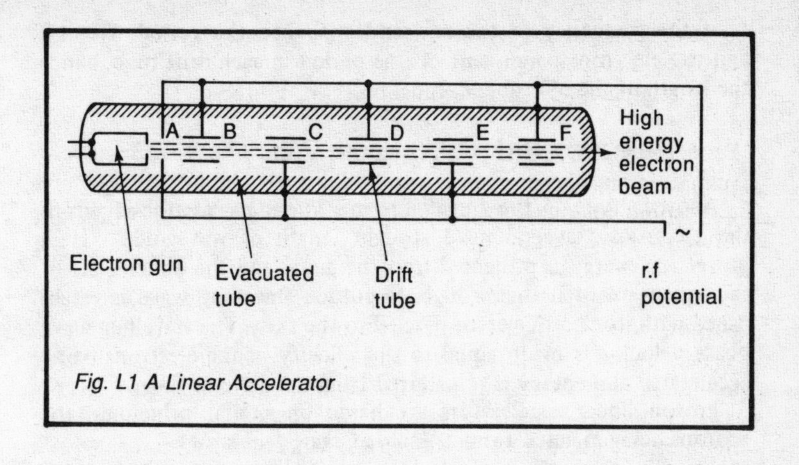

Fig. L1 A Linear Accelerator

potential supplying adjacent tubes at a 180° phase difference. The potential is derived from a high power klystron or magnetron. Electrons projected into the linear system by the electron gun are first accelerated by the potential on the electrode A when this is positive. Now when electrode B is positive with respect to A the electrons are accelerated across the gap from A to B. Within tube B the electrons are said to *drift* because there is negligible field within the tube. Each tube length is such that the electrons take exactly half a period of the r.f. field before emerging. At the time the electrons do emerge from tube B, the potential on C has become positive and again there is acceleration but now across the gap from B to C. The drift tube C is slightly longer than B because the velocity of the electron beam has increased hence it travels further during the half-cycle of the r.f. potential. The action continues similarly through drift tubes D, E and F so that for a given frequency of accelerating potential, correct choice of tube lengths ensures that electrons receive a boost of energy at each gap. The chamber is evacuated to avoid collisions between electrons and air molecules.

Let us assume that an electron of mass m starts off with zero energy (an impossible situation really but the supposition allows us to obtain some approximate relationships). Assume also that it receives an increment of energy, E at each gap and that relativistic effects can be ignored, then:

$$\text{kinetic energy at the n}^{\text{th}}\text{ gap} = nE = \tfrac{1}{2}mv^2$$

where v is the velocity. Therefore $v = \sqrt{(2nE)/m}$.

If the frequency of the r.f. field = f, then the period, $T = 1/f$ and the electron spends half of one period in each drift tube, hence the length of the nth tube, l_n must be:

$$l_n = \text{average velocity} \times \text{time} = \sqrt{(2nE)/m} \times T/2 .$$

Another type is the *travelling-wave linear accelerator* in which the electrons travel along a straight length of waveguide. High power r.f. energy is projected into the guide and the dimensions of the guide are such that a high amplitude travelling wave is established with its electric vector parallel to the axis. The travelling wave phase velocity is made equal to the velocity of the electrons being accelerated and energy is transferred from the wave to them.

Proton linear accelerators are based on similar principles, the protons being injected from a Van de Graaff generator.

(* Electron Gun, Klystron, Magnetron, Travelling-Wave Tube, Van de Graaff Generator >> Electron, Proton, Energy, Kinetic Energy, Period, Relativistic Effect, Phase, Phase Velocity, Waveguide)

LINEAR INDUCTION MOTOR – see Electric Motor.

LIQUID CRYSTAL DISPLAY (LCD) is a type of electronic display usually of black characters on a semi-reflective background. The system has the significant advantage of being inexpensive and of consuming almost negligible current. Most work by modifying the transmission of ambient light. The units are attractive for use in portable, battery-operated equipment such as digital watches, calculators, remote control handsets, cameras, etc. Generally they are driven by CMOS logic circuits.

There are several types of liquid crystal available and various methods of operating them but the one much favoured for general use is the *twisted nematic* or *field effect* liquid crystal. This is an organic compound (contains carbon in the molecule) which has long cigar-shaped *polar* molecules (*polar* means that they exhibit positive and negative poles). The effect which is useful is illustrated in Figure L2(i) where at (a) the liquid is contained between two plates carrying no charge and therefore, because they are polar, the molecules are aligned uniformly. In the drawing they are shown perpendicular to the plates. When as at (b) an electric field is present, it produces a torque on each molecule trying to turn it in a direction parallel to the electrodes. In this condition the plane of polarization of light passing through the crystal is rotated, hence the additional term "field effect".

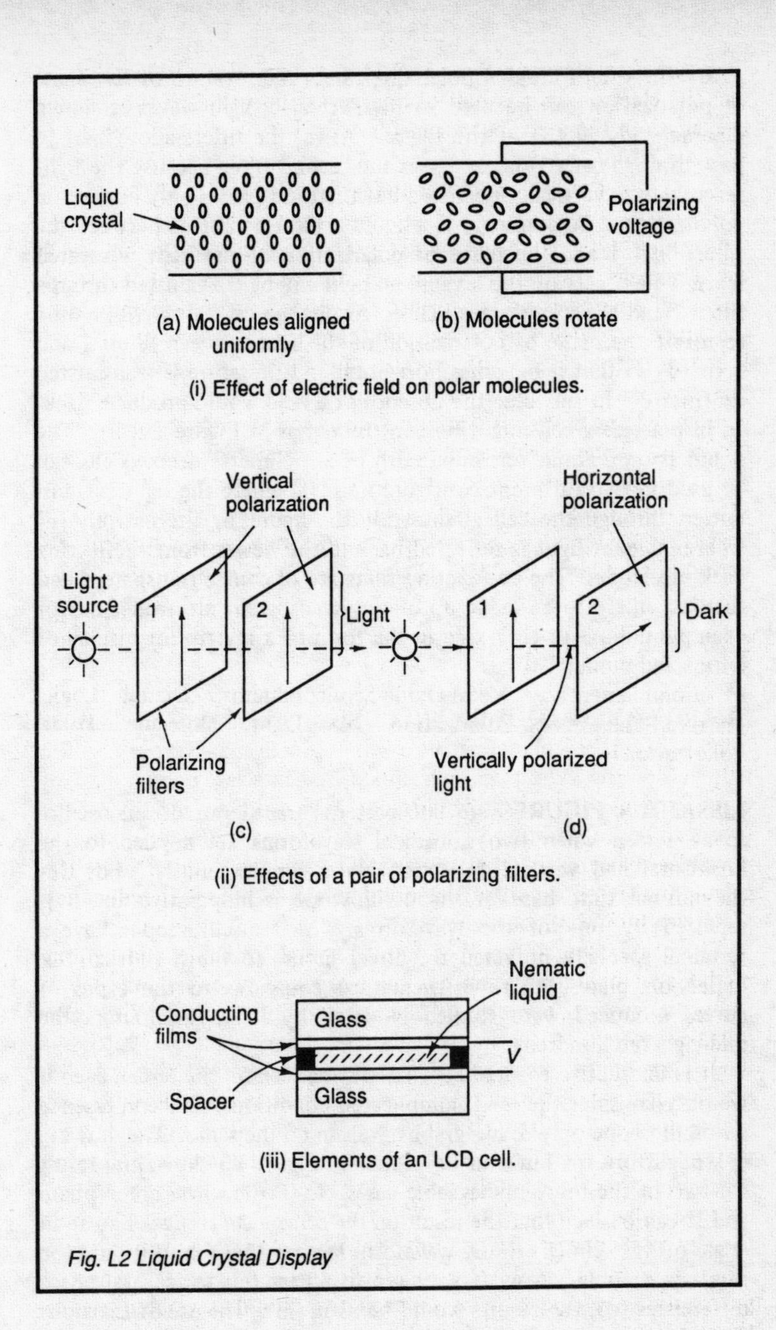

Fig. L2 Liquid Crystal Display

By the use of crossed polarizing filters the rotation of the plane of polarization can be used to pass or reject light waves as shown schematically in (ii) of the figure. At (c) the filters allow light to pass through, at (d) none passes the second filter because the light reaching it is vertically polarized but the filter passes only horizontal polarizations. Accordingly if a liquid crystal is inserted between the filters in (c) and the plane of polarization of the light is rotated when a field acts on the crystal, no light will be transmitted through filter 2 and the viewer sees black. Again, the crystal might be used to rotate the plane of polarization of the light between filters 1 and 2 of (d) so that it becomes horizontal and therefore is transmitted by filter 2. In this case the absence of a field would produce black.

In practice a cell might be constructed as in Figure L2(iii). The liquid is only about one-hundredth of a millimetre deep. Cells can be used in two different configurations: (i) where the light is transmitted through the cell as shown in the figure, or alternatively (ii) where incident light is reflected back to the viewer from a reflecting back electrode. The conducting films are of course transparent and they are likely to be made up of tiny transparent electrodes of, for example indium or tin oxide in the form of a matrix for display of letters and numerals.

(* Complementary Metal-Oxide-Semiconductor, Digital Logic, Matrix, Plane of Polarization >> Light, Molecule, Polar, Polarization)

LISSAJOUS FIGURES are line patterns traced out on an oscilloscope screen when two sinusoidal waveforms are applied to the horizontal and vertical deflection plates simultaneously. For this the normal time base of the oscilloscope is inoperative and it is replaced by one of the waveforms. Most oscilloscopes have a terminal specially provided for direct inputs to the X (horizontal) deflection plates. The mathematical equations to the types of curves produced were studied in detail by J. A. Lissajous in the mid-eighteen hundreds.

It is instructive to predict what will be seen on the screen even if we only consider the least complicated conditions. Since in essence an oscilloscope only draws graphs, we can do the same. The drawing is straightforward but can be tedious. Figure L3 shows the result for two of the more manageable cases. In (i) the waves are in phase and it can be seen that the result on the screen is a straight line at an angle of 45°. In (ii) the X waveform lags on the Y by 90° and the result is a circle. Now if we were to repeat this for several phase differences (ϕ), the results would be as in (iii). The use of Lissajous figures to measure phase differences is now apparent. The actual

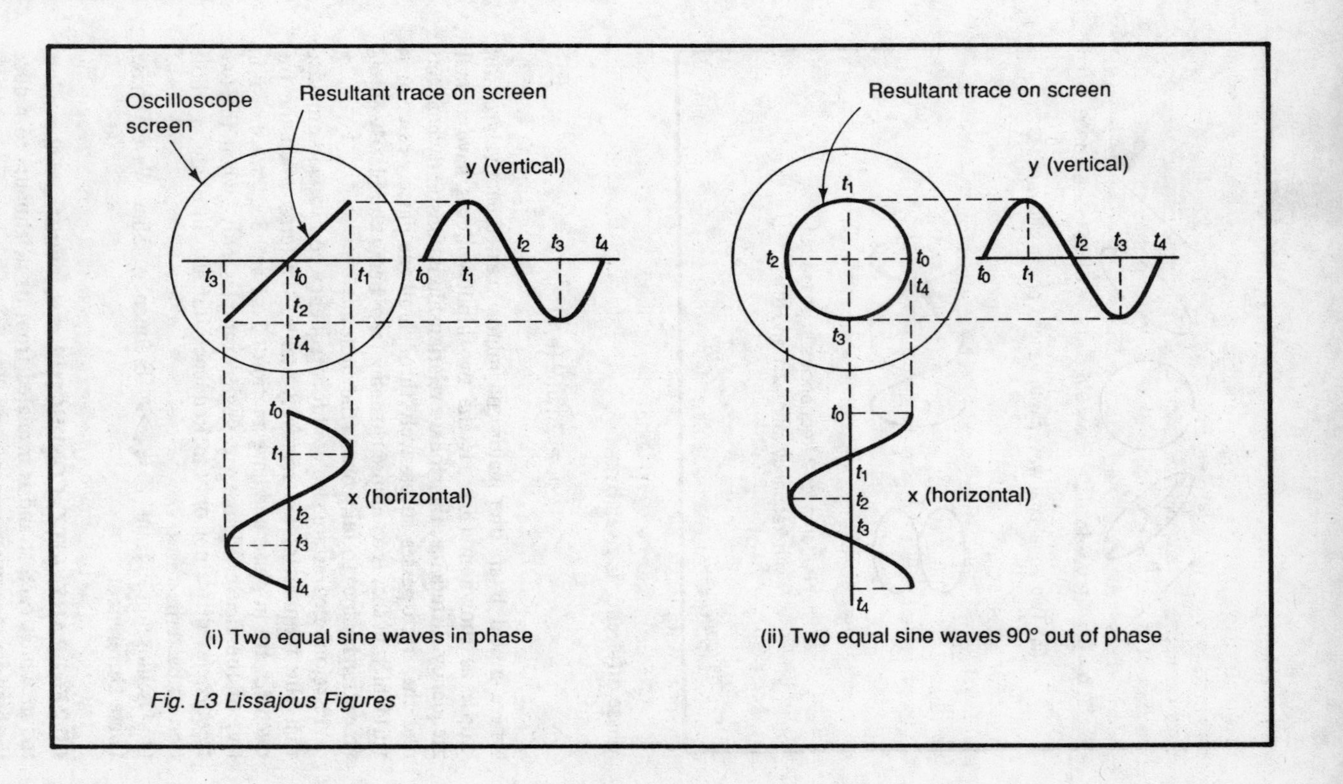

(i) Two equal sine waves in phase

(ii) Two equal sine waves 90° out of phase

Fig. L3 Lissajous Figures

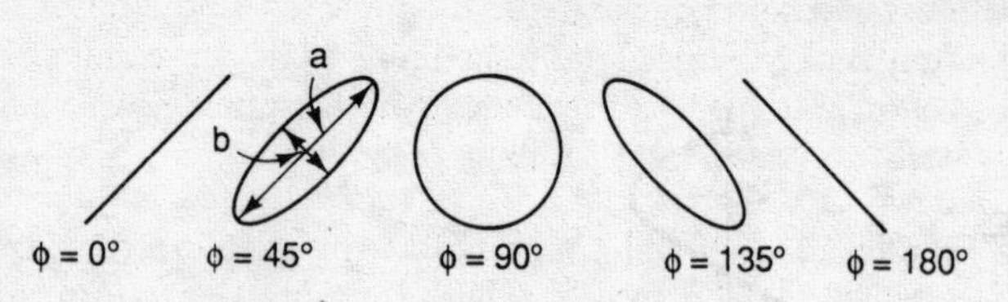

(iii) Two equal sine waves with various phase differences

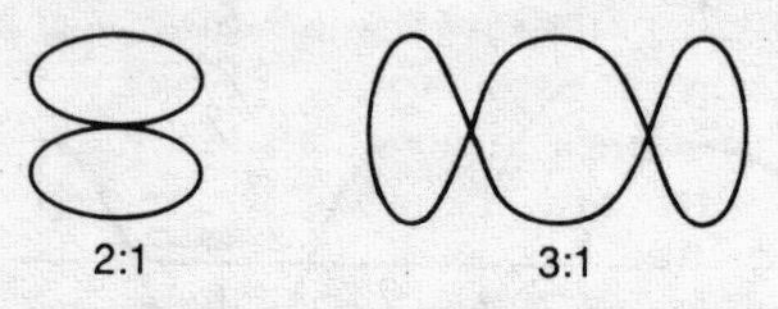

(iv) Patterns for 2 frequencies in phase but with frequency ratios 2:1 and 3:1

Fig. L3 (continued)

phase difference is given by:

$$\phi = 2\tan^{-1}(b/a)$$

where a and b are the major and minor axes respectively of the ellipse as shown in (iii). If the two input voltages have a small frequency difference, their phase relationship is constantly changing and the trace passes successively through all the patterns shown in (iii) which in fact is an ellipse changing from being completely closed (the straight line) to fully open (the circle).

Lissajous figures are also used for frequency comparison provided that the frequencies are relatively stable. Patterns when the frequencies are in phase and have a ratio of 2 : 1 and 3 : 1 are shown in (iv) of the figure. These are single examples only, when the two frequencies differ not only in frequency but also in phase, a whole host of patterns arises.

(* Oscilloscope, Time Base >> Frequency, Sine Wave, Phase, Phase Difference)

LITZENDRAHT (LITZ) CONDUCTOR A multistranded conductor in which each strand is insulated from its neighbours to reduce the high frequency resistance – see Skin Effect.

LNB (LOW NOISE BLOCK) CONVERTER This is a device used in satellite television reception. It is connected at the output of a receiving antenna to amplify the incoming radio wave and convert it to a lower, intermediate frequency for transmission over a cable to the satellite receiver – see Satellite Television.

LOAD is a device or circuit connected to the output terminals of a signal source and which absorbs power from it. Generators, amplifiers, networks and transmission lines are said to be terminated in a load. An everyday example of a load is the loudspeaker, this is the load of the power amplifier driving it. In this case the load is expressed as a resistance or impedance.

With electrical machines (generators) and with the electricity mains, load usually refers to the actual power delivered in watts, kilowatts, etc.
(* Matching, Loudspeaker, Generator >> Power, Impedance, Amplifier)

LOADING is the addition of inductance to a line to improve its attentuation/frequency characteristic.
(>> Transmission Line)

LOAD LINE is a line drawn on a set of static characteristics of an active device (e.g. a transistor or thermionic valve) for a particular value of load. The purpose is to examine the electrical conditions in the load when a given input signal is applied to the device. This is most easily understood from a practical example. In Figure L4 is a set of static characteristics as measured and supplied by the manufacturer for a bipolar transistor. These simply show how the collector current (I_C) changes with collector voltage (V_C) when various levels of base current (I_B) flow. With no load, when an a.c. signal is applied and therefore I_B varies, the static curves apply. This means that at any value of V_C the collector current can be read off directly from the curve for any value of I_B. However, when a load is connected to the transistor, there is a voltage drop across it and V_C changes in some way and unless V_C is known it is not possible to read off I_C. A load line takes care of the problem for us.

Referring again to the figure, consider for example a load of 75 Ω and supply voltage of 9 V. Load lines are always straight so the position in each case can be determined by plotting two points only. The easiest to calculate are at the extremes of the line and in this example are (i) at $V_C = 0$ for then $I_C = 9/75$ A = 120 mA and (ii) at $I_C = 0$ for then $V_C = 9$ V. Drawing a line between these two points produces the load line for 75 Ω. Lines for other values are similarly calculated and drawn. Next suppose that the transistor

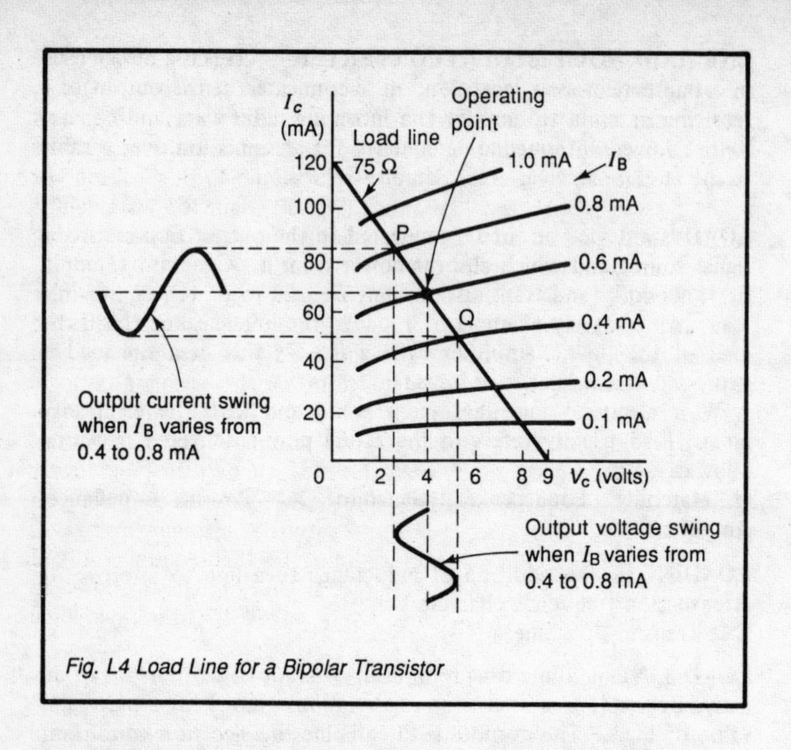

Fig. L4 Load Line for a Bipolar Transistor

base bias is set at 0.6 mA (the *operating point*). The load line then indicates that V_C = 4 V, I_C = 67 mA as shown in the figure. Any swing in I_B due to an incoming signal, say from 0.4 – 0.8 mA is also directly given from the load line (also indicated in the figure).

A load line can be summed up as being a useful graphical tool for choosing the value of a transistor load, the optimum operating point and subsequently for examining the output waveform to ensure that the transistor is not driven into distortion.
(* Load, Operating Point >> Characteristic, Transistor, Distortion)

LOCAL OSCILLATOR In a superheterodyne radio receiver or mixer a (local) oscillator is used to provide a radio frequency waveform for mixing with the incoming signal to generate the intermediate frequency.
(* Mixer >> Superheterodyne Reception, Oscillation)

LOCKING is a means of synchronizing the frequency of an oscillator with that of a constant frequency external signal.
(>> Oscillation, Beat Frequency)

LOGIC is really the science of thinking and reasoning but because computers cannot (yet) think or reason for themselves, logic in electronics has a rather restricted meaning. In a way it does deal with reasoning but only in a limited and exact fashion, outputs from electronic logic circuits are always in the form of "true" or "false", "high" or "low" or more generally labelled just plain 1 or 0. Facts entered into an electronic logic system are also precise and unambiguous and are of the same form.

A simple, homely example is perhaps the best way to illustrate the use of electronic logic. Take the little boy caught with the garden hose in his hands (A) and the family cat soaking wet (B). This gives two sets of input data from which reasoning or logic comes to only one conclusion (f), he did it. Logically A and B on their own do not allow the conclusion f, only A and B together. The electronic device which sorts this out is known as a *logic gate.* In this case it is called an AND gate which functions by having an output of logic 1 only when both the inputs A and B are at logic 1. Different gates are employed according to the requirement and many may be used in tandem. A special kind of algebra is used in design known as *Boolean algebra.* Every gate works to the two logic levels 1 and 0 only.

(* Digital Logic, Logic Gate, Boolean Algebra, Logic Level)

LOGIC GATE is a circuit which provides a *logic function.* On a black box basis a gate has a number of input terminals and one output terminal. In the binary system the electrical condition on the output terminal is a logic 1 or logic 0 depending on the various states of the input signals. The full range of input conditions with the appropriate output is shown by a *truth table.*

The circuits used to provide gates vary but practically all are semiconductor, generally part of an integrated circuit. As an easy to understand example of gate circuitry we can consider the simple diode AND gate (see Figure D6 for the graphical symbols). A circuit is shown in Figure L5. The AND gate has an output (f) of 1 only when the x and y inputs are both at 1 (usually some 5 V) otherwise f remains at 0 (approximately zero potential). If a logic 0 is applied to either x or y the corresponding diode is forward biased, therefore conducts so the voltage drop across R maintains f at low voltage (a logic 0). Hence if only one input is at 1, f remains at 0. However if a logic 1 is applied to both inputs, neither diode conducts, consequently f rises to 1. The same conditions apply irrespective of the number of inputs.

Generally gate circuits are more complex than the elementary AND gate above, they may also be designed specifically for

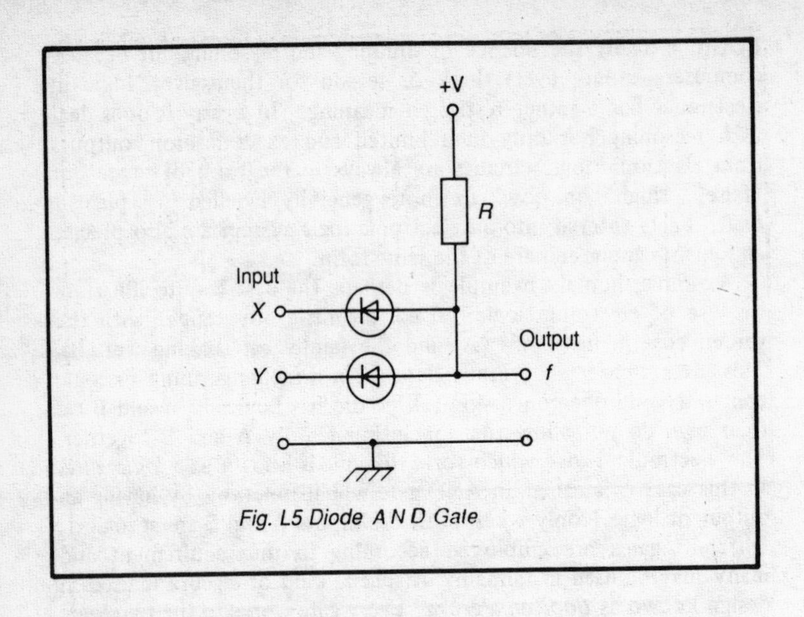

Fig. L5 Diode AND Gate

integration and up to 4 or 5 transistors may be needed per gate. Gates may be connected in tandem [e.g. see Fig.D6(vi)] and any overall function is possible (but only on a 1 and 0 basis).
(* Logic, Digital Logic, Logic Level, Black Box, Truth Table, Coincidence Circuit, Diode–Transistor Logic, Transistor–Transistor Logic, Integrated Injection Logic >> Binary, Diode)

LOGIC LEVEL refers to the voltage used to represent a logic 0 or logic 1. The two levels can be made anything we choose as long as equipment can recognize which one it is without error. A commonly used pair of values may be quoted as 0 V for logic 0 and 5 V for logic 1. If logic 1 is more positive the system is known as *positive logic*, if more negative then it is *negative logic*.

The variations normally encountered and the fact that many different devices must work to one another implies that some tolerances must be allowed and a typical example for a 5 V system is illustrated by Figure L6. The tolerances are shown in (i) and are expressed as a graph in (ii) where the time, t is usually of the order of nanoseconds. The graph indicates that under the *worst* conditions the receiver must recognize any incoming voltage greater than 2.4 V as a logic 1 and a voltage between zero and 0.6 V as a logic 0. Many 5 V computer systems work quite happily to tolerances such as these.
(* Logic, Digital Logic, Logic Gate >> Binary)

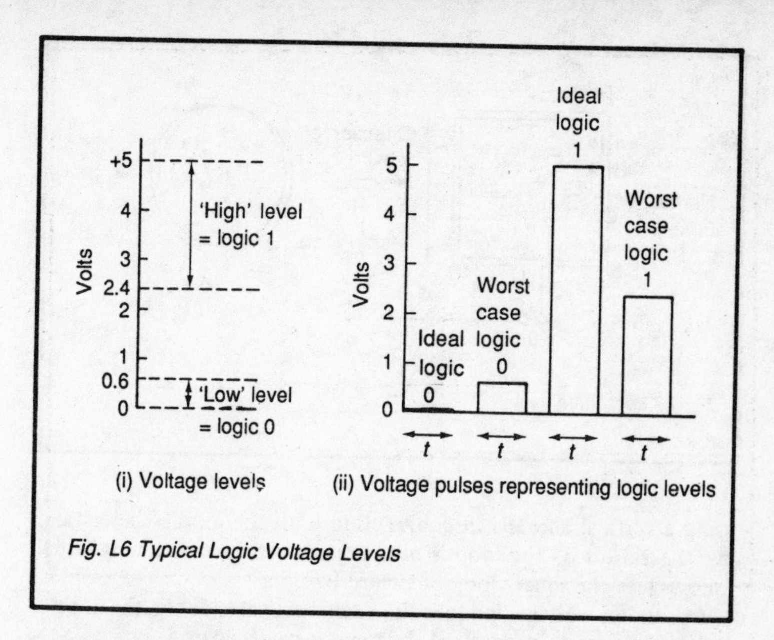

Fig. L6 Typical Logic Voltage Levels

LONG PERSISTENCE TUBE is a cathode-ray tube with its screen coated with the normal fluorescent materials but to which has been added a phosphorescent compound. This allows the visible trace to persist for several seconds.
(* Cathode-Ray Tube >> Fluorescence, Phosphorescence)

LONG-TAILED PAIR is a special transistor circuit in which two matched bipolar transistors have the same value individual collector resistors but share a common emitter resistor. The circuit is used as a differential amplifier or phase-splitter – see Differential Amplifier and/or Figure D4(i).

LOOP ANTENNA is a type used in many situations for direction finding. It is essentially a large open coil of square or circular shape as shown in Figure L7 or in fact of any other shape. When the plane of the loop is perpendicular to the direction of travel of the incoming wave, the response of the loop is zero but when the plane of the loop is parallel with the direction of travel of the wave, the response is maximum. Accordingly by connecting the loop to a radio receiver and tuning to the wave, then by rotating the loop for zero or maximum response, the *direction of wave travel* can be determined. Note however that there is a 180° uncertainty as to the actual direction of the radio transmitter. This can be resolved by

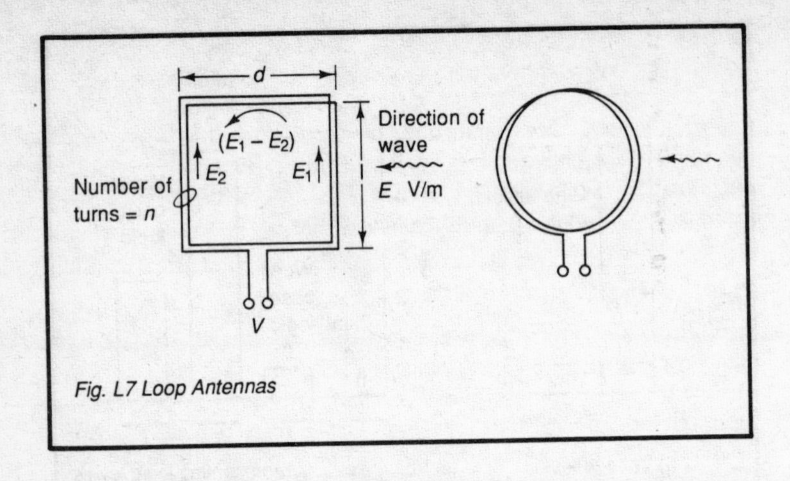

Fig. L7 Loop Antennas

using a vertical antenna in conjunction with the loop. Understanding the action of the loop is best gained from the reasoning which follows (see the square loop of Figure L7).

Maximum voltage induced in each vertical side of the loop = Enl where E is the strength of the radio wave (V/m).

Phase difference between vertical sides of loop = $2\pi/\lambda \times d \cos\theta$ where λ is the transmission wavelength and θ is the angle between the plane of the loop and the direction of the wave (the wave travels $d \cos\theta$ in passing from one side of the loop to the other).

From the above, by subtracting the voltages in the two sides of the loop and taking into account the phase difference:

$$\text{Resultant loop voltage, } V = E_1 - E_2 = 2Enl \sin[(\pi d/\lambda)\cos\theta]$$

and clearly when $\theta = 0$ (i.e. the plane of the loop is parallel to the wave direction), then the loop voltage is maximum. When $\theta = 90°$ (i.e. the plane of the loop is perpendicular to the wave direction), the loop voltage is theoretically zero. Furthermore since d is very small compared with λ, $\sin[(\pi d/\lambda)\cos\theta]$ is also very small hence we can use $[(\pi d/\lambda)\cos\theta]$ without appreciable error, giving:

$$V = \frac{2\pi En \cos\theta}{\lambda} \times \text{(loop area)}$$

which applies to all loops whatever their shapes.
(* Antenna, Goniometer >> Electromagnetic Wave, Phase, Phase Difference)

LOOSE CONTACT MICROPHONE A variable resistance microphone – see Microphone.

LOSS is a term concerned with the extent to which a signal is reduced in being transmitted over a channel or network, it is akin to attenuation. It is usually expressed as the ratio of the output power, voltage or current to the input power, voltage or current. The result is most conveniently quoted in decibels. Loss also occurs when energy is dispersed, e.g. as heat.
(>> Attenuation, Dissipation, Decibel, Loss Factor)

LOSS FACTOR applies to dielectrics and is a measure of the loss occurring due to the absorption of energy from the electric field of an alternating wave. The effect of the field is to displace charges within the atoms or molecules from their normal positions or orbits. Because the field is alternating, there is a continual readjustment of the alignment of the particles. The field therefore does work on the atoms and molecules and for work to be done a supply of energy is required. For any given material the loss factor is calculated from the product of the power factor and the relative permittivity. The absorption of energy creates heat and this is proportional to the power factor. For most dry materials at room temperature and 30 GHz the loss factor is less than 0.5, for pure water it is 12 or more.
(* Microwave Heating >> Dielectric, Energy, Electric Field, Power Factor, Permittivity)

LOUDSPEAKER is an electroacoustic device for converting electrical audio frequency signals into corresponding sound waves. Loudspeaker frequency ranges, power handling capacities, efficiencies and quality of reproduction vary over a wide range. There are also many different types but generally the principle involves electrical vibration of a diaphragm or cone which sets up sound pressure variations in the air.

Moving coil loudspeaker – this type is the most widely used and is to be found in almost all domestic sound reproducing equipment. There are many variations in construction but the basic drive principle based on electromagnetic motor action, is the same in all. Figure L8(i) illustrates how the motor action is used. The coil former is attached to the cone and is free to move forward and backward (to left or to right in the sketch). It moves within the strong magnetic field of a permanent magnet and when a current flows in the coil the cone moves according to the current direction. Hence with an alternating audio frequency current the cone vibrates

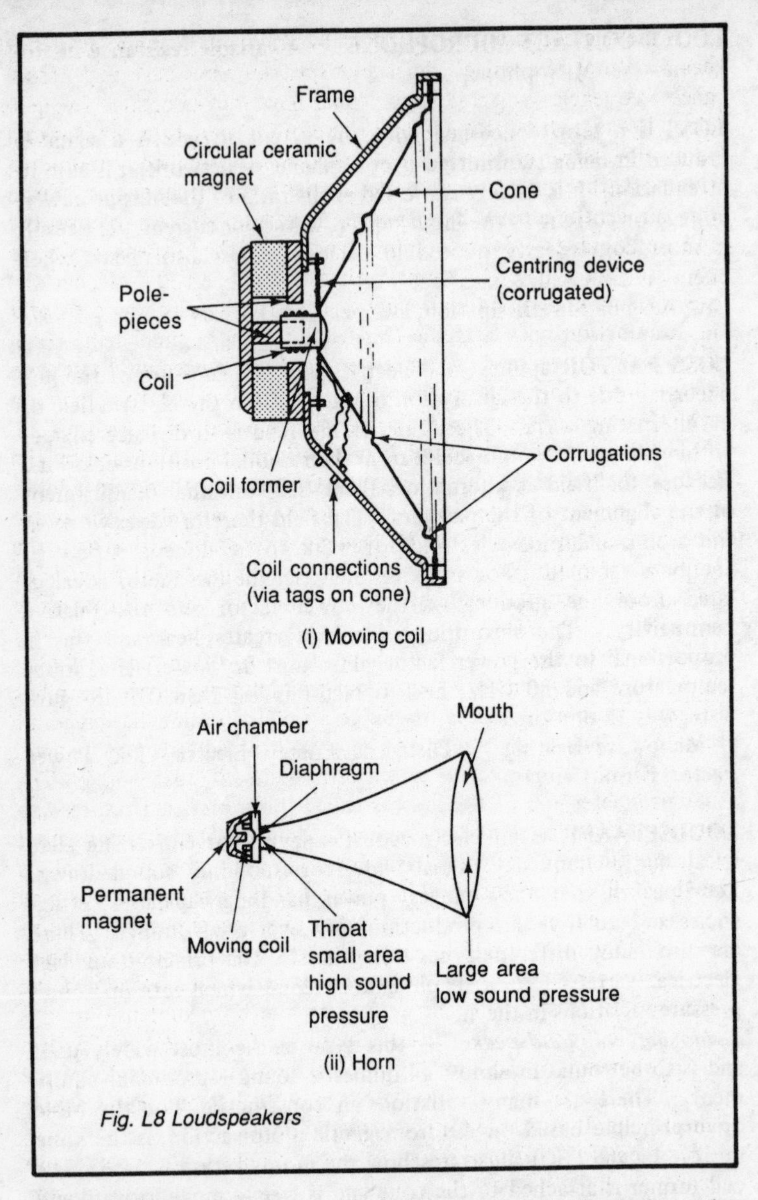

Fig. L8 Loudspeakers

and sound waves are set up at the same frequency. Typically with a 3 cm diameter coil and an input power of 20 watts, the force exerted by the coil on the cone is about 6 newtons, depending on the flux density of the magnet.

A moving coil unit is a mechanical vibrating system and as such it has a natural resonance. Small loudspeaker cones have high resonance frequencies whereas larger cones have low resonance frequencies. Because the efficiency and therefore output is greater around resonance, larger cones are more suited to low frequency reproduction with the smaller units better at the higher frequencies. From this springs the idea of using two or more loudspeakers to cover the full audio range. Most commonly used is the 2-speaker system consisting of a bass (l.f.) unit with a large cone (20 – 40 cm diameter) and known to high fidelity (hi-fi) enthusiasts as a *woofer* in conjunction with a treble (h.f.) unit having a small light cone, known as a *tweeter*. A *crossover network* preceding these two units directs the appropriate range of frequencies to each and typical response/frequency characteristics are shown in Figure C23.

The cone produces sound waves both at its front and at the back and these meet out of phase. On its own therefore a loudspeaker tends to spoil its own performance unless the wave emanating from the rear can be brought into phase with that at the front or be removed altogether. This is the purpose of a *baffle* or of a special acoustic cabinet such as the *bass reflex* or *acoustic labyrinth*.

Horn loudspeaker – the shape is seen often especially in musical wind instruments and in fact as a loudspeaker the horn has the same purpose which is to couple a small vibrating diaphragm or reed to a much larger volume of air than it could affect on its own. This results in energy conversion efficiencies of up to 50%. The small diameter end of the horn is called the *throat*, it is tapered to the larger diameter open end known as the *mouth*, names consistent with the human vocal tract. The drive unit at the throat is usually a moving coil system as shown in Figure L8(ii). The horn shape may be conical, exponential or hyperbolic, of these exponential horns are probably most used. Clearly all horns have directional properties. Horns have a lower *frequency of cut-off* below which the output fails, this is naturally related to the horn dimensions. As an example, for a lower cut-off frequency of say, 60 Hz, with a throat diameter of 2.5 cm, it can be shown that the length of the horn must be over 4 metres with a mouth diameter approaching 3 metres, hardly suitable for the drawing room!

Electrostatic loudspeaker – this is a less well-known type yet it is capable of high efficiency and wide frequency response, e.g. from about 50 Hz to 20 kHz. It is basically nothing more than two large plates close together as in a capacitor. The back plate is rigid, the other is of light metal or metallized plastic and acts as a diaphragm of low mass but large area. The plates may be some ½ to 1 metre long with the gap between them extremely small at about 0.025 mm (this is the difficult part!). A high voltage d.c. polarizing supply is required. In action an incoming signal varies the charges on the plates, this creates forces between them which cause the front plate or diaphragm to vibrate accordingly.

The *response* of a loudspeaker is measured by the acoustic sound pressure output for a given electrical power input over the working frequency range. The input must not be sufficient for overload. (* Crossover Network >> Electromagnetic Motor Action, Newton, Resonance, Electrostatic Induction, Charge, Capacitor, Magnetostriction)

LSI Abbreviation of Large Scale Integration – see Integrated Circuit.

LUMINANCE is an expression of the amount of light emitted from a surface, i.e. the level of brightness. A luminance signal is transmitted in both black and white and colour television systems.
(>> Colour)

LUMINANCE SIGNAL is part of the complex video signal on which colour television is based. For compatibility with black-and-white receivers the colour signal is made up essentially of a luminance signal to which is added a chrominance component. From the luminance signal the brightness of the received picture is derived hence generating a black-and-white picture. The chrominance signal adds the colour – see Television Signal.

MAC is an acronym for *Multiplexed Analogue Components.* It is a colour television system which improves the colour quality compared with PAL, SECAM, etc. by keeping the chrominance and luminance signals strictly separated in time (multiplexed). Figure T5(iii) shows the waveform envelope for one line. Because colour and luminance components are not transmitted together, no *cross colour* or *cross luminance* effects can arise. The first shows itself as swirling coloured patterns over parts of the picture containing fine detail while the second results in variations in brightness where extreme colour changes occur.

Essentially the system is time division multiplex in which the analogue picture signal is time compressed and then combined with a "data burst" carrying sound, data and synchronization signals [see Fig.T5(iii)].

In each D-MAC line the data burst occupies 10.2 of the 64 μs. The transmission rate is at 20.25 Mbit/s (i.e. 20.25 bit/μs) hence the data burst contains $20.25 \times 10.2 = 206$ bits. This is per line, when the number of lines per frame and the number of frames per second are considered, the data rate for the data burst is over 3 Mbit/s, ample for 8 high quality digital sound channels (15 kHz) plus other data and synchronization signals. D2-MAC is similar except that it carries only half the amount of data (i.e. 4 high quality sound channels etc.) but therefore in a slightly lower bandwidth channel. With several sound channels accompanying a single picture it is therefore possible to serve several countries of different languages at the same time.

Time compression of the vision components of the signal into 52 μs results in an increase in the overall bandwidth (to about 8.5 MHz). Expansion in the receiver is achieved by sampling the analogue signal, storing the samples and then reading them out at the required rate.

The MAC system also provides a firm basis for large-screen, high definition television.

There are also B-MAC and C-MAC, used mainly in commercial broadcasting.

(* Television, Television Signal, Television Receiver, Multiplex System, Binary Notation, Bit, Digital Transmission, Sampling >> Colour, Pulse)

MAGNETIC AMPLIFIER is a device based on the saturable reactor either used alone or in conjunction with other circuit components for the purpose of amplification or control. An elementary circuit of a saturable reactor is given in Figure M1 and it can be shown that the average values of the load current and the control current are related (although in a rather complicated way) by the turns ratio of what is effectively a transformer. Many different amplifier configurations are used, quite a few being difficult to analyse mathematically – see Saturable Reactor.

MAGNETIC BUBBLE is a microscopic magnetic domain in a thin magnetic film and these in their thousands are used as a magnetic storage system in computer memories. In certain thin materials such

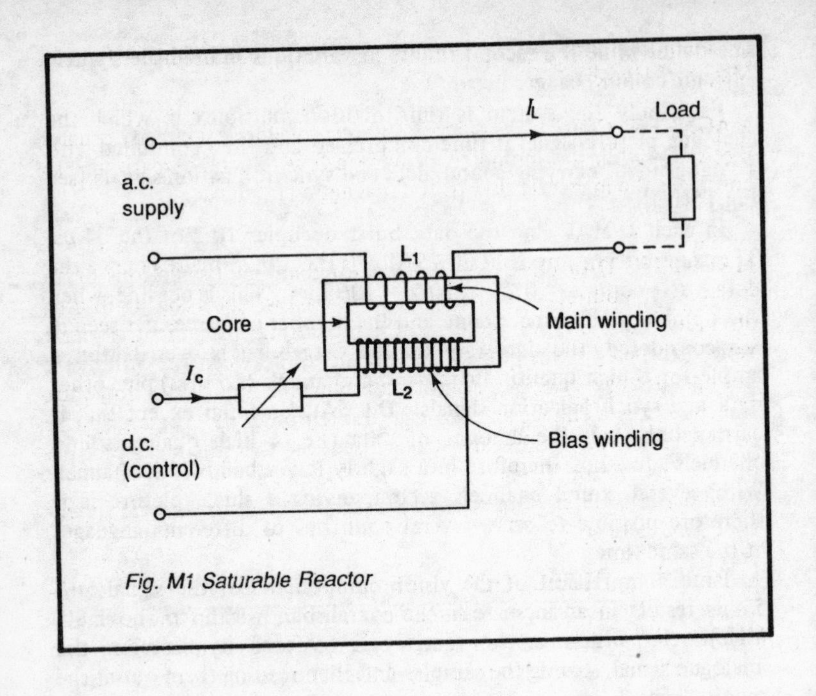

Fig. M1 Saturable Reactor

as magnetic garnet the natural direction of magnetisation is perpendicular to the surface. The thin film (of only a few micrometres) is deposited on a substrate of non-magnetic garnet. An external magnetic field (the *bias field*) is then applied perpendicular to the film surface and those domains which have a magnetisation opposite to that of the bias field shrink in area until at a sufficiently strong field they are reduced to a diameter of less than 10 μm. These domains are stable regions of magnetisation and are the *magnetic bubbles.*

Bubbles can be moved through the film by the application of a second external magnetic field known as the *drive field.* This is applied parallel to the plate surface. For the production of computer memory, lines of a soft magnetic material (e.g. a nickel-iron compound) are deposited on the film so that the bubbles can be moved along the tracks underneath them. The bubbles can subsequently be created, moved or destroyed by the application of appropriate external fields.

If we consider the main direction of polarization of the bubbles to be perpendicular to the surface of the film and downwards then in use as a digital memory a bubble can be polarized upwards to represent a logic 1 and for no bubble, a logic 0.

(* Memory, Binary >> Domain, Magnetic Field, Magnetisation, Magnetic Hysteresis)

MAGNETIC CORE A block of ferromagnetic material usually inserted within a winding to provide a low reluctance path and so constrain the magnetic flux to the magnetic circuit.
(>> Core)

MAGNETIC DAMPING is a method of damping oscillations of an instrument pointer or bringing quickly to rest the rotating disc of an induction (energy) meter. In a measuring instrument a metal vane attached to the pointer system moves between the poles of a permanent magnet. Electromotive forces are induced in the vane since there is a change in magnetic flux through it. These give rise to currents which flow in such a direction that their effect is to oppose the motion.
(* Induction Meter, Moving-Coil Meter >> Electromagnetic Induction, Lenz's Law)

MAGNETIC DEFLECTION is more correctly termed *electromagnetic deflection.* It is most commonly used in the cathode-ray tube in which electromagnets external to the tube deflect the electron beam – see Electromagnetic Deflection.

MAGNETIC MEMORY is that type of digital store in which binary information is represented by the direction of magnetisation of a magnetic material on for example, magnetic tape, disc or drum, or magnetic bubbles.
(* Digital Signal, Magnetic Recording, Magnetic Tape, Magnetic Bubble >> Magnetisation)

MAGNETIC RECORDING is a technique of recording the information content of electrical signals on a moving magnetic medium. The original signal can be regained by *playback* once or many times. The magnetic system is universally used for sound and television recording on magnetic tape which for the home is contained in a cassette but on the big machines, on reels. Magnetic discs are used to record data and computer signals and even credit cards have their magnetic strips. Because the most popular application is sound recording on magnetic tape, this is described in outline below to illustrate the general principles.

The elements of a complete system are shown in Figure M2(i). The input signal is amplified as necessary and supplied together with an a.c. *bias* to the *record head* over which the tape moves at constant speed by the action of the tape drive roller or *capstan*

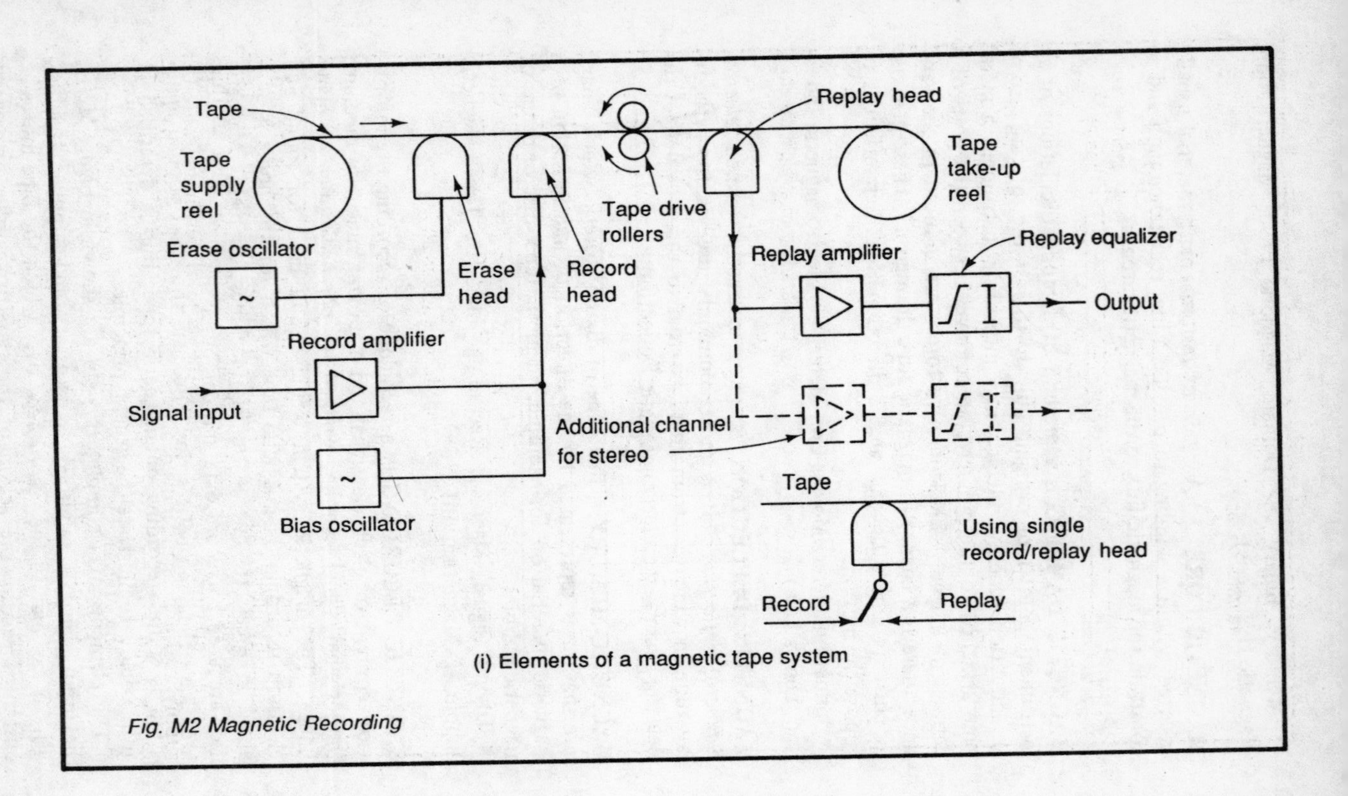

(i) Elements of a magnetic tape system

Fig. M2 Magnetic Recording

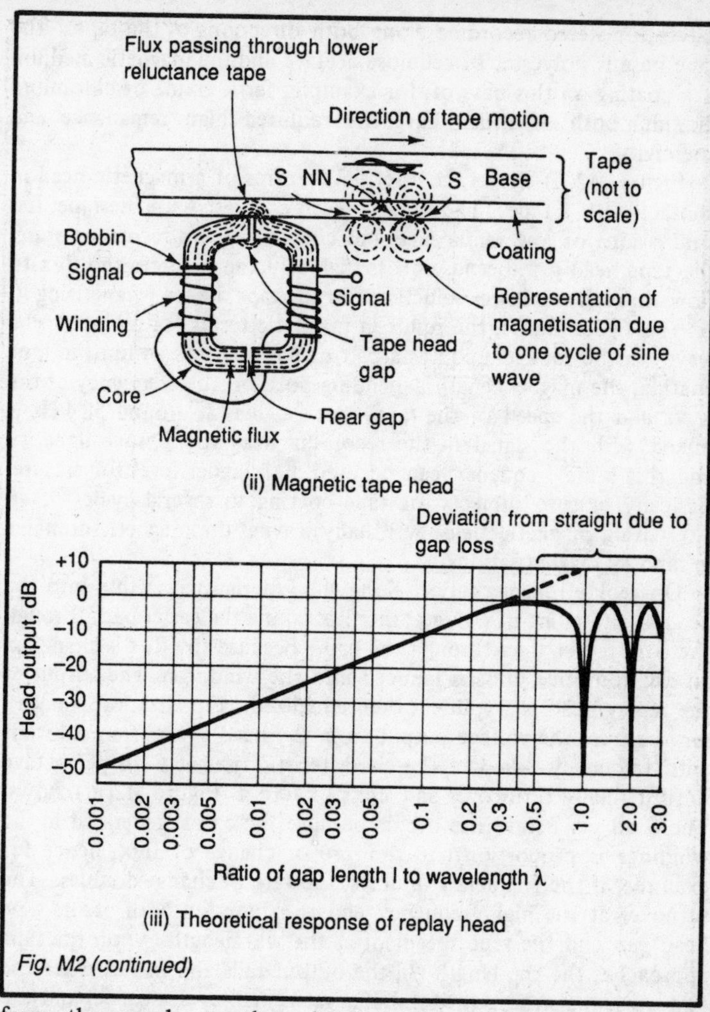

(ii) Magnetic tape head

(iii) Theoretical response of replay head

Fig. M2 (continued)

from the supply to the take-up reel. The signal is recorded magnetically along the tape. The record head follows an *erase* head which demagnetises the tape in advance so clearing it of anything recorded previously. For replay the tape is rewound onto the supply reel and again moved at the same speed but now with the *replay* head effective. The magnetisation on the tape induces a replica of the original signal frequencies into the replay head, this is amplified, equalized and then appears at the output terminals.

The popular audio cassette tape is 3.8 mm wide on which 4 separate magnetic tracks only 0.6 mm wide may be recorded, this caters for stereo recording along both directions of the tape. The tape base is polyester or cellulose acetate and the magnetic medium is a coating on this base of, for example, ferric oxide or chromium dioxide, both of which have the required high remanence and coercivity.

Figure M2(ii) shows the essential features of a magnetic head in contact with a tape. The head core, in contrast with the tape, has laminations of low remanence and coercivity. On record or erase, the tape head gap, because of its high reluctance forces the flux to flow through the lower reluctance of the tape, hence magnetising it. As the figure shows, the result in magnetic terms for an input sine wave can be looked upon as a pair of bar magnets within the tape coating, the magnet length depending both on the frequency of the wave and the speed of the tape. An a.c. bias at around 50 kHz is mixed with the signal in the recording head to improve linearity and this same frequency can be used at a higher level for erasure. Basically erasure subjects the tape coating to several cycles of an alternating magnetic field, eventually leaving the magnetic domains in random magnetisations.

On replay, magnetisation along the tape induces a flux into the head at the point of contact, the flux taking the easier path through the core rather than through the gap. Because the flux is changing, an electromotive force is induced into the windings. The output of the replay head is amplified, then equalized. Equalization is necessary because the voltage output from the head is far from constant with frequency. In fact the characteristic rises at 6 dB per octave until it finally turns over and sinks to zero as Figure M2(iii) shows. The 6 dB per octave rise occurs because the e.m.f. generated in the windings is proportional to the *rate* of change of flux, hence for example, if the frequency doubles, the rate of change doubles. The turnover at the high frequency end is a function both of the tape head *gap* and the tape speed for as the wavelength (λ) on the tape approaches the gap length (l), the output falls and in fact when the two are equal, the positive and negative half-cycles cancel and the output is zero. This is clearly shown on the drawing at $l/\lambda = 1.0$. Working in decibels, the formula for the relative output levels from a playback head is:

$$\text{output level} = 20 \log [\sin (\pi l/\lambda)] \text{ dB} \qquad (\pi \text{ in radians})$$

This is for the theoretical characteristic and in fact practical ones are not very different. Typically for a 3 μm head gap and tape speed of 4.75 cm/s, maximum output is at just under 8 kHz (where $l/\lambda = 0.5$), falling to zero just below 16 kHz ($l/\lambda = 1.0$). At double this tape speed, λ is halved so these figures are doubled, hence the big machines use high tape speeds for good high frequency response. So we demonstrate the need for equalization, hence as mentioned above, the replay amplifier is followed by the replay equalizer, then to power amplifier and to loudspeakers or headphones as required.

When it comes to recording television signals which have frequencies up to several megahertz, then so that the wavelength on the tape is always smaller than the tape head gap, a very high head-to-tape speed is required. At such tape transport speeds there would be tape handling problems and a requirement for reels of impractical size, e.g. many thousands of metres for a one-hour recording. This problem is overcome by using tape for example, 25.4 mm (1 inch) wide at a speed of 24 cm/s reel-to-reel with special mechanical arrangements to ensure a head-to-tape speed which is much greater than the reel-to-reel speed. These figures are for some broadcast machines, narrower tape and slower speeds are employed for home use.

There are two main systems of operation, *quadruplex* and *helical.* The first employs four magnetic heads mounted around a *head drum* which rotates at right angles to the tape as it moves so producing sweeps across the tape at an angle. The helical method employs one or two heads on a drum which rotates at the field rate with the tape wrapped around the drum in the form of a helix. By so doing the signal is not recorded longitudinally along the tape but at an angle of a few degrees to the edge. Many tracks can therefore be packed onto the tape and the required head-to-tape speed obtained. Sound accompanying the vision is recorded along the edge of the tape at the normal reel-to-reel tape speed.
(* Magnetic Tape, Equalization, Television Signal, Videotape Recording >> Magnetic Field Strength, Magnetic Flux Density, Magnetic Hysteresis, Bias, Remanence, Coercivity, Reluctance, Domain)

MAGNETIC SCREEN is a high permeability magnetic material used as a screen to protect electronic components or circuits from extraneous magnetic fields – see Screening.

MAGNETIC TAPE is used in magnetic recording systems and consists of a base of pliable yet strong plastic such as polyester or cellulose acetate with a coating of fine particles of a magnetic oxide powder mixed with a binder which coats the particles to prevent bunching when magnetised and which presents a smoother surface on the tape to minimize head wear. In the coating is also a lubricant,

again to minimize head wear. The magnetic oxide powder is an acicular (needle-like) derivative of ferric oxide or chromium dioxide. In manufacture the particles (not the domains) are aligned to a certain extent lengthwise along the tape, this enables more particles to be accommodated than if they were scattered randomly. High remanence and high coercivity are required, the ranges for audio tape being from about 0.08 – 0.16 tesla for the remanence and 20 000 – 40 000 amperes per metre coercivity. Tape widths vary according to the application, e.g. 25.4 mm for broadcast television recorders, 3.8 mm for the popular audio cassette and even smaller for microcassettes.
(* Magnetic Recording >> Magnetisation, Remanence, Coercivity)

MAGNETOSTRICTIVE TRANSDUCER is one which depends on the interchange of magnetic energy with mechanical energy. It is based on magnetostriction in which there is a minute change in dimensions of a magnetic material when subjected to magnetic stress. This type of transducer usually employs a nickel alloy or a ferrite. The material may be used as a rod or a tube with a coil wound around it. The transducer is particularly suitable for underwater acoustic systems, it is capable of radiating acoustic powers up to several kilowatts at frequencies up to around 100 kHz.
(* Transducer >> Magnetisation, Magnetostriction)

MAGNETRON is a microwave oscillator now entering our homes as the generator in microwave ovens. It functions on the interaction of an electric field generated between a central cathode and a cylindrical anode surrounding it. The anode is divided into two or more segments or cavities, each of which operates as a cavity resonator. Figure M3 shows the basic construction of the type mainly in use, the *cavity magnetron.* The anode structure which is normally fabricated from a block of copper, forms part of the vacuum enclosure. It is of course the positive electrode. Eight resonant cavities are shown but other numbers are used. External to the anode structure, a magnetic field is arranged to provide a flux which is perpendicular to the electrostatic field created between cathode and anode.

Electrons emitted from the cathode which would normally travel straight to the anode are therefore deflected by the magnetic field. The strength of the field is adjusted so that in the absence of a radio frequency field, the electrons are just unable to reach the anode and instead would be constrained to rotate around the cathode within the *interaction space.* However this electron stream induces currents in the cavities and a.c. electric fields are set up between the poles.

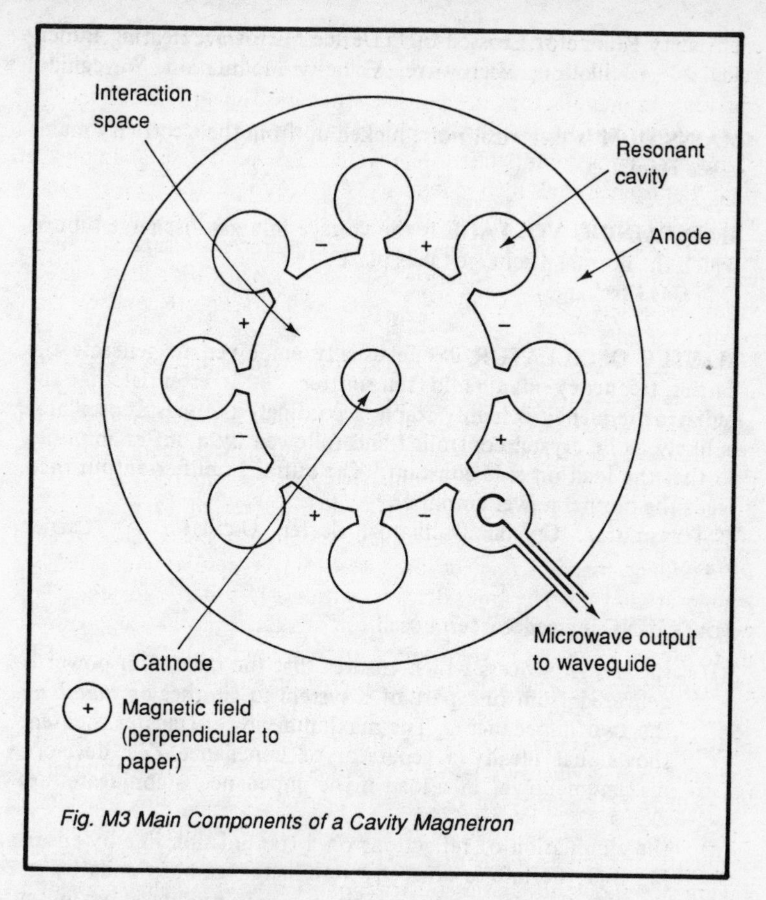

Fig. M3 Main Components of a Cavity Magnetron

The radio frequency field generated in each cavity takes up energy from electrons moving within the interaction space, these electrons move further towards the anode, effectively therefore energy is transferred from the d.c. electric field to the radio frequency field, so maintaining oscillation. Bunching occurs between alternate cavities resulting in a 180° phase difference between each pair as shown (hence this is known as the *π-mode*). It can be seen therefore that alternate poles are one wavelength apart, hence an even number of cavities must be provided. The output is taken from one of the cavities into a waveguide or coaxial cable.

Magnetrons are highly efficient microwave generators, they range over some 1 – 3 GHz (domestic microwave ovens, 2 – 3 GHz) at powers from a few watts up to megawatts. Some types are tunable.

(* Cavity Resonator, Crossed-Field Device, Microwave Heating, Bunching >> Oscillation, Microwave, Velocity Modulation, Waveguide)

MAINS HUM is electrical noise picked up from the electricity mains – see Hum.

MAINTAINING VOLTAGE is the voltage in a gas-discharge tube at which the normal discharge takes place.
(>> Gas Discharge)

MASTER OSCILLATOR is one usually employed to generate the carrier frequency in a radio transmitter. It is essential that the radiated frequency is highly stable accordingly the master oscillator is likely to be crystal controlled and followed by a buffer amplifier so that the load on it is constant. The buffer amplifier output then feeds the normal power amplifier.
(* Transmitter, Crystal Oscillator, Buffer, Oscillator >> Carrier Wave)

MATCHING is a general term used for:

(i) the design process which ensures that the maximum power is delivered from one part of a system to another by *matching* the two impedances. The maximum power transfer theorem shows that ideally a generator of impedance $Z\angle\phi$ develops maximum power in a load if the impedance is conjugate, i.e. $Z\angle-\phi$.

(ii) the elimination of reflections on a transmission line by ensuring that the line is correctly terminated at both ends by its characteristic impedance. This not only produces maximum power into the termination but by avoiding reflections along the line, standing waves cannot arise.

In both the above, when generator (or line) and load have different impedances, it is often desirable to provide matching between them by inserting a network so that each part of the system "sees" the impedance it needs. A transformer of suitable turns ratio may be employed, this is capable of good matching over a wide frequency range and the transformer itself inserts only a small loss. The ratio of the impedances a transformer matches is equal to the square of its turns ratio and this is illustrated by Figure M4 where n_1/n_2 or n_2/n_1 represent the turns ratio according to which way we are looking at it. As an example, suppose the requirement is for matching a 1200 Ω line (Z_1) to a 600 Ω line amplifier (Z_2):

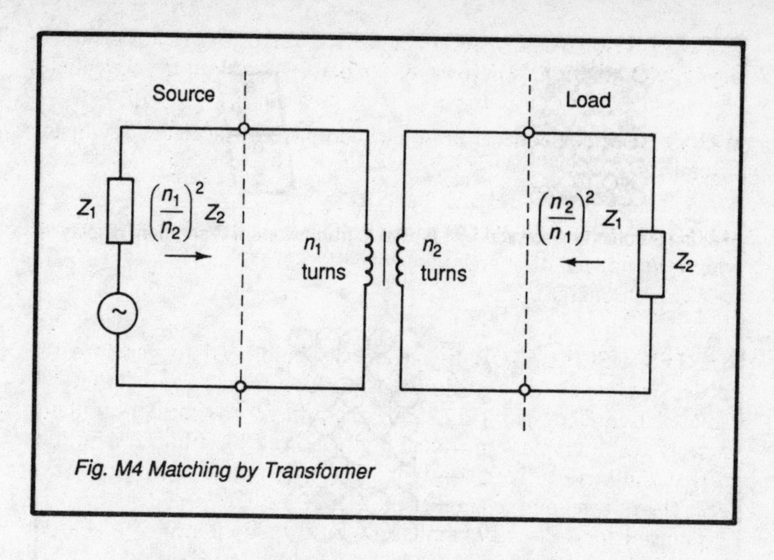

Fig. M4 Matching by Transformer

$$1200/600 = (n_1/n_2)^2 \qquad \therefore n_1/n_2 = \sqrt{2} = 1.414$$

i.e. the turns ratio of the two windings is 1.414 : 1. (This only determines the ratio, the actual numbers of turns depend on many other factors such as frequency range, type of core, etc., usually a compromise to keep losses at a minimum). Such a transformer might have a loss of about 0.5 – 1.0 dB. A useful reminder is that the higher of the two impedances to be matched is connected to the winding with the greater number of turns.

Alternatively an L-network can provide any degree of matching. This type of network however may create too great a loss for there is no point in matching for maximum power transfer if more is lost in the matching network.

Matching is also the term employed when components are selected as having certain similar electrical characteristics, e.g. power transistors may be matched in pairs for push-pull operation.
(* Push-Pull Operation >> Maximum Power Transfer Theorem, Transmission Line, Transformer, Image Impedance)

MATRIX Technically this is a rectangular array of items in rows and columns that is treated as a single quantity. In electronics we usually use the term to refer to a logic array of elements which can change their form (e.g. become light or dark) and so produce the alphanumeric displays seen on so many electronic devices. Two examples are given in Figure M5. In (i) is an 8 × 9 dot matrix in which the illuminated dots generate the capital letter S as might be

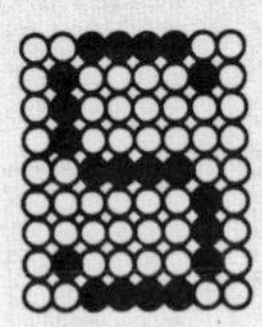

(i) 8 × 9 dot matrix (capital S)

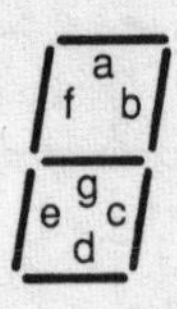

(ii) Basic framework of 7-segment display

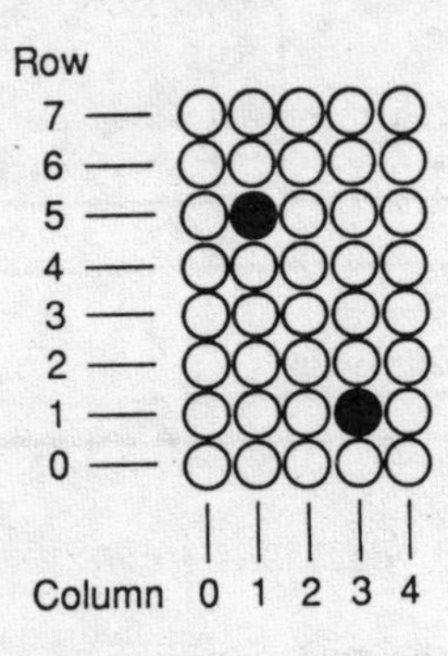

(iii) An 8 × 5 matrix

Fig. M5 Alphanumeric Matrices

used on a computer screen. In (ii) is the basic framework of the 7-segment numeric display in which all figures 0–9 are obtained by omission of various segments, for example, with f and e "off" a figure 3 is displayed. This is not strictly a matrix as defined above but is added because there are so many of this type of display around. Running a wire to each dot or segment is unnecessary because the display can just as easily be driven on a row and column basis.

Take the simple 8 × 5 matrix shown in (iii) of the figure and suppose that we are about to illuminate the lamps shown (e.g. light-emitting diodes). Applying the exciting voltage to row 5, column 1, and also to row 1, column 3 lights both lamps. A matrix of 40 points is therefore fully operated by 13 wires (plus one extra for the common wire to each point to connect the opposite pole of the supply).

(* Liquid Crystal Display >> Light-Emitting Diode)

m-DERIVED FILTER This type of filter section has an improved attenuation/frequency characteristic compared with a constant-k section. This is because it contains an additional resonant circuit such that the resonance produces (theoretically) infinite attenuation at some desired frequency. The basic sections for both low and high pass filters are given in Figure M6 (compare with Fig.C19 for the constant-k type). The problem is what value of m should be chosen because sharp cut-off has to be traded for attenuation in the cut-off band. The factor m is related to the frequency of cut-off f_c and the frequency of resonance f_r by:

$$m = \sqrt{1-(f_c/f_r)^2} \quad \text{for the low pass}$$

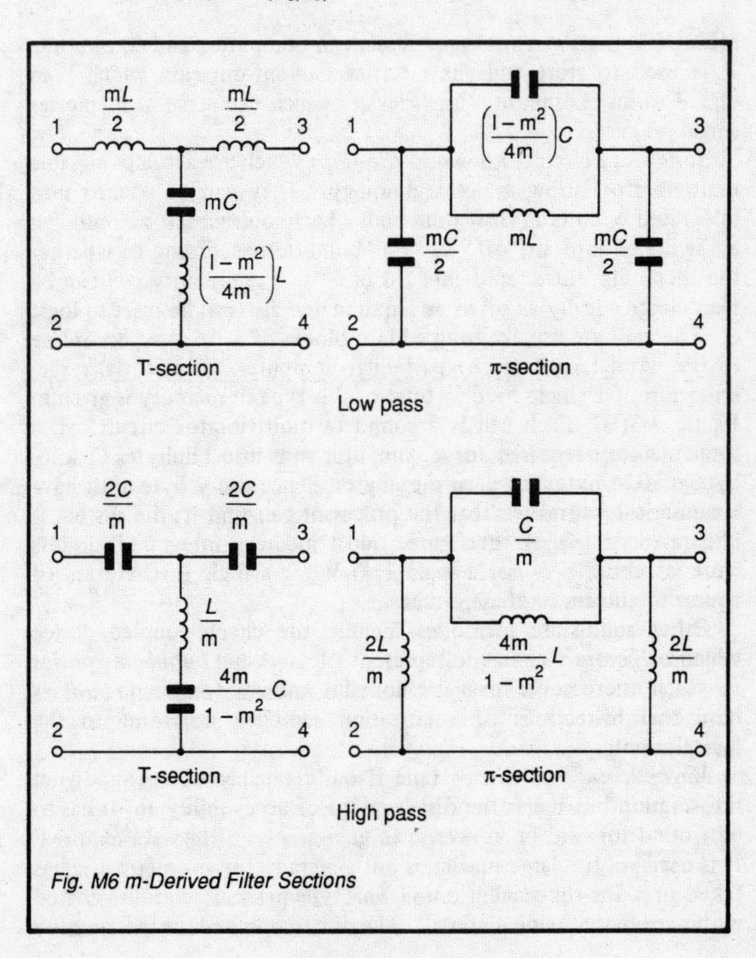

Fig. M6 m-Derived Filter Sections

and

$$m = \sqrt{1 - (f_r/f_c)^2} \qquad \text{for the high pass .}$$

The choice of value to be used for m is made easier by plotting attenuation/frequency characteristics for a range of values. Generally m might lie between 0.4 and 0.9.
(* Constant-k Filter >> Filter, Reactance, Network)

MEAN TIME BETWEEN FAILURES (MTBF) is one of the measures of the reliability of a component or an equipment – see Reliability.

MEDIUM-SCALE INTEGRATION (MSI) – see Integrated Circuit.

MEMORY is an essential requirement in computers and computing. It is used to store and allow retrieval of information which is in digital form. Commonly used devices which can serve as memories (or *stores*) are:

Solid-state circuits known as *flip-flops* which are actually bistable multivibrators using m.o.s. technology. They can be packed into integrated circuits in their thousands. Each multivibrator circuit can be switched into an "off" or "on" condition according to whether the incoming pulse represents a 0 or a 1. The memory *cell* can be read electronically as often as required and also can be reset to logic 0. The cells are usually grouped into blocks of 8, 16, etc., according to the word length of the particular computer. A pictorial representation of a single *byte* (8 bits) of this type of memory is given in Figure M7(i). Each cell is a complete multivibrator circuit. The total memory required for a computer runs into kilobytes (1 kilobyte = 1024 bytes) or even megabytes, hence every byte must have a numerical address so that the processor can find it, the system is illustrated in (ii) of the figure. Most memory integrated circuits work at about 5 V for a logic 1, 0 V for a logic 0, there are of course tolerances on these values.

Other solid-state memories include the charge-coupled device which can store a charge to represent a logic 1 and *bubble memories* in which microscopic magnetic domains known as *magnetic bubbles* have their directions of polarization switched according to the logical input.

Magnetic tape or *disc* – tape is quite capable of storing digital information but it has the disadvantage of accessibility for it has to be wound forward or in reverse to gain access to the data required. It is used on the large machines but generally the magnetic disc has taken over for the smaller ones. This type has a circular disc coated with a magnetic oxide material. The disc rotates and the information

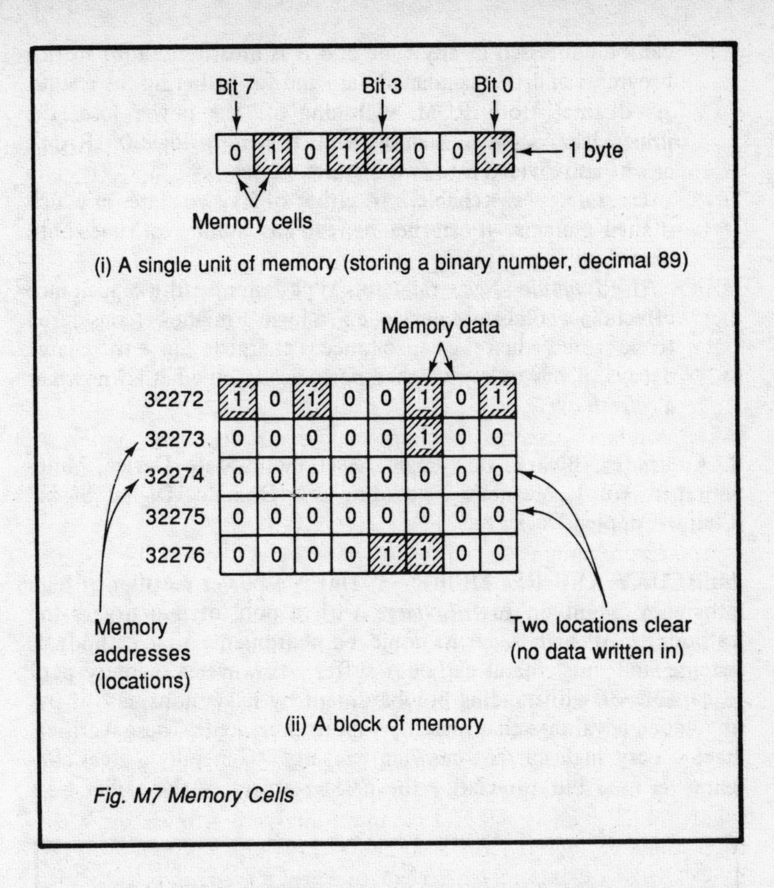

Fig. M7 Memory Cells

is recorded in a number of concentric tracks on the surface. "Read" and "write" magnetic heads can be speedily moved into position over any track.

Of the many different types of memory, two classifications are worth noting:

(1) ROM is an abbreviation for *read-only memory*. This contains memory cells which once set, cannot be changed. It is used for internal programs which must not be corrupted such as those for mathematical operations, constants (e.g. the value of π) and system operational data. The information in a ROM is not lost when power is switched off.

(2) RAM is an abbreviation of *random access memory*. Data can be both written in and read out of this type of memory as often as is required. Any one of the total number of locations

can be addressed at any time and it is mostly used for storing programs and the associated data and for gathering the results. As distinct from ROM, switching off the power loses the information since all memory cells restore to logic 0. RAM's can be sub-divided into two distinct classes:

(i) *static* – switchable into either of its two states in which it then remains. It can then be read any number of times until a reset pulse is applied.

(ii) *dynamic* – generally this type relies on the capacitance effects in a solid-state device, e.g. a logic 1 might be considered to be stored when the capacitance is charged. Since the charge decays, it has to be refreshed periodically on what is known as a *refresh cycle.*

(* Computer, Binary, Bit, Logic Level, Solid-State Device, Multivibrator, Word, Magnetic Recording >> Domain, Digital Signal, Charge-Coupled Device)

MERCURY ARC RECTIFIER This is a power rectifier of high efficiency based on *gas discharge* with a pool of mercury as the cathode. At high currents ionic bombardment of a cathode is intense and most metal cathodes suffer. However a mercury pool is capable of withstanding bombardment by heavy ions, also it has the added advantage that mercury vapour is created. These rectifiers have a very high current carrying capacity. Generally a steel container is used but for clarity the basic features of the earlier glass

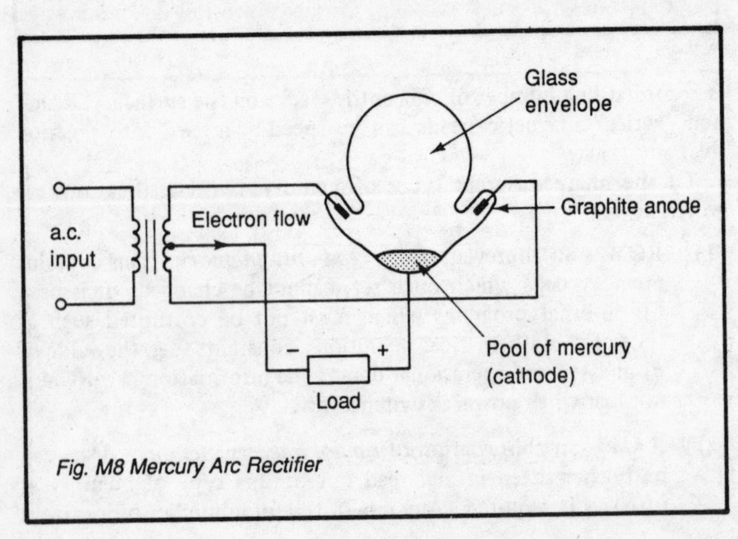

Fig. M8 Mercury Arc Rectifier

type are shown in Figure M8 together with its external circuit. An arc is struck between the mercury pool and each of the anodes in turn when they are made sufficiently positive. Direct current only therefore flows in the load. The arc itself has very low resistance, hence even at high currents the voltage drop cathode – anode is small, usually between 15 and 25 V, hence the high efficiency of the rectifier.
(* Ignitron >> Rectifier, Gas Discharge, Ionization, Arc)

MERCURY VAPOUR RECTIFIER is a gas-filled rectifier working on the gas discharge principle, using a heated cathode and mercury vapour as the gas. When ionization takes place between cathode and anode, the path is of very low resistance, hence even at high currents the voltage drop is small, typically around 15 V. The rectifier is therefore very efficient.
(* Mercury Arc Rectifier >> Rectifier, Gas Discharge, Ionization)

MESA TRANSISTOR A bipolar transistor fabricated by the diffusion process in which regions are etched away to leave the base and emitter on a raised plateau (from Spanish, mesa = *table*) as shown in Figure M9. Firstly the base is diffused into the substrate to a depth of about 1 μm, a circular mask is then used so that the diffused region is removed except in the centre. Finally the emitter is diffused into the small elevated region remaining and the contacts are made.

The base region width is small as are the junction areas. Mesas are therefore especially suitable for amplification at microwave

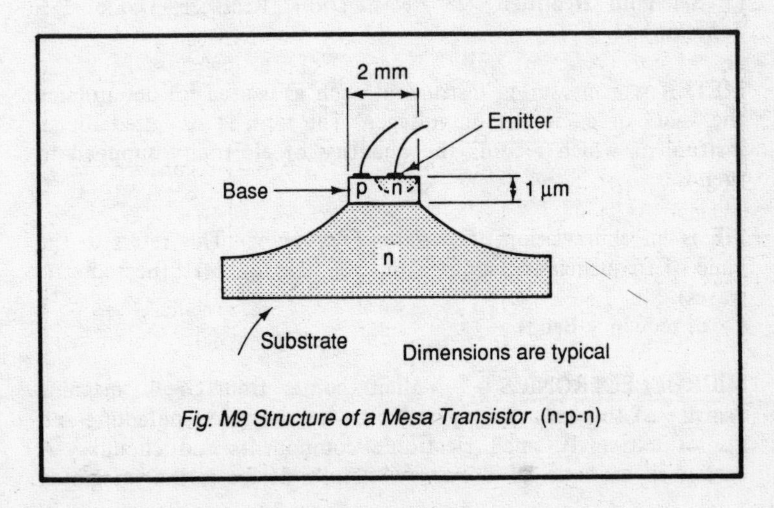

Fig. M9 Structure of a Mesa Transistor (n-p-n)

frequencies up to as high as 10 GHz but because of the complex construction techniques required, they are relatively expensive. (* Diffusion >> Transistor, Microwave)

METAL-FILM RESISTOR is one which is manufactured by evaporating metal (in a vacuum) onto a ceramic rod. The desired resistance value is obtained by either controlling the thickness of the film or by cutting a spiral pattern into the film after deposition. By this method closer tolerances than with carbon resistors are obtained. As an example, 0.6 watt metal-film resistors are generally available at ± 1% tolerance with values from 1 Ω to 10 MΩ.
(* Ceramic, Resistor >> Resistance)

METAL RECTIFIER is one in which each element consists of a metal plate or disc pressed into contact with a suitable compound such as a semiconductor or metal oxide. As an example, a copper oxide rectifier is made up of a series of elements each of a copper disc in contact with cuprous oxide on the face of a second disc. The resistance to electron flow is much lower in the direction copper → oxide than in the opposite direction. The elements are rarely used singly since the forward voltage drop is only around 0.5 V and the oxide layer can withstand a back voltage of only a few volts, a number of elements is therefore stacked in series.

The selenium rectifier is also a metal rectifier and generally is preferred to the copper oxide type because overall its operating characteristics are better. Both copper oxide and selenium are little used compared with the p-n junction type.
(* Selenium Rectifier >> Rectification, Rectifier, Diode, P-N Junction)

METER is a measuring instrument such as is used for determining the value of a current or voltage. The term is also used for an instrument which records the quantity of electricity supplied to premises.

MF is an abbreviation of *Medium Frequency*. This refers to the band of frequencies extending from 300 kHz to 3 MHz (hectometric waves).
(>> Frequency Band)

MICROELECTRONICS Micro comes from Greek, meaning "small" so this term simply refers to the design, manufacture and use of extremely small electronic components and circuits. A particular example of a *microminiature* device is the integrated

circuit in which many thousands of individual components may be contained within a small package of only a few square centimetres area and probably less than one centimetre in depth.
(* Integrated Circuit)

MICROPHONE is a device which converts the energy of a sound wave into electrical energy. The process firstly involves the production of mechanical energy in which sound waves strike a diaphragm and cause it to vibrate. The vibrations of the diaphragm are then applied to some type of voltage generator. The conversion efficiency of a microphone is generally poor because energy has to be transferred between media of very different densities such as air to metal.

The performance of a microphone is usually assessed by measurement of its sensitivity, i.e. how it responds to a given stimulus. In practical terms this requires measurement of the output electromotive force (e.m.f.) generated for a given sound pressure at a certain point in front of the diaphragm. The measurements are made at various frequencies over the usable frequency range. A sensitivity/frequency graph is then plotted. Another important feature of a microphone is its *directivity* and this can be illustrated by a *polar diagram*. Most microphones have to be supported by an amplifier so the impedance must be known because this determines the type of amplifier input required. Microphones are also classified by the two ways in which the diaphragm may be made to respond: (i) if the back of the diaphragm is sealed off from the front, then the response is proportional to the pressure of the sound wave (*pressure operation*); and (ii) the wave may have access to both front and back of the diaphragm which is therefore caught up in the motion of the wave particles. In this case the response corresponds to the particle velocity, this is known as *pressure gradient operation.* Brief descriptions of the main types of microphone follow:

Variable resistance microphone – in this type a sound wave varies the resistance of a chamber partly filled with minute granules of special carbon. A sketch of such a microphone as used in a telephone handset is shown in Figure M10(i). As the diaphragm moves inwards, pressure is increased on the granules and their resistance falls. When the diaphragm moves outwards the resistance increases. A d.c. supply of some 10 – 100 mA is required so that the resistance changes can be detected resulting in an a.c. output for a normal talker of up to one volt. This type is also known as a *loose contact* microphone and because the back of the unit is sealed, it is said to be *pressure* operated. This microphone has many failings,

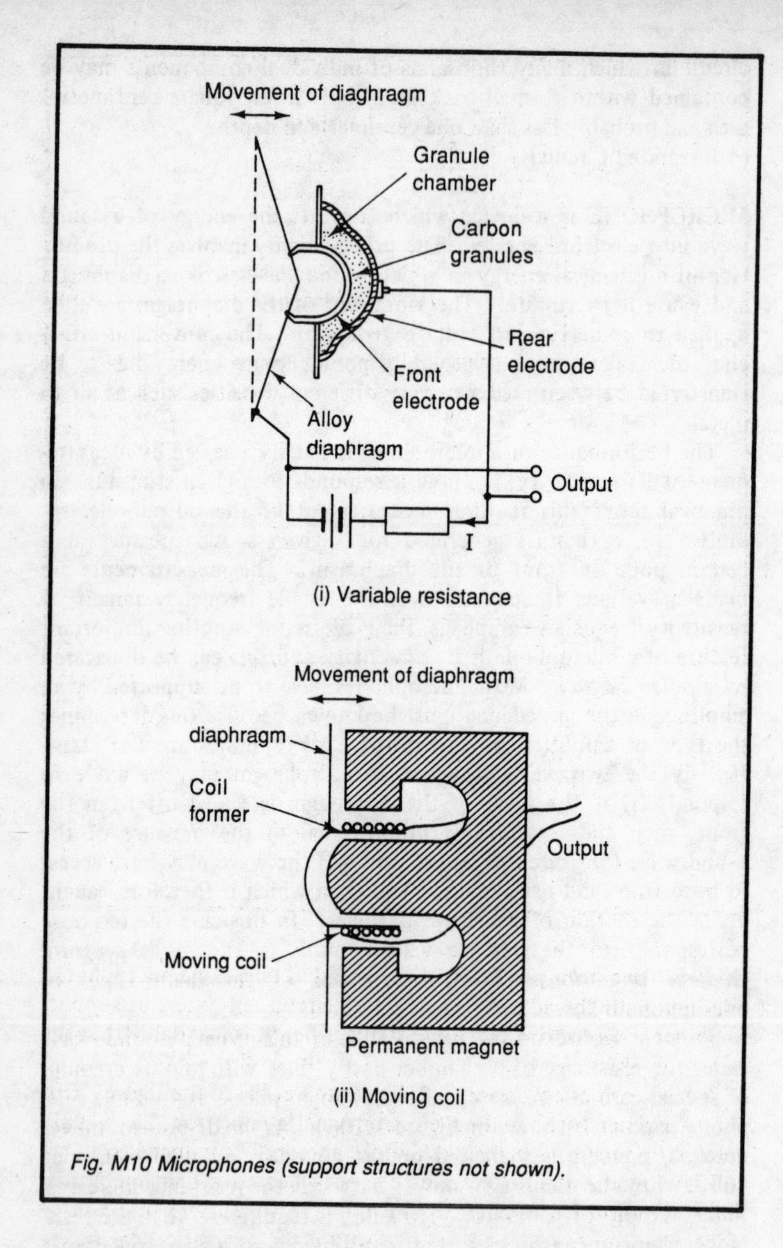

Fig. M10 Microphones (support structures not shown).

especially in its poor sensitivity/frequency characteristic (not much output above 4 kHz) and generation of harmonics, nevertheless it has one great advantage, that of high output. Thousands of millions

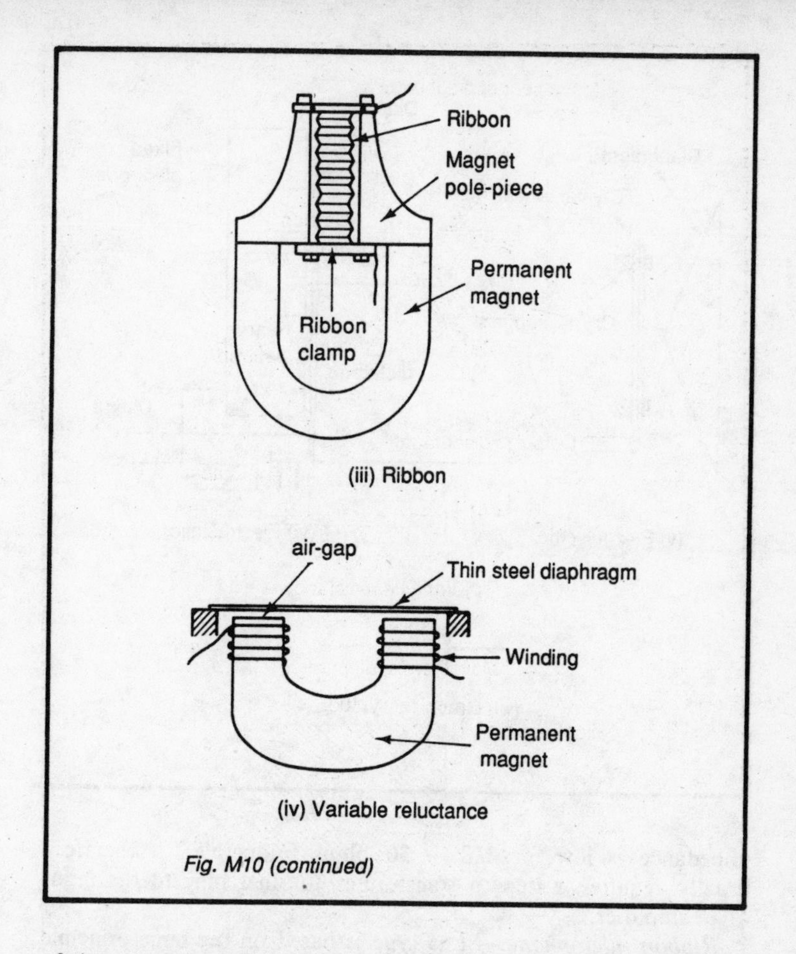

Fig. M10 (continued)

of these have been produced in the World as telephone microphones although with the advent of integrated circuit amplifiers as support for other less sensitive but more stable types, it is inevitable that the latter are taking over.

Moving coil microphone – is illustrated in (ii) of the figure. This is a true generator, based on electromagnetic induction, i.e. when a conductor moves in a magnetic field an e.m.f. is induced in it. A coil is wound on a former which is attached to a light metal diaphragm. Vibration of the diaphragm due to an incident sound wave causes the coil to move to and fro within the magnetic flux, hence an e.m.f. is generated. This type has a good, fairly level frequency response, typically from about 30 Hz up to well over 10 kHz. Because the coil consists solely of several turns of fine wire, its

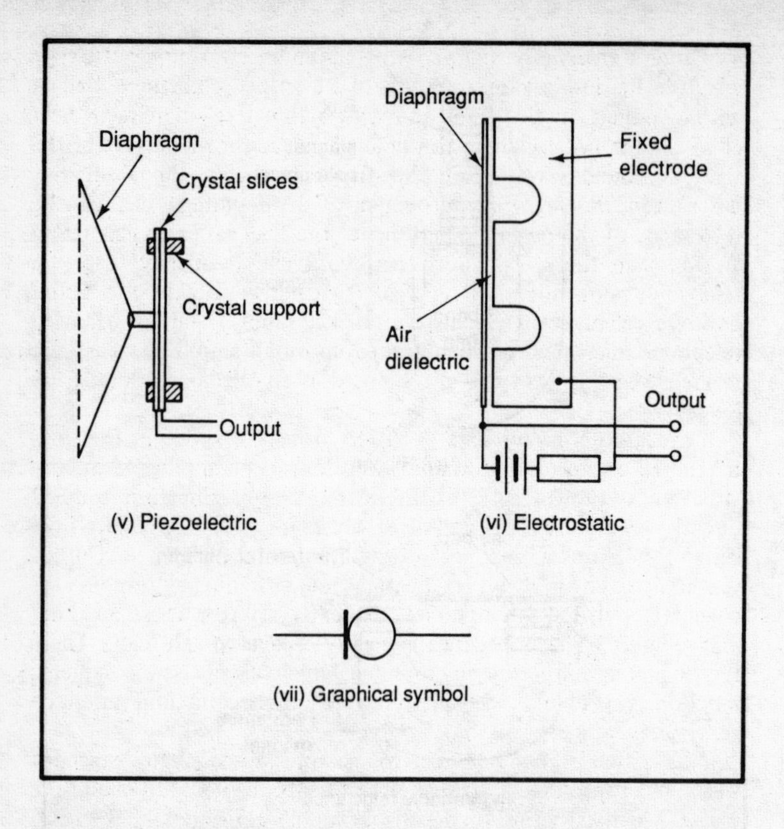

(v) Piezoelectric

(vi) Electrostatic

(vii) Graphical symbol

impedance is low, say 10 – 30 ohms (inductive), it therefore usually requires a step-up transformer for matching to the input of an amplifier.

Ribbon microphone – this type is based on the same principle as the moving coil but in this case a ribbon shaped conductor which is also the diaphragm, moves in the magnetic field. A sketch showing the essential features is given in (iii) of the figure. The ribbon is usually of soft aluminium, extremely thin and hence fragile. It is corrugated to allow motion and being thin it responds well to transients. It can be shown that the velocity attained by the ribbon is proportional to the particle velocity of the sound wave. This is a high quality microphone used mainly for studio work, it has a low sensitivity but its frequency response is excellent, covering the range from about 25 Hz to well over 18 kHz. The impedance being that of the ribbon is of course very low, only a small fraction of one ohm; a step-up transformer is therefore required. This type is also known as a *pressure-gradient* or *velocity* microphone.

Variable reluctance microphone – again an electromagnetic type which in its simplest form consists of a U-shaped permanent magnet with windings on the limbs and with a thin steel diaphragm held close to but not touching the pole pieces as shown in (iv) of the figure. Sound waves move the diaphragm hence the alternative description, *moving iron*. Movement of the diaphragm changes the reluctance of the magnetic path hence the flux varies, so generating an e.m.f. in the coils. Both sensitivity and frequency range are relatively poor but this type is particularly suitable for *sound powered* telephones (which have no d.c. supply) and for ordinary telephone microphones when backed up by an amplifier. They are reversible in that they can also be used as an earphone or miniature loudspeaker.

Piezoelectric microphone – differs from the above in that it is not based on magnetism in any way. It is less complicated in construction as shown in (v) of the figure. The diaphragm is coupled directly to a pair of crystal slices which respond to pressure by a shift of electrons within, so creating a potential difference. Output can be up to the millivolt level with adequate frequency response for a general purpose microphone, frequently referred to as a *crystal microphone*. The impedance is mainly capacitive and high. There is also a *piezo-junction* microphone which uses a semiconductor junction instead of a crystal. Pressure on the junction varies the transconductance.

Electrostatic microphone – is simply a two-plate capacitor varying its capacitance by the effect of the sound wave on one of the plates which is acting as the diaphragm. Appropriately it is also known as a *capacitor* microphone (it also happens to be a case where the term *condenser* lingers on, i.e. a *condenser microphone*). A sketch is shown in (vi) of the figure. The capacitance varies inversely as the separation between the plates and these variations are easily converted into similar variations in output voltage. The gap between the fixed electrode (the back plate) and the diaphragm is extremely small and a d.c. supply is needed of a relatively high value, 50 – 200 V. These microphones can be quite small, they are of very good frequency response, up to some 20 kHz and are therefore suitable for high quality work. Impedance is high, in the megohm range and capacitive.

Electret microphone – is an advancement on the capacitor type above in that no d.c. supply is required, instead a permanent charge is implanted on the plates. Needless to say, very high internal insulation is necessary to avoid the charge leaking away. Size is small.

Lavalier microphone – this type is named after the Duchess de la Vallière who was always seen with a locket on a chain around her neck. These are the microphones which we see on the clothing of people on television. They have specially shaped characteristics for their position on or near the chest and for this purpose electret microphones are particularly suitable owing to their small size.

The graphical symbol for microphones generally is shown in (vii).
(* Transducer, Polar Diagram, Electret, Matching >> Electromagnetic Induction, Piezoelectric Effect, Crystal Piezoelectric Crystal, Impedance, Capacitance, Reluctance)

MICROPROCESSOR is a microminiature digital processor. It is only micro in size, not in capability, in fact it is the major component of most computers. A microprocessor consists mainly of the central processing unit (CPU, i.e. the control unit and the arithmetic logic unit) packed into a single monolithic integrated circuit (see Fig.C17) together with the memory required.

Although developed specifically for computers, the capacity of microprocessors for electronic control and their reasonable cost make them applicable to many other activities such as control of machine tools, control of chemical processes, washing machines, microwave ovens, video recorders and in fact, all types of robotic action.
(* Computer, Integrated Circuit, Digital Logic, Memory)

MICROSTRIP TRANSMISSION LINE A miniature transmission line consisting of a thin conducting strip running close to an earthed conducting plane – see Strip Transmission Line.

MICROWAVE HEATING is a process of heating, not through I^2R, i.e. passing a current through a resistive material, but through the dissipation of microwave energy in a dielectric which in fact might have a sufficiently high resistivity that I^2R heating is negligible. When a dielectric experiences an electric field its atoms and/or molecules become elongated in the direction of the field. The electrons are pulled one way, the nuclei in the opposite direction according to the direction of the field, in a way circular particles are pulled into being oval. Now we have particles with poles at each end (*dipoles*), positive at one end, negative at the other, aligned with the field. Energy is needed to bring about this redistribution of charge and this is supplied by the field, the dissipation of energy producing heat. Reversal of the electric field causes the dipoles to realign in the opposite direction and if the field alternates at some high frequency the energy dissipation results in a continuous generation of heat.

It can be shown mathematically that the heat generated is proportional to the wave frequency and also to the *loss factor.* This leads to the conclusion that frequencies in the microwave band are the most suitable. The loss factor of a dielectric is an indication of the rate of the power absorption. Water has a high loss factor, many times that of most other dielectrics.

In a practical microwave heating system, for example the domestic microwave cooker, a magnetron supplies the microwave energy which is fed via a waveguide into a closed cabinet, constructed of a conducting material such as aluminium or stainless steel. The microwaves are constantly reflected from the cabinet walls (the loss factor of a conducting material is practically zero so there is no loss by absorption) and generally so that standing wave patterns do not cause uneven heating, a *mode stirring fan* is fitted at the open end of the input waveguide. The rotating blades of the fan project the microwave energy in different directions to vary the field pattern.

In the domestic oven the food may be placed on a motor-driven turntable, again to distribute the heat evenly. It is mainly the water in the food which heats up because of its high loss factor. In industry large cabinets or tunnel ovens are employed but the same basic principles apply.
(* Magnetron, Loss Factor >> Electromagnetic Wave, Microwave, Dielectric, Energy, Electric Polarization, Waveguide, Standing Wave)

MILLER INTEGRATOR is an active stage used to improve the linearity of a pulse generator such as a sawtooth generator used as a time base. The integrator is based on the charge and discharge of a capacitor. As an example, the capacitor may be connected between base and collector of a transistor so that the Miller effect is increased, hence effectively the additional feedback introduced keeps the discharge current of the capacitor almost constant. The discharge portion of the sawtooth waveform is therefore almost straight.
(* Time Base, Time Base Generator >> Miller Effect, Integrating Circuit, Capacitance)

MISMATCH occurs between a generator and its load when the load is not correctly matched, i.e. its impedance is not equal to the conjugate impedance of the generator. The condition of maximum power transfer from generator to load therefore does not apply.

The degree of mismatch may be indicated at any particular frequency by the *mismatch factor* calculated as the ratio between the current delivered to the non-matching load and the current which would be delivered if the generator and load were matched.
(* Matching, Generator, Load >> Ohm's Law, Conjugate Impedance)

MIXER is that part of a frequency changer which converts a low power level input signal from one carrier frequency to another by combining it with a higher power signal to produce sum and difference frequencies. Mixers are used for example in superheterodyne receivers where an incoming radio signal is changed to the intermediate frequency and also in domestic satellite reception where the signal received by the "dish" antenna has to be reduced in frequency for transmission over a cable. In addition mixing is employed in telephony carrier systems where channels are changed in frequency for transmission over high frequency circuits.

Most mixers rely on the non-linear properties of a single diode or diode bridge. Under small-signal conditions the current – voltage relationship of a diode can be represented approximately by $i = av + bv^2$ where a and b are constants depending on the particular diode. In the circuit of Figure M11 the two signals $v_0 \sin 2\pi f_0 t$ and $v_s \sin 2\pi f_s t$ are applied in series to the diode. They are additive, hence let $v = (v_0 \sin 2\pi f_0 t + v_s \sin 2\pi f_s t)$. Substituting this in the equation for i and expanding by normal trigonometrical formulae shows the several new components which are produced. The important one is:

$$bv_0 v_s[\cos 2\pi(f_0 - f_s)t - \cos 2\pi(f_0 + f_s)t]$$

from which it is evident that sum and difference frequencies are present. If the mixer is followed by a band-pass filter, it is possible for only one of these components to have an appreciable voltage level at the output.

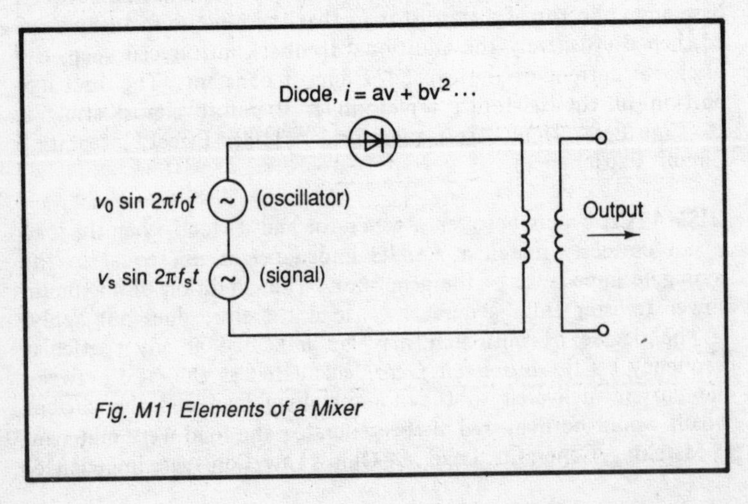

Fig. M11 Elements of a Mixer

Figure F4 shows how a mixer fits into a frequency changer. In this drawing the mixer is shown as the non-linear device, the sole purpose of which is to carry out the mixing, while two other components (oscillator and band-pass filter) are required to make up a complete frequency changer. However the term "mixer" may frequently be found to include the band-pass filter and sometimes the terms "mixer" and "frequency changer" are used synonymously. (* Frequency Changer, Conversion Conductance >> Heterodyne, Superheterodyne Reception, Diode, Modulation, Non-Linearity)

MODEM The term stands for modulator/demodulator, a device which converts signals of one type into a different type. It is most frequently used in data transmission, e.g. a computer transmitting data to another computer over a line. This often takes place over a voice-frequency telephone circuit but a problem arises in that the circuit is analogue whereas the computer signals are digital. Accordingly at the transmitting end the digital signals from the computer are changed into an analogue form (modulation) and at the receiving end the analogue signals are converted back to digital (demodulation). This process is illustrated by Figure M12 which shows one end of the circuit only, a modem is similarly connected at the distant end.

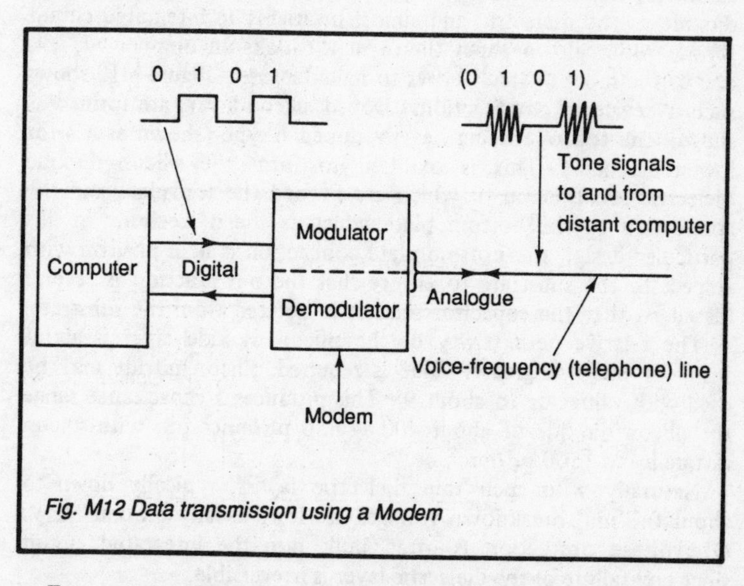

Fig. M12 Data transmission using a Modem

For a voice-frequency circuit the tone signals might have a frequency of around 3 kHz. The speed of transmission over such a

circuit of limited bandwidth is necessarily low for clearly each burst of tone representing a logical 0 or 1 must consist of several cycles. For higher speeds therefore, special circuits of greater bandwidth are provided.
(* Digital Logic, Computer, Analogue-to-Digital Conversion, Digital-to-Analogue Conversion >> Analogue Signal, Digital Signal, Modulation, Demodulation, Bandwidth)

MONOCHROME Literally means containing only one colour, hence by considering black to be a colour, we use the term to describe a television system in which the luminance only of a scene is transmitted. More technically it means light of a single frequency only. This is impossible to achieve so in electronics the term *monochromatic* describes light occupying a very narrow range of frequencies.
(>> Frequency, Light, Visible Spectrum)

MONOSTABLE MULTIVIBRATOR A multivibrator which always returns to a single latching state – see Multivibrator.

MOS CAPACITOR is a shortened form of *metal-oxide semiconductor capacitor.* It is a parallel plate capacitor using silicon dioxide as the dielectric and almost invariably in integrated circuit form. Although on paper the capacitor looks uncomplicated, it is one of the more difficult types to manufacture. Figure M13 shows such a device in cross-section. Doped silicon layers are formed as shown, the top one being heavily doped n-type (shown as n^+) for low resistance. This is oxidised to form the silicon dioxide dielectric, on the top of which are formed the top plate and the connection to the bottom plate which is the n^+ region. In this particular design the bottom plate connection is held positive with respect to the substrate to ensure that the p-n junction is reverse biased so that the capacitor section is isolated from the substrate.

The relative permittivity of the silicon dioxide layer is about 2.5 – 4 but if a greater value is required, silicon nitride may be used with values up to about 9. This produces a capacitance range for silicon dioxide of about 400 – 650 pF/mm^2 but with silicon nitride up to 1500 pF/mm^2.

Naturally with such thin dielectric layers, typically down to about 0.1 μm, breakdown voltages are low, usually around 50 V. Overvoltage protection is often built into the integrated circuit since any failure of the dielectric layer is irreversible.
(* Integrated Circuit, Planar Process >> Capacitance, Doping, P-N Junction, Breakdown)

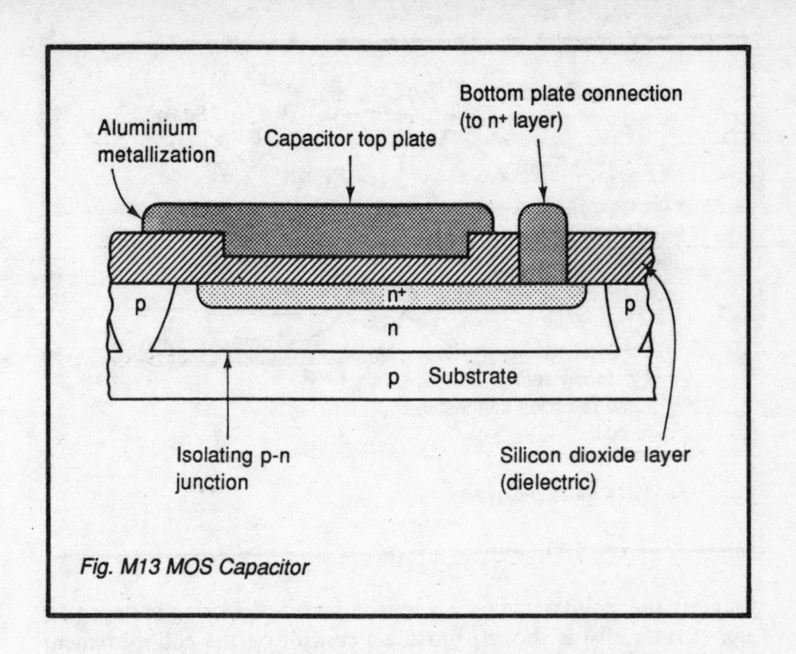

Fig. M13 MOS Capacitor

MOS INTEGRATED CIRCUIT is one comprising insulated-gate field-effect transistors (i.g.f.e.t.). MOS stands for metal-oxide semiconductor which in fact indicates the basis on which the i.g.f.e.t. is constructed. When packed into an integrated circuit, these transistors can be biased not only to act as transistors but also as resistors. Manufacture is therefore comparatively uncomplicated and packing density is high. Because the gate is capacitively coupled to the channel the input impedance is extremely high.
(* Integrated Circuit, Planar Process >> Field-Effect Transistor)

MOVING-COIL METER is a general measuring instrument operating on the interaction between a fixed magnetic field and a coil carrying the current (or part of it) being measured, i.e. one which is based on the galvanometer principle. A basic form of construction is shown in Figure M14. The magnetic field is produced by a permanent magnet, the poles only of which are shown in the sketch. The soft iron core is fixed between the poles and serves to distribute the flux uniformly so that it is always at right angles to the vertical wires of the coil. This ensures that the deflection of the pointer is directly proportional to the current being measured. The coil itself is wound on a non-magnetic former such as aluminium and is free to rotate about the pivot. Fixed to the coil former is the pointer so as the coil

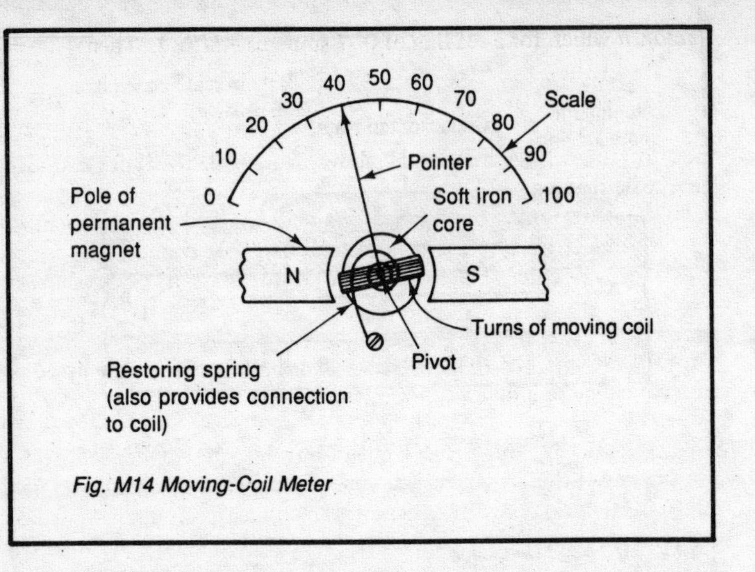

Fig. M14 Moving-Coil Meter

rotates, the pointer moves across the scale. Restoring springs (the upper one only is shown) provide a control on the coil movement and also bring it back to its zero position when no current flows.

Design aims at a "dead beat" instrument, i.e. one in which the pointer does not overshoot the correct reading. Apart from the effect of the springs, damping arises from eddy currents generated in the coil former as it moves in the magnetic field. These eddy currents flowing against the resistance of the former cause power to be consumed which effectively puts a brake on the coil movement.

A typical work bench meter might produce a full scale deflection (f.s.d.) with a coil current of 50 μA, i.e. the scale would read 0–50 μA in 1 μA steps. Coil resistance might be around 4000 Ω. Such a basic meter *movement* can be converted for general work as a bench voltmeter and ammeter by the addition of series and shunt resistors respectively. If the coil current for f.s.d. is i_m and the coil resistance, r_m, then the series resistance, R_{SE} required for reading 0–V volts is given by:

$$R_{SE} = (V/i_m) - r_m \text{ ohms}$$

e.g. for the 50 μA movement above, R_{SE} = 196 kΩ for a 0–10 V scale reading.

For direct current measurements, it is convenient to calculate the shunt resistance, R_{SH} required in terms of its *multiplying factor*, *n* which for a reading of 0–*I* amperes = (I/i_m). Then:

$$R_{SH} = r_m/(n-1)$$

e.g. for the 50 μA movement above, R_{SH} = 2.001 Ω for a 0–100 mA scale reading.

The meter may be further adapted for the measurement of alternating current by use of a suitable rectifier connected in series. (>> Galvanometer, Electromagnetic Motor Action, Eddy Current, Rectifier)

MOVING-COIL MICROPHONE A type of microphone based on electromagnetic induction – see Microphone.

MOVING-IRON METER is a measuring instrument depending for its action on the attraction or repulsion between the magnetic field from a coil carrying the current to be measured and a soft-iron armature. Figure M15 shows the essential features of both the attraction and the repulsion types. In (i) the soft-iron armature is attracted into the coil, thereby moving the pointer over the scale. An air piston damps vibration. The force turning the pointer is dependent on the magnetic flux within the iron and on that of the coil, both of which are proportional to the coil current, hence the force is proportional to the square of the current.

In (ii) the current in the coil induces magnetic poles in the fixed and moving iron rods which are situated axially in a short solenoid. Similar poles are developed in adjacent ends of the rods which therefore repel each other so moving the pointer over the scale. Since the bars are equally magnetized by the coil current and the repulsion is proportional to the pole strengths, it is again proportional to the square of the current. Hence this type of meter is especially suitable for measuring a.c. (although not at high frequencies) because it gives the root mean square value directly.
(* Solenoid >> Magnetic Field, Magnetic Flux, Root Mean Square)

MULTIPLEXED ANALOGUE COMPONENTS is more commonly known by its acronym MAC. It is a colour television system used especially with satellite television – see MAC.

MULTIPLEX SYSTEM In a few words is a transmission system which carries a multiplicity of individual channels. There are two main techniques in use:

Frequency Division Multiplex – in this system each channel is allotted its own individual band of frequencies. Taking telephony as

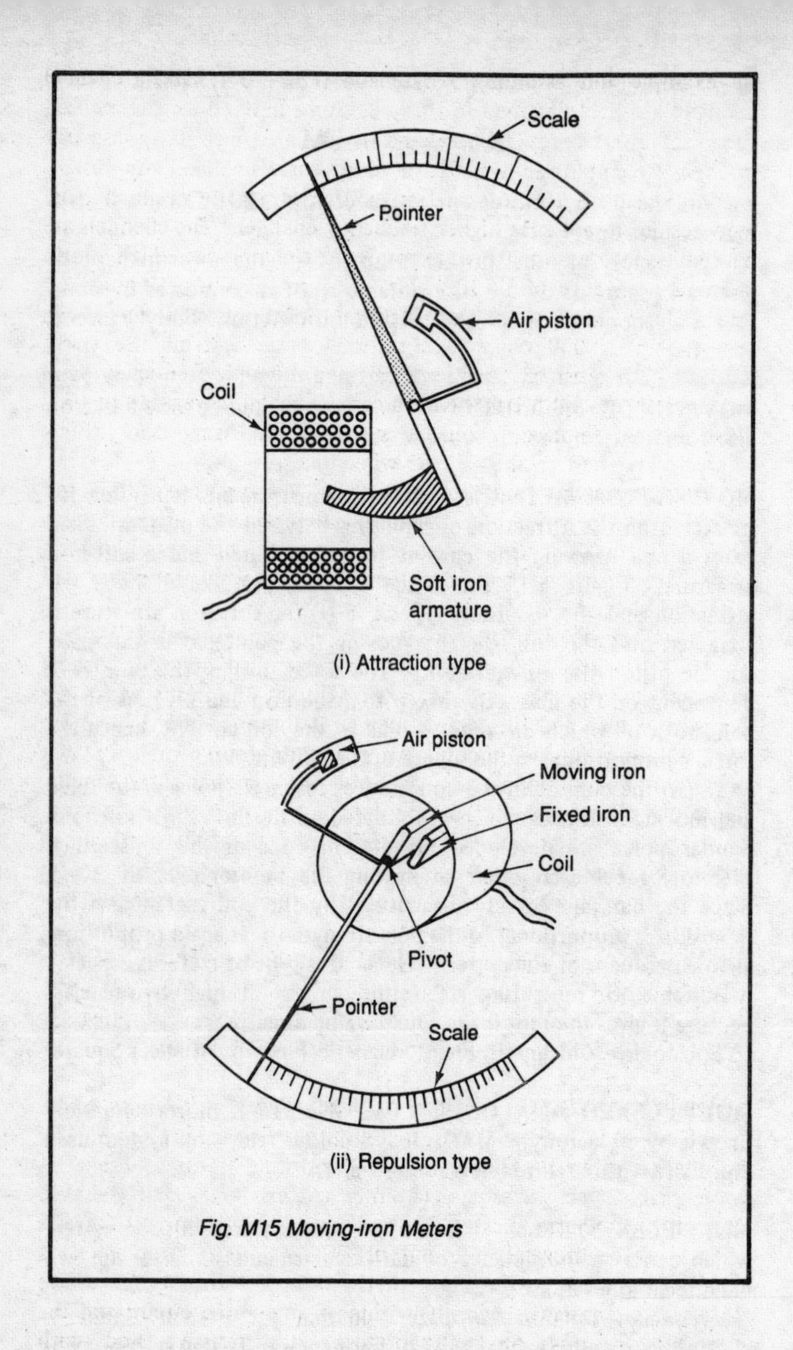

Fig. M15 Moving-iron Meters

an example and assuming a baseband 0.3 – 3.4 kHz, a channel requires a 4 kHz bandwidth, this gives some in hand for the inefficiencies of filters etc. The baseband is translated into its appropriate channel by amplitude modulation using single sideband suppressed-carrier hence all the information contained in the original signal now resides in a 4 kHz higher frequency channel. The channels are assembled into *groups* of for example, 12 channels contained within a frequency range 60 – 108 kHz. Groups may be assembled by further frequency translation into multiplex systems which can carry over 10 000 channels. For such large systems the transmission path must be capable of carrying the wide frequency band required (up to 60 MHz), hence a coaxial cable, waveguide or glass fibre system is used. Smaller systems comprising only a few channels may be transmitted over wire circuits.

At the receiving end, further frequency translation, filters and demodulators separate the channels and regain the original audio inputs. To do this, each system carries in addition to the channels a *pilot* carrier which is required for controlling the receiving and demodulation oscillators.

Time Division Multiplex – in this the communication path is available to each input signal and to that signal only for a short duration of time at regular intervals. Usually the input signals are sampled in turn and the sample may be in the form of a single pulse as in a pulse-amplitude modulation system or group of pulses as in a pulse-code modulation system. Whatever the contents of the sample, it is switched into its allotted time slot.

At the receiving end the time slots must be made available to the correct channels hence switching at the two ends of the system must be in synchronism. To ensure this, marker pulses are transmitted at regular intervals. System line requirements vary but for example, for a 32 channel system a bandwidth of 1 – 2 MHz is required.

(* Baseband, Suppressed Carrier Transmission, Mixer, Sampling >> Pulse Modulation, Amplitude Modulation, Demodulation)

MULTIVIBRATOR is a device originally developed for its *multi-vibrations* or in modern terms, for an output rich in harmonics. The output consists of periodic abrupt transitions as for square, saw-tooth, triangular waves etc. (Fourier analysis shows all these to contain many harmonics). The basic multivibrator circuit consists of two active devices, the output of each being coupled via a coupling network to the input of the other. Normally the active devices are transistors, usually within an integrated circuit and the essential features of multivibrators with resistive and with

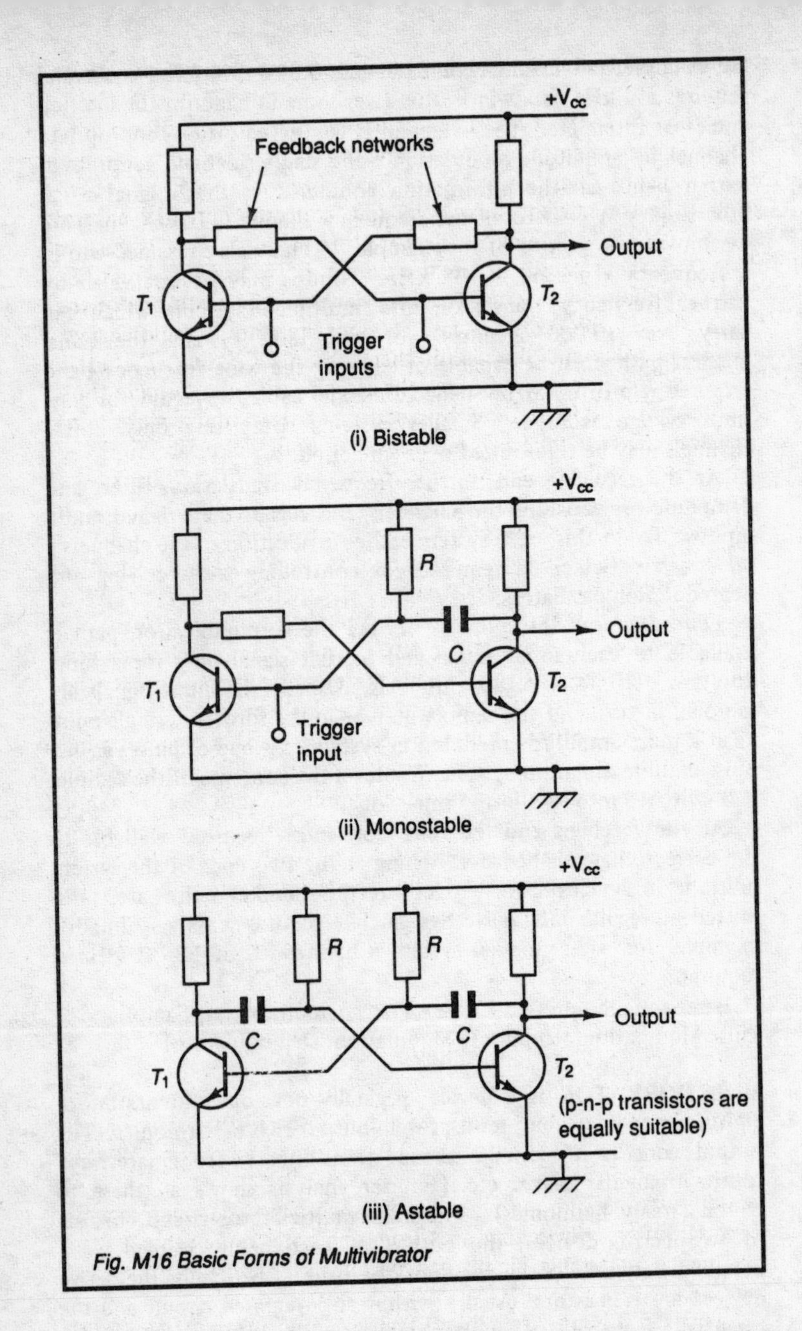

Fig. M16 Basic Forms of Multivibrator

resistance–capacitance coupling networks are shown in Figure M16.

Bistable – in this type the two coupling networks as shown in (i) of the figure are single resistors. The transistors operate as switches and when, say T_1 is "on" (i.e. the base potential is such that saturation collector current flows), its low collector potential ensures that T_2 is "off". The high collector potential of T_2 equally ensures that T_1 is held "on", hence the circuit is *latched,* T_1 "on", T_2 "off". If now an external (trigger) signal is applied to one of the bases to swing the transistor into its opposite state, a rapid change-over takes place and the circuit then locks to T_2 "on", T_1 "off". The two latched conditions give the circuit its name, *bistable* (bi = 2). Accordingly, if triggered by a series of pulses, square waveforms appear at the two collectors. Because an input pulse can "flip" the circuit over while a second one causes it to "flop" back, the bistable is known in the computer world as a "flip-flop" and is especially suitable for use in computer memories.

Monostable – the circuit is shown in Figure M16(ii). In this case T_1 is held "on" via resistor R, T_2 is therefore "off". This is the single state (mono = 1) to which the circuit always returns. A triggering pulse to T_1 to cut it "off" causes a rapid change-over. The circuit then reverts to its stable state controlled in time by the discharge of C through R. The output is a single pulse.

Astable – this type has two resistance–capacitance coupling paths as shown in (iii). The circuit operation follows from the explanation above for the monostable, only in this case it cannot latch in either state, accordingly it switches regularly and symmetrically between the two states. It is therefore classed as astable (a = not) and is said to be *free running* and is in fact an oscillator. If for example, both capacitances and resistances are made equal, the output is a 1 : 1 square wave of frequency:

$$f_{osc} = \frac{1}{1.386\,CR} = \frac{0.722}{CR}$$

where C is the capacitance in farads, and R the resistance in ohms. As an example, for capacitors of 0.01 μF and resistors of 30 kΩ, f_{osc} is 2400 Hz.

Multivibrators are also designed embodying standard operational amplifiers. Switching over from one state to the other is very rapid hence an astable circuit can produce an almost exact square wave.

(* Integrated Circuit, Switching Transistor, Memory, Operational

Amplifier >> Fourier Analysis, Harmonic, Transistor, Oscillator, Pulse, Square Wave)

MUTING is to silence. An example commonly met is the muting switch on a television receiver, when this is operated the sound is cut off. F.M. receivers are sometimes equipped with an automatic muting facility which is effective on weak signals only so that noise is not constantly heard as the tuning control is adjusted.
(* Television Receiver >> Frequency Modulation)

N

NAND GATE A logic gate which has an output of logic 0 only when all the inputs are at logic 1 – see Digital Logic.

NEGATIVE LOGIC refers to logical signals and is the condition where of the two levels, a logic 1 is the more negative. Most logic systems however use positive logic.
(* Binary, Digital Logic, Logic Level, Positive Logic)

NEON TUBE is a cold-cathode gas-discharge tube filled with neon gas at low pressure. When a sufficiently high voltage is applied between the electrodes the neon ionizes and glows in its characteristic red colour. Neon tubes are used in illuminated signs and as small indicators in electrical equipment.
(>> Gas Discharge, Cold Cathode, Neon, Ionization)

NEUTRAL For safety reasons many circuits, especially the electricity supply mains, have one wire of the circuit connected to earth. In the case of the electricity mains the line which is connected to earth at the power station or local transformer is known as the neutral line or neutral as shown marked N in Figure P8(iii).
The term is also used to indicate the condition when positive and negative charges are in balance, i.e. there is no net charge.
(* Polyphase System >> Charge)

NEUTRALIZATION The high frequency response of an amplifying stage is affected not only by the interelectrode capacitances of

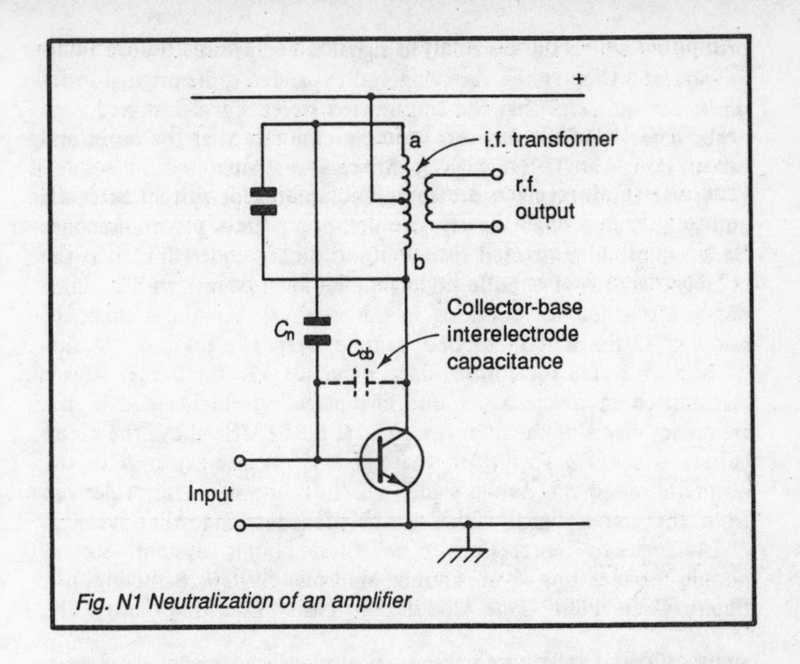

Fig. N1 Neutralization of an amplifier

the active device (e.g. a transistor) but also by reactive components in the external circuit. These together affect the phase-shift through the amplifier and it is possible for sufficient positive feedback to arise to cause high frequency oscillation. This problem can be overcome by the technique of neutralization which deliberately feeds back a fraction of the output to the input but in antiphase to the unwanted feedback. Usually all that is required is a single capacitor as shown in Figure N1. The circuit is that of an intermediate frequency (i.f.) amplifier with the centre of the primary winding of the i.f. transformer connected to chassis via the positive supply line. Points a and b are therefore opposite in phase hence the feedback due to C_n (a few picofarads) opposes that due to C_{cb}, i.e. the circuit is neutralized and therefore stable.
(* Interelectrode Capacitance >> Transistor, Amplifier, Feedback, Intermediate Frequency, Phase, Phase Angle, Oscillation)

NICAM (STEREO) is the acronym of *Near Instantaneous Companded Audio Multiplex*. It is a system which converts analogue stereophonic signals to digital and then processes them for transmission with a television picture. Looking at its rather complicated title, *near instantaneous* refers to the high speed at which the analogue to digital conversion takes place, *companding* is the process by which the transmitted signal is compressed before transmission and then at the receiving end expanded to its original form, *multiplex* indicates that the transmitted stereo signal is mixed with other data. *Audio* of course refers to the fact that the input and output signals are in the (high quality) audio range.

At the transmitting end of a particular working system both left and right stereo channels are sampled at 32 times per millisecond. Each sample is converted into a 10-bit binary code (similar to the coding method of a pulse code modulation system) with a single parity bit added for checking in the receiver. For the 2 channels, sampled 32 times at 11 bits per sample, there is a total of 704 bits. 24 bits are added for control data, making a 728 bit frame. This is transmitted in a separate sound channel at the higher end of the frequency band of the picture signal [at 6.552 MHz above the vision carrier – see Fig.T5(iv)] so that there is no interaction with the normal monophonic sound signal, i.e. the mono signal is not derived from the stereo signal which is the procedure in earlier systems.
(* Analogue-to-Digital Conversion, Stereophonic System, Stereophonic Broadcasting, Companding, Multiplex System, Sampling, Bit, Binary Code, Pulse Code Modulation, Parity Checking, Parity Bit)

NICKEL-CADMIUM CELL A secondary cell, usually of cylindrical or "button" shape. Being rechargeable, these cells are often used as replacements for dry cells or batteries and can do so because, unlike the lead-acid cell, no gases are evolved, hence the cell can be sealed. The positive electrode is nickel oxide, the negative, cadmium and the electrolyte a solution of potassium hydroxide. The cell has a voltage 1.2 – 1.25.
(>> Cell, Secondary Cell, Electrolyte)

NICKEL-IRON CELL is a secondary and therefore rechargeable cell with an electromotive force of 1.2 – 1.3 volts. It is a robust type of cell suitable for heavy duty work such as traction. The plates are steel grids, the positive plate contains nickel and nickel compounds, the negative plate is of iron and iron oxide. A potassium hydroxide (caustic potash) electrolyte is used which ionizes into K^+ and OH^-. The cell has an advantage over the lead-acid cell in that it is lighter, the main disadvantage is that the cell voltage is lower.
(* Lead-Acid Cell >> Cell, Secondary Cell, Electrolyte, Ionization)

NOISE FACTOR is a means of specifying the performance of an item of equipment such as a radio receiver. It is defined as the relationship between the input and output signal-to-noise power ratios and so indicates the extent to which the noise generated within the equipment degrades the signal-to-noise ratio as the signal passes through. Noise factor is given the symbol F. Then:

$$\text{Noise factor, } F = \frac{P_{si}/P_{ni}}{P_{so}/P_{no}}$$

where P_s and P_n represent signal and noise powers and the added suffixes i and o refer to input and output.

As an example, if the input signal-to-noise ratio is 10 and the output signal-to-noise ratio is 8, then $F = 10/8 = 1.25$. If now the internally generated noise increases so that the output signal-to-noise ratio falls to 5, F rises to $10/5 = 2$. Hence the higher the value of F, the worse the equipment is from the point of view of internal noise generation.
(* Signal-to-Noise Ratio, Noise Figure >> Noise, Power)

NOISE FIGURE – first see Noise Factor. Noise figure is the noise factor F of an item of equipment, expressed in decibels, hence:

$$\text{Noise Figure, } F_{dB} = 10 \log F.$$

0 dB is therefore perfection because as a signal passes through the equipment, the signal-to-noise ratio does not change. As with noise factor, the higher the noise figure, the worse is the equipment noise performance.
(* Signal-to-Noise Ratio >> Noise, Decibel)

NOISE GENERATOR A gas discharge device makes an excellent white noise generator because it develops a stable and repeatable noise output when in the conducting condition. The ionization of the gas molecules in the tube is a random process hence the current flow through the tube has a minute random fluctuation imposed on it. The noise has a flat frequency spectrum and is therefore classed as "white". A noise generator comprises a gas discharge device using for example, helium, neon or argon, coupled to the input of an amplifier. This gives an output of white noise and an appropriate filter following the amplifier is inserted if a different noise power/frequency characteristic is required.
(* Noise, White Noise >> Filter, Gas Discharge, Ionization)

NOISE LIMITER Both radio and television are particularly susceptible to incoming impulsive noise signals. These are usually in the form of high amplitude, short duration pulses covering a

wide range of frequencies. To reduce the effects however is moderately simple and frequently a semiconductor diode in or following the demodulator is employed. The method is to clip all signals which are of appreciably greater magnitude than the desired signal and perhaps the simplest form of limiter is a pair of diodes connected "back to back" across the audio frequency path. Also a series diode may be used, conducting for the desired signal level but biased to be non-conducting for noise pulses. In more complicated systems the noise pulses can be used to momentarily reduce the receiver gain. In this case the wanted signal is also reduced but it has been determined that the ear is less disturbed by very short reductions in audio amplitude than it is by peaks of noise.
(* Limiter >> Noise, Diode, Pulse)

NON-LINEAR ELEMENT is a component or part of a circuit exhibiting non-linearity, i.e. two quantities (such as current and voltage) do not vary in proportion. With current and voltage therefore, Ohm's Law does not apply except for instantaneous values. Many components exhibit non-linearity, e.g. diodes, thermistors, barretters. The graphical symbol used generally for a non-linear resistor is shown in Figure N2(i), for those with characteristics

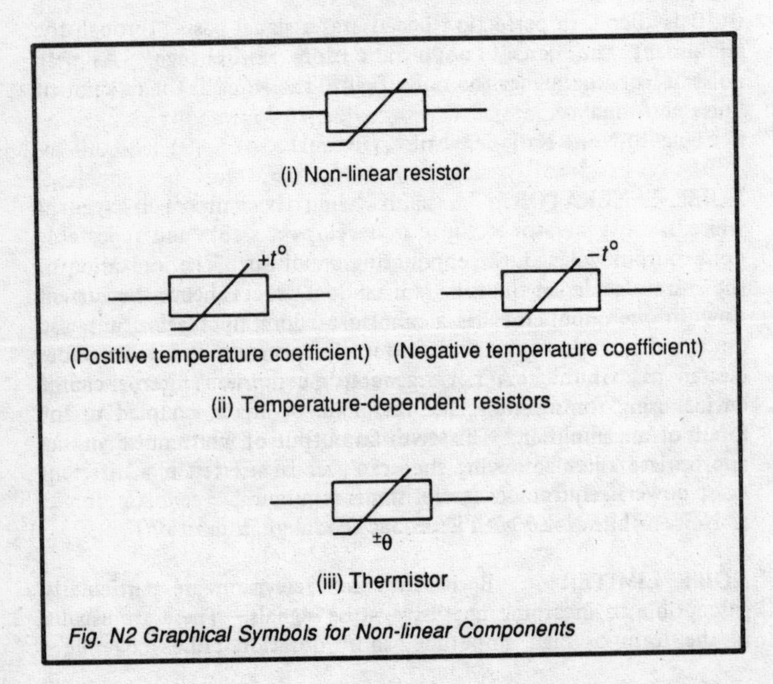

Fig. N2 Graphical Symbols for Non-linear Components

controlled by temperature the addition of $+t^\circ$ indicates a positive temperature coefficient, while $-t^\circ$ indicates a negative one as shown in (ii). Although the addition of $+t^\circ$ or $-t^\circ$ covers thermistors, a symbol as in (iii) may be used for this particular component instead. (>> Non-Linearity, Ohm's Law, Temperature Coefficient of Resistance)

NOR GATE A logic gate which has an output of logic 0 when one or more of the inputs is at logic 1 – see Digital Logic.

NOT GATE A logic gate which has an output of logic 1 when the input is at logic 0 and vice versa – see Digital Logic.

NTSC is an abbreviation of *National Television Systems Committee.* It is the name given to the colour television system used in North America, Japan and some other countries. An important feature of the system is that the colour information is mixed with the video signal so that there is no increase in bandwidth compared with black and white transmissions.

See also PAL, SECAM.

(* Television, Television Signal, Television Receiver >> Colour, Bandwidth)

NYQUIST DIAGRAM This is a technique used with amplifiers employing negative feedback to predict whether the amplifier will be stable and if not, at which frequencies instability is likely to occur. The mathematics were first unravelled by H. Nyquist, an American scientist. We can only look at his work in a simplified fashion and even then an appreciation of complex notation is essential.

The phase shift between the input and output of an amplifier is ideally a multiple of π radians (180°). However reactances within the amplifier cause deviations from this especially at the lower and higher frequencies. Even though reactive networks may not be used in the amplifier, transistors have various internal capacitances, hence unwanted phase shifts are bound to occur even with the most careful design. Phase shifts outside of the frequency range for which an amplifier is designed can also cause trouble.

The general formula given under the term Feedback for an amplifier of gain $A\angle\theta$ with a feedback network $\beta\angle\phi$ is:

$$\text{gain with feedback} = \frac{A\angle\theta}{1 - \beta A\angle(\theta + \phi)}$$

To simplify the explanation let us replace $-\beta A\angle(\theta + \phi)$ by T, remembering that T is complex. Then:

(i) for negative feedback, $(1 + T)$ must be greater than 1 so that the gain is reduced. T must therefore be positive;

(ii) when T is negative the gain increases (positive feedback) until eventually at $T = -1$ the gain is infinite and the amplifier unstable and oscillatory.

Consider an amplifier with negative feedback applied for the design frequency range. It is necessary to check whether at some frequency (or frequencies) outside of the chosen range T reaches -1 for as shown above, if it does so the amplifier will be unstable. Nyquist has shown that it is possible to predict the likelihood of such an occurrence by measuring the loop gain (i.e. the amplifier–feedback loop is broken at some point and the gain measured round the loop) and plotting the rectangular coordinates of T as a function of frequency. Figure N3 will help to make this clear. The two curves shown cover the range of frequencies from 0 to ∞.

The *Nyquist criterion* is that the curve must not pass through nor enclose the point $-1 + j0$. The amplifier with frequency curve (a) does not do this (point P is *between* 0 and -1) so it is stable at all frequencies. On the other hand, for the amplifier with curve (b), T is beyond $-1 + j0$ at one of the higher frequencies as indicated

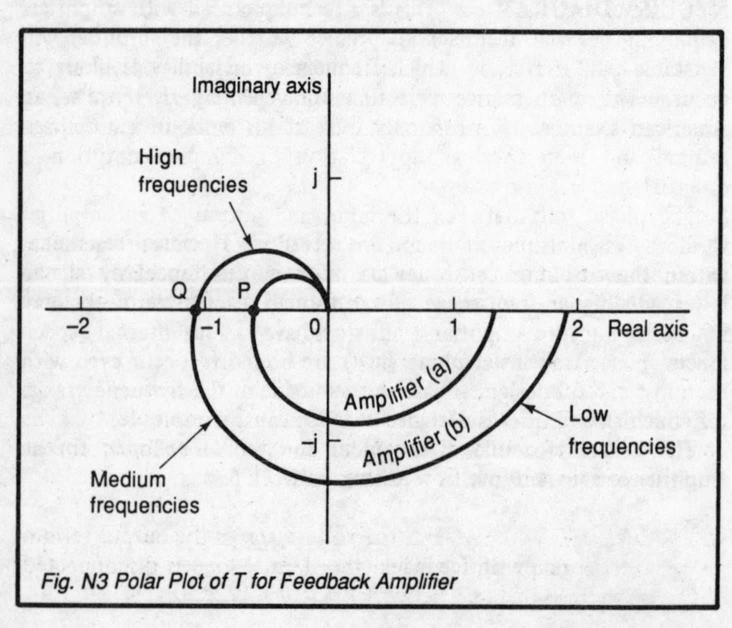

Fig. N3 Polar Plot of T for Feedback Amplifier

by point Q. This predicts that the amplifier will be unstable at this frequency and oscillation will occur of increasing amplitude until limited by overloading the amplifier.
(* Instability >> Amplifier, Feedback, Phase, Phase Shift, Complex Notation, Oscillation)

O

OCTAVE is a frequency interval with a range 2 : 1. Its association with the number 8 (Latin, *octo* = 8) comes from the original use of the word with the piano on which a doubling or halving in the frequency of the note is obtained by playing an octave (8 keys) higher or lower.

If f is any frequency, then one octave higher is $2f$, 2 octaves higher is $4f$ etc.
(>> Frequency)

OHMIC CONTACT is an electrical contact which is purely resistive and therefore Ohm's Law applies, i.e. the potential difference across the contact is directly proportional to the current flowing through it.
(>> Resistance, Ohm's Law)

OHMMETER – an instrument for measuring electrical resistance. It passes a small current through the unknown resistance; the current is provided by an internal small battery or a d.c. generator operated by hand.
(* Meter >> Resistance, Ohm's Law)

OPEN CIRCUIT When a circuit is broken for example, by a disconnection or a switch, it is said to be *open* or *on open circuit*. Current cannot therefore flow at this point.

OPEN-CIRCUIT VOLTAGE is the voltage across the output terminals of a network or device when the normal load is disconnected.
(* Open Circuit, Load >> Network)

OPERATING POINT Operating conditions for an active device such as a transistor are usually determined by graphical construction. The operating point is a position established on a characteristic to determine the current and voltage conditions when no signal is present or the mean conditions when a signal is applied. This is best explained by reference to a set of characteristics as shown in Figure L4. Assume that we are considering a small-signal amplifier which must not run into distortion. The load line is first drawn, then a point is chosen on it so that the positive and negative swings due to the incoming signal are equal. For example, in Figure L4 an operating point might be chosen at 0.6 mA base current as shown. Then if the signal swings the base current from a no signal value of 0.6 mA to between 0.4 and 0.8 mA, both the output current and voltage swings indicate little distortion. The position of the operating point on the load line is determined by the bias applied to the base of the transistor (in this case a bias current of 0.6 mA). With no input signal the operating point is also known as the *quiescent point* (quiet, motionless).

If the instantaneous values are considered when a signal is applied, then the operating point moves away from the quiescent point with the signal, i.e. it moves up and down the load line, in the case of Figure L4, between the points P and Q.

(* Load, Load Line >> Transistor, Characteristic, Bias, Distortion)

OPERATIONAL AMPLIFIER These were originally used in early computing for performing mathematical "operations". Nowadays the name is used to describe a general purpose linear integrated circuit amplifier which can be controlled by external circuits to do a whole range of jobs. The graphical symbol is basically a triangle as will be seen from Figure O1. Within the integrated circuit are some 10 – 30 transistors, all as components of direct-coupled amplifiers. Because the use of coupling capacitors is avoided, the operational amplifier is usable as either an a.c. or d.c. amplifier.

The device has two inputs, marked + and –. These signs indicate the phase of the output relative to the input, + for both in phase, – to show that they are 180° out of phase with each other. The signs must not be confused with d.c. supply polarities.

For d.c. amplification it is arranged that the output terminal is at zero volts when both the inputs are connected to zero volts so that the output can swing either positive or negative. Ideally with balanced supply voltages as in (i) of the figure, this should be so but to compensate for any minor irregularities, two *offset null* pins are provided which may be connected to a potentiometer for adjustment to zero on the output voltmeter as shown.

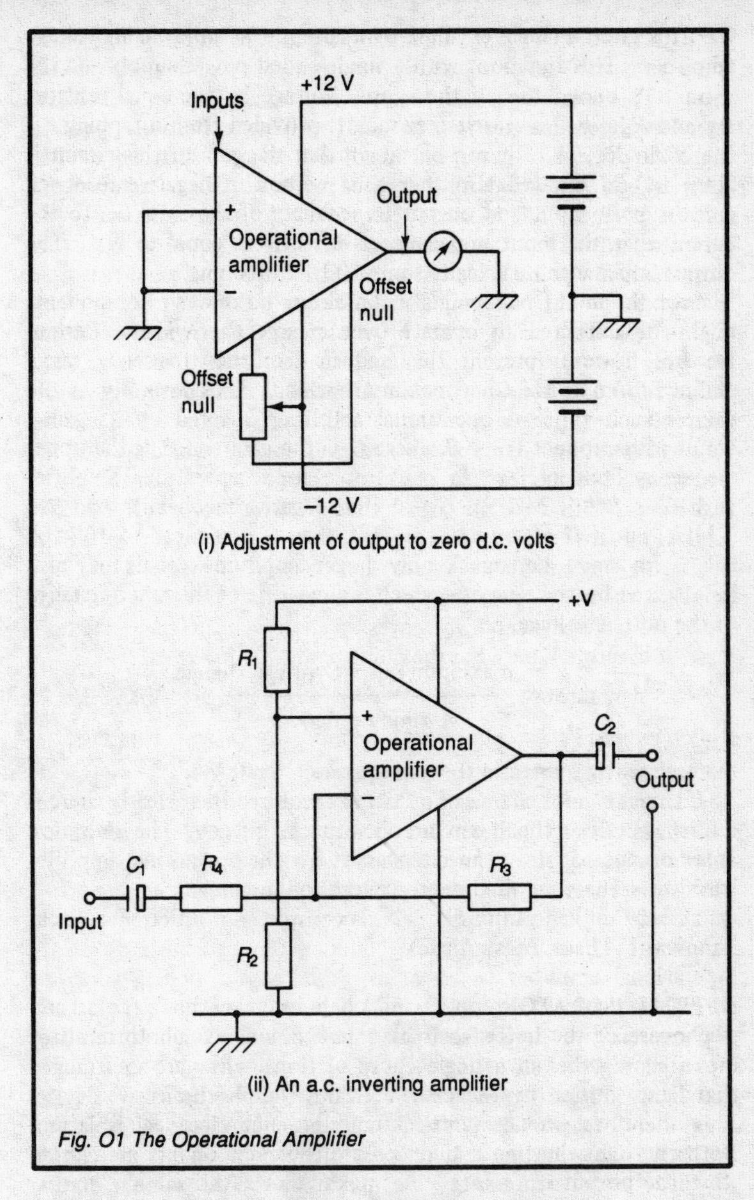

Fig. O1 The Operational Amplifier

The gain is an almost unbelievable 100 – 200 000 or even more. Such a gain is unusable in practice so it is reduced to the required value by application of negative feedback. This technique makes the operational amplifier an extremely useful device. In Figure

O1(ii) is given a single example of its use, i.e. as an inverting voltage amplifier. This functions with a single-ended power supply and the + input is biased to half the supply voltage by the equal resistors R_1 and R_2. A.C. negative feedback is provided from a tapping off the chain R_3, R_4. It can be shown that the gain of this circuit is given by R_3/R_4 and also that this method of negative feedback reduces both input and output impedances of the amplifier to the extent that the input impedance is effectively equal to R_4. The output impedance is typically some 100 – 200 ohms.

Such an amplifier, seemingly containing no reactive components might be expected to operate over a large bandwidth. Certain features however prevent this and in fact the frequency range extends from 0 Hz to a maximum which varies inversely as the gain. Each type of operational amplifier is rated by its gain–bandwidth product ($G \times B$ where G is the gain and B is the upper frequency limit in Hz). As an example, for an operational amplifier with $G \times B = 1$ MHz, if $G = 1$ (full negative feedback), then $B =$ 1 MHz, but if G of only 100 is used, then B is reduced to 10 kHz. this is for small a.c. signals only, larger amplitude signals may also be affected by the *slew rate* which is a measure of the *rate of change* of the output voltage, i.e.:

$$\text{slew rate} = \frac{\text{maximum output voltage change}}{\text{time needed}} \text{ V/s},$$

but frequently quoted in the more practical unit, V/μs.

If things cannot change as quickly as required then clearly there is a further limit on the maximum operating frequency. The limitation arises because of stray capacitances within the operational amplifier transistors, these require time to charge and discharge.

(* Direct-Coupled Amplifier >> Transistor, Amplifier, Feedback, Bandwidth, Phase, Phase Angle)

OPTICAL ISOLATOR consists of a light-emitting diode (l.e.d.) and a photosensitive device such as a photodiode or phototransistor mounted together in a single encapsulation. They are so arranged that light emitted by the l.e.d. activates the photosensitive device. This therefore provides optical coupling but electrical isolation. Both the light-emitting and photosensitive components are chosen so that their performances are maximum at the same radiation frequency (often in the infra-red). Figure O2 shows the circuit of a simple unit suitable for miniaturization.

(* Infra-Red >> Light-Emitting Diode, Photodiode, Phototransistor, Light, Visible Spectrum)

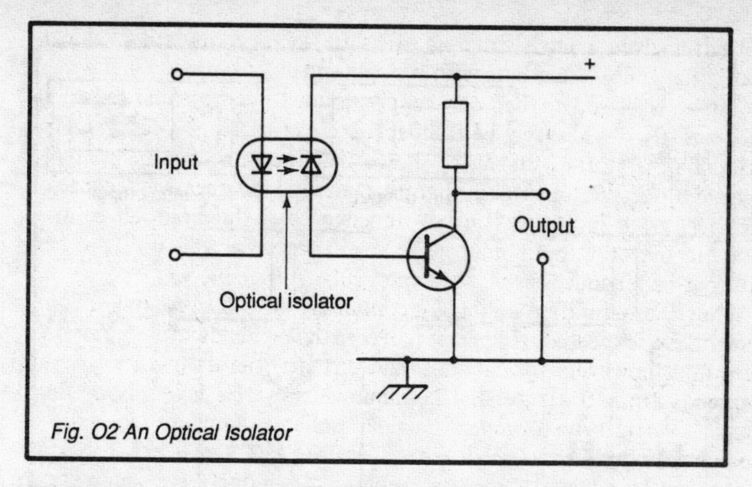

Fig. O2 An Optical Isolator

OR GATE A logic gate which has an output of logic 1 when one or more of the inputs is at logic 1 – see Digital Logic.

OSCILLATOR This is an instrument which, given a power supply, produces alternating current at either a single frequency or over a range of frequencies. Possible frequencies range from a few hertz up to GHz. The graphical symbol is given in Figure O3(i). Waveforms produced may conveniently be subdivided into the smooth *sinusoidal* and *relaxation*, the output of which exhibits abrupt transitions. The sinusoidal fall generally into the class known as *harmonic oscillators* although in fact in most cases no harmonics should be generated, this being the province of the relaxation type.

Many designs of harmonic oscillator have been produced and several which use positive feedback round an amplifier with a passive circuit controlling the frequency are shown in Figure O3(ii). Power supplies are not included.

The *tuned input* and *tuned output* oscillators shown employ a straightforward *LC* circuit with energy fed back into the inductor. For these the oscillation frequency, $f_r = 1/2\pi\sqrt{LC}$, where L is the inductance in henries and C, the capacitance in farads.

The *Colpitts* and *Hartley* oscillators (named after their American engineer inventors) are shown in more detail. In both types the frequency control network is basically *L-C* but the method of tapping the circuit for an emitter connection differs. From the point of view of the emitter, if at resonance one side of the *L-C* circuit is positive, the other side is negative and so the signal returned from collector to base changes phase by 180°. Together with the 180° change through the transistor, the complete loop has a

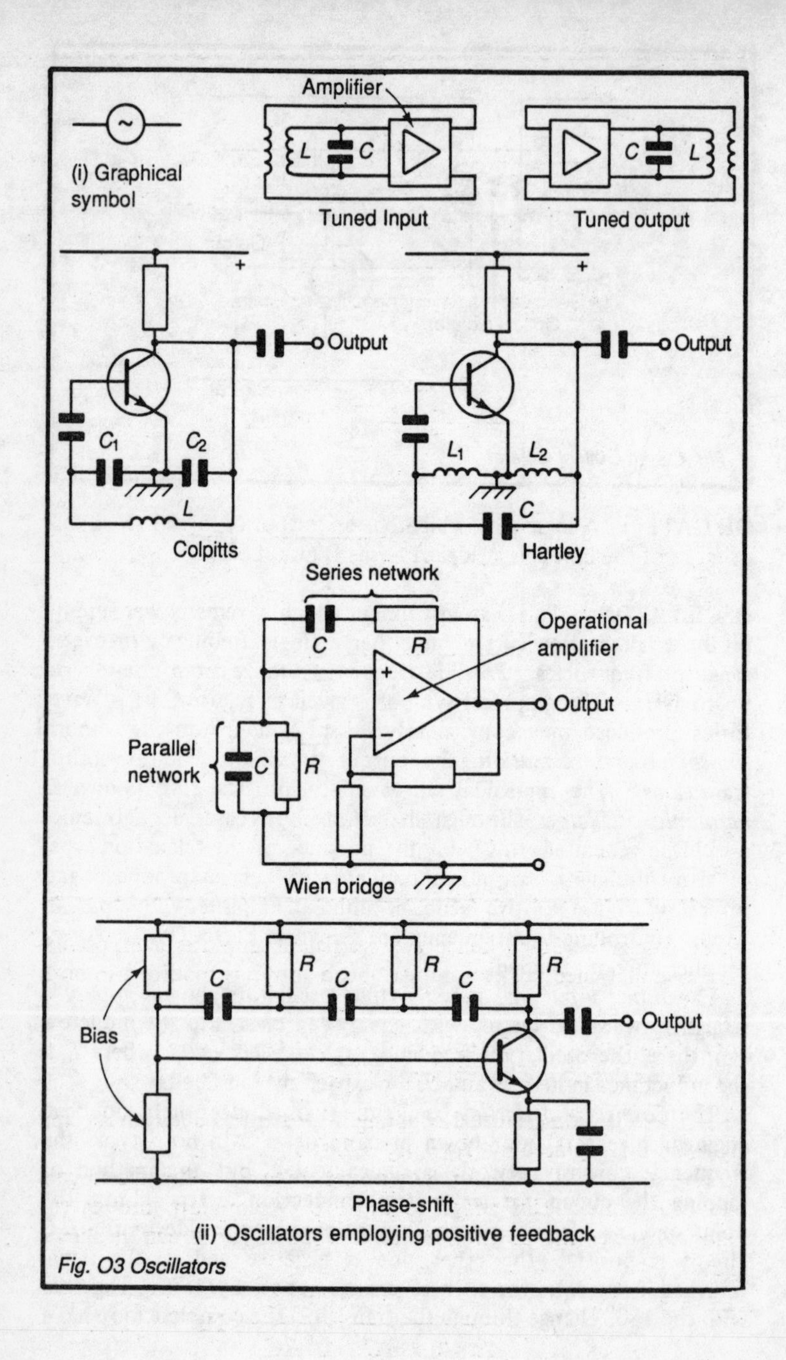

Fig. O3 Oscillators

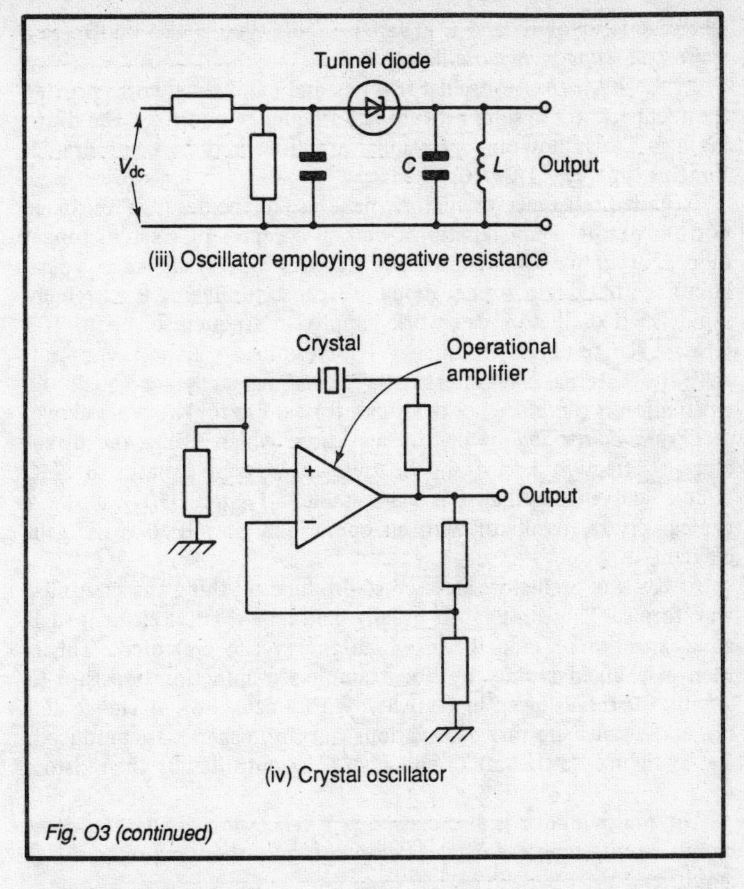

Fig. O3 (continued)

phase change of 360°, hence with sufficient amplifier gain, oscillation is maintained. The formula above for f_r is modified in both cases:

for the Colpitts, C is replaced by $C_1 C_2/(C_1 + C_2)$
for the Hartley, L is replaced by $(L_1 + L_2)$

or if there is aiding mutual coupling of M henries between L_1 and L_2, then L is replaced by $(L_1 + L_2 + 2M)$.

The phase-shift oscillator shown uses three RC networks to gain the 180° shift. This added to the 180° phase shift through the transistor gives the positive feedback required and it can be shown that:

$$f_r = \frac{1}{2\pi\sqrt{6} \times RC} = \frac{0.065}{RC} \quad \text{Hz}$$

where R is in ohms and C in farads. This type is also known as a *resistance–capacitance* oscillator.

In the *Wien Bridge* oscillator series and parallel networks provide the feedback and also constitute the frequency control. The drawing also shows how an operational amplifier may be incorporated. For this type, $f_r = 1/2\pi RC$.

Negative resistance oscillators make use of the negative resistance portion of the characteristic of certain components such as tunnel diodes or unijunction transistors. Figure O3(iii) shows a typical circuit employing a tunnel diode. Because tunnelling is extremely rapid, such oscillators can work happily at frequencies up to 100 GHz. The resonance frequency is determined on the assumption that the external and internal circuit admittances are equal, the calculation is therefore not as straightforward as for the types above.

Crystal-controlled oscillators are those which utilize the piezoelectric effect in a crystal. In these the crystal replaces the *L-C* circuit and the oscillator is very stable. Figure O3(iv) shows a typical crystal oscillator with an operational amplifier as the gain element.

Relaxation oscillators are used to produce anything but sinusoidal waveforms. These oscillators usually contain a reactive element such as a capacitor or inductor in which energy can be stored. This is then discharged rapidly by, for example a unijunction transistor (a circuit for this is given in Fig.R5). With a capacitor, as charge and discharge times are varied, so various waveform shapes are produced, e.g. in Figure R5 the rate of charge of C is controlled by the resistor, R.

The multivibrator is also classed as a relaxation oscillator. Many circuit arrangements are used, again often embodying operational amplifiers.
(* Multivibrator, Operational Amplifier, Backward-Wave Oscillator, Relaxation Oscillator >> Oscillation, Resonance, Amplifier, Negative Resistance, Phase, Phase Shift, L-C Circuit, Piezoelectric Effect, Wien Bridge)

OSCILLOSCOPE often described as a *cathode-ray oscilloscope* and abbreviated to *c.r.o*. This is one of the most widely used tools in electronics for with it pictures in the form of graphs of any waveform can be examined. The essential feature of a c.r.o. is the cathode-ray tube. For most work an X-axis is drawn horizontally by a saw-tooth time base. Controls are added so that the horizontal line can be moved up and down on the screen, the X-shift, see Figure O4. The figure shows the arrangements for a medium priced c.r.o. with electrostatic deflection. The X-amplifier enables the sweep to

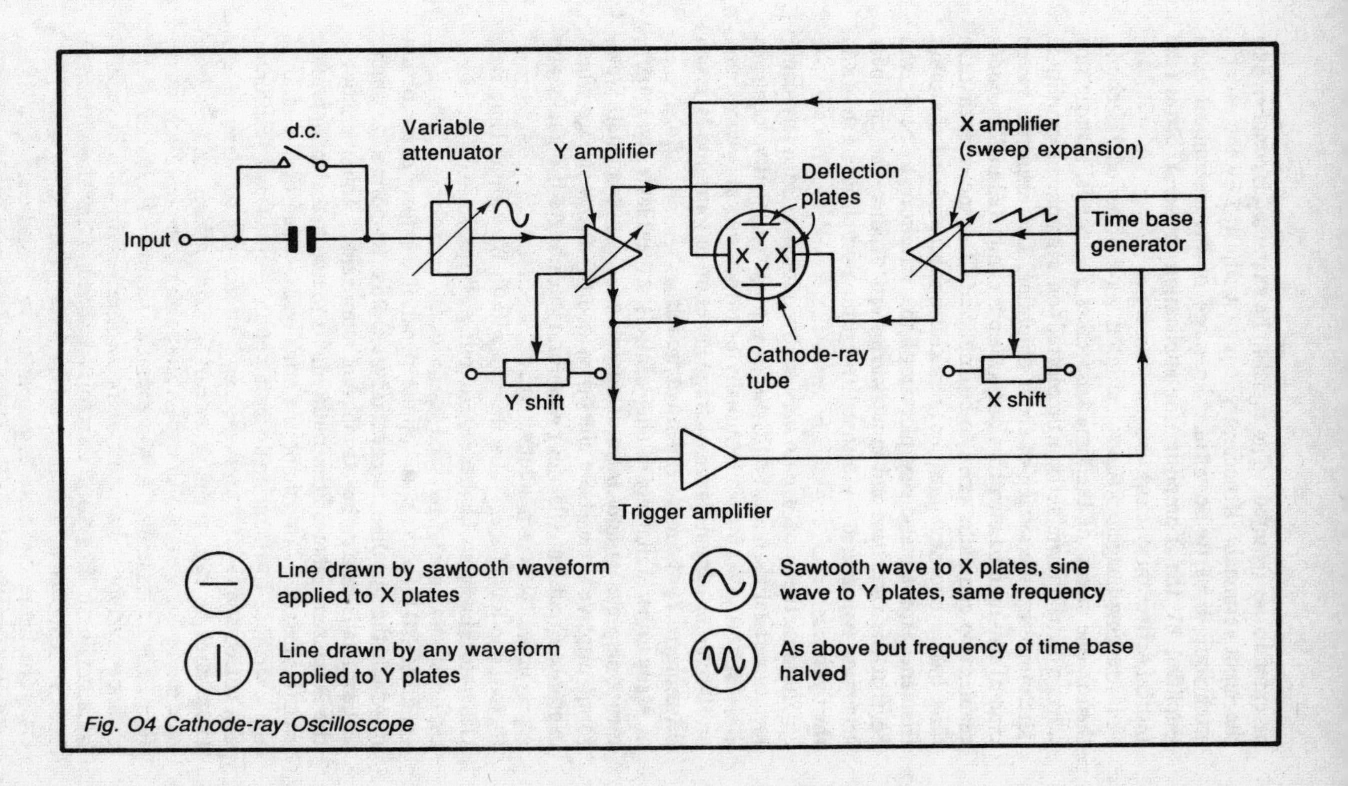

Fig. O4 Cathode-ray Oscilloscope

be extended as required. The signal to be examined is connected to the input terminal. If necessary it is first adjusted by the variable attenuator so as to be within the range of the instrument then amplified by the Y-amplifier for application to the Y plates (the vertical deflection system).

If we now imagine a sinusoidal input wave of period T seconds, then if one sweep of the time base takes T seconds, a single sine wave will be drawn as though plotted on a graph, its amplitude determined by the setting of the Y-amplifier. Decreasing the sweep time of the time base so that one sweep is completed in $2T$ seconds enables two complete waves to be displayed. This indicates that the time base frequency must be an exact sub-multiple of the input frequency for a stationary picture of the waveform to be drawn. So that the time base and input wave start together, the time base generator is triggered by a signal from the Y-amplifier as shown in the figure.

The sensitivity of a c.r.o. is usually quoted as so many centimetres vertical movement of the spot for a given input voltage, e.g. 1 cm per 50 mV, this would usually be turned the other way round as 50 mV/cm. Input signals at frequencies up to some 400 MHz can be displayed by the more expensive models.

Many other refinements and controls are available, two worth mentioning are (i) *dual trace* or *dual beam*, i.e. two separate waveforms displayed one above the other; and (ii) *digital storage* which captures a transient (fleeting) waveform, memorizes it digitally and repeats it on the screen indefinitely.
(* Cathode-Ray Tube, Time Base, Sawtooth Waveform, Time Base Generator, Lissajous Figures >> Amplifier, Period)

OVERSHOOT occurs with a pulse signal, it is a form of distortion in which the response momentarily exceeds the normal maximum value or falls below the normal minimum value. The overshoot is the maximum value of the pulse minus the normal step amplitude and the degree of overshoot is normally expressed by the ratio of the overshoot to the normal step amplitude, either as a fraction or as a percentage.
(>> Pulse)

P

PAD is a term commonly used for a fixed attenuator – see Attenuator.

PADDING CAPACITOR (PADDER) is a capacitor connected in series with the oscillator tuning capacitor of a superheterodyne radio receiver. This is to arrange as far as possible that the oscillator and signal frequency circuits keep in step (i.e. track) together for all settings of the tuning control – see Tracking.

PAIR is a general name for a transmission line comprising two conductors. Such lines may be in the form of open wires carried on poles, wires in a cable or a coaxial cable.
(* Coaxial Cable >> Transmission Line)

PAL is an abbreviation of *phase alternation line*. It is the colour television system used in the UK, many European countries, South Africa, Australia and New Zealand. It can be seen from Figure T5(iv) that the colour signals are added to the luminance signal and that the colour occupies a lower bandwidth compared with the luminance. The colour information is transmitted as two signals in quadrature which modulate a chrominance sub-carrier and in the receiver the colour information is regained from the vector sum of these components. Any shift in the phase of the colour sub-carrier relative to the colour burst results in a change of hue of the picture. The PAL system provides protection against such phase errors by reversing the relative phase of the quadrature components on alternate lines. There is a small loss in picture sharpness but this is not generally noticeable because colour on its own does not require high resolution.

See also SECAM, NTSC.
(* Television, Television Signal, Television Receiver >> Colour, Quadrature)

PARABOLIC ANTENNA is a transmitting or receiving antenna of parabolic shape. The important feature of the parabola of which we make much use in antenna design is that as a receiving antenna all electromagnetic energy arriving parallel to the principal axis is directed to the focus as shown in Figure P1(i). Conversely on transmitting, energy launched at at the focus is radiated as a parallel, concentrated beam as with a searchlight. A parabolic antenna is

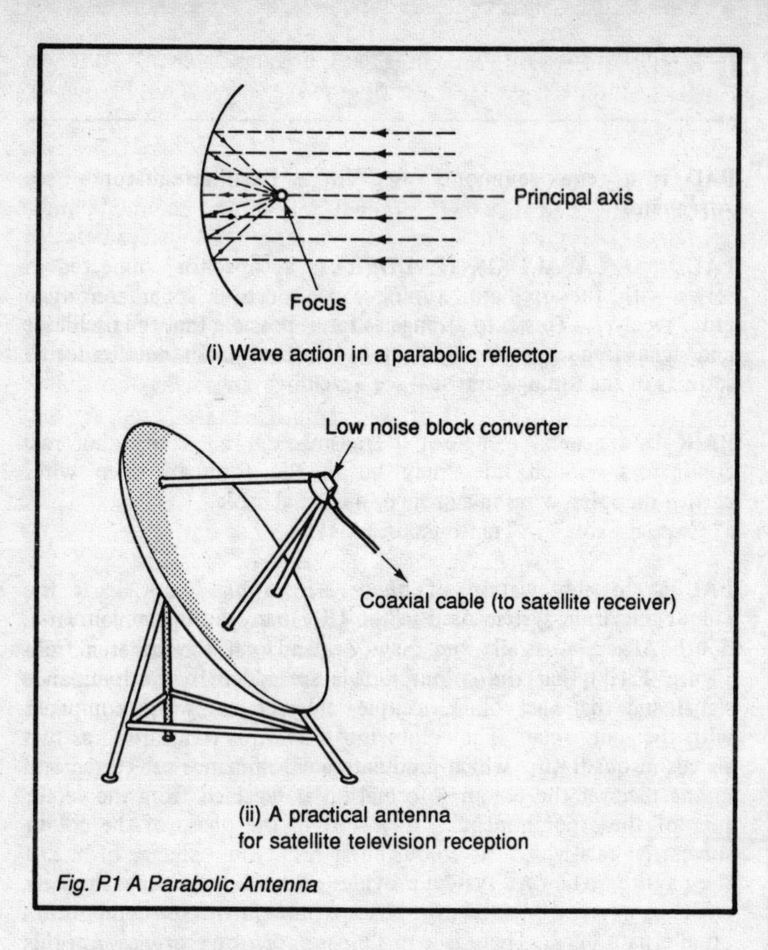

Fig. P1 A Parabolic Antenna

therefore highly directional.

Parabolic antennas are used principally for microwave point-to-point transmission, e.g. for terrestrial microwave systems and also for satellite transmission and reception. Colloquially these are known as "dishes", a simplified sketch of one is shown in Figure P1(ii). Transmitting antennas radiate energy from the focus fed by a waveguide, receiving antennas collect the incoming energy at the focus. For domestic satellite reception because use of a waveguide is unthinkable a special *low noise block converter* LNB) is placed at the focus. This collects the electromagnetic wave and shifts it down in frequency so that the feed into the premises can be by coaxial cable. Because this type of antenna is directional, mechanical stability and accurate alignment are all important.

(* Satellite Television, Antenna, LNB, Coaxial Cable >> Antenna, Parabola, Electromagnetic Wave, Microwave, Waveguide, Frequency Changing)

PARALLEL CONNECTION (1) is the technique of connecting circuit elements so that their terminals join at two common points. The current at the input of a parallel arrangement divides between the various paths and reunites at the output.

(2) cells, batteries and generators are said to be in parallel when all positive terminals are connected together to form the positive pole of the arrangement and all negative terminals are connected similarly. As an example, with a parallel arrangement of n similar cells (or generators), each of electromotive force (e.m.f.) e and internal resistance r, the parallel system has an e.m.f. e and internal resistance r/n.

See also Series Connection.
(>> Electromotive Force, Resistance, Positive, Negative)

PARAMETER In analysis of networks this is a quantity which is constant in the particular case under investigation but which varies in value for other cases. As we see with hybrid parameters, it is one of a number of variables referring to a network or active device which may be held constant while the effects of other network variables are assessed.

The term is also used loosely to describe any variable associated with electronic activity. See Hybrid Parameters as an example.
(>> Network)

PARAMETRIC AMPLIFIER This is used at microwave frequencies and differs from the normal amplifier in that the energy source is at a high frequency instead of being a direct current. Another difference is that whereas the "straight" type of amplifier employs an active device such as a transistor or thermionic valve, the parametric amplifying element is a reactance. In a way the operation of a parametric amplifier can be appreciated from the build up of the amplitude of a child's swing (i.e. amplification). Energy is supplied to the swing in pulses regularly by the child so this is a case of energy being added periodically rather than continually. The swing frequency does not change since it is determined by the swing length.

In place of the swing, consider a capacitance, C which is part of a resonant circuit. If it has a charge, q, then the voltage across it, $v = q/C$. Now if C is suddenly decreased (and this is quite a practical consideration), the charge is still there, hence v rises proportionately. However the energy stored by the capacitor is $\frac{1}{2}Cv^2$, so being proportional to the *square* of the voltage, rises accordingly. This energy must have been supplied by the external source which was employed to change the capacitance of C. This external source is known as the *pump frequency* because it "pumps up" the voltage across C at the required times. Within the resonant circuit, this is amplification. C can be increased to its original value when v has fallen to zero.

The same considerations can be applied to the inductance of the resonant circuit. However the capacitance is chosen above for illustration because a suitable variable one exists in the form of the varicap diode which varies its capacitance with the reverse voltage applied. A suitable variable inductor is not so easy to find.

This is the basic idea of the parametric amplifier. Many other considerations must be taken into account, especially the pump frequency. This normally differs from the signal frequency and when it is twice the signal frequency as is commonly the case, the amplifier is described as *degenerate*.

The parametric amplifier has the important advantage of low noise generation, very useful when an incoming signal is weak as for example, from a satellite.

(>> Amplifier, Reactance, Capacitance, Energy, Resonance, Charge)

PARASITIC OSCILLATION is an undesired oscillation occurring in a system containing one or more active devices, i.e. in an amplifier or oscillator circuit. Oscillations may occur when there is positive feedback over one or more stages of amplification. The circulating energy increases until oscillations are maintained. Feedback is usually via interelectrode capacitances of the active devices, stray capacitances and inductances or even by coupling of one stage to an earlier one via the common power supply impedance. Because for example the strays are very small, parasitic oscillations are often at higher frequencies than that at which the equipment works. It is also possible for several separate oscillations to be present at one time in a system. In transmitters where power levels are high, parasitic oscillations may be particularly troublesome if not prevented for they can be responsible for distortion, low efficiency and interference with other services if radiated.

There are several methods of prevention of which perhaps the most obvious is a sensible wiring layout so that stray capacitances and inductances are minimized. Common power supplies should be of very low impedance. However, if oscillations persist, *parasitic stoppers* may be inserted to provide *damping*. These are, for example

resistors or series inductors (chokes) in the input and output circuits of transistors to create a high impedance within the oscillatory path. Even a tiny capacitor connected across the signal path (in parallel) may be effective.
(* Interelectrode Capacitance, Stray Capacitance, Choke >> Oscillation, Amplifier, Feedback, Damping)

PARASITIC STOPPER is a component inserted in an active circuit to suppress parasitic oscillation – see Parasitic Oscillation.

PARITY BIT is used in binary data transmission and is the 8th bit within a byte of data used to make up the overall parity as even or odd. The parity of data received by the system is then checked to reveal any errors which have occurred during transmission – see Parity Checking.

PARITY CHECKING Binary digits do not always travel well especially on lines where there is always the risk, be it ever so small, that interference voltages and other malfunctions may change a 0 for a 1 or vice versa. Using the ASCII code as an example, this must be 7 bits in length in order to express all (one language) characters. The word length of computers is 8 bits or a multiple thereof, hence the ASCII code leaves one bit spare in an 8-bit word and this spare bit position is conveniently used for a *parity* (equality) bit, a single bit used solely as an indication that all is or is not well.

An *odd-parity generator* adds a single logical 1 when doing so makes the total number of 1's in the byte odd. An *even-parity generator* similarly arranges for an even number of 1's. Thus as an example the decimal number 78 (capital N in ASCII) is transmitted as:

1 (parity) followed by 1001110 for odd parity

0 (parity) followed by 1001110 for even parity

(the parity bit might equally *follow* the code). At the receiving end every byte is tested for the chosen parity. A positive result in the test is a good indication of successful transmission. The system has some weaknesses but in most situations these are greatly outweighed by the overall reduced likelihood of undetected error.
(* Binary, Binary Code, Bit, Byte, Word, American Standard Code for Information Interchange (ASCII) >> Digital Signal)

PCM Abbreviation of Pulse Code Modulation – see this term.

PEAK INVERSE VOLTAGE (p.i.v.) is the maximum instantaneous reverse voltage which may be applied to a component such as a diode. If the reverse bias voltage applied to a diode is steadily increased the breakdown point is ultimately reached where there is a large increase in current. The voltage across the diode which gives rise to this condition is known as the *peak inverse voltage.* A safe value for the p.i.v. is therefore quoted by the component manufacturer.

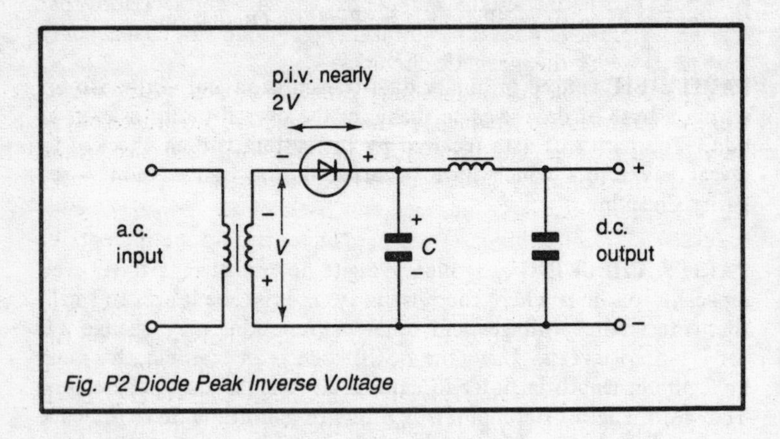

Fig. P2 Diode Peak Inverse Voltage

The importance of the p.i.v. in circuit design is highlighted by the case of the rectifier. As an example Figure P2 shows the elements of a half-wave circuit from which it is evident that the input voltage V to the diode is in series with the rectified voltage across C (only a little less than V). When V is at its negative peak therefore the two voltages add up to a p.i.v. of nearly $2V$. Hence for a d.c. output of say, 200 V, the diode p.i.v. must be in excess of 400 V for minimum risk of breakdown.
(>> Diode, P-N Junction, Rectification, Breakdown)

PERMANENT MAGNET In its simplest form consists of a bar or horseshoe-shaped sample of a magnetically hard material such as steel which has been magnetised. The material possesses high remanence so that the magnetisation is not easily destroyed. The magnet exhibits North and South poles situated close to the ends.
(>> Magnetism, Magnetisation, Remanence, Ferromagnetism)

PERMEABILITY TUNING A method of changing the inductance of a coil by moving its core. The frequency of resonance (f_r) of a tuned circuit is determined by the values of the capacitance and the inductance, either of which can be varied for tuning to a different frequency. Usually the capacitance is varied but it is sometimes more convenient to vary the inductance instead. Frequently this is done by screwing a ferromagnetic core (sometimes referred to as a *slug*) in or out of the inductor to vary the proportion of it in the magnetic circuit. Adjusting the position or amount of core within the coil changes the reluctance of the magnetic path. The inductance is inversely proportional to the reluctance hence decreasing the reluctance increases the inductance and vice versa. (Note that the permeabilities of the air and magnetic core do not change, only the reluctance of the magnetic circuit).

Typical examples of permeability tuning are given by the inductors in intermediate frequency transformers of superheterodyne radio receivers [see Transformer T2 in Fig.F4(ii)] and also in the channel tuners of many domestic television receivers.
(* Television Receiver, Frequency Changer >> Tuned Circuit, Inductance, Permeability, Reluctance, Superheterodyne Reception)

PERSISTENCE is a term used mainly with regard to cathode-ray tubes. When an electron beam strikes the phosphor coating on the face of the tube the energy of the beam is transferred to the electrons in the phosphor crystals. This raises their energy levels and when each electron returns to the ground state it emits a quantum of light energy (photon). This process of light emission decays approximately exponentially for a period of time which is known as the *persistence* or *afterglow.* The chemical composition of the phosphor determines the persistence which can vary from a fraction of a second to several minutes, depending on the application. For example, long persistence tubes are used in oscilloscopes for examination of fleeting waveforms, on the other hand, tv tubes require a persistence (to the 10% level) of less than one millisecond.
(* Cathode-Ray Tube, Oscilloscope >> Energy Levels, Luminescence, Planck Constant)

PHASE DISCRIMINATOR is a detector circuit used in frequency or phase modulation systems. It produces an output proportional to the deviation of the frequency or phase from the unmodulated value – see Frequency Discriminator.

PHASE-SHIFT OSCILLATOR An oscillator which relies for its positive feedback partly on the phase shift introduced by resistance –capacitance networks – see Oscillator.

PHASE SPLITTER This is a circuit or component which accepts a single input signal and produces at its output two separate identical copies of that signal but with a predetermined phase difference, usually 180°. Such circuits are mostly used to drive push-pull stages. The simplest phase splitter is a transformer with a centre-tapped secondary winding. Given an input signal on the primary winding, then relative to the centre-tap on the secondary, the secondary terminals reproduce the input but with 180° phase difference between them [see Fig.P13(i)]. Alternatively a transistor stage may be employed as a phase splitter. A single stage with collector and emitter resistors of approximately the same value can produce collector and emitter voltages 180° out of phase (there is a small difference in the two resistors due to base current flowing in the emitter resistor).
(* Push-Pull Operation, Differential Amplifier >> Transformer, Transistor, Phase Angle)

PHOTOLITHOGRAPHY is the process through which the insulating silicon dioxide formed on the surface of a silicon slice is removed from certain predetermined areas for the doping elements to be added. In the manufacture of an integrated circuit for example, the initial layout is several hundred times the size of the final mask. The large, more workable mask patterns are cut in plastic sheets and are then known as *rubyliths*. These are then reduced photographically down to the final mask dimensions. The reduced mask is reproduced many times by a photographic step and repeat process to produce multiple images side by side and line by line over a transparent glass slide. This is the final mask which now contains rows of images of the required pattern for placing over the silicon wafer. The process is illustrated by stages 1 to 4 in Figure P3.

Photoresist is a lacquer coating which is applied over the silicon dioxide film formed on the substrate. The lacquer reacts to ultraviolet light by changing its chemical composition. Thereafter it is insoluble in certain solvents whereas the unexposed lacquer is soluble (and vice versa).

At this stage we therefore have a silicon wafer with an insulating silicon dioxide film on the upper surface. This is next coated with a photoresist lacquer, the masking plate put into position and exposed to ultraviolet light. There are two types of photoresist, labelled positive and negative. The negative variety becomes hardened when exposed to the light. Subsequent action by a *developer* dissolves the resist which has been masked and therefore *not* exposed. The wafer is next immersed in hydrofluoric acid which etches away the silicon dioxide where the photoresist has been removed. The acid does not

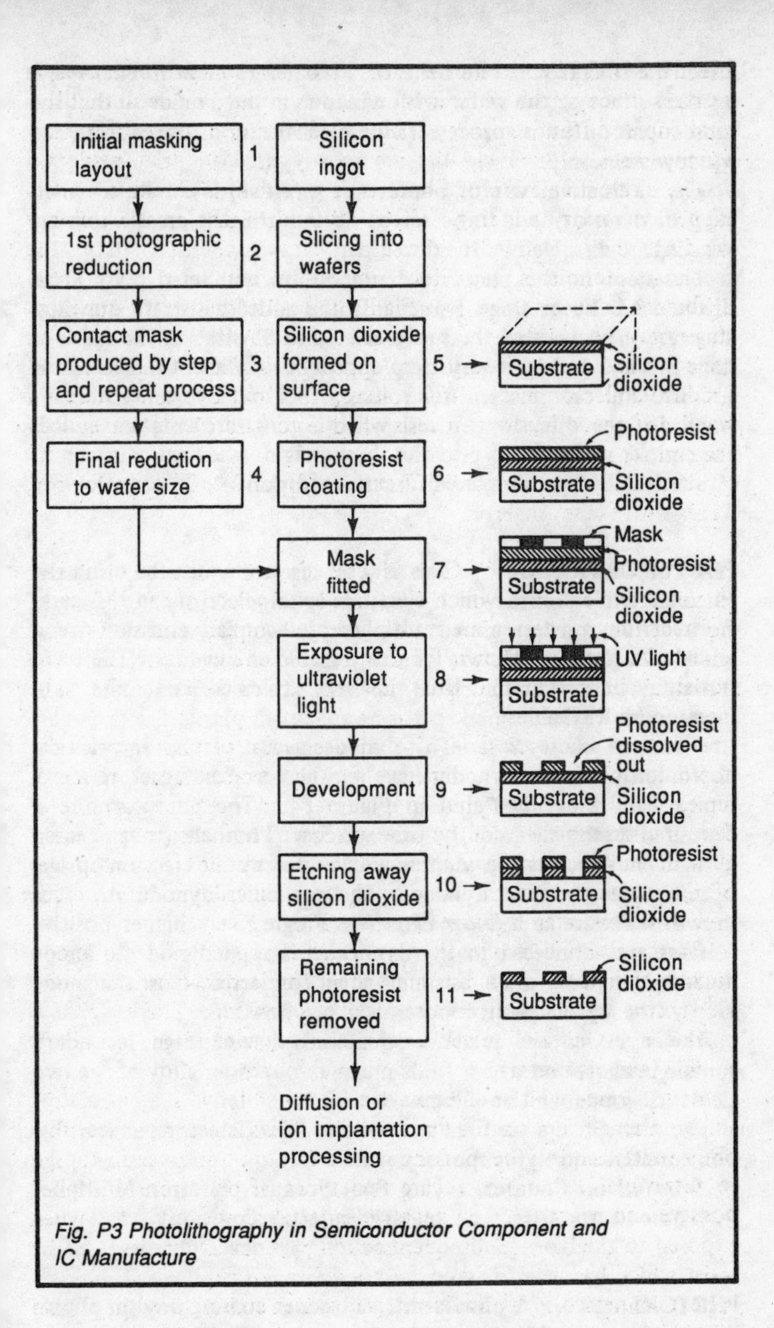

Fig. P3 Photolithography in Semiconductor Component and IC Manufacture

affect the silicon substrate beneath. This leaves a *photoresist mask* on the surface of the wafer with windows in the dioxide so that the subsequent diffusion process (adding in the dopants) affects the window areas only.

The alternative type of photoresist (positive) is employed when most of the dioxide is to be removed, with this the areas which *are* exposed are dissolved by the developer.

The steps in the photoresist process are numbered 5 to 11 in Figure P3. From stage 5 onwards the added substrate drawings illustrate the results of the processing. For illustration the mask at stage 7 is reduced to a very simple form but sufficient to show how a single chip progresses. When stage 11 is completed the wafer is ready for the diffusion process when doping elements are added. Finally the wafer is cut into the thousands of identical chips on it.
(* Substrate, Chip, Integrated Circuit, Diffusion >> Silicon, Doping)

PHOTOMULTIPLIER This is a special form of tube using the photoelectric effect in which electrons (photoelectrons in this case) emitted from a cathode are multiplied by secondary emission over a series of electrodes, known for this purpose as *dynodes.* The basic system is illustrated in Figure E8 and explained under the term Electron Multiplier.

Figure E8 shows a series of dynodes as flat plates. In practical photomultipliers the dynodes have a more complex structure and a typical one is as illustrated in Figure P4. The photocathode is deposited on the inside of the tube window. Photoelectrons released by light illuminating the window are directed by the electron optical system onto the first dynode. The particular dynode structure shown is known as a *linear cascade.* Progressively higher positive voltages are connected to the dynodes from 1st dynode to anode usually by tapping off a resistance chain connected across the anode supply (the highest positive potential).

The dynodes are made of materials having high secondary emission ratios, one which finds much favour is an alloy of the two elements, copper and beryllium.

Photomultipliers are used as low-level light detectors, in scintillation counters and flying spot scanners.
(* Scintillation Counter, Flying Spot Scanner, Electron Multiplier >> Photoelectric Effect, Secondary Emission, Collision)

PHOTORESIST A photosensitive lacquer coating used in photolithography – see this term.

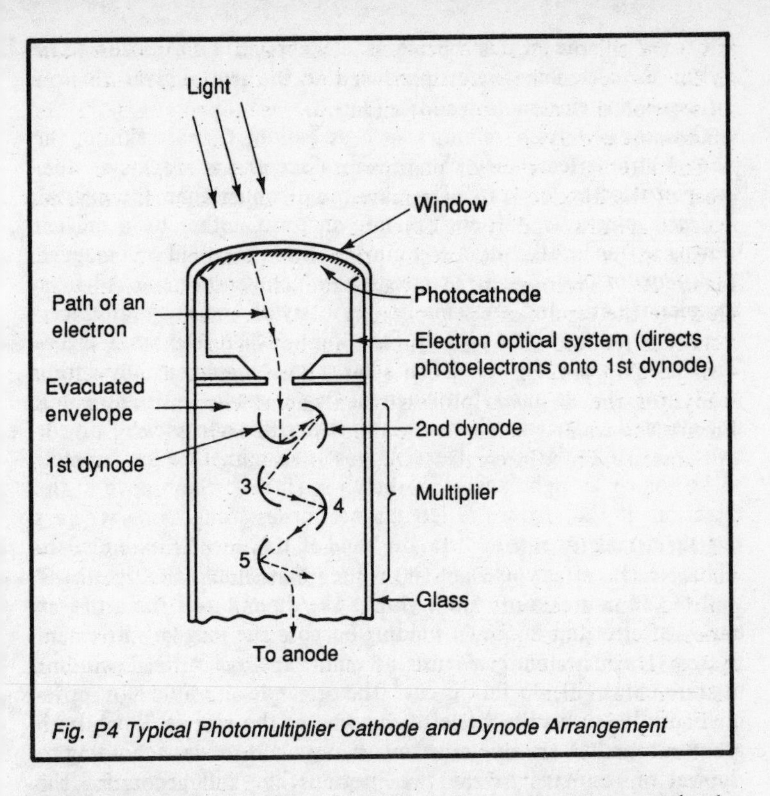

Fig. P4 Typical Photomultiplier Cathode and Dynode Arrangement

PHOTOTUBE is a vacuum or gas-filled glass, ceramic or metal tube containing a photocathode (typically 0.5 – 5 cm diameter) fixed at a window in the tube and also an anode. The anode is held positive relative to the cathode. Light falling on the photocathode releases electrons from it and these are collected by the anode. Gas-filled tubes may use argon at low pressure, ionization of the gas produces positive ions which reduce the space charge surrounding the cathode and so provide a higher anode current with higher sensitivity.

The sensitivity may be defined as the ratio of the alternating component of the anode current to that of the incident radiation. (>> Gas Discharge, Photocathode, Ionization, Space Charge)

PICK-UP is a transducer for converting signals recorded as variations in the groove of a (gramophone) disc into their electrical counterparts. A stylus (or needle) runs in the groove and "picks up" the signals from the walls. There are several different types of transducer by which the vibrating stylus produces corresponding electrical signals. Those mostly used are:

Crystal – the stylus vibrations are applied to a piezoelectric crystal, the alternating stress produced on the crystal gives rise to a corresponding electromotive force (e.m.f.).

Ceramic – certain ceramics such as barium titanate exhibit the piezoelectric effect, they can therefore act as transducers as does the piezoelectric crystal. They are more robust than the crystal.

Electromagnetic – these generate an e.m.f. either by a magnet moving within a coil or by a coil moving within the field of a magnet.

A *pick-up cartridge* is an assembly which can be removed from the pick-up arm and contains both the stylus and the transducer.

How a stereophonic pick-up functions may be seen from Figure P5. As a reminder (i) shows that a bar magnet moving axially within a coil generates an e.m.f. but when moving as shown in (ii), no e.m.f. is generated. The two channels have their signals impressed on the two walls of the groove. Next suppose two miniature bar magnets to be joined at right angles as shown in (iii). If they move in the direction of the arrow the left magnet moves "length-on" whereas the right magnet moves "end-on" and if this idea is extended to include coils and stylus as in (iv) we see that should the right-hand wall of the groove move the stylus in the direction of the arrow an e.m.f. is generated in the R winding because the magnet movement is as in (i) of the figure whereas no e.m.f. appears in the L winding because, as in (ii), no flux is cut. The principle also holds for movement of the stylus by the left-hand wall of the groove. When both grooves together are operative on the stylus it moves according to the vector resultant of the two motions but still generating the appropriate e.m.f.'s in the two coils.

Because piezoelectric transducers are sensitive to stress in one direction but not at 90° to this direction, they are also suitable for stereophonic pick-ups; a basic arrangement is shown in (v) of the figure. High quality pick-ups can have a frequency response varying by only a few decibels over the range 20 – 20 000 Hz.
(* Disc Recording, Transducer, Stereophonic System, Ceramic >> Piezoelectric Effect, Piezoelectric Crystal, Electromagnetic Induction, Decibel)

PICTURE ELEMENT is a term used with television screens and visual display units. Frequently and especially with computers the term *pixel* is used instead. A picture element is the smallest area on the screen which can be displayed. For an example we can estimate the number of picture elements on a 625-line television screen. For a picture of this number of lines each picture element must be about 1/600 of the picture height (allowing for the fact that not all lines are effective in drawing the picture). Assuming that the width of a

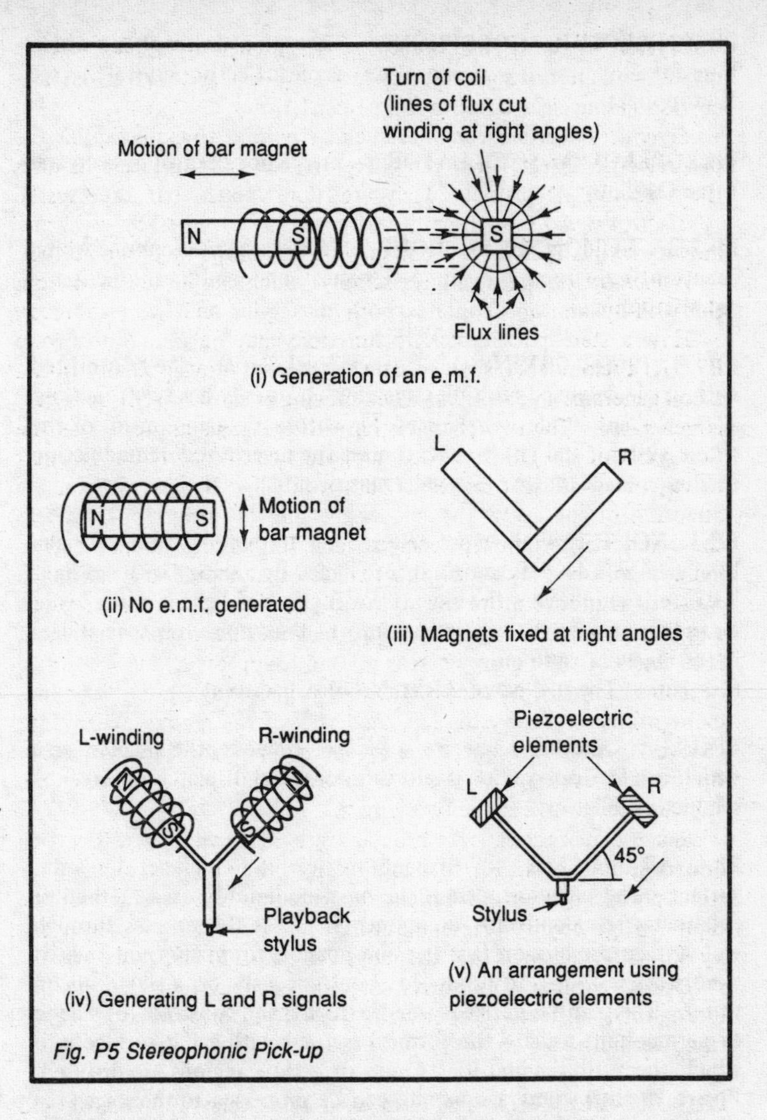

Fig. P5 Stereophonic Pick-up

picture element is the same as its height and with a screen width 4/3 times the height, there are therefore 600 × 4/3 elements per line. The total number of picture elements per frame therefore is 600 × 600 × 4/3, i.e. nearly half a million.

In practice however the number is usually somewhat less because of bandwidth restrictions (see Kell Factor)
(* Television, Television Receiver, Visual Display Unit, Kell Factor)

PIEZOELECTRIC MICROPHONE A type of microphone which functions by varying pressure on a piezoelectric crystal – see Microphone.

PIEZOELECTRIC OSCILLATOR Frequency control by a crystal – see Oscillator.

PIEZOJUNCTION MICROPHONE A type of microphone which functions by varying pressure on a special semiconductor junction – see Microphone.

PILOT (PILOT CARRIER) A low level carrier wave transmitted with single sideband multiplex systems. It usually has two functions – (i) the amplitude is measured for automatic gain control of the whole system; and (ii) it synchronizes the receive end demodulation oscillator – see Single Sideband Transmission.

PINK NOISE is white noise tailored by filtering so that its mean level falls at 3 dB per octave. It is so called by analogy with red light because it emphasizes the lower frequencies (red light is at the lower frequency end of the visible spectrum). Pink noise has special uses in testing audio systems.
(>> Noise, Thermal Noise, Light, Visible Spectrum)

PIXEL Another name for a *picture element*, the smallest area which can be displayed on a television or visual display unit screen – see Picture Element.

PLANAR PROCESS Planar means "related to a plane", i.e. a flat surface. The planar process is the most commonly used method of producing semiconductor components. It is the process through which mass production first became possible for many thousands of transistors etc. can be produced simultaneously on a single silicon wafer. The name is derived from the fact that a substrate (of silicon or germanium, usually the former) is used with a flat surface into which the various impurities for n- or p-type regions are diffused. Figure P3 shows how a substrate can be processed to the stage (11) where a silicon dioxide mask adheres to the surface, hence allows diffusion products or ion implantation to affect the substrate only where apertures or "windows" are present.

In the planar process impurity atoms (e.g. boron for p-type, phosphorus for n-type), acting on the plane surface of the substrate, are able to diffuse into the material. However diffusion of the impurity atoms takes place not only normal to the surface but to a

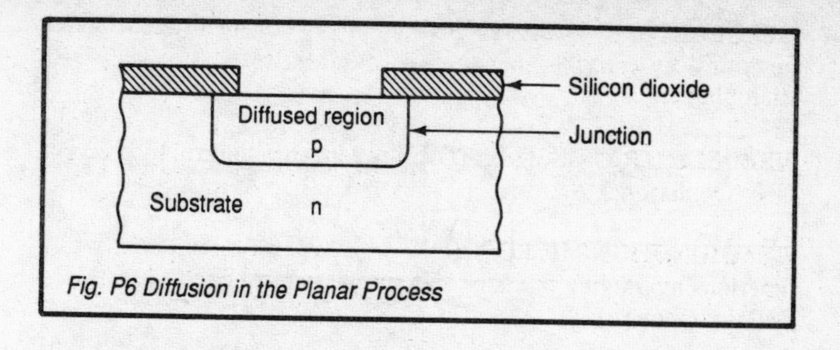

Fig. P6 Diffusion in the Planar Process

lesser extent beneath and parallel to the surface. This results in a diffused region as illustrated in Figure P6. The figure shows a single junction only, by suitable masking an n-p-n transistor for example, has a further n region diffused into the centre of the p region. Metal contacts (such as aluminium) are evaporated onto the various regions and wires are bonded to them as required.

The same type of processing is capable of making interconnections between devices, hence it is suitable for the manufacture of integrated circuits.
(* Substrate, Diffusion, Epitaxy, Photolithography >> Doping, Ion Implantation)

PLANE OF POLARIZATION A *polarized* beam of transverse waves is one with vibrations occurring in a single direction which is perpendicular to the direction of wave travel. The wave is restricted to a plane called the *plane of polarization.*

The plane of polarization is important in radio transmission because over a certain range of frequencies the transmitting and receiving antennas must match in their polarizations. In optical transmission also light beams can be modulated by polarization sensitive devices which rotate the plane as the beam passes through.
(* Antenna >> Antenna, Wave, Electromagnetic Wave, Polarization)

POLAR DIAGRAM is drawn for a quantity which varies with direction such as the sensitivity of a microphone, output of a loudspeaker or signal pick-up of an antenna, i.e. any quantity which has *directivity*. From a chosen central point a vector representing the magnitude of the quantity and its direction is considered to rotate through 360°. An example is given in Figure P7 of a polar diagram illustrating the directivity pattern of a certain type of microphone. The response directly in front, labelled 0° is maximum as indicated by the length of the vector OF. To the sides it is less as indicated by OS_1 and OS_2. To the rear of the microphone there is no

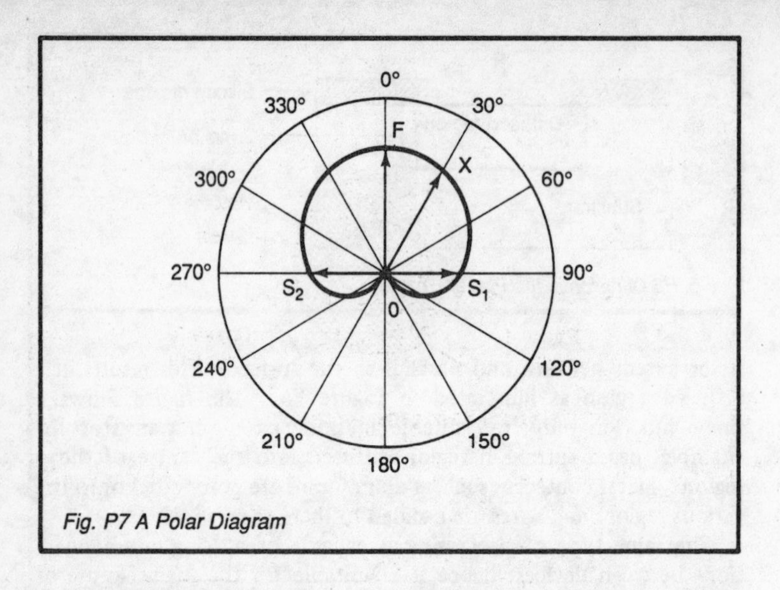

Fig. P7 A Polar Diagram

response, hence no vector. In any other direction the response is given by the vector length in that direction, e.g. at 30° by OX. (>> Vector)

POLE Each of the two terminals of an electrical network, cell or battery may be referred to as either the positive (+) or negative (–) pole. Similarly each of the two opposite points on the surface of a magnet at which the magnetic force is concentrated is known as either the North pole (N) or South pole (S).
(>> Positive, Negative, Magnetic Pole)

POLYPHASE SYSTEM "Poly" is derived from Greek meaning *many*. The term refers to an electrical system which has two or more alternating supply outputs but which are not in phase with each other. In most cases the outputs are at the same frequency and at the output terminals have the same amplitude. The polyphase system which we all know and use daily is the 3-phase electricity mains supply hence this is the system discussed here. Happily all other systems are based on the same principles. Alternating current power systems are more efficient compared with direct current systems mainly because voltages can be more easily changed and the generators do not require commutators.

The huge generators which supply our electrical power consist basically of an electromagnet (the *rotor*) rotating within a set of windings on the *stator*. This we might crudely illustrate as in Figure

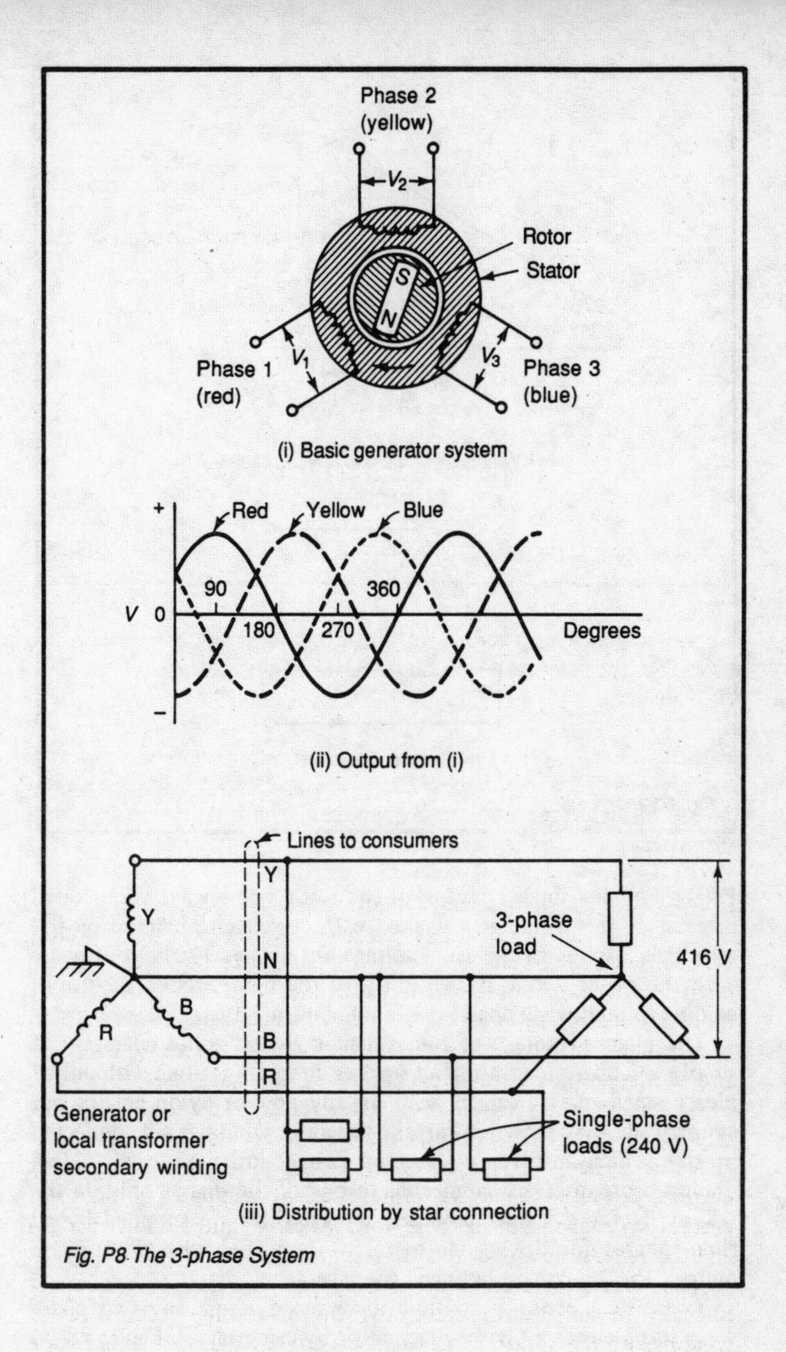

Fig. P8 The 3-phase System

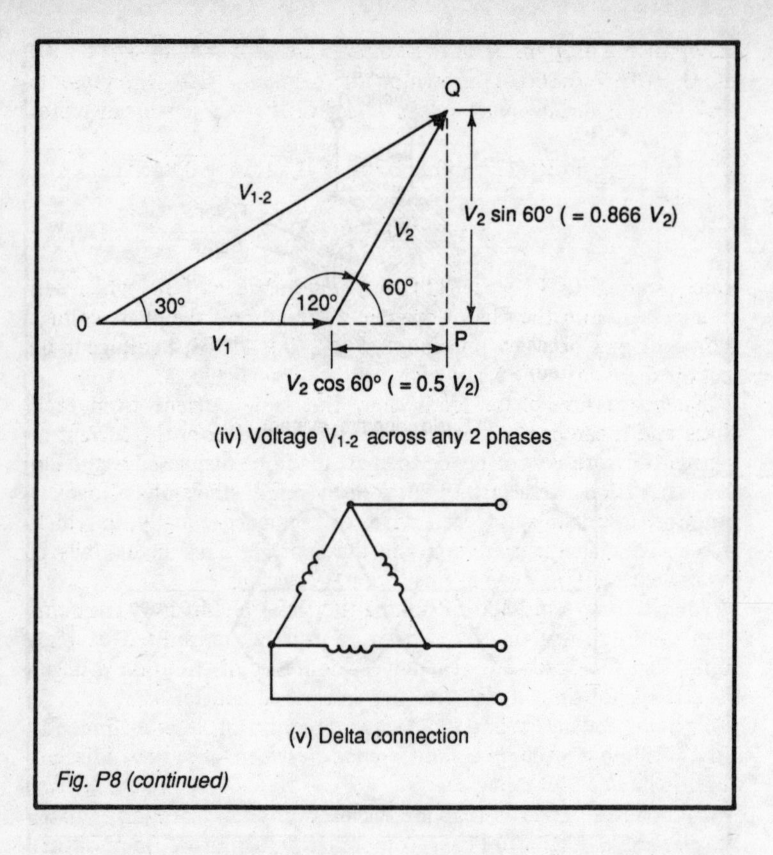

(iv) Voltage $V_{1\text{-}2}$ across any 2 phases

(v) Delta connection

Fig. P8 (continued)

P8(i). For one single rotation of the rotor a sine wave is generated in each of the windings. There are three separate pairs of output terminals, each with the same voltage but always 120° out of phase with the other two as shown in (ii) of the figure. Note the use of colours to mark each phase, this is standard practice.

The main advantage of the system is that it is not necessary to supply a 3-phase load using all 6 wires, in fact it is done with only 3 plus a small one as can be seen on any pole or pylon gracing our countryside. As shown in (iii) the generator windings are connected in *star* which involves a common connection with each. Most domestic premises are connected to one of the phases only, in the UK at 240 V. Larger premises and factories are supplied by all three phases for driving motors etc. Compared with single-phase motors, the 3-phase do not need special starting gear.

A useful exercise is to find the voltage across any two phase wires using either a phasor diagram or by calculation. Figure P8(iv) shows such a diagram. The two voltages are expressed by $V_1(1 + j0)$ and $V_2(0.5 + j0.866)$ as shown on the diagram. Here V represents peak or root mean square values. Because $V_1 = V_2$, we can write:

$$V_{1\text{-}2} = V_1(1.5 + j0.866) = V_1\sqrt{(1.5^2 + 0.866^2)}$$

$$\angle \tan^{-1}(0.866/1.5)$$

which is equal to $V_1 \times 1.732$ (i.e. $\sqrt{3}$) at an angle of 30° which can be checked from the phasor diagram. Therefore if the phase voltage is 240 V, that between phases is $\sqrt{3} \times 240 = 416$ V, a voltage to be reckoned with!

Balanced three-phase loads draw the same current from each phase and it can be shown that under these conditions the current in the neutral wire is zero hence the wire could be dispensed with. On the other hand, when power is taken by many single-phase loads it is almost impossible for each phase to be loaded equally, in which case an unbalance current flows in the neutral. This incidentally is usually earthed as shown in (iii) for safety reasons.

An alternative method of linking the three phases is by the *delta* connection, shown in (v). Power is usually transmitted at high voltages in this form but generally at domestic distribution voltages the star is used since it also provides an earthed neutral.

Systems having *n* phases normally require at least *n* lines for distribution and the phase difference between any two adjacent phases must be 360/*n* degrees.

(* Generator, Load >> Sine Wave, Complex Notation, Phase, Phasor, Phase Angle, In-Phase Component, Quadrature Component)

POSITIVE LOGIC refers to logical signals and is the condition where of the two levels, the logical 1 is the more positive. Generally in computer systems positive logic means that logical 1 is represented by +5 V and logical 0 by zero voltage (with tolerances).

(* Binary, Digital Logic, Logic Level)

POTENTIAL DIVIDER is a series arrangement of components connected across a voltage source. The current through each component is therefore the same but the voltage developed across each depends entirely on its impedance. The most common potential divider comprises two resistors in series as shown in Figure P9(i) and from Ohm's Law it is easily established that the *division ratio*, $v_o/v_i = R_2/(R_1 + R_2)$ which must always be less than 1. Clearly the division ratio does not change with input voltage. Such a circuit is frequently employed for obtaining a particular voltage from a

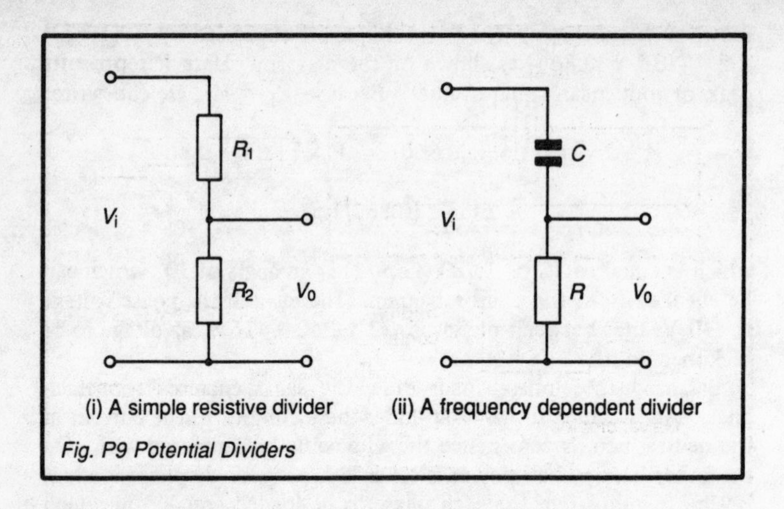

(i) A simple resistive divider (ii) A frequency dependent divider

Fig. P9 Potential Dividers

higher voltage source. Several resistors may be used to obtain a range of voltages.

The resistive circuit in (i) has the same division ratio at all frequencies. If however one of the components is a capacitor or an inductor then the division ratio becomes frequency dependent. As an example, in (ii) of the figure the potential divider consists of a capacitor and a resistor in series. As the frequency of v_i rises so the reactance of C falls hence more of the voltage is dropped across R, i.e. the division ratio rises. For a practical use of this, see R_1C_1 of Figure D3.

If we exchange the capacitor C for a diode, the circuit is still that of a potential divider but now things become more complicated because the division ratio changes with the value of the voltage applied.
(>> Ohm's Law, Reactance, Diode)

POTENTIOMETER (1) is an instrument for measuring or adjusting electric potential in terms of the length of a uniform resistance wire acting as a potential divider. The essential features are shown in Figure P10(i), connected for example for measurement of the voltage of the battery or cell B_2.

AB is a length of uniform resistance wire with a sliding contact, C which is connected to the unknown potential and galvanometer G. Connected across the wire is a battery B_1 of voltage greater than that expected from B_2. This battery therefore provides a constant current flowing through the resistance wire. A most important corollary is that no current must flow through the slider otherwise

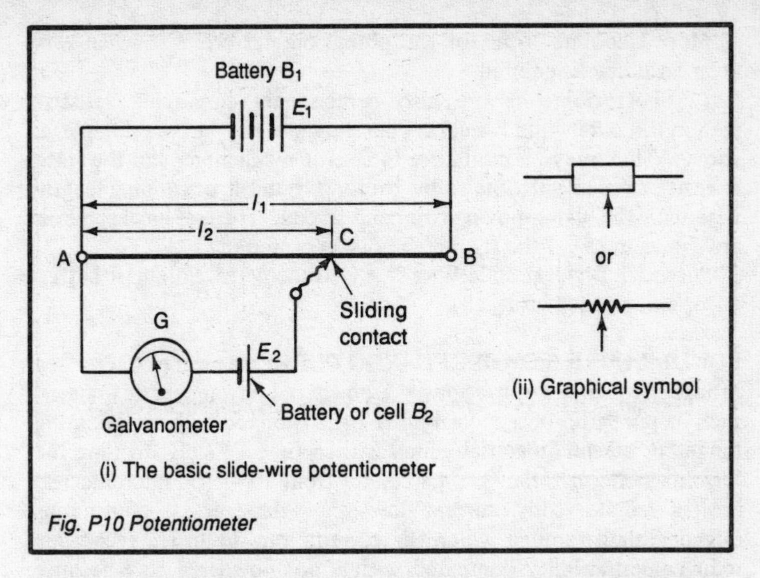

Fig. P10 Potentiometer

the potential difference along the wire per unit length is not constant. In use therefore the slider is adjusted until this condition is obtained, i.e. G (which preferably is a centre-zero instrument) registers zero current. The potentiometer is then said to be balanced.

If the lengths of the potentiometer wire are l_1 and l_2 and the battery voltages are E_1 and E_2 as shown, then the potential difference per unit length of the wire is E_1/l_1 volts per metre, hence:

$$E_2 = \text{potential difference per unit length} \times l_2\ ,$$

i.e.:

$$E_1/l_1 = E_2/l_2$$

so if E_1 is known, E_2 can be determined.

If the value of E_1 is not known accurately (remember it may not be possible to use a standard cell directly since its voltage is only about 1 V) then a standard cell (C_s) is brought in to replace the unknown battery or cell, B_2. The potentiometer is again balanced and if the length of wire for balance is now l_2, then if E_s is the voltage of the standard cell:

$$E_s/l_s = E_1/l_1$$

so that E_1 can be determined from which the original unknown, E_2 follows.

More elaborate forms of the potentiometer are used when very great accuracy is required.

(2) Potentiometers are also components employing resistive carbon or wire-wound tracks operating on the basic principle as above. They may be miniature in size or much larger and the track is either circular with the slider rotating round it or running lengthwise with the slider moving from end to end. The graphical symbols are shown in (ii) of the figure (the first is preferred).
(* Potential Divider, Slide Wire >> Galvanometer, Potential Difference, Weston Standard Cell)

POWDER CORE (POWDERED-IRON CORE) is a magnetic core used in high frequency applications. A powdered ferromagnetic material such as pure iron or a special alloy of it is mixed with an insulating binder or ceramic material which is then fired. Finely dividing the ferromagnetic material (grain sizes are from 10 – 100 micrometres) greatly reduces eddy current loss since there is no continuous electrical path through which the currents can flow. The technique reduces permeability compared with a non-powdered core because there is less magnetic material. Permeabilities are around 100 to 125.
(>> Core, Core Loss, Ferromagnetism, Eddy Current)

POWER AMPLIFIER is one which delivers a relatively large output power into a load, usually by an appreciable current into a low impedance load such as a moving-coil loudspeaker. The term is used to distinguish this type of amplifier from a *voltage amplifier* which normally drives an amplifying stage with high input impedance, therefore with insignificant power output. Power amplifiers may have output powers ranging from a fraction of one watt up to many hundreds for audio work, robots etc. but up to many kilowatts when the amplifier supplies power to a transmitting antenna.
(* Antenna, Loudspeaker >> Amplifier)

PREAMPLIFIER This is an amplifier which precedes a main amplifier, e.g. most audio power output amplifiers require a preamplifier to provide a sufficiently high input signal. Generally but certainly not in all cases, preamplifiers are voltage amplifiers and they may contain frequency correction networks. As an example, magnetic tape playback heads are likely to work directly into a preamplifier which boosts the very small audio signal to a level suitable for driving a power amplifier and also contains the required equalization (frequency correction).
(* Power Amplifier, Equalization, Magnetic Recording >> Amplifier)

PRE-EMPHASIS When coupled with *de-emphasis* is a technique for improving the signal-to-noise ratio over a transmission system. It has been established that a good signal-to-noise ratio is more important at the higher audio frequencies than at the lower ones for satisfactory articulation or understanding of speech. Accordingly the technique is to use pre-emphasis of the audio signal at the transmitter by progressively raising the audio level at the higher frequencies then using de-emphasis in the receiver to restore to the original overall frequency response. In the journey over the channel therefore the signal-to-noise ratio at the higher frequencies is improved because the signal level has been raised and this improvement remains when the audio signal is de-emphasised at the receiving end.

Figure P11 illustrates this graphically, showing at (i) that if for example, the noise is constant at all operational frequencies, the signal-to-noise ratio is constant with frequency. In the figure at (ii) and (iii) is shown how the improved signal-to-noise ratio is obtained at the higher frequencies. Of course care must be taken that the higher signal levels do not give rise to overloading on the channel. Very simple networks for pre-emphasis and de-emphasis are also shown. In practice values of pre-emphasis (and de-emphasis for one must match the other) of some 4 – 6 dB per octave above a specified frequency (say, around 400 Hz) are used so giving an *overall* signal-to-noise ratio improvement of well over 10 dB.

The technique is also used particularly with frequency or phase modulation communication systems. In these the modulation index is increased at the higher frequencies at the transmitter and the original frequency response is restored in the receiver.

Pre-emphasis with accompanying de-emphasis is similarly employed in magnetic tape recording to reduce the effect of tape noise. The principles are the same.

(* Channel, Signal-to-Noise Ratio, Magnetic Recording >> Decibel, Frequency Modulation, Modulation Index)

PREFERRED VALUES are those designed specifically to reduce the enormous range of values a component such as a resistor or capacitor may have to a range which is manageable. In electronic design for example, the value of say, a transistor collector load may be calculated as 1224 Ω. To expect such a value to be available "over the counter" is more than a little optimistic, so the nearest preferred value of 1200 Ω is accepted, the difference in performance of the design, considering all the other tolerances which are around, may be negligible.

Each value in the system differs from its predecessor by a constant multiplier but rounded to two significant figures. As the

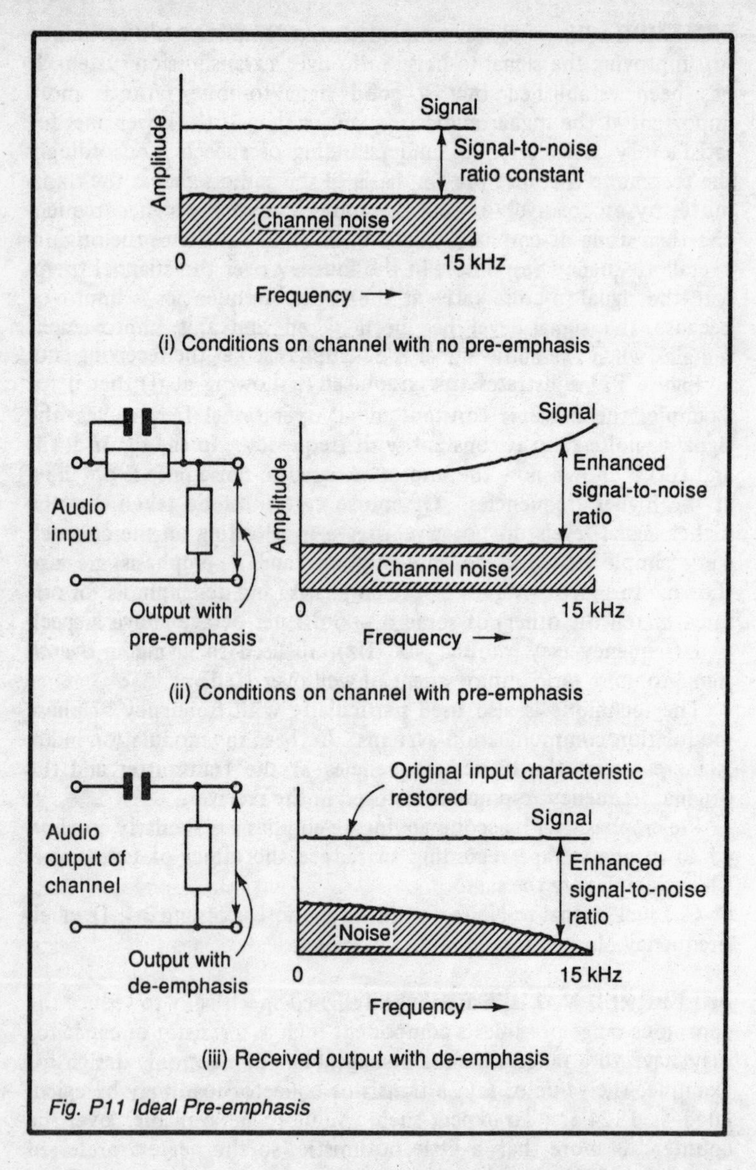

Fig. P11 Ideal Pre-emphasis

component tolerance falls so the number of preferred values available increases. This provides minimum overlapping between one value and the next due to tolerance spreads. Because ± 20%, ± 10% and ± 5% tolerances are in greatest use, a basic series of values has been adopted as shown in the table following. The values may be multiplied by a multiple of 10 or divided by 10:

Tolerance																									Series
20%	10				15				22				33				47				68				E6
10%	10		12		15		18		22		27		33		39		47		56		68		82		E12
5%	10	11	12	13	15	16	18	20	22	24	27	30	33	36	39	43	47	51	56	62	68	75	82	91	E24

Each series is coded by an E number as shown above.

A designer calling for discrete components uses preferred values if possible. If not, then series or parallel combinations of two or more preferred values are likely to produce a value almost as required, e.g. a resistor of value 59 Ω is not likely to be easily available because it is not a preferred value but it can be made up from a 20 and a 39 in series. Again a 460 Ω comes almost exactly from a 510 and 4700 in parallel. Tables are available showing all combinations.
(* Colour Code, Tolerance, Resistor >> Capacitor)

PRESSURE-GRADIENT MICROPHONE is a microphone which has an output proportional to the instantaneous particle velocity of the incident sound wave, the *ribbon* microphone is an example. Both faces of the ribbon are accessible to the sound wave. However because the wave reaching the back of the ribbon has a greater distance to travel its effect on the ribbon is out of phase with that of the wave at the front, the magnitude of the phase difference depending on the length of the various paths existing between front and back. It is the difference between front and back pressures which moves the ribbon and the net pressure multiplied by the ribbon area gives the total force acting at any particular time. It can be shown that the velocity attained by the ribbon is proportional to this force and hence to the particle velocity of the wave. For this reason it is also known as a *velocity* microphone. Sensitivity of this type of microphone is generally lower than that of most others – see Microphone and/or Figure M10(iii).

PRINTED CIRCUIT – see Printed Wiring.

PRINTED WIRING This is a system of flat conductors formed on one or both sides of an insulating board for the interconnection of electronic components. These are fitted onto the board in such a way that their connecting tags can be soldered to the conductors. The board is usually a rigid epoxy resin glass fibre laminate. Copper conductors are formed on it by:

(i) an additive process in which the metal is deposited on the surface of the laminate to the pattern required; or

(ii) a subtractive process in which the laminate is coated completely on one side with the copper foil which is etched away where not required (see Photolithography).

Where very small values of resistance, capacitance or inductance are required, these may also be provided by printing. Capacitors for example, can be produced by printing conducting areas on both sides of the laminate, the laminate therefore acting as a dielectric. Inductors may be formed by printing wiring spirally. In such cases the unit containing both wiring and printed components is known as a *printed circuit.* However this term now generally finds favour to describe also any printed wiring board on which discrete components are mounted.

The printed wiring board lends itself especially to automatic assembly. Machines are capable of mounting the components and soldering them in even with the most complex circuits.
(>> Resistance, Capacitance, Inductance)

PROBE is a resonant conductor inserted in a waveguide or cavity resonator for injecting or extracting energy, see for example, Figure K1.

A probe is also a pointed conductor on the end of a test lead used for exploring voltages in a practical circuit. The probe may contain the input stage of an electronic voltmeter or oscilloscope so that loading of the circuit under test by the capacitance of the test leads is minimized.
(* Cavity Resonator, Oscilloscope >> Waveguide)

PROGRAM In the computer world this is a set of instructions written in a particular computer language which the computer understands. This enables the machine to carry out a series of operations as required. The versatility of a computer lies solely in the fact that it can be instructed (programmed) to carry out many different tasks, for example, calculations, control of machines, word processing, sorting.

The instructions are typed in on a keyboard and a special program in the machine recognizes each instruction and changes it into the appropriate binary code which the processor understands. The program is then held in the computer memory in this form or may be output onto a magnetic disc for storage and subsequent use.
(* Computer, Binary, Binary Code, Programming Language)

PROGRAMMING LANGUAGE Data supplied to a computer and processing within the machine is effected solely in binary notation, this is known as *machine code*. To program a computer directly in machine code (i.e. to key everything in as 0's and 1's only) is time consuming and fraught with the possibility of error. Accordingly special *high-level languages* are used which are built up from everyday words and symbols. Instructions in such languages are therefore entered by the programmer and a special program held in the computer memory known as an *interpreter* does just that, it changes the high-level language instructions into the appropriate machine code.

There are several high-level languages, each being especially suitable for a particular type of work. Examples are: FORTRAN (Formula Translation) for scientific work; COBOL (Common Business Oriented Language) for business computing; BASIC (Beginners' All-Purpose Symbolic Instruction Code), a general easy-to-learn code.
(* Computer, Binary, Binary Notation, Program)

PROPORTIONAL COUNTER – see Geiger Counter.

PSOPHOMETER is a noise-measuring instrument used especially on commercial telephone circuits. The noise power is measured through a weighting network, i.e. a network which results in the measurements giving reasonable estimations of subjective results (using human listeners).
(* Weighting Network >> Noise)

PULSE CODE MODULATION (p.c.m.) is a modulation system widely used over transmission lines, especially in telephony. It has an inherent resistance to corruption from external noise although it does have its own unhelpful way of generating noise within itself. This latter noise however can be kept low at some 40 – 80 dB below the signal level depending on the system used. The system also lends itself to multi-channel working on a time-division basis.

To convert an analogue signal into its pulse code equivalent involves firstly sampling and quantizing the signal regularly then coding the quantization levels using the binary code. The complete modulation process is shown graphically in Figure P12. In this drawing a mere 16 quantization levels are shown (labelled 0 – 15), practical systems however work with 100 or so for commercial speech up to over 8000 for high quality sound. The actual figure is a function of the number of digits in the binary code and of course the more digits there are, the more transmission bandwidth is required. As shown in the figure, a binary code of 4 digits allows 16 quantization levels ($2^4 = 16$). A high quality sound system might have $2^{13} = 8192$ levels.

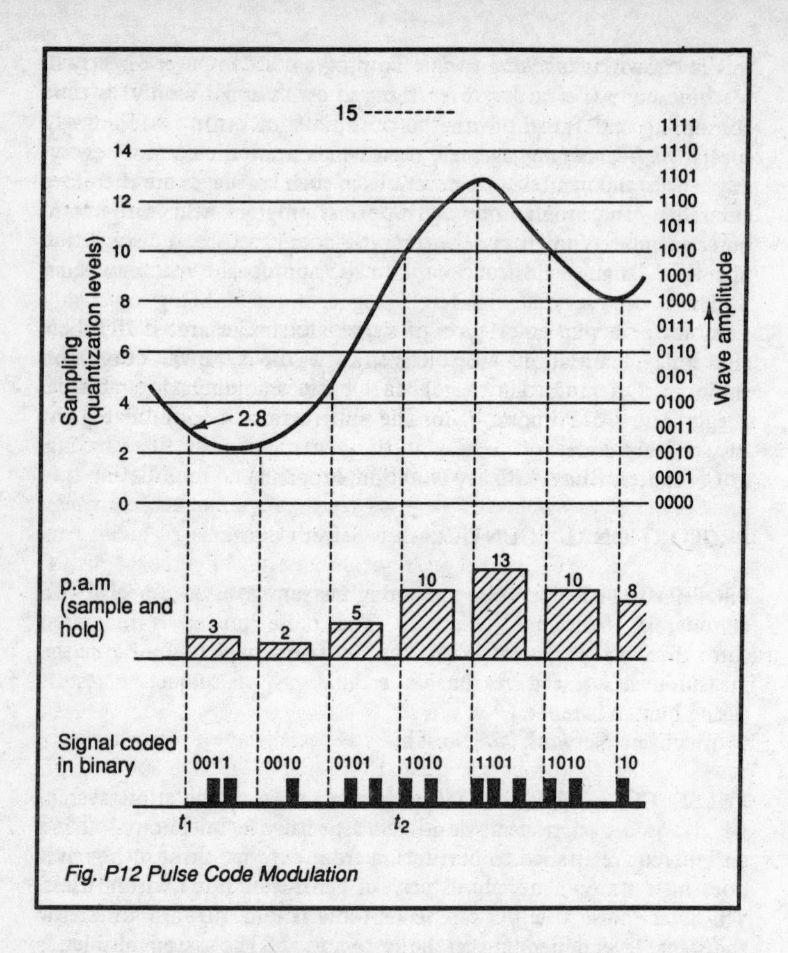

Fig. P12 Pulse Code Modulation

At time t_1 the wave is sampled resulting in quantization level 3. Note the small *quantization error* in that 3 does not represent exactly the level of the signal at that instant. It takes time to set up the binary signal of (in this case) 4 digits, hence the amplitude of each sampling pulse is held constant until the binary code corresponding to it has been generated. The figure shows the "sample and hold" pulses. Each of these is then converted into the group of binary digits which represents that particular amplitude. Also in the figure at the right hand side is the appropriate binary code for each quantizing level. As a second example, at t_2 the binary code 1010 sent to line indicates that at that instant the analogue signal amplitude was nearest to quantization level 10.

The pulses transmitted to line now have constant amplitude and this is where p.c.m. scores. No matter how much distortion a pulse suffers in transmission or how much noise is picked up on the way, as long as a pulse (or no pulse) can be recognised electronically at some distant point, then a new "clean" one can be generated (the equipment is known as a *regenerator*). Normal amplification which in fact amplifies not only the distortions but also the noise, is not required. Over long distances the pulse train can be regenerated as often as is necessary.

At the receiving end the coded signal is first regenerated and then it meets a decoder. This is followed by a converter, the output of which is a p.a.m. train, a replica of the sending end quantized samples shown in Figure P12. The p.a.m. train is demodulated by the simple process of passing it through a low-pass filter having a cut-off frequency just above the highest original modulating frequency. This may be contrary to all reasonable expectations when most other demodulation processes require non-linearity but it can be shown that although the pulses contain frequency components theoretically up to infinity, the modulating frequency resides at the low frequency end.

(* Sampling, Quantization Distortion, Binary, Binary Code >> Pulse, Pulse Modulation, Filter)

PUSH-PULL OPERATION This is a special way of operating two transistors so that they conduct 180° apart. In one method of operation the positive half-cycles of the incoming wave are fed to one transistor, the negative half-cycles to the other. The output of the two transistors is combined in such a way that the normal wave is reconstructed. The transistors can be operated as Class A, Class AB, or as Class B amplifiers, usually the latter. Figure P13 shows at (i) the elements of the earliest type of transistor push-pull amplifier in which an input transformer with a centre-tapped secondary winding is used to achieve the 180° phase difference and a second centre-tapped output transformer combines the two half-waves.

As an alternative, to dispense with the input transformer, a *phase-splitting* stage may be used. This develops two signals in antiphase (180° apart) from a single input signal as does the transformer.

It is of course desirable to avoid the use of transformers altogether so to this end complementary push-pull operation has been developed. This requires a matched pair of output transistors, one n-p-n, the other p-n-p. These generally work in Class B with a small quiescent current to minimize crossover distortion. A phase-

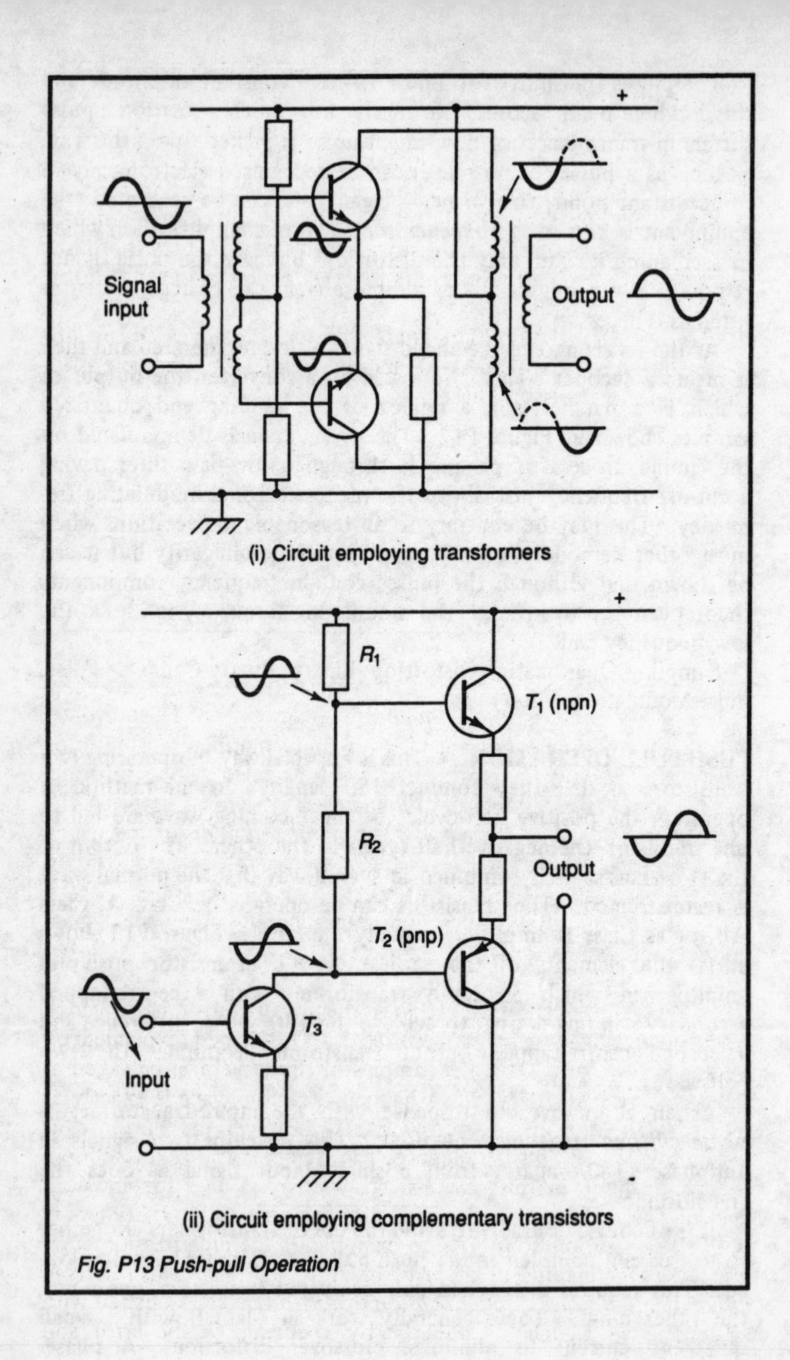

Fig. P13 Push-pull Operation

splitting stage is not required and a basic circuit is shown in (ii) of Figure P13. T_1 and T_2 are the matched pair of transistors. R_1 and R_2 in conjunction with T_3 are of such values that the positive bias applied to T_1 and negative bias to T_2 (both forward) provide the small quiescent currents. The input signal is applied to the base of T_3 (biasing not shown). T_1 and T_2 are fed with in-phase signals but being complementary transistors, when one conducts the other is driven "off". The two outputs together therefore meet to form a complete wave as shown.
(* Class A, AB, B Amplifier, Phase Splitter, Crossover Distortion, Complementary Transistors, Operating Point >> Characteristic, Transformer, Transistor, Phase)

Q

QUANTIZATION is the process of representing an analogue signal by steps or discrete levels (*quantum* = amount). This involves division of the analogue range into a finite number of amplitude levels, each of which is represented by an assigned value. Information as to the movements of the analogue waveform between the discrete levels is lost, this is known as *quantization distortion* which is apparent as an added (quantization) noise – see Quantization Distortion.
(* Analogue-to-Digital Conversion, Sampling >> Analogue Signal, Pulse, Pulse Modulation)

QUANTIZATION DISTORTION is the distortion or noise added when an analogue signal is *quantized*. This is best explained by reference to Figure Q1. Let samples of the waveform be taken at times t_1 and t_2. At t_1, it so happens that the wave is exactly at quantization level 10, no error. At t_2 however the waveform is between levels 11 and 12. Suppose the system is arranged to choose the nearer level, in this case 12. Now there is an error and it is evident that the maximum uncertainty or error is $\pm\, Q/2$ where Q is the quantization step. As an example, if the quantization steps are 1 mV, there could be an error of up to 0.5 mV. This results in a *quantization noise* or *quantization distortion* being associated with all quantized signals. Evidently by reducing Q the error and

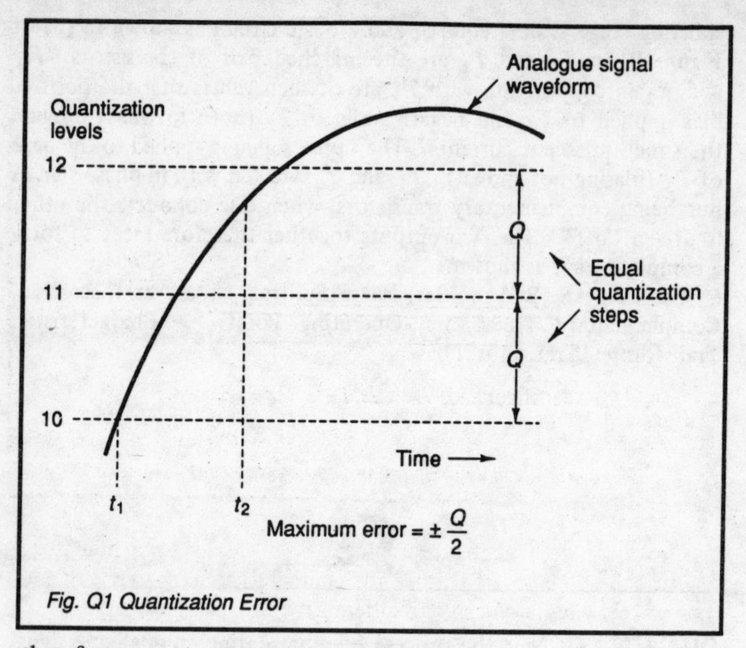

Fig. Q1 Quantization Error

therefore quantization noise is reduced but it cannot be completely eliminated.
(* Quantization, Sampling >> Analogue Signal)

QUANTIZATION NOISE The noise added when an analogue signal is sampled – see Quantization Distortion.

QUARTER-WAVE LINE This is a transmission line one-quarter of a wavelength long ($\lambda/4$) at the operating frequency. It is a particularly useful device for it can be used for matching two unequal impedances, especially an antenna to its feeder and also it is able to present a theoretically infinite impedance at one end when the other end is short-circuited. Generally it is a high or very high frequency device at which wave-lengths are short enough to be manageable.

The special condition which arises on such a line is that if, for example, we wish to match the characteristic impedance, Z_f of an antenna feeder to that of the antenna itself, Z_a, then:

$$Z_0 = \sqrt{Z_f Z_a}$$

where Z_0 is the characteristic impedance of the section of line to be used for matching.

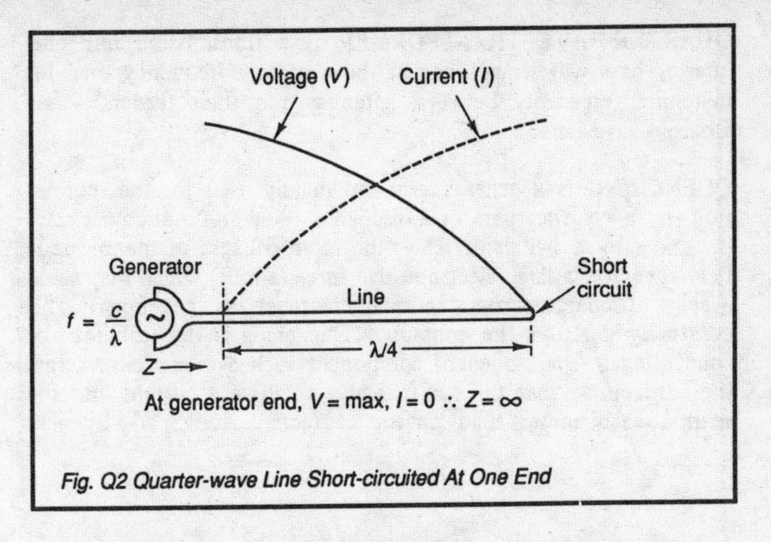

Fig. Q2 Quarter-wave Line Short-circuited At One End

For example, if a coaxial cable of Z_f = 75 Ω is to be matched to an antenna of Z_a = 36 Ω, then the characteristic impedance of a λ/4 line which will match cable to antenna:

$$Z_0 = \sqrt{75 \times 36} = 52\ \Omega$$

and such a line is known as a *quarter-wavelength transformer*. This particular condition arises not only when the transmission line is one-quarter of a wavelength long but also for any odd number of quarter wavelengths.

Next consider a transmission line λ/4 long and fed by a generator of the appropriate frequency. As shown in Figure Q2, if the end remote from the generator is short-circuited, the voltage at that end must be zero, whereas the current is maximum. This establishes current and voltage standing waves as shown. Clearly for the λ/4 line, with voltage maximum and current zero at the generator end, the impedance there looking into the line must be infinite (never forgetting that this is only at the operating frequency corresponding to λ). This gives the line an isolating property which makes mechanically strong λ/4 structures useful for supporting lines and antennas with practically no loss. Note however that although the λ/4 line presents an extremely high impedance at a carrier frequency, it will be somewhat less for any sidebands.

See Balun. See also Dipole Antenna for use of a quarter-wave line open-circuited at one end.
(* Matching, Antenna, Coaxial Cable >> Transmission Line, Characteristic Impedance, Standing Wave, Node)

QUARTER-WAVE TRANSFORMER is a transmission line one-quarter of a wavelength long at the operating frequency used for matching, especially between antennas and their feeders – see Quarter-Wave Line.

QUENCHING is a general term but mainly used for the suppression of an electric spark or a discharge. When an inductive circuit is broken by a switch or relay, the rapid collapse of the magnetic field generates a large electromotive force (e.m.f.) which may cause a spark discharge across the switch contacts as they open. This eventually destroys the contacts. Quenching is the technique of connecting a (spark-quench) component such as a capacitor across the contacts so that the e.m.f. is able to drive a current into the spark-quench rather than via the contacts – see Spark Quench.

R

RADAR is an acronym of *Ra*dio *D*etection *A*nd *R*anging. It is a method for detecting and measuring the range of a distant *target* using beamed microwaves (or alternatively optical waves). Detection of a target relies on the fact that there is reflection of an electromagnetic wave at any discontinuity in the atmosphere. The technique is therefore to transmit regular pulses of radio energy from a highly directional antenna then examine any returned signals for direction and time of the round trip.

The basic layout of a microwave radar system is given in Figure R1. The sequence is started by the synchronizer, this causes the modulator to apply a pulse to the radio frequency (r.f.) power amplifier and at the same time a drive signal is applied to the power amplifier by the exciter. The pulse of radio frequency energy is fed via the duplexer to the antenna. In the return direction the signal is received by the same antenna, then mixed with the output of a local oscillator to produce an intermediate frequency which is demodulated, processed and passed to the display cathode-ray tube. The synchronizer ensures that the display time base operates at the right time. The figure shows both transmitted and received signals, the distance between them on the screen being used to calculate the target distance. Frequently the antenna is rotated mechanically with

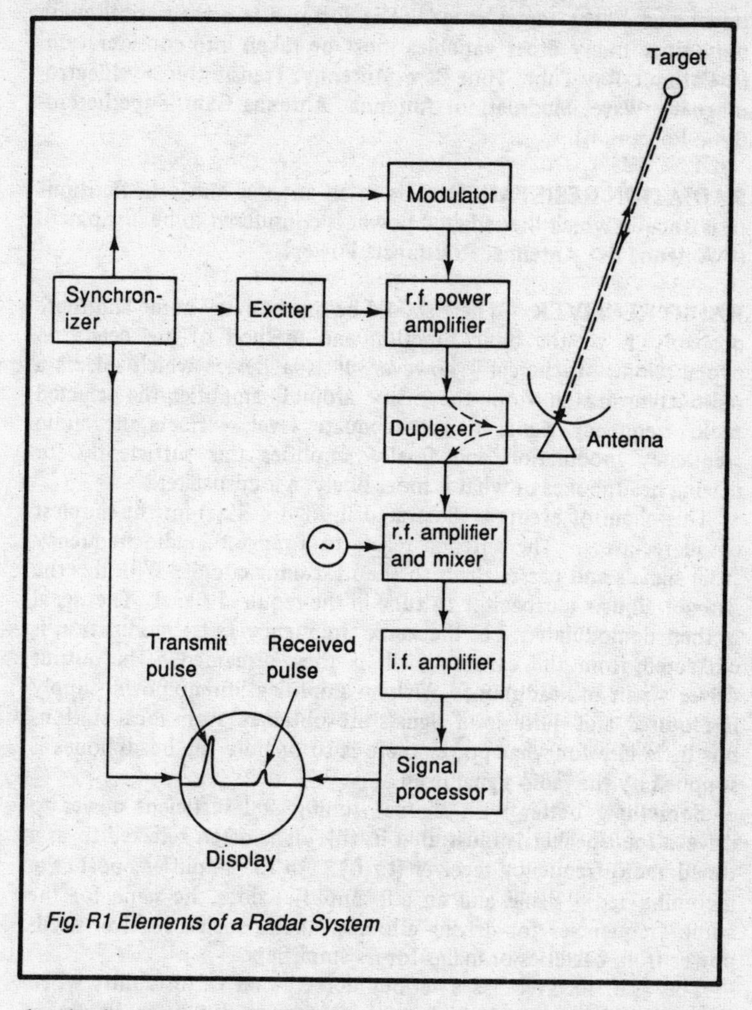

Fig. R1 Elements of a Radar System

the display time base running from centre to edge of the tube and rotating in synchronism with the antenna. In this case the range is measured radially from the centre of the tube.

The basic radar equation for the received signal power is:

$$P_r = \frac{P_t G^2 \lambda^2 \sigma}{(4\pi)^3 R^4}$$

where P_t is the transmitted power, G, the antenna gain, λ, the wavelength of transmission, σ, the effective reflecting area of the target and *R* the target range. The formula is a theoretical guide only since many other variables must be taken into consideration. (* Cathode-Ray Tube, Time Base, Antenna, Transmitter >> Electromagnetic Wave, Modulation, Antenna, Antenna Gain, Superheterodyne Reception)

RADIATION RESISTANCE refers to an antenna and is the fictitious resistance in which the radiated power is considered to be dissipated. (* Antenna >> Antenna, Resistance, Power)

RADIO RECEIVER There should be one in every home and there probably is so the basic function and method of use needs no explanation. Technically however, it is a device which selects a radio transmission from the many around, amplifies the selected radio frequency signal to an adequate level, extracts the audio frequency modulation and finally amplifies this sufficiently for driving headphones or what is more likely, a loudspeaker.

This chain of events is illustrated in Figure R2(i) for the simplest of all receivers. The antenna reacts to a range of radio frequency (r.f.) signals and passes them to the r.f. tuning circuit. With this the listener adjusts a capacitor to tune in the required signal. The signal is then demodulated, i.e. the audio frequency (a.f.) modulation is extracted from the carrier which is then discarded. The output drives a pair of headphones. With no amplification, no power supply is required and quite loud signals are obtained from local stations but little else for what power there is to operate the headphones is supplied by the radio signal itself.

Something better with sharper tuning and sufficient power to drive a loudspeaker is illustrated in (ii). It is often referred to as a tuned radio frequency receiver (t.r.f.). An r.f. amplifier boosts the incoming radio signal and an a.f. amplifier does the same for the audio frequencies for driving a loudspeaker. Such a receiver needs power from batteries or mains for its amplifiers.

The t.r.f. receiver has a serious defect, that of instability when r.f. amplifier gains are high as is necessary for weak incoming signals, for then the receiver whistles or "howls". This brings us to a more complex type of receiver, the *superheterodyne* or for short, *superhet*. This type is almost universally used and generally the t.r.f. remains the province of amateur constructors and experimenters.

The *superheterodyne* principle introduces another frequency known as the *intermediate frequency* (i.f.) into the receiver chain. In practice for a.m. receivers the antenna is often a *ferrite rod* type so that it can be contained within the cabinet or case. The tuning and amplifying stages are followed by a demodulator (detector)

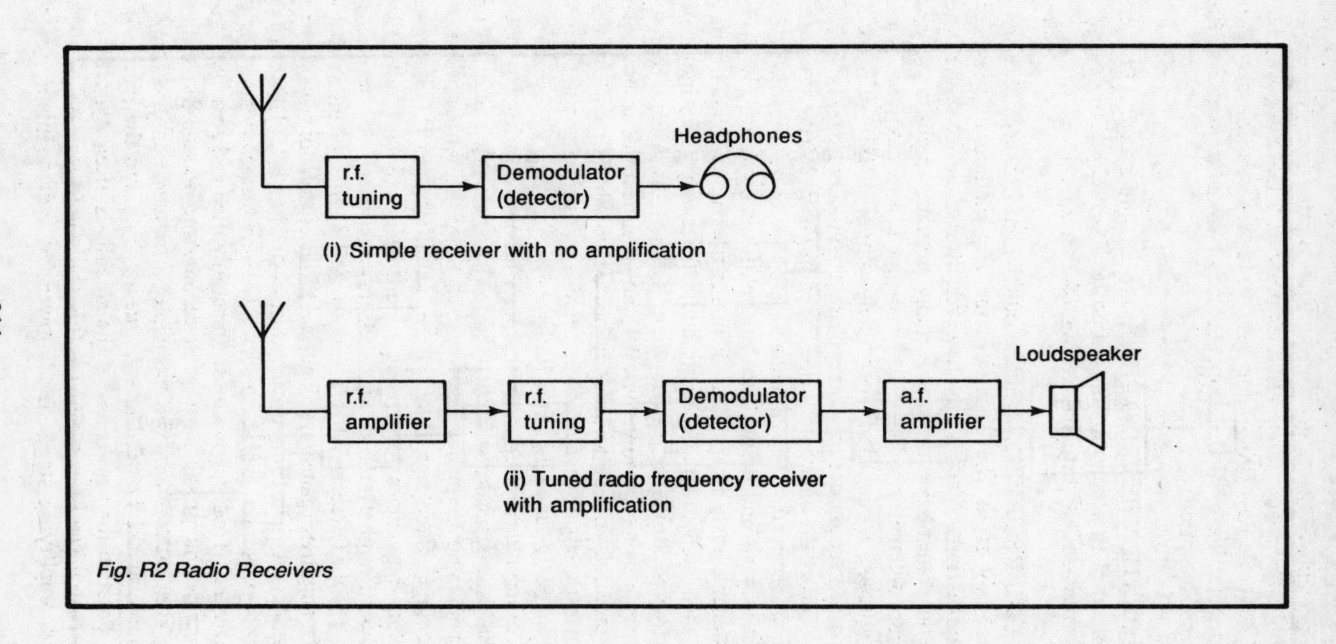

Fig. R2 Radio Receivers

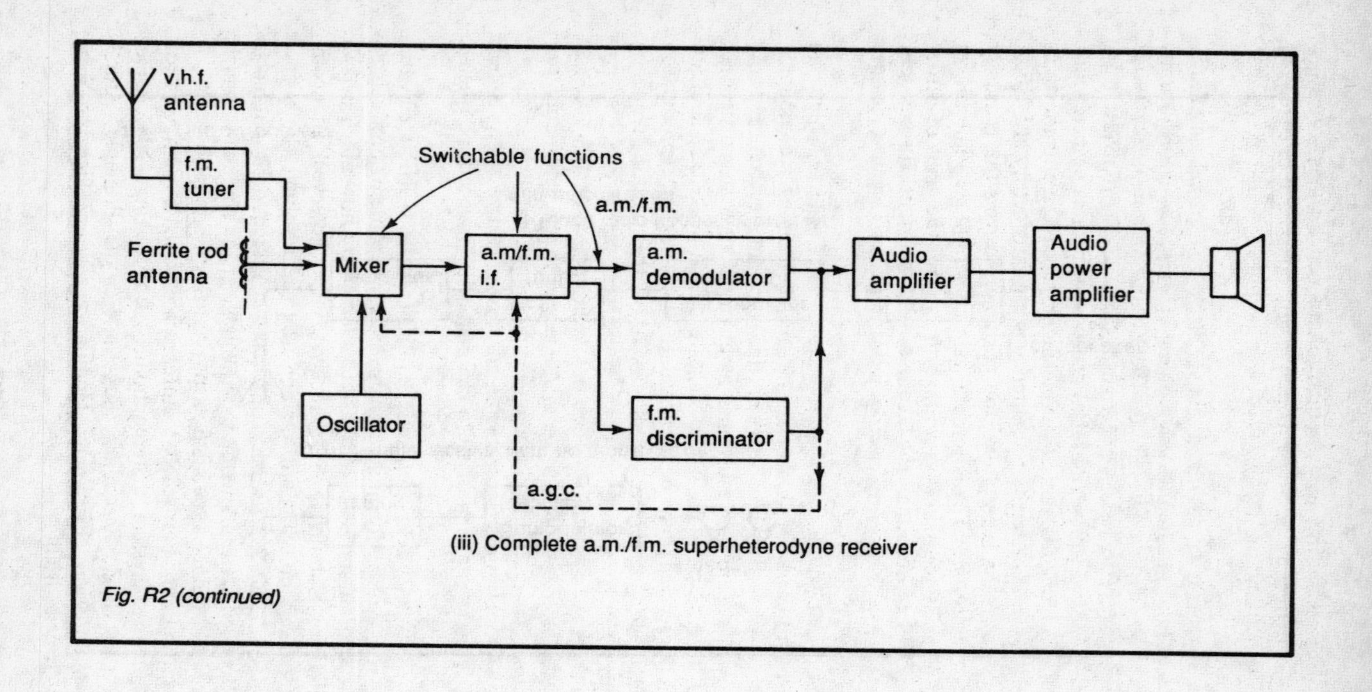

(iii) Complete a.m./f.m. superheterodyne receiver

Fig. R2 (continued)

which regains the original modulation frequencies. Lastly comes the audio frequency section which typically consists of one stage of voltage amplification feeding a power amplifier which drives the loudspeaker.

The receivers as described above work to normal amplitude modulated (a.m.) or frequency modulated (f.m.) radio transmissions. A.M. transmissions are usually on the LF and MF frequency bands (30 kHz – 3MHz) whereas f.m. transmissions are more likely to be in the VHF band (30 – 300 MHz) because of the greater bandwidth required. A block diagram of a typical a.m./f.m. receiver is shown in Figure R2(iii). The ferrite rod antenna is not satisfactory at VHF so a separate antenna is employed, on portable receivers this is usually an extendable rod. The automatic gain control (a.g.c.) line shown in the diagram feeds back a voltage to control the gains of earlier stages so as to maintain the audio output substantially constant irrespective of variations in the input signal. This is a feature common to most receivers.

More complicated is the *stereophonic* f.m. receiver which can demodulate and reproduce transmissions containing stereophonic sound. The difference between this type of receiver and the *monophonic* is in the additional requirement of a stereo decoder and of duplication of the audio stages and loudspeaker. In addition the audio section may be designed for high-fidelity reproduction and include controls for modification of the output frequency response.

Much of the modern receiver employs integrated circuits (IC) and in fact all in Figure R2(iii) from the mixer to the audio amplifier (and including both of these) may be contained within a single IC. In addition microprocessors enable automatic controls to be added, e.g. automatic sampling of radio channels with an interrupt when a signal is detected.

As with any system containing amplifiers, noise is generated within it. The weakest incoming signal which is capable of producing a satisfactory output is therefore not governed by how much overall amplification is available in the receiver but by how weak an incoming signal can be while still making itself heard above the output noise level. Hence sensitivity of a receiver is frequently quoted in these terms, i.e. the minimum signal voltage at the antenna terminals required to produce a specified output signal-to-noise ratio.

(* Loudspeaker, Ferrite Rod Antenna, Automatic Gain Control, Stereophonic System, Stereophonic Broadcasting >> Radio, Frequency Band, Resonance, Superheterodyne Principle, Amplitude Modulation, Frequency Modulation, Noise, Signal-to-Noise Ratio, Tuned Circuit)

RAM is an abbreviation for *random access memory*, a type of memory used in computers. Any single location in the memory can be accessed directly – see Computer.

RATIO DETECTOR is a detector (i.e. a demodulator) employed in frequency and phase modulation systems. It is based on the circuit of a phase discriminator [see Fig.F5(iii)] but with a limiter added and although in a frequency modulation (f.m.) system there is slightly higher distortion the circuit is generally preferred because of the added facility of limiting, although the number of circuit components is almost the same.

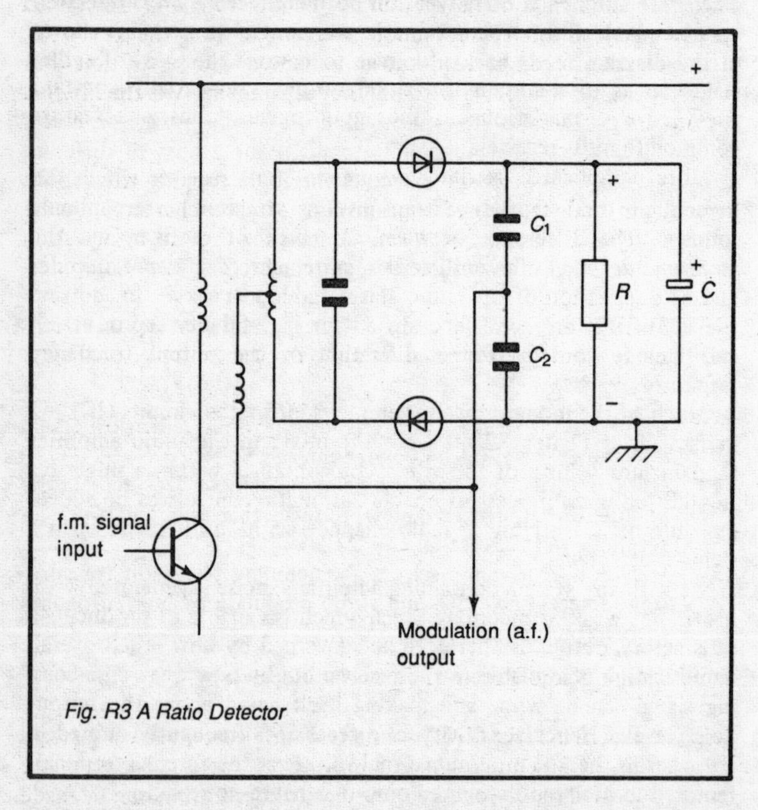

Fig. R3 A Ratio Detector

A typical ratio detector (or ratio discriminator) circuit is given in Figure R3 and it is immediately evident that, compared with the circuit of Figure F5(iii), one of the diodes is reversed. With an unmodulated carrier therefore, instead of producing zero output by cancellation of the two diode outputs, the ratio detector adds them together resulting in a voltage across R as shown. When the carrier frequency changes, this voltage stays relatively constant (and is held so by capacitor C) but the *ratio* between the diode outputs varies, hence the description *ratio detector.* The variations appear across C_1 and C_2 and are the modulation output.

Many variations of the circuit exist, especially when integration is required.
(* Frequency Discriminator, Limiter >> Demodulation, Diode, Distortion)

READ-ONLY MEMORY (ROM) is a computer memory store in which the information is set during manufacture and is retained permanently, it therefore cannot be changed from the keyboard. The information can be read out an unlimited number of times but nothing can be written into it. This type of memory is the internal permanent memory of the machine and it is read by the processor to find out what to do and how to do it for a host of different manipulations. As a single example, the ROM supplies the various binary instructions required for display of each character on the screen. ROM is classed as *non-volatile* meaning that the information is not lost when the machine is switched off – see Computer.

RECEIVER is a general term for a device which converts an electrical signal into a desired form of output. Typical examples of the use of the term are:

(1) telephone receiver – converts the incoming electrical signal into sound waves (also known as an *earphone*);
(2) radio receiver – selects an incoming radio wave, detects the modulation it carries and reproduces this as sound from an earphone or loudspeaker;
(3) television receiver – selects an incoming television transmission, detects the video and audio modulations and reproduces them as picture and sound.

(* Earphone, Radio Receiver, Television Receiver)

RECTIFIER INSTRUMENT is an alternating current (a.c.) measuring instrument based usually on a moving-coil meter. Such a meter on its own is suitable for direct current (d.c.) only but can be made to read a.c. if this is first rectified. A diode bridge circuit is commonly employed, connected as shown in Figure R4. In most cases the maximum meter current is less than 1 mA hence the diodes may be miniature semiconductor types. The value indicated is the root mean square if the alternating current being measured is a sine

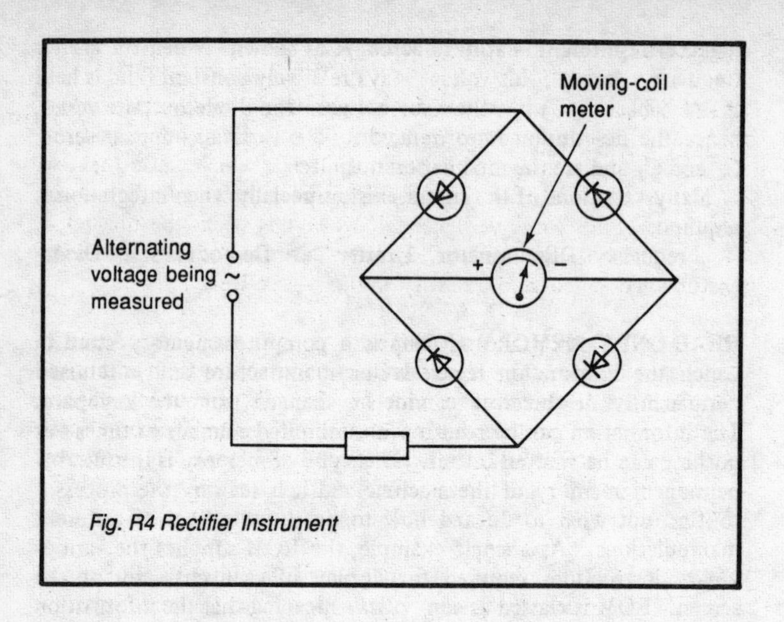

Fig. R4 Rectifier Instrument

wave.
(* Moving-Coil Meter >> Diode, Bridge, Rectification, Rectifier, Sine Wave, Root Mean Square)

REDUNDANCY is the term used for the fraction of the total information content of a signal which can be omitted without loss of significance. Redundancy is employed to enhance the *reliability* of a system:

(1) in a binary system for example, a technique is to transmit additional binary digits to those essential for defining a particular character. The added digits are said to be *redundant*, they add nothing to the information but they do in fact decrease the chance of error;
(2) in a continuously operating system redundancy is necessary to allow for periodic maintenance or failure, i.e. standby (redundant) equipment is provided so that the system can be kept going;
(3) where very high reliability is essential as in space travel, whole redundant systems may be involved. Components too may be backed up by redundancy, for example a resistor may be replaced by a series-parallel combination of four resistors of the same value, similarly with diodes. The risk of catastrophic failure is therefore greatly reduced.

(* Reliability, Binary, Parity Checking)

REED RELAY is one comprising magnetisable reeds sealed into a gas-filled glass tube and surrounded by a coil. Magnetic flux from the coil produces magnetic poles in the reeds which cause them to attract each other and close an external circuit. A permanent magnet may be employed instead of a coil; when the magnet is brought close to the reeds it similarly deflects them (a technique used in window and door security alarms) – see Relay.

REGENERATION is another name for positive feedback. A particular use of this is in the *regenerative receiver.* This is an amplitude modulation radio receiver in which in the radio frequency stages a small amount of positive feedback is employed to overcome some of the damping (not all, otherwise instability arises). This improves both the sensitivity and the selectivity of the receiver.
(* Radio Receiver >> Feedback, Damping, Selectivity)

REGENERATOR A device which accepts pulses in poor condition and generates new "clean" ones – see Pulse Code Modulation.

REGULATION is a general term for the maintenance of voltage or current levels at a certain point in a system. Regulators are commonly used with d.c. power supplies in which the voltage may vary because of (i) ripple from the a.c. mains, (ii) mains voltage variations, (iii) load current changes. The regulator is expected to iron out such fluctuations. Many techniques exist for regulation, generally they are divided into series and shunt types. In the series type, when the load voltage tries to increase, the regulator increases its series resistance and vice versa. In the shunt type, when the load voltage tries to increase, the regulator draws more current, e.g. as with a gas-filled tube or zener diode, in fact the zener diode is also known as a *voltage regulator diode.*
(* Stabilization, Constant Voltage Source, Load >> Rectifier, Gas Discharge, Zener Diode)

RELAXATION OSCILLATOR This is one which has an output waveform exhibiting a sudden change or changes per cycle as opposed to the smooth flow of a sine wave. A typical use of such an oscillator is as a generator of a saw-tooth waveform as used in a television time base. However, Fourier analysis indicates that the output waveform is very rich in harmonics, hence the oscillator can be also used as the basis of a simple electronic organ. The essential action is the build up of energy in a capacitance or inductance

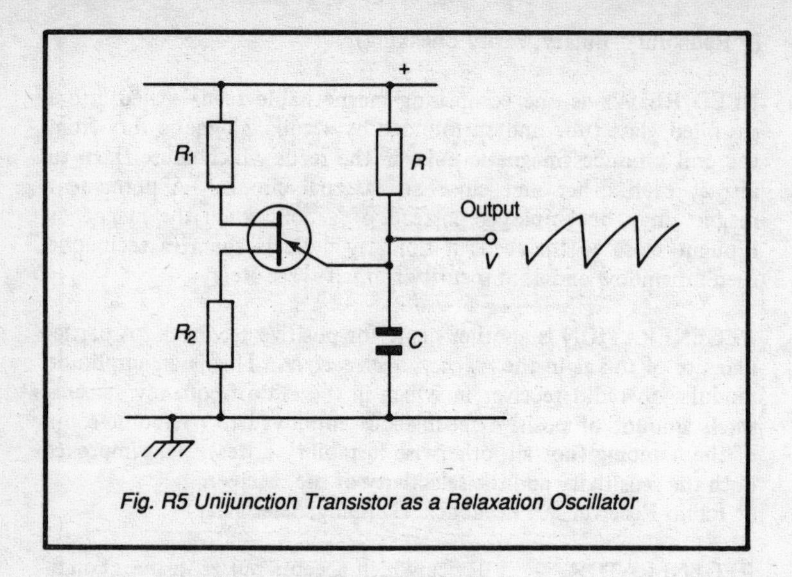

Fig. R5 Unijunction Transistor as a Relaxation Oscillator

(usually the former) during the "relaxation" period. This culminates in a sudden discharge so that equilibrium is restored each cycle (see Fig.T12).

Unijunction transistor circuits and multivibrators are in common use as relaxation oscillators and a typical basic unijunction circuit is shown in Figure R5. Briefly the circuit action is as follows:

(i) on switching on, C charges through R and the voltage, V at the output terminal rises towards the supply voltage;
(ii) however when V reaches the *peak point* for the unijunction transistor, it triggers "on" and moves onto the negative resistance part of the characteristic. C then discharges through the transistor and R_2 in series;
(iii) V therefore falls rapidly until the *valley point* is reached whereupon the transistor triggers "off";
(iv) the charge/discharge cycle repeats continuously with an output waveform as shown.

(* Blocking Oscillator, Time Base, Time Base Generator, Multivibrator >> Unijunction Transistor, Fourier Analysis)

RELAY is a switching device actuated by changes in the circuit of which it is a part and controlling changes within another separate and independent circuit, in essence, a remotely controlled switch. There are many different types of relay but generally they fall into two different classes, *electromagnetic* and *solid state*. The electro-

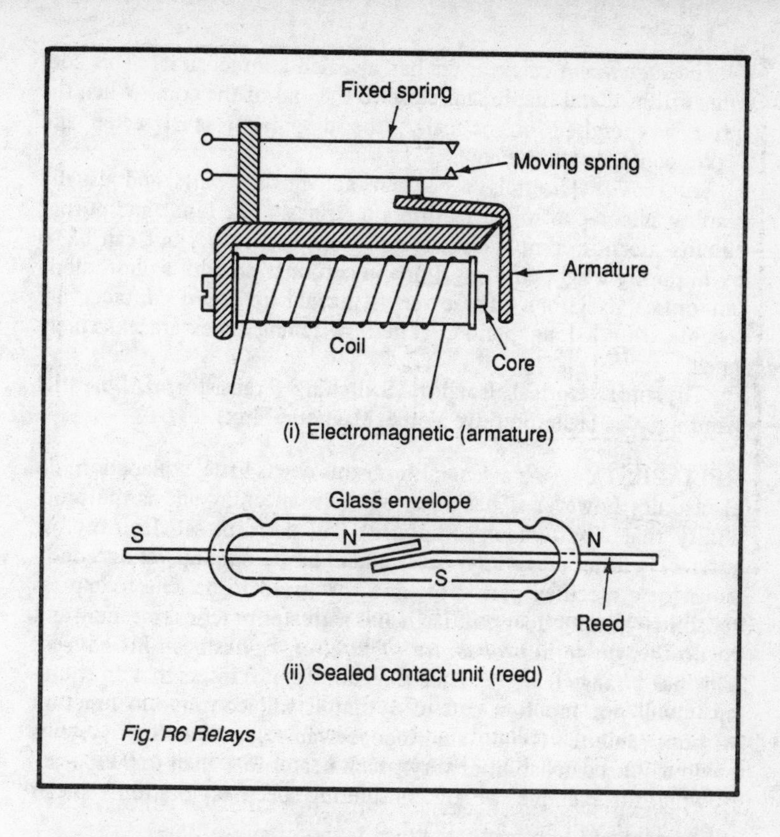

Fig. R6 Relays

magnetic relay may be typified by the *armature relay*, a sketch of one is shown in Figure R6(i). A small current flowing through the coil creates a high flux density in the magnetic circuit and causes the iron armature to be attracted towards the core. This closes the contacts which may then carry a relatively large current. One set of contacts only is shown but many sets may be operated together. There is complete isolation between the coil and contact circuits. Switching time is comparatively long, say up to 25 ms.

The *reed relay* is similarly an electromagnetic type with a much shorter switching time of about 1 ms or less. Its contacts are bonded into a glass tube (usually gas filled) to reduce corrosion. The contacts for example are thin nickel-iron strips (the reeds), flattened at their ends and sealed into the tube as sketched in (ii) of the figure. A surrounding coil, when energised creates a magnetic flux in each reed, producing poles which might be as shown. The unlike poles at the contact position cause attraction and the contacts close. The reeds are springy hence when the flux is removed, they fly apart.

The *diaphragm relay* again has a sealed contact unit. This contains a thin metal diaphragm close to the end of the core. When the latter is energised magnetically, the diaphragm is attracted and makes contact with the core.

True *solid state* relays contain no moving parts and usually employ silicon-controlled rectifiers or triacs. The input and output circuits are not completely isolated from each other but can be so by imposing a light-emitting diode in conjunction with a photodiode (an optical isolator). These relays, having no metal contacts, are reliable over a long period. Their switching times are extremely small.

(* Thyristor, Optical Isolator, Switching Transistor, Differential Winding >> Magnetomotive Force, Magnetic Flux)

RELIABILITY As a general term this needs little explanation. In electronics however it has a more precise meaning and is the probability that a system or component will perform satisfactorily (or survive) within previously determined limits and operating conditions for a specified period of time. We need to be able to express reliability as a number so that it has a greater practical meaning and to do this the term *probability of survival,* P_s has been introduced. This has a range 0 to 1. Thus a reliability of 0 infers that an equipment will not function and of 1 that it will continue to function without failure (both are inconceivable). Practical systems obviously need reliabilities very much nearer to 1 than to 0 especially when for example, we are considering space exploration vehicles for which P_s will have a value up to 0.9999.

Reasonable estimates of reliability can be determined through tests in advance and/or by observation of working equipment. For electronic systems or components usually a fundamental to the concept of reliability is the factor of time for clearly the longer an item or system functions without failure, the greater is its reliability. However time is not used to the exclusion of all else for reliability could for example, be assessed on the number of operations as in the case of a mechanical switch for which failure through wear may be better assessed with use rather than with time.

On the assumption that the failures are random and independent, reliability can be estimated from the *mean time between failures* (m.t.b.f.). The *failure rate* λ is the reciprocal, hence

$$\text{Reliability (as a function of time),} \quad R_t = e^{-\lambda t}$$

As an example, if similar components put on test for one year are found to have an m.t.b.f. of 10 years then the failure rate, λ = 1/m.t.b.f. = 0.1 and

$$R_t = e^{-0.1} = 0.905 .$$

System Reliability – in the above emphasis is on batches of similar components. Seldom does a system use only one type hence for an estimate of system reliability the effects of the numbers and failure rates of all components must be included. It can be shown that for a given time interval, n_1, n_2, n_3 . . . components with failure rates $\lambda_1, \lambda_2, \lambda_3$ . . . give rise to a system failure rate, λ_s where:

$$\lambda_s = n_1\lambda_1 + n_2\lambda_2 + n_3\lambda_3 + \ldots$$

When very high system reliability is essential then additional similar units are added so that should one unit fail, the remainder continue to carry the load. Putting several units in series is useless because failure of one unit puts all others out of action. Parallel and sometimes series-parallel arrangements are therefore used. As a single example, if two similar units having reliabilities of 0.9 are connected in parallel, the overall reliability can be shown to be 0.99, a considerable improvement.
(* Failure/Failure Rate, Redundancy >> Probability, Random)

REPEATER is a device inserted in a communication channel which accepts signals at its input and delivers corresponding signals at its output. In telephony channels a repeater provides amplification to ensure that the signal amplitude remains well above the general noise level. Telegraph repeaters regenerate the incoming pulses so that "clean" pulses are transmitted onwards – see also Regenerator.
(* Signal-to-Noise Ratio >> Amplifier, Pulse)

RESERVOIR CAPACITOR is a capacitor (usually a large value electrolytic type) connected in parallel with the output of a rectifying system, shown as the capacitor C in Figure R10(i) and (iv). It is aptly named because it acts as a reservoir of current. While the rectifier is conducting, C is charged to the maximum value but while the rectifier output is below this, current flows out of C to supply the load. The variation in voltage of C can be judged from Figure R10(i) – see Ripple Filter.

RESIDUAL CHARGE is a relatively small amount of charge remaining in a capacitor when it is discharged rapidly and so in effect is not fully discharged. The arrangement of the molecules in a dielectric changes when a charge is present and some charge remains within the dielectric, this charge is not as quickly removed as is the main charge.
(>> Charge, Capacitor, Dielectric)

RESIDUAL CURRENT CIRCUIT BREAKER is a device concerned with our safety. Electricity is normally a friend, but it can also be a killer, the opportunity most frequently arises when we get mixed up with the electricity mains, for in many countries the supply is at well over 200 volts. Generally one wire of the supply is connected to earth, called the *neutral* and contact with it presents no danger, conversely the other *live* wire is at mains voltage relative to earth and will drive a current through a human body in series with its resistance to earth. Ohm's Law applies, even to us.

The real danger from electricity arises from its interference with the heart beat, not through damage to the heart itself. The main function of a heart is to pump, but it is told when to do this by a *pacemaker* situated at the top. The pacemaker generates impulses which travel through the heart muscle fibres and when the fibres receive an impulse, the heart beats once. In electronic parlance we call this *triggering*. Hence if the pacemaker pulse does not arrive, the heart does not beat and the owner becomes null and void. An electronic current flowing across the chest of a human being of only about 100 mA can be fatal simply by its interference with the triggering pulse.

Modern technology has evolved the residual current circuit breaker (formerlly known as an *earth leakage circuit breaker*). This is inserted at a socket-outlet or in the main supply to a particular circuit and it measures the current flow in both live and neutral. If these currents balance as they should under normal conditions, there is no action. However, should the current on the live wire exceed that on the neutral by only some 10 – 30 mA because there is a leakage to earth through somebody, then the device cuts off the power within about one-thirtieth of a second and the danger to life is removed.

In addition, in responding to such low and normally undetected leakage (or residual) currents, the circuit breaker minimizes the risk of fire by simply disconnecting the circuit, it will not restore until the leakage is cleared.
(* Circuit Breaker, Trigger)

RESISTANCE-CAPACITANCE COUPLING (R-C COUPLING) Generally this applies to the coupling between amplifier stages. The signal output of one stage is the input of the next and the coupling between the two stages is usually via a capacitor. By this means the biasing arrangements of the second stage are independent of conditions in the first stage. Two stages with resistance-capacitance coupling are shown in Figure R7. The coupling derives its name from the capacitor *C* in conjunction with the resistive signal source,

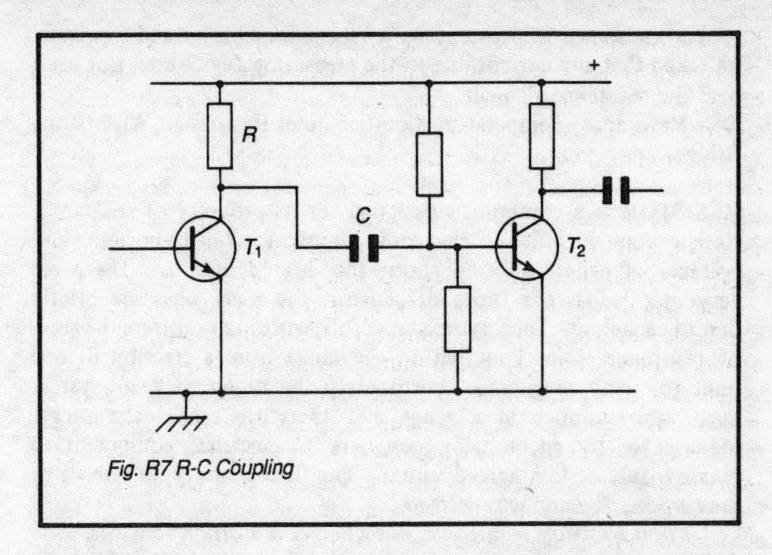

Fig. R7 R-C Coupling

R which here is the collector load of T_1. Whatever the combined input resistance of T_2 plus its biasing resistors, the reactance of C must be very much less (say to one-tenth) at the lowest frequency to be transmitted. This is to avoid excessive signal voltage drop across it. There are practical limits to the value of C when frequencies get very low, in which case recourse is made to direct coupling in which C is eliminated and other arrangements are made for biasing.
(* Direct-Coupled Amplifier >> Transistor, Amplifier, Reactance)

RESISTANCE-CAPACITANCE OSCILLATOR is another name for a *phase-shift* oscillator, relying as it does on the creation of the required phase shift for positive feedback by use of resistance-capacitance networks – see Oscillator and/or Figure O3.

RESISTANCE THERMOMETER The resistance of most conductors varies with temperature hence it is possible to measure temperature by measuring the resistance of a wire exposed to it. The measuring element is usually in the form of a small coil of wire wound on a mica former. Several materials are suitable, all having the necessary high positive temperature coefficient of resistance. Platinum and nickel are used extensively, the former has the advantage of having a linear temperature coefficient of resistance over a wider temperature range (from about −200°C to over 600°C) whereas nickel has a higher coefficient.

The resistance is measured by a Wheatstone bridge and care must be taken that any current due to the measuring device does not itself heat the resistance element.
(>> Resistance, Temperature Coefficient of Resistance, Wheatstone Bridge)

RESISTOR is a component designed for its property of resistance. Resistors are included in electronic circuits to control currents and voltages in order to bring about the desired effects. There are very many different types of resistor, the main ones are briefly described below. Each type is available with many different values of resistance, sometimes within the range from a fraction of one ohm to many megohms. Fortunately the *preferred value* system limits the number in a range and therefore makes the ranges manageable by encouraging designers of electrical equipment to employ only certain agreed values. The three main types of resistor are *carbon*, *film* and *wire-wound*.

Carbon Resistors – are also known as *composition* resistors. The resistance element is a mixture of finely ground carbon with a ceramic material, contained in a small insulating tube or alternatively coated with an insulating compound. The two connecting wires are embedded in the ends, typically as shown in Figure R8(i). The resistance value depends on the proportions of carbon and ceramic in the mix. These resistors are inexpensive, available in a wide range of values and are easily soldered into the practical circuit. The resistance value is usually marked on the body in *colour code* together with the tolerance value.

The power which a carbon resistor can handle without overheating is usually indicated by its size as shown typically in the figure. As indicated above, this type has several advantages, however its stability with time is poor, the resistance may vary with current and noise performance is not particularly good.

Carbon composition resistors are also manufactured in variable form, usually as a disc of the composition over which rotates a sliding contact or a strip along which the contact slides.

Film Resistors – generally comprise carbon film, metal alloy or metal oxide film. In one process the metal is evaporated onto a substrate in a vacuum with the resistance value controlled by the thickness of the film. Alternatively the resistance can firstly be made too low, then raised to the required value by cutting a spiral into the film. Marking is by colour code and generally preferred values only are used.

For printed wiring and integrated circuits either thick or thin metal films may be deposited onto an insulating base. These two

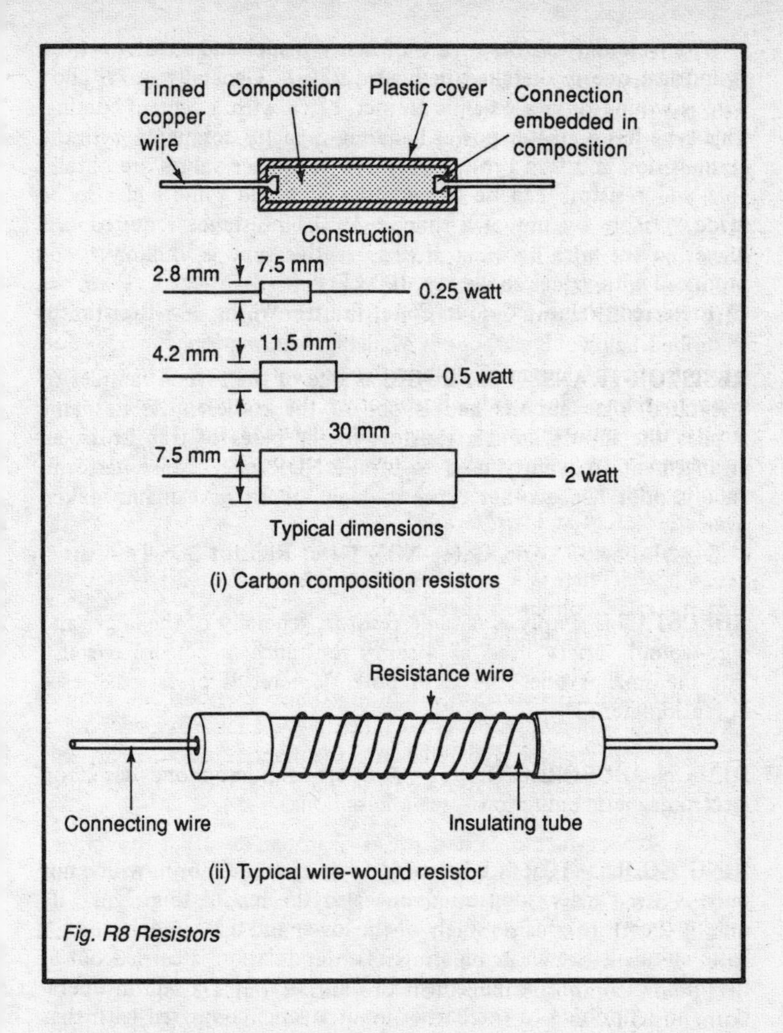

(i) Carbon composition resistors

(ii) Typical wire-wound resistor

Fig. R8 Resistors

types are manufactured by quite different processes. Thin film resistors consist of, for example, tantalum or a nickel-chromium alloy evaporated or sputtered onto an insulating base. Compared with composition type resistors their range is limited to a few ohms up to less than 100 kΩ but they can be manufactured to tighter tolerances and have good frequency response. Thick film resistors may be formed for example by depositing a resistive *ink* of metal or metal oxide particles onto an alumina substrate. The width, length and thickness of the ink control the resistance value.

Wire-wound Resistors – are of many shapes and sizes, a typical cylindrical one is sketched in Figure R8(ii). Generally metal alloy wire is wound onto a ceramic former, often with a cement coating. This type has a greater power handling capacity compared with the composition and film types. Very low resistance values are obtainable and resistors can be wound to a specified value and also be made variable by use of a slider. As the resistance required gets higher so the wire becomes thinner so this type is unlikely to be produced with values above say, 100 kΩ.
(* Preferred Values, Colour Code, Printed Wiring >> Resistance)

RESISTOR-TRANSISTOR LOGIC is one of the several families of integrated logic circuits and is one of the earliest. As its name implies the inputs are via resistors to the bases of transistors, an arrangement frequently used to form a NOR gate. Noise performance is poor hence other types of logic circuit have mainly taken over.
(* Digital Logic, Logic Gate, NOR Gate, Resistor >> Transistor)

RHEOSTAT is simply a variable resistor, generally of the larger and wire-wound variety used as a series resistance to control current. For the smaller ones the term potentiometer is preferred – see Potentiometer (2).

RIBBON MICROPHONE A type of microphone based on electromagnetic induction – see Microphone.

RING MODULATOR is a balanced type of modulator in which not only is the carrier suppressed but also the modulating signal, its output therefore consists solely of the lower and upper sidebands. A basic circuit is shown in Figure R9(i). Modulation is carried out in the bridge (or ring) arrangement of diodes D_1 to D_4 and in operation the amplitude of the carrier input is large compared with that of the modulating signal. When, for example, the carrier input terminal 1 is positive, diodes D_1 and D_3 are forward biased and therefore conduct, diodes D_2 and D_4 are reverse biased and they are therefore ineffective. Accordingly the modulating signal current flows via D_1 and D_3 to reach T_2. When the carrier polarity changes over however (positive to 2), diodes D_2 and D_4 conduct and it will be seen that the modulating signal current again flows through T_2 but now in the opposite direction. The carrier signal flows in opposite directions in the centre-tapped windings of T_1 and T_2 hence results in no carrier frequency output.

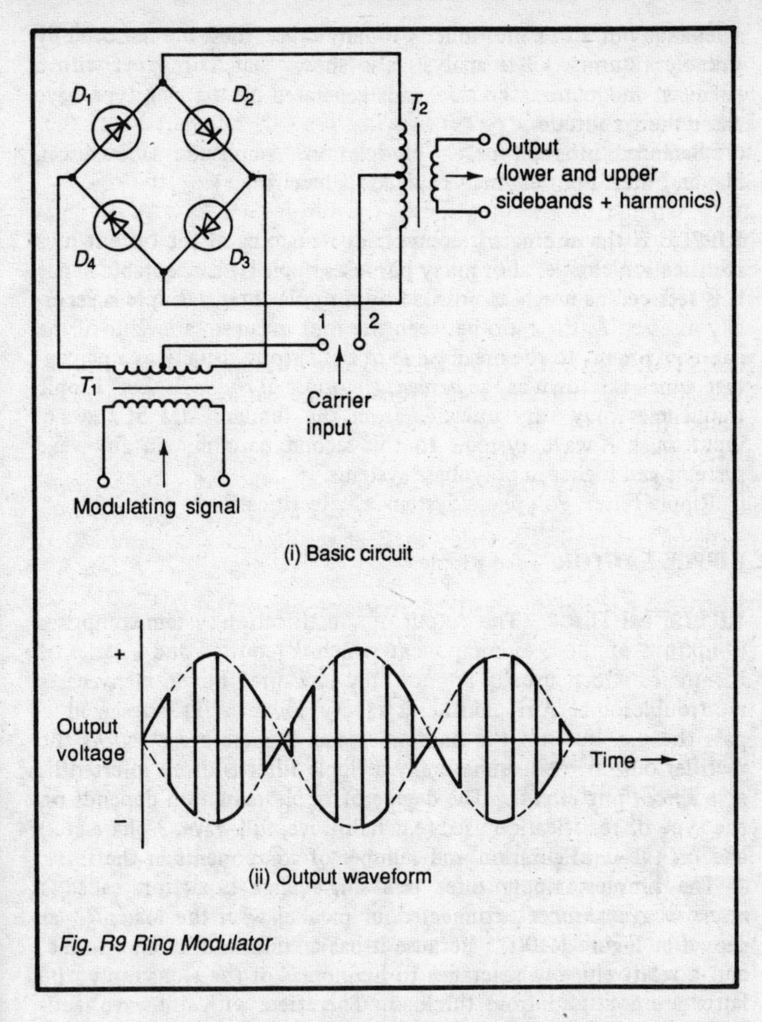

Fig. R9 Ring Modulator

The net result is that after each half-cycle of the carrier the output signal undergoes a phase-shift of 180°. Carrier frequencies are always much higher than the signal frequencies being modulated hence this phase change occurs many times per signal cycle, resulting in an output which might be pictured as in Figure R9(ii). In this drawing, for the sake of illustration, the ratio between carrier and modulating frequencies is greatly reduced, it would normally be at least 30 and probably several hundred.

Fourier analysis shows that because the output waveform includes some "squaring", it contains not only the lower and upper

sidebands but also a multiplicity of harmonics, these are removed by suitable filtering. The analysis also shows that, compared with a balanced modulator, the sidebands generated by the ring type have twice the amplitude.
(* Balanced Modulator >> Modulation, Amplitude Modulation, Diode, Filter, Fourier Analysis, Phase, Phase Angle)

RIPPLE is the alternating component remaining in the output of a rectification circuit. For many purposes ripple is unacceptable hence it is reduced as much as possible by a *ripple filter.* Ripple is generally assessed as the ratio between the root mean square value of the a.c. component to the mean value of the output, usually as a percentage which is known as the *percentage ripple* or *ripple factor.* Ripple frequencies may vary upwards from the fundamental of the a.c. input in half-wave systems to the second harmonic in full-wave systems and higher in polyphase systems.
(* Ripple Filter, Polyphase System >> Rectification)

RIPPLE FACTOR – see Ripple.

RIPPLE FILTER The output of a rectification system comprises a mixture of the d.c. component which is required and a series of harmonics which usually are not only unwanted but in many cases are troublesome. A ripple filter is a (very) low pass filter designed to pass the d.c. but not the harmonics and it therefore *smooths* the rectifier output. Not unnaturally a ripple filter is often referred to as a *smoothing circuit.* The degree of ripple reduction depends on the type of rectification used (e.g. half-wave, full-wave, 3-phase etc.) and on the configuration and number of components in the filter.

The simplest ripple filter is a single large capacitor, called a *reservoir capacitor C,* connected in parallel with the load, R_L as shown in Figure R10(i). Because it has an infinite reactance to d.c. and a relatively low reactance to harmonics of the a.c. supply, the latter are bypassed from the load. The effect with full-wave rectification is illustrated in the figure. The larger the capacitance therefore, the greater is the ripple reduction.

A single inductor (choke) is more expensive and bulky. A circuit and its effect are illustrated in (ii) of the figure in which L is the inductor. This works on the principle that an inductor opposes current changes in it so its reactance is higher at the harmonic frequencies. Accordingly, being in series in the filter it effectively "chokes" back the harmonics yet the steady d.c. component appears in the load reduced only by the resistance of the inductor. This is kept low. Technically, for maximum attenuation of the harmonics,

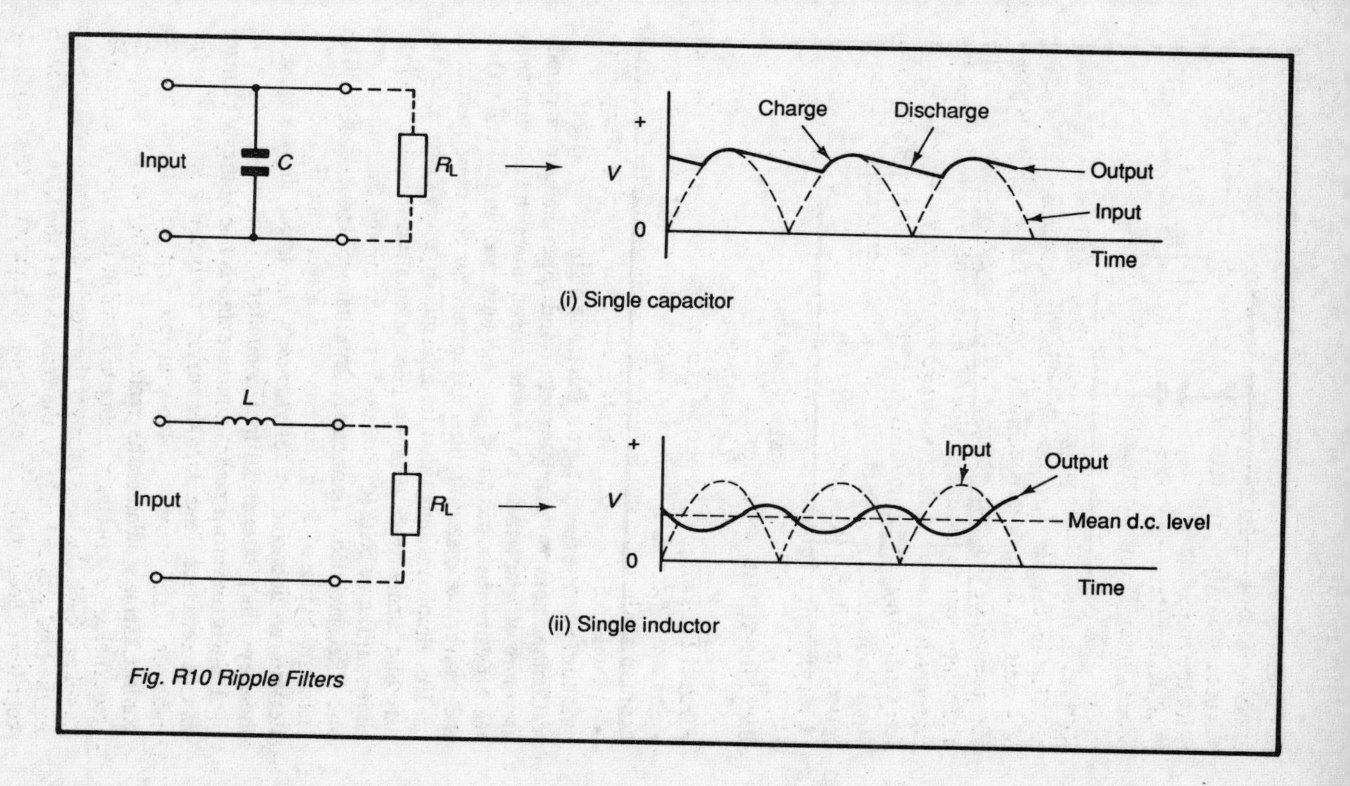

Fig. R10 Ripple Filters

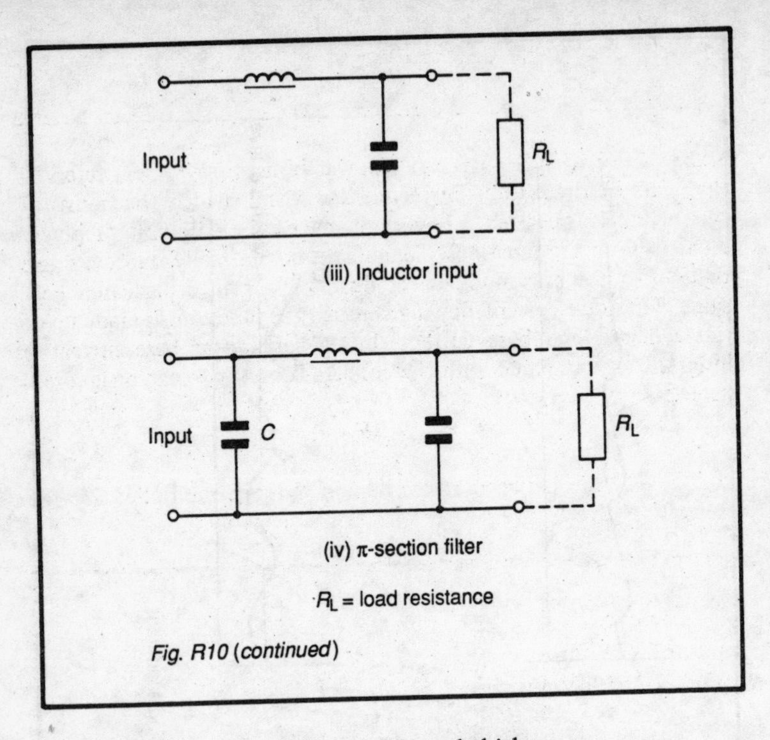

Fig. R10 (continued)

ωL must greatly exceed R_L, i.e. L is made high.

Combinations of shunt capacitor and series inductor naturally are more efficient than single component filters and the principles are basically the same. Just two are illustrated in (iii) and (iv) of the figure, the π-section filter being perhaps the most frequently used in circuits such as those for high quality audio systems. In the very best where ripple is almost eliminated altogether, a (iv) followed by a (iii) may be used.
(>> Rectification, Harmonic, Capacitance, Inductance, Filter)

ROM is an abbreviation for *read-only memory*. It is a type of memory which is essential in a computer or microprocessor. The data is written into it on manufacture and is not normally changed by the user – see Read-Only Memory.

RUBYLITH – see Photolithography.

S

SAFE OPERATING AREA of a power transistor. "Area" refers to that part of the output characteristics within which the transistor can be safely operated, i.e. without exceeding the limit of power dissipation in the junctions. Manufacturers normally quote a single figure P_{tot} for maximum power dissipation with a particular heat sink. The total current flowing through the junctions is made up of the collector and base currents but generally the base current is insignificant compared with the collector current so can be ignored, hence:

$$P_{tot} = V_{CE} I_C$$

i.e. the voltage between collector and emitter multiplied by the collector current.

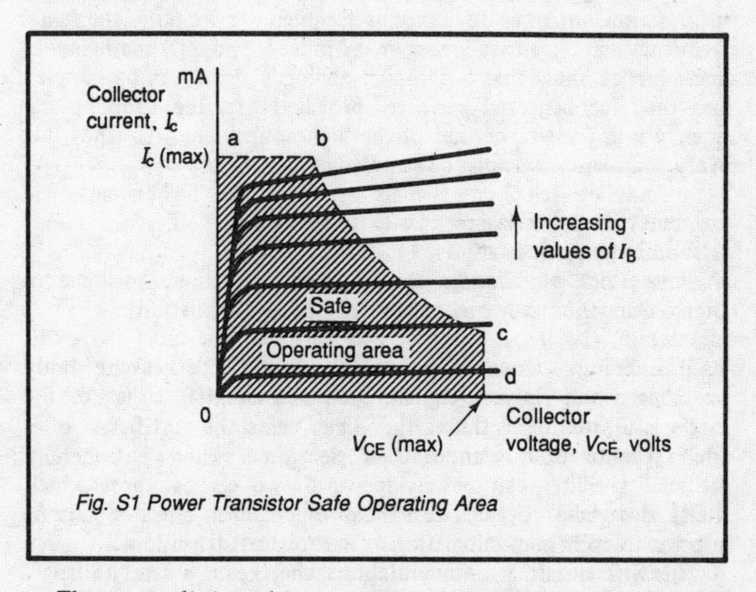

Fig. S1 Power Transistor Safe Operating Area

The power dissipated in a transistor is maximum under no-signal conditions for then none is being passed to the output. Thus because the output characteristics are drawn from d.c. values it is only necessary to draw the operating curve through the points where the above equation applies. A typical one is shown in Figure S1 between points b and c. From a to b and c to d we also get from the manufacturer's data. The safe operating area is therefore

completely determined. In circuit design therefore any load line must lie within the safe operating area otherwise there is the risk of overheating and breakdown.
(* Heat Sink, Load Line >> Transistor, Power, Breakdown)

SAMPLING is measuring the amplitude of a signal at certain (usually regular) time intervals. To obtain a single value for the sample it should be measured over a very short period of time so that amplitude changes are insignificant. Sampling is used in digital systems where the input is an analogue signal, i.e. in analogue/digital conversion. It generates a train of amplitude modulated pulses and clearly the greater the sampling frequency, the more information about the original signal is transmitted. For example it is not sufficient to sample a single sine wave only once per cycle because if the sample happened to be taken on each positive swing, there would be no information to show that a negative swing even existed. On the other hand, sampling at every 5° of the cycle would give ample information but now the sampling frequency is 72 times the signal frequency, an expensive arrangement indeed. Happily mathematics and practice show that a complex analogue signal can be sampled and then reconstituted perfectly provided that the sampling frequency is *at least* twice that of the highest analogue frequency, i.e. every complete wave must be sampled at least twice.

In practice telephony signals in which the highest analogue frequency is 3.4 kHz are usually sampled at 8 kHz and a colour television signal needs at least 11 MHz.
(* Pulse Code Modulation, Quantization Distortion, Analogue-to-Digital Conversion >> Analogue Signal, Pulse Modulation)

SATELLITE Originally this term referred to a heavenly body revolving round a planet, e.g. the earth is a satellite of the sun, the moon is a satellite of the earth. Then came the "artificial" ones which cannot exist without their electronic systems. Generally artificial satellites can be divided into two classes, those which transit data back to earth and those which act as repeater stations in point to point communication or in broadcast television.

The first question is, no doubt, "what keeps a satellite up?". Firstly, up in space there is no air to cause friction so bodies, once given motion, go on seemingly for ever. But this would be in a straight line and a body would be lost were it not for the pull of the earth. To maintain the body in orbit the centrifugal force (centre-fleeing, due to motion) which tries to pull a body away from the earth must be exactly counterbalanced by the centripetal force (centre-seeking) provided by gravity. For any satellite in a circular

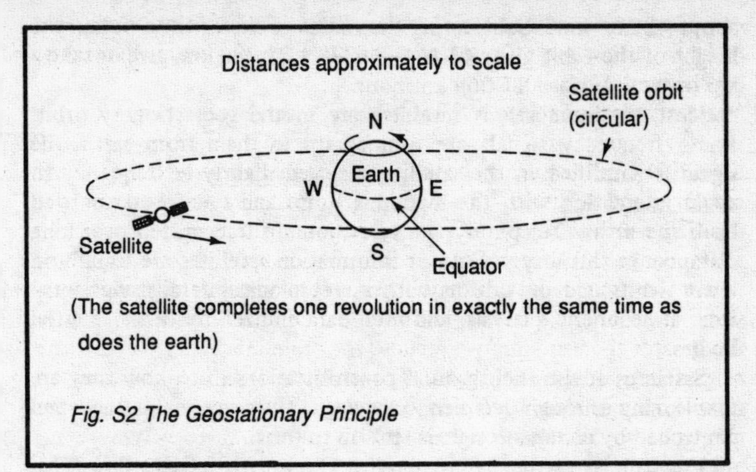

Fig. S2 The Geostationary Principle

orbit the centrifugal force:

$$F_C = m_s v^2/r$$

where m_s is the mass of the satellite, v is its velocity and r the radius of orbit (i.e. the distance from the centre of the earth). The centripetal force is given by:

$$F_G = Gm_s m_e/r^2$$

where m_e is the mass of the earth and G is its *gravitational constant.*

For a stable orbit, F_C must be equal to F_G and for a given r, this is controlled by the satellite velocity which follows as:

$$v = \sqrt{Gm_e/r}\,.$$

Many data or information satellites are in elliptical orbits for which the formulae become slightly more complicated. However of perhaps greater interest is the *geostationary* orbit which brings us television (Greek, *geo* = earth). This is a circular orbit directly above the equator at such a height that each satellite completes one revolution in exactly the same time as the earth rotates once, hence to an observer on earth the satellite appears to be stationary, see Figure S2. Let T be the orbital period (i.e. the time for one revolution), then:

$$T = 2\pi r/v$$

which now gives sufficient information for r to be calculated at about 42 164 km. Subtracting the radius of the earth to obtain the height of the orbit gives 42 164 – 6378 = 35 786 km, give or take a km or two. Also v = 11 069 km/hour.

Most communications satellites are in the geostationary orbit. Radio frequency signals are beamed up to them from earth, the signal is amplified in the satellite, changed slightly in frequency to avoid interaction with the incoming beam and then re-transmitted back to earth. Telephony and television are transmitted over long distances in this way. Data or information satellites are usually in lower orbits and provide us with meteorological data, navigational aids, atmospheric analysis, and even data emitted by other celestial bodies.

Satellites advise their ground control stations as to how they are functioning through *telemetry* signals. They are maintained and controlled by *command* signals sent up to them.

Frequencies used are from about 0.1 to over 100 GHz. Power for the electronics is obtained from the sun by use of banks of solar cells either spread out on flat, wing-like panels or alternatively fixed round the outer surface of the satellite body.
(* Repeater, Satellite Television, Telecommunication System, Solar Cell)

SATELLITE TELEVISION Television programmes are transmitted to viewers by three main methods: (i) terrestrial broadcast which even for a small country requires many transmitting stations (e.g. more than 600 for the UK); (ii) by cable which requires expensive wiring to all premises; or (iii) via a special communications satellite.

The television baseband signal occupies up to 8 MHz and for satellite working frequency modulation is employed resulting in a bandwidth on modulation of some 27 MHz. This can only be carried by a frequency in the VHF or a higher band. To reach a satellite the radiated wave must pass straight through the ionosphere, this and the need to avoid the pick-up of "sky noise", places the transmission frequency in the low gigahertz region.

The path from the broadcast transmitting station to the viewer's television set can be divided into (1) the *uplink* to the satellite, (2) the satellite itself and (3) the *downlink* from the satellite into the viewer's premises.

(1) the uplink is based on a large parabolic antenna (see Fig.P1), fed by the main transmitter. The antenna is highly directional and aims its narrow beam directly at the satellite.

(2) a similar type of antenna but smaller on the satellite picks up the signal which is first amplified and then changed in frequency.

Then follows a power amplifier (usually a travelling-wave tube) which feeds the satellite transmit antenna via a waveguide. This antenna (or it may be a group of antennas) is again parabolic and sends a slightly divergent beam to earth to cover the area required as shown in Figure S3(i). The basic satellite equipment is known as a *transponder* with main components as outlined in (ii). Satellite output power, unlike that of the ground station, is very limited simply because the power itself is derived from the sun. Transmitted frequences are around 12 GHz.

(3) on its way down to earth the radio frequency signal suffers attenuation, not through space for there is none, but through the earth's atmosphere. This is of course, a very variable quantity,

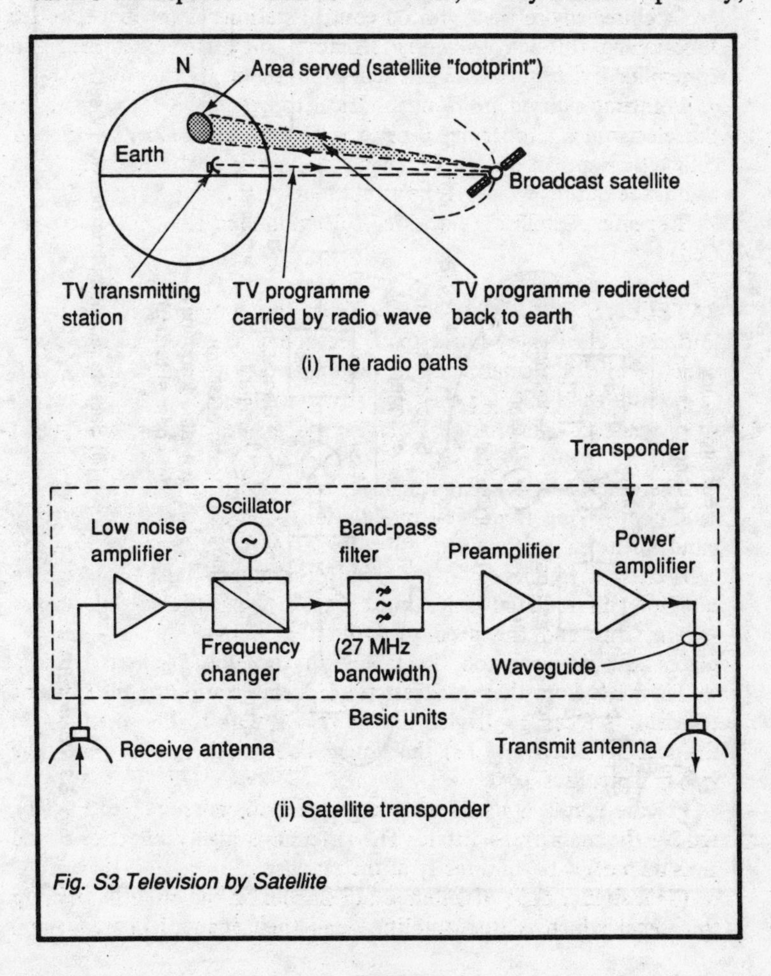

Fig. S3 Television by Satellite

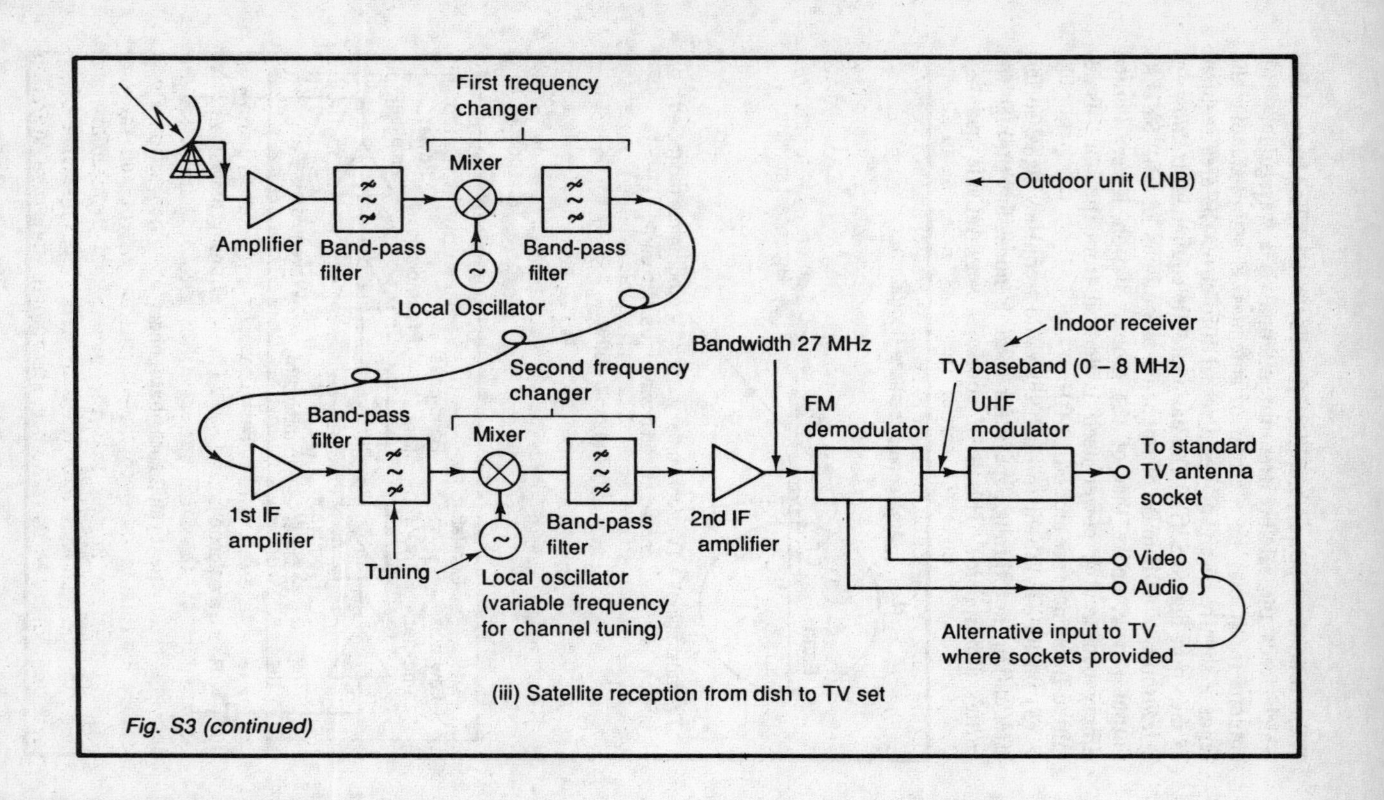

(iii) Satellite reception from dish to TV set

Fig. S3 (continued)

creating a loss of say 2 to 5 dB depending on the length of the path through the atmosphere but increasing in wet weather due to absorption of the wave by water drops. The viewer's antenna output depends on its area hence must be sufficiently large so that the signal does not get lost in noise. The antenna (or dish), must be accurately aligned to the satellite and there must be no objects in the path otherwise the wave is blocked. The wave is reflected by the dish into a horn or waveguide which is followed (at the dish) by a *low noise block converter* (LNB) which changes the frequency down to the first intermediate frequency (i.f.) so that the signal can be fed into the premises by coaxial cable rather than by waveguide. This is shown in Figure S3(iii). Within the premises is the satellite receiver which changes the carrier frequency down again to the second i.f. A demodulator then extracts the baseband for connection to the television receiver.
(* Satellite, Baseband, Parabolic Antenna, Ionosphere, Travelling-Wave Tube, Coaxial Cable, Television Receiver, PAL, MAC, Transmitter >> Electromagnetic Wave, Frequency Modulation, Noise, Antenna, Waveguide, Superheterodyne Reception)

SATURABLE REACTOR (TRANSDUCTOR) is a device used in power control, it is also the basis of the magnetic amplifier. Their ruggedness and tolerance of environmental and overload conditions makes them preferable to semiconductors in certain circumstances. Generally control of an alternating current (a.c.) can be by (i) series resistance but this wastes energy as heat, or by (ii) a series inductance for which resistance heat losses are much smaller. The series inductance is obviously preferable but then comes the problem as to how to vary the inductance according to the current requirements of the load.

The saturable reactor provides load current control by the simple expedient of saturating or partly saturating the core of a series inductor by means of a small direct current (d.c.). The method is illustrated by the elementary circuit of Figure M1, it is in fact a flux-controlled switch in series with a load. The core has a highly rectangular hysteresis loop and the average core flux is biased by the direct current flowing in L_2. The alternating magnetomotive force set up by the main current drives the core into saturation during part of the cycle, the phase angle at which saturation is reached depending on both the alternating current and the d.c. bias. Saturation implies that the incremental permeability and therefore the reactance have fallen to zero. The impedance of L_1 therefore reduces to its resistance, accordingly while core saturation conditions apply, the current from the a.c. supply into the load is at maximum. Of each half-cycle of alternating current the time before saturation is known as the *exciting interval*, after saturation it becomes the *saturation interval* and clearly these intervals can easily be adjusted to suit many control requirements. Note from the drawing that L_2 has a large number of turns so that only small control (bias) currents are required.

A main disadvantage of the elementary circuit of Figure M1 is that the device is also a transformer hence the current and control circuits are linked. Practical saturable reactors are therefore likely to embody more complicated core arrangements to neutralize this effect. It is however useful in the magnetic amplifier.
(* Saturation, Magnetic Amplifier >> Alternating Current, Inductance, Inductive Reactance, Core, Magnetic Hysteresis, Magnetomotive Force, Phase Angle, Incremental Permeability)

SATURATION The term in electronics indicates a condition where some quantity which normally increases with the input of another quantity suddenly or gradually fails to increase. Generally on a characteristic relating two quantities, this condition is indicated by the curve turning over and then running horizontally. An example is given by the transfer characteristics in Figure C8 which are all showing saturation at the top end, indicating that no matter how much further the base current increases, the collector current does not.

A switching transistor can be driven to its saturation point by the input signal [see Fig.S16(iii)]. When this happens the collector current is maximum irrespective of any further increase in the input signal. The transistor is then said to be saturated.
(* Switching Transistor >> Transistor, Characteristic)

SAW Abbreviation of Surface Acoustic Wave Device – see Acoustic Wave Device.

SAWTOOTH WAVEFORM is a periodic waveform moving regularly between its minimum and maximum values. The time taken in one direction, say minimum to maximum is considerably longer than that required for a move in the opposite direction so producing a waveform of shape similar to that of the tooth of a saw as shown in Figure T12. This is a sketch of an ideal waveform in which the changes are linear, practical waveforms differ. The longer time interval is known as the *active interval*, the return is known as the *flyback*. This type of waveform is most frequently used as a time base and is conveniently generated by a relaxation oscillator or a

multivibrator. Although a multivibrator is fundamentally a generator of rectangular pulses, it can produce sawtooth waveforms by applying these pulses to a capacitor.
(* Time Base, Time Base Generator, Relaxation Oscillator, Multivibrator >> Waveform)

SCANNING is the process of resolving a scene, object or picture into its elements of light, shade and colour in a prearranged pattern. An everyday example of scanning is the way in which we read a page from a book. We start at the top left and read the first line. Then our eyes fly back to the beginning of the second line, this is read, then the third and so on to the bottom of the page. The page has been scanned and the information gained from it committed to memory. Television scanning works in the same way. In the camera an image of the scene being viewed is scanned as though it were a page of about 600 lines. Each complete scan takes 1/25 seconds.

In an oscilloscope a scan is a horizontal or vertical sweep of the spot on the screen, controlled by a time base. Generally in radar systems circular scanning is used, the radar antenna rotates and scans through 360°, the resulting display is a radial line on the screen rotating in sympathy with the antenna.
(* Cathode-Ray Tube, Time Base, Oscilloscope, Flying-Spot Scanner)

SCHMITT TRIGGER is a bistable device of the multivibrator family with an output controlled by two threshold input values. Calling these v_1 and v_2 where $v_2 > v_1$, the device triggers to output HIGH when the input voltage reaches v_2. If next the input level is reduced to v_1, the device triggers to its alternative stable state, output LOW. The difference between the two triggering points is known as the *hysteresis.* Summing this up; as with a bistable multivibrator, there are two stable states but which state the circuit remains in at any time is controlled by the input voltage.

Figure S4(i) shows a basic circuit. Note that the emitter resistor R_e is common to both transistors, therefore there is feedback between them. In contrast with the bistable multivibrator circuit, T_1 is controlled directly by the input signal instead of by T_2. Also the collector of T_2 is connected to the output terminal. The circuit operation is more complicated compared with that for the multivibrator but the features which interest us most are as follows.

If the input voltage is initially zero, T_1 is OFF, T_2 is ON. When the input voltage increases positively and reaches v_2, the circuit rapidly switches over to T_1 ON, T_2 OFF. Note that when T_2 is OFF, the output is HIGH and vice versa. Now on decreasing the input voltage to a less positive value v_1, the circuit switches back to

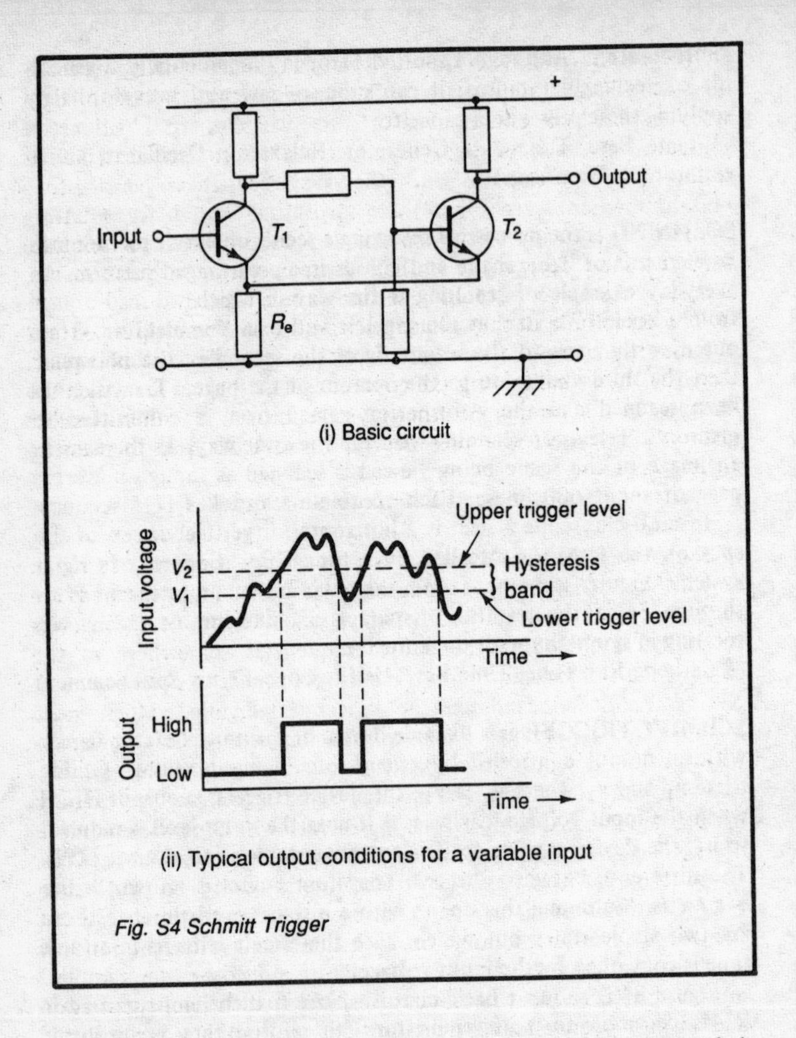

Fig. S4 Schmitt Trigger

T_1 OFF, T_2 ON. The action is shown graphically in (ii) of the figure.

It is evident that much information can be gained from the recurrence and duration of the output pulses and perhaps the simplest operation is to change a sine wave into a square wave. Even waveforms of speech, known for their complexity, can to a certain extent be analysed.

(* Multivibrator, Counter, Switching Transistor >> Transistor, Hysteresis, Pulse)

SCINTILLATION COUNTER This is a device consisting basically of a scintillator (a special phosphor) which emits a flash of light when exposed to gamma rays or other particles from radioactive sources. The flash of light illuminates a photocathode which is followed by an electron multiplier (together these constitute a photomultiplier – see Fig.P4) and an output system for counting the rate of reception of the flashes. It is essential that the scintillator has a short decay time so that events occurring in quick succession (e.g. within 10^{-11} to 10^{-9} seconds) are recorded.

The magnitude of the voltage pulse at the photomultiplier output is proportional to the number of photons reaching the phosphor. Accordingly by calibrating the counter against sources for which the energies of the gamma or other rays are known, it is then possible not only to detect the presence of the rays but also to measure their energies.

(* Photomultiplier >> Scintillation, Gamma Rays)

SCRAMBLING is the technique used to change the form of a signal so that it is unintelligible to unauthorized users. Many methods are employed dating back to earlier days when telephone speech was scrambled by dividing the audio frequencies somewhere in the middle and transposing the two bands so formed. A *descrambler* at the receiving end rendered the speech intelligible. Much more sophisticated techniques have replaced this one so that nowadays unauthorized descrambling is difficult to almost impossible.

In satellite television systems the term scrambling is generally used but so is *encryption* (making secret) which perhaps is more correct. Again highly sophisticated techniques are available. As a single example, it is possible with computer control to "cut" each line of a television picture and transpose the two portions. The cut is made at a different point on each line and a different series is used for each frame. To view the picture a *decoder* (descrambler) must be fitted to identify the cut position in each line, cut it again and change over left and right portions so that they are restored to their original positions. Obviously when scrambled the picture is totally unrecognizable and unauthorized decoding is to say the least, extremely difficult.

(* Television, Television Receiver >> Signal, Audio Frequency)

SCREENING is a general term relating to the technique of (i) enclosing apparatus or components within a screen or shield for protection from extraneous electric or magnetic fields, (ii) containing fields from a component so that they do not spread out and affect other nearby components and (iii) minimizing stray capacitance or stray magnetic couplings between two adjacent circuits.

Electric (Electrostatic) Screening: requires a screen of a material of low resistivity to eliminate direct stray capacitance between two circuits. In Figure S5(i) two circuits, A and B, have a stray capacitance C_{AB} between them. An earthed screen between the circuits as shown in (ii) changes the capacity so that there is no direct capacitance but only stray capacitances C_{AE} and C_{BE} from each circuit to earth. The need for such screening generally increases with frequency because stray capacitances have lower reactances at high frequencies.

Gauss's theorem also shows that circuits or devices may be surrounded by an electrical conducting screen to prevent interference from external electric fields. The screen need not be solid but may be in the form of a wire mesh, i.e. a Faraday cage.

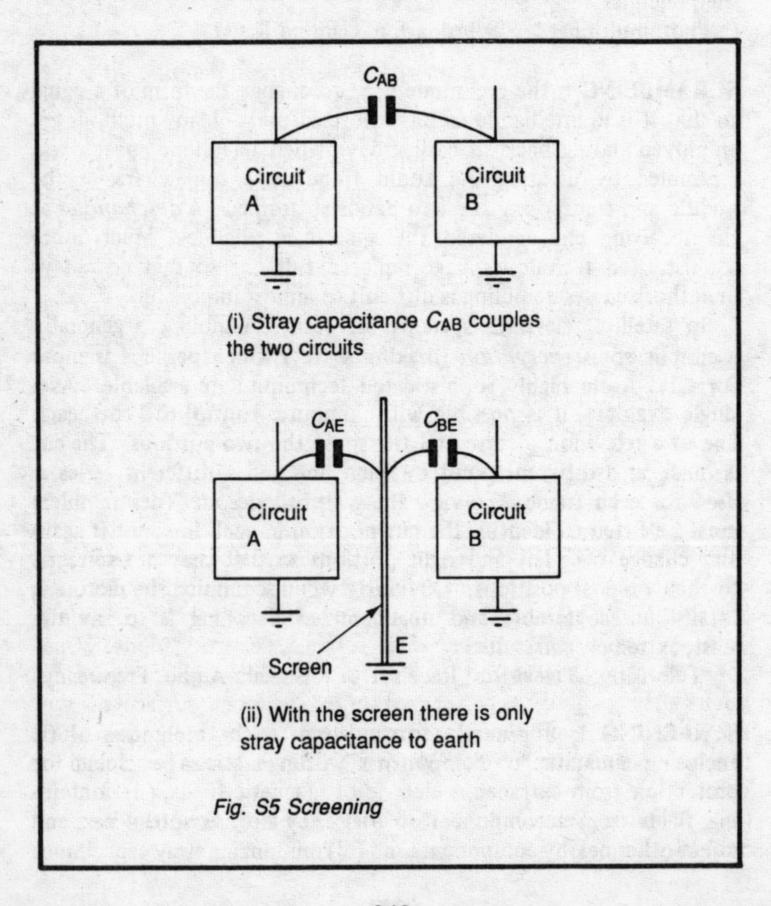

Fig. S5 Screening

Magnetic Screening: is accomplished by use of a screen or shield composed of a magnetic material of high permeability. Effectively the material acts as a magnetic short-circuit which prevents the magnetic flux from extending to the space inside the container. This is because the screen offers a lower reluctance path to the magnetic flux than does the space outside. If however the source of magnetic flux is within the container, the same type of screening prevents the flux from extending outwards.

Tuning coils and intermediate frequency transformers are typical components which are shielded by screening cans.
(* Faraday Cage >> Gauss's Theorem, Electric Field, Magnetic Field, Magnetic Flux, Permeability, Reluctance)

SCREENING CAN is one which surrounds a component such as a radio frequency coil or transformer to prevent electric or magnetic fields from entering or leaving – see Screening.

SECAM is an acronym for *Séquentiels Couleurs A Mémoire.* It is the colour television system used in France, USSR and Eastern Europe and some Middle East and African countries. The system transmits one colour-difference signal on one line followed by the other colour-difference signal on the subsequent line. By this technique of imposing the colour signals sequentially on alternate lines, the process of extracting the basic red, green and blue components is simplified. However to do this it is necessary to store the colour information for a full line period so that when one colour-difference signal is received it can be combined with its partner from the previously transmitted line.

See also PAL, NTSC.
(* Television, Television Signal, Television Receiver >> Colour)

SECOND CHANNEL INTERFERENCE is encountered in superheterodyne radio receivers – see Image Frequency.

SELENIUM RECTIFIER is a rectifying element based on selenium which is a semiconducting material. It is manufactured by depositing a thin, crystalline layer of doped selneium (about 0.1 mm) onto a steel or nickel plate. This forms a Schottky diode. One connection is made to the base plate, the other to a low melting point alloy (e.g. of tin) sprayed onto the open surface of the selenium. This produces a forward current of more than 100 mA/cm^2 at less than 1 volt. Many such elements can be stacked in series.
(>> Selenium, Semiconductor, Rectifier, Doping, Schottky Barrier, Schottky Diode)

SELF-CAPACITANCE is the capacitance belonging naturally to a component such as an inductor or a wire-wound resistor. Self-capacitance of inductors is the most troublesome because a minute capacitance exists between adjacent and near-adjacent winding turns and layers, the wires acting as the capacitor plates and the insulation as the dielectric. The wire insulation is frequently a very thin coating of enamel hence the thickness of the dielectric is small and the capacitance therefore high. The self-capacitance of an inductor is difficult to calculate but it can be measured and is usually represented as a single capacitance connected in parallel (i.e. across the inductor terminals). For radio frequency coils many winding techniques are used which reduce the self-capacitance, e.g. *wave winding* in which the wires cross each other at an angle rather than lying parallel to each other.
(>> Capacitance, Resistor, Inductor)

SENSITIVITY is the degree of response to a given stimulus. The term is particularly applicable to transducers all of which respond to some input stimulus, for example, microphones, loudspeakers, photocells. Measuring instruments also have their sensitivities as the input required for full-scale deflection.

Radio receiver sensitivity expresses how well the receiver responds to weak signals and it is usually quoted as the smallest radio frequency input at a given frequency which will produce a specified signal-to-noise ratio at the output.
(* Transducer, Microphone, Loudspeaker, Meter, Radio Receiver, Signal-to-Noise Ratio >> Photocell)

SERIES CONNECTION (i) is the technique of connecting circuit elements in sequence so that the same current passes through each in turn.

(ii) cells, batteries and generators are said to be connected in series when the positive terminal of one is connected to the negative terminal of the next (or vice versa) in a chain. In this case both the electromotive forces and the internal resistances are additive.

See also Parallel Connection.
(>> Electromotive Force, Resistance, Internal Resistance)

SERVOMECHANISM is a control system for operation of mechanical devices such as robots, drilling machines, vehicles etc. – see Closed-Loop Control System.

SEVEN-SEGMENT DISPLAY is a numeric display generally of 7 light-emitting diodes or 7 liquid crystal elements arranged as a figure of eight as shown in Figure M5(ii). There is one additional element for the decimal point when required. This type of display is used extensively in electronic equipment and is seen in the home on television sets, video recorders, microwave cookers, calculators and clocks. The display works by energising two or more of the elements for example, if elements a, b, g, c, and d are illuminated, a figure 3 is displayed; a, f, g, c and d produce a 5. Quite a few letters can also be displayed.

A 4-bit binary code can cater for 10 different numerals but there are 7 or 8 elements in the display for each one hence a *7-segment decoder* is required which examines the input code and then produces an output energising the appropriate elements.
(* Matrix, Liquid Crystal Display, Binary Code >> Light-Emitting Diode)

SHADOW MASK is a special metal mask used in colour television cathode-ray tubes. It is fitted directly behind the screen and ensures that each of the three electron beams (red, blue and green) strikes the appropriate phosphor dot – see Colour Picture Tube.

SHELF-LIFE is the time for which an item kept in store remains usable. The term is frequently used with batteries which may slowly deteriorate even when not in use.

SHELL-TYPE TRANSFORMER is a construction in which the core of a transformer has three limbs with the centre limb carrying all the windings as shown diagrammatically in Figure S6(i). In practice it is more likely that the secondary winding will be wound on top of the primary as sketched in (ii), this method gives rise to less magnetic leakage.

See also Core-Type Transformer.
(* Lamination >> Transformer, Core, Magnetic Circuit)

SHF is an abbreviation of *Super High Frequency*. This refers to the band of frequencies extending from 3 to 30 GHz (centimetric waves).
(>> Frequency Band)

SHIFT REGISTER A register is a temporary storage location used by the processor in a computer system so that it can perform its various functions. A *shift* register is a special kind of register in that it can contain a string of binary digits (bits) each in a separate memory cell (we can image them as being in a row) and these can be shifted one position to left or right by an input *shift pulse*.

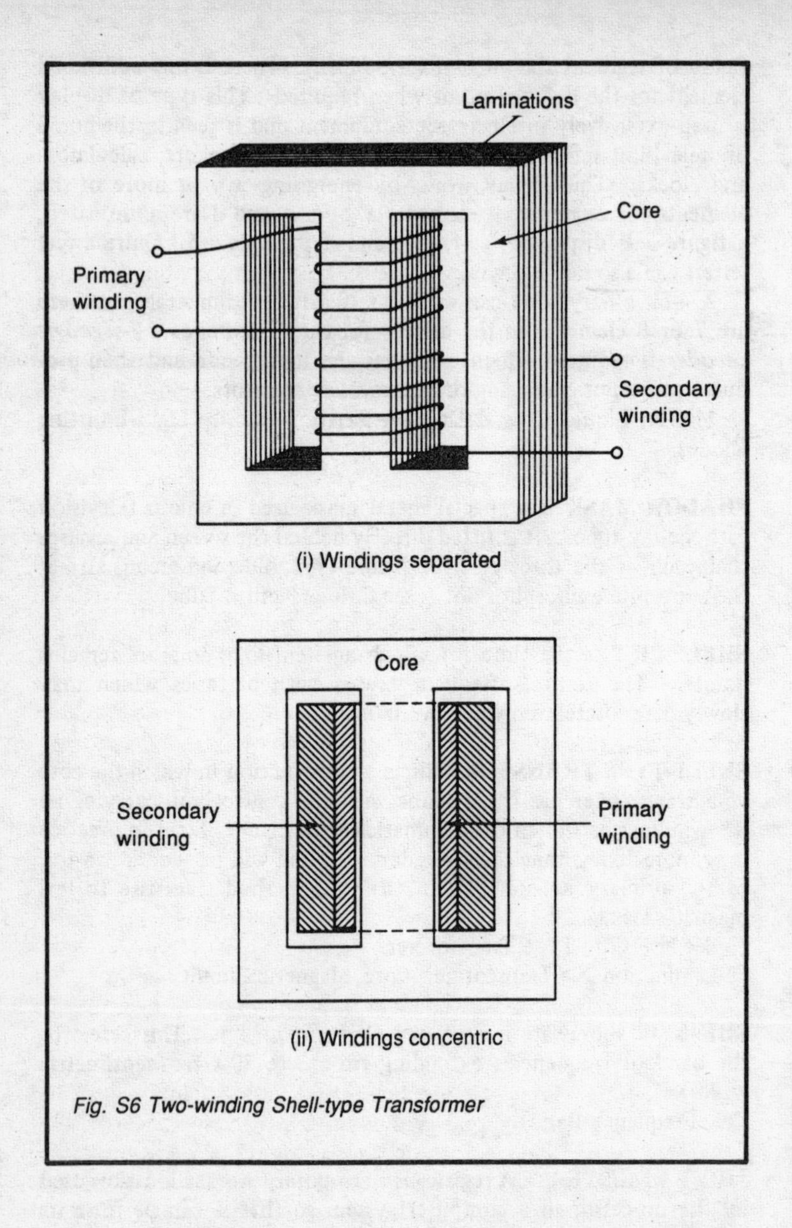

Fig. S6 Two-winding Shell-type Transformer

As a simple example of the use of a shift register, consider a register of 4 cells only, all set at logic 0, then let a logic 1 be inserted at the right-hand end followed by the insertion of logic 0's as shown below:

0 0 0 0 (initial condition)	equivalent to decimal 0
0 0 0 1 ← logic 1 inserted	equivalent to decimal 1
0 0 1 0 ← logic 0 inserted	equivalent to decimal 2
0 1 0 0 ← logic 0 inserted	equivalent to decimal 4
1 0 0 0 ← logic 0 inserted	equivalent to decimal 8

Clearly each shift to the left multiplies the binary number by 2.

Irrespective of the direction of shifting, a bit is shifted out at each move and might be considered lost. However it is possible to take such a bit and re-enter it at the opposite end so that all the bits circulate. A shift register with this capability is known as a *ring counter.*
(* Computer, Binary, Binary Notation, Binary Code)

SHOCK EXCITATION When a dormant resonant system is provided with a sudden burst of energy it will oscillate at its natural frequency. The oscillatory current quickly dies away owing to *damping*, i.e. the dissipation of the oscillatory power in the resistance element of the system.
(>> Oscillation, Natural Frequency, Forced Oscillation, Damping)

SHORT-CIRCUIT An electrical connection having a relatively low resistance, across two points in a working circuit.
(>> Resistance)

SHORT WAVE A general term for radio waves in the high frequency band, i.e. of wavelengths 10 – 100 metres or of frequencies 3 – 30 megahertz.
(>> Frequency Band)

SHUNT is an electrical conductor through which current may be diverted, i.e. it is a resistance connected in parallel with another circuit. A common use of shunts is in moving-coil measuring instruments. If the moving coil produces a full scale deflection with say, 10 mA, then on its own no greater currents can be measured. For these therefore a low resistance shunt is connected across the coil so that only a fraction of the current being measured passes through it, most being diverted via the shunt. By providing a number of shunt resistors which can be switched in individually, the meter range for current measurement can be increased to any required degree.

See Moving-Coil Meter for shunt value calculations.
(* Parallel Connection)

SIGNAL GENERATOR is basically an oscillator of variable frequency, amplitude and waveform used for testing electronic equipment. For assessing the performance of radio receivers the signal generator output is in the radio frequency range and may be modulated at an audio frequency. The overall sensitivity of the receiver is determined by connecting the signal generator to the antenna socket and measuring the receiver output at the loudspeaker terminals. Such a generator is also used for "lining up" a receiver, i.e. adjusting both radio frequency and intermediate frequency circuits for maximum output.
(* Radio Receiver, Sensitivity, Oscillator >> Audio Frequency, Intermediate Frequency)

SIGNAL-TO-NOISE RATIO is generally defined as the ratio of the signal power to that of noise accompanying it. Other parameters however are used, e.g. root mean square values for both signal and noise or even peak values.

Signal-to-noise ratios are most conveniently expressed in decibels, a positive result indicating that the signal power is greater than the noise power, a negative figure indicating that the noise is the greater. Suppose the signal power, P_s is 16 times greater than the noise power, P_n, then:

$$\text{signal-to-noise ratio} = P_s/P_n = 16 \quad \text{or} \quad 10 \log 16 = 12\,\text{dB}$$

(>> Signal, Noise, Decibel)

SILICON CONTROLLED RECTIFIER is a p-n-p-n semiconductor device in which the main current is controlled by one of the p-regions, known as the *gate* – see Thyristor.

SILICON CONTROLLED SWITCH (S.C.S.) This is a four-layer semiconductor device similar to the thyristor but with connections to all layers. Being a 4-terminal device it is also known as a *tetrode thyristor.* There are two gate connections as shown in Figure S7(i). The basic action is similar to that for the thyristor except that:

(i) the "on" state can be initiated not only by a positive pulse on the cathode gate but also by a negative pulse on the anode gate. In both cases junction J_2 changes over from reverse to forward bias;

(ii) as with the thyristor, the s.c.s. "off" state is achieved by reducing the main current to a value below the holding value, I_H. This for the s.c.s. is done by applying a positive pulse to the anode gate or a negative pulse to the cathode gate.

The graphical symbol is given in Figure S7(ii).
(* Thyristor >> Semiconductor, P-N Junction)

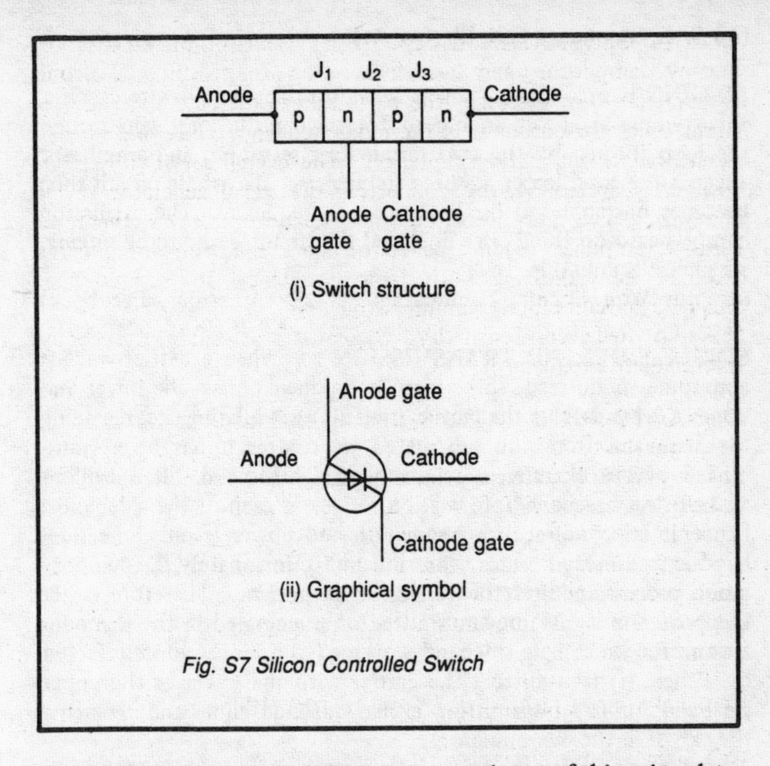

Fig. S7 Silicon Controlled Switch

SILVERED MICA CAPACITOR is one made up of thin mica plates which form the dielectric, silvered on both sides and stacked together, the plates then bond together on firing. The capacitor is usually flat with a solid wax impregnant and cement coating. This type is noted for its low power factor, capability of high voltage operation and good long-term stability. A typical range of values is from 5 picofarads (pF) to 4700 pF with an overall thickness of only around 3 mm.
(>> Capacitor, Power Factor, Mica)

SILVER-ZINC (SILVER OXIDE) CELL is a sealed secondary cell, more expensive than an equivalent size nickel-cadmium cell but having more than double the capacity. A silver mesh coated with silver oxide forms the positive plate, the negative electrode is a perforated silver-coated copper plate which is covered with zinc oxide. The electrolyte is potassium hydroxide (KOH). Cell voltage is 1.5 which can be maintained even at relatively high current drains. This type of cell is especially useful in button construction for watch and calculator batteries.

(>> Cell, Secondary Cell, Electrolyte)

SINGING is a condition which arises on telephone 4-wire circuits, for example as shown in Figure T6(i), when the total gain around the loop formed by the two terminating sets, lines and amplifiers, exceeds the total losses at some frequency. The whole circuit then becomes unstable and oscillates at this frequency. The oscillation can be heard on the 2-wire lines and the circuit is said to be *singing*. As such it is unusable.
(* Four Wire Circuit, Terminating Set >> Amplifier, Feedback)

SINGLE SIDEBAND TRANSMISSION When a carrier wave is amplitude modulated, three main components arise, the lower and upper sidebands plus the carrier itself. Demodulating, i.e. regaining the baseband from the modulated wave after it has been transmitted over a channel, is relatively straightforward. It is evident that all the baseband information resides in each of the sidebands, hence it is economical in bandwidth and power if only one sideband is transmitted. This is possible but unfortunately the demodulation process requires the carrier to be present. Therefore either the carrier must also be transmitted or regenerated in the demodulation process. Single sideband working (s.s.b.) is therefore effected by either: (i) transmitting the carrier with the lower or the upper sideband; or (ii) transmitting either sideband alone and replacing the carrier in the demodulator.

The carrier contains no information and in (i) accounts for a large proportion of the transmitted power. It is sensible therefore to transmit the carrier at a lower power (known as a *pilot carrier*) and use it to lock in an oscillator at the receiving end. Compared with normal double sideband transmission therefore an s.s.b. system with pilot carrier requires less bandwidth and lower power for the same baseband signal output.

Transmitting a single sideband with suppressed carrier (s.s.b.s.c.) economizes further on bandwidth and power but there is the complication of reintroducing the carrier in correct frequency and phase at the distant end.
(* Balanced Modulator >> Carrier Wave, Sideband, Amplitude Modulation, Bandwidth)

SKIN EFFECT When a current flows through a conductor it creates a magnetic flux in the form of concentric circles around the conductor. Accordingly if the current is alternating, the magnetic flux continually develops and then collapses, with a flux reversal each time the current reverses. Some of the flux exists within the conductor and therefore links more with the current flowing at the centre than with the current flowing near the surface. This increases the inductance at the centre more than at the surface because of the greater number of flux linkages. The impedance of the conductor is therefore greatest at the centre so the current there is least. Conversely more current flows at or near the surface or "skin" of the conductor. Since the inductive reactance which is the major component of the impedance increases with frequency, then clearly the skin effect also increases with frequency.

When the current cannot take full advantage of the whole cross-sectional area of a conductor, this indicates a rise in resistance and the conductor is then said to have an *effective resistance* which is higher than its d.c. resistance. It can be shown that the ratio of effective to d.c. resistance varies approximately as the square root of the frequency.

At very high frequencies, skin effect is so pronounced that virtually no current flows along the conductor centre, hence a tube of the same diameter can be used to replace the conductor. Alternatively, another way of using the conducting material more effectively is to use a bunch of smaller gauge enamelled wires connected together at the ends but insulated from each other along the length (the *Litzendraht* or *Litz* conductor). Because each strand is small, there will be relatively little skin effect over its cross-section, accordingly all the material is effective in carrying current.
(>> Inductance, Effective Resistance)

SKIP DISTANCE Long distance radio communication (up to some 15 MHz) is accomplished via the sky wave, i.e. the wave reflected back to earth by the ionosphere. At the higher frequencies waves entering the ionosphere with nearly vertical incidence pass straight through and are lost, however as the angle of incidence increases so the likelihood of a sky wave return also increases. The result is that no sky wave reaches earth until some distance from the transmitter.

If also at the frequency of operation the ground wave is ineffective because of ground absorption then there is a certain distance over which practically no signal is received. The distance from the transmitter to where the first sky wave arrives is known as the *skip distance*.
(* Ionosphere, Ground Wave >> Electromagnetic Wave)

SKY NOISE arrives from up above and can be subdivided into (i) *atmospheric noise* and (ii) *galactic* noise. Both types affect radio systems and arise on the transmission path. The atmospheric variety comes from disturbances such as lightning or other discharges in the atmosphere or ionosphere while galactic noise has a character of its own and emanates from the galaxy (the myriads of far-off stars). (* Signal-to-Noise Ratio, Noise Factor, Noise Figure, Lightning, Ionosphere >> Noise Temperature)

SKY WAVE The energy radiated from a transmitting antenna located on the earth's surface consists of a ground wave which travels along the surface of the earth and a sky wave which is propagated via the atmosphere. When the sky wave reaches the ionized regions in the upper atmosphere (the ionosphere), it can either be bent earthwards and therefore be useful for long distance radio transmissions or pass through for use in satellite communications. This depends on its frequency – see Ionosphere.

SLEW RATE of a signal is its rate of change of voltage, measured in either volts per second (V/s) or more usually, volts per microsecond (V/μs) – see Operational Amplifier.

SLIDE WIRE A resistive wire stretched taut between two terminals, it has uniform resistance along its length and a sliding contact makes a connection with it at any point. It has a scale attached, usually 0 – 100. With it a desired value of resistance can be obtained in terms of the length of wire in use. Resistance ratios are also available directly from the scale.
(* Potentiometer, Potential Divider >> Ohm's Law)

SLIP RING – see Generator.

SLOW-WAVE STRUCTURE – see Travelling-Wave Tube.

SLUG A core which can be screwed in or out of a coil to vary its inductance.
(>> Inductor)

SMOOTHING CIRCUIT A circuit designed to reduce the amount of ripple remaining on the direct current output of a rectifying system. It usually consists of a low-pass filter – see Ripple Filter.

SOFTWARE is a term used in computer usage for the programs. These are mainly held in the memory or magnetically on tape or disc and although the memory, tape and disc are classed as *hardware*, the actual program on them is the software.
See also Hardware.
(* Computer)

SOLAR CELL is a photovoltaic cell, i.e. it generates an electromotive force according to the intensity of light falling on its input electrode. It is used especially for conversion of solar energy into electrical energy, for example, for the power supply of satellites and in remote terrestrial areas for telephone and radio equipment.

If photons which are incident on or near the depletion layer of a p-n semiconductor junction have sufficient energy to release electrons from their parent atoms, electron-hole pairs are created. These become separated by the electric field existing across the depletion layer with the result that holes move into the p-region, electrons into the n-type. A potential therefore exists across the junction which can be employed to drive a current round an external circuit.

Silicon and gallium arsenide are commonly used for the semiconductor, either with a thin translucent p-type layer on an n-type substrate or vice versa. Typically an open-circuit voltage of 0.5 V and a short-circuit current of 0.1 A are available from a single cell. Cells are therefore combined in series and parallel arrangements to provide the required values of voltage and current. Efficiencies are not particularly high, around the 20% level but continued research is likely to improve on this.

(>> Photovoltaic Effect, Photovoltaic Cell, Semiconductor, P-N Junction)

SOLENOID Basically this is a coil of wire in the form of a helix which, when carrying a current, acts as a bar magnet. If the turns are closely wound and the length of the solenoid is much greater than its diameter, then the magnetic field within it is uniform and parallel to the axis except at the ends. This is sketched in Figure S8.

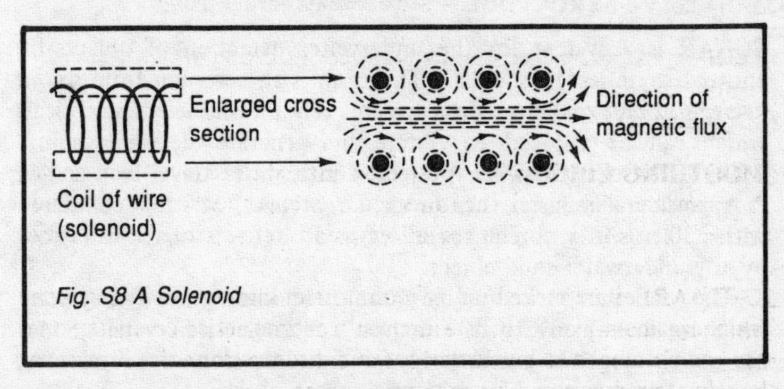

Fig. S8 A Solenoid

For such a solenoid, the flux density, B within the coil in air is given by:

$$B = \mu_0 IN/l \text{ tesla}$$

where μ_0 is the permeability of free space (magnetic constant), I is the current in amperes, N the number of turns and l the length of the coil in metres (the diameter of the coil is not included provided that it is small compared with the length). The direction of the magnetic flux for a given current direction can be determined from Fleming's Rules.
(>> Electromagnetism, Magnetic Field, Magnetic Flux, Permeability)

SOLID-STATE CAMERA is one which does not rely on thermionic emission in an evacuated envelope but employs solid-state devices only. The main component generally used is the charge-coupled device (CCD). Photons of light generate electron-hole pairs in a silicon substrate according to the light intensity [see the input side of Fig.C4(ii), in this case known as the *photosite*]. The minority carriers fill the potential "wells" in the substrate and the charge is transferred along the CCD, eventually to its output. The CCD's are in integrated form and are therefore minute and may be arranged with their photosites constructed as a matrix to cover a given area. This turns a picture into electrical signals which can result in a video output signal when suitable clock pulses are applied.
(* Solid-State Device, Charge-Coupled Device, Clock Pulse >> Semiconductor, Photon, Electron-Hole Pair, Photoconductivity)

SOLID-STATE DEVICE is one which employs solid materials only, especially semiconductors and its operation is entirely due to the movement of charge carriers within the solid.
(>> Semiconductor, Charge, Charge Carrier)

SONAR is a system for the underwater detection of objects by emitted or reflected sounds. The term is an acronym from *sound navigation and ranging.* Most systems rely on piezoelectric crystals which can be induced to vibrate and generate ultrasonic sound waves. These waves when projected into water travel well and in fact considerably faster than in air, i.e. around 1500 m/s compared with 330 m/s in air. The sound waves are reflected back as echoes by any underwater solid object.

The echoes are picked up by a transducer known as a *hydrophone* which again is likely to be based on a piezoelectric crystal. Sonar has many uses but particularly for the detection of submarines, locating fish shoals and for measuring ocean depth.
(* Transducer >> Ultrasonics, Piezoelectric Effect, Piezoelectric Crystal)

SOUND-LEVEL METER is one in which the electrical output of a microphone is, after some manipulation, displayed as a reading on a meter. It provides a convenient objective measurement which can be interpreted as an assessment of the loudness of noise or other sounds. A simplified diagram of a typical instrument is given in Figure S9.

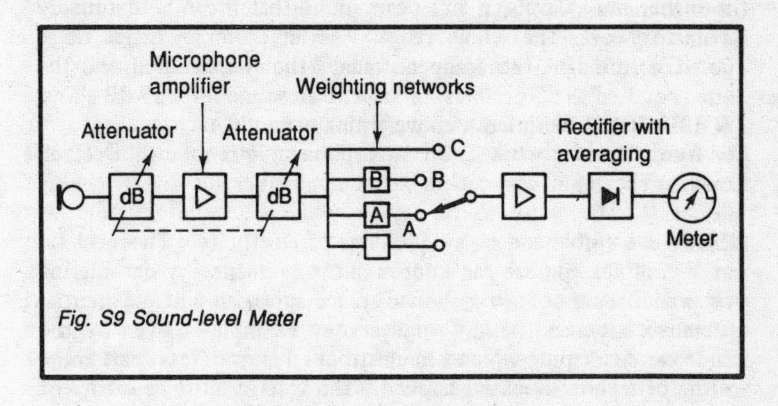

Fig. S9 Sound-level Meter

Ignoring the *weighting networks*, the system must be "flat" in that, irrespective of frequency, equal sound pressures at the microphone give rise to the same meter deflections. The range of sound levels is large hence an attenuator follows the microphone so that the microphone amplifier is not overloaded at high levels. The *averaging* circuit prevents the pointer from trying to follow peaks and it averages over 0.2 up to 1 second as required. The longer time is especially useful for high-energy, short duration, but relatively infrequent peaks.

In listening to sounds our ears tell a different story from a microphone system with a flat response because our ears are less sensitive at the lower frequencies especially for weak sound levels. The weighting networks therefore give predetermined "weights" or compensation to certain frequencies. Taking the commonly used A network which is used mainly for measuring noise, this simply creates a loss at the lower frequencies increasing as frequency falls. Accordingly a higher sound level is needed for the same meter reading compared with that for the higher frequencies. This particular network which is designed for low to medium sound levels attempts to simulate average hearing by gradually introducing some 50 dB loss as frequency falls from 1000 Hz to 20 Hz. A weighting network B is used for higher sound levels and C for even higher and experimetal work. There are other special networks.

The actual sound level figures used are quoted in decibels relative to a generally known reference level of 2×10^{-5} newtons per square metre (N/m^2) at 1000 Hz. So that it is clear as to which weighting network has been used, the sound level is quoted with the weighting code, e.g. dBx where x is the code.

Although theoretically the B and C weightings are necessary for the higher noise levels, it has been found that the A is reasonably satisfactory over the whole range. As an example, office noise quoted as 65 dBA (generally nowadays the A is ignored and the noise is quoted as 65 decibels) infers a mean sound level 65 dB above 2×10^{-5} N/m^2 measured with weighting network A.

(* Weighting Network >> Microphone, Attenuator, Decibel, Newton)

SPARK is a visible and noisy discharge of electricity. The mechanism is complex but we can understand it in essence by considering two points separated by a short distance and with a high potential difference between them. An everyday example is given by the motor car spark plug which has electrodes 1 mm or less apart and a voltage of several thousand applied. The voltage must be sufficient to give rise to ionization by collision. This increases the number of electrons and ions in the gap between the electrodes and the intense electric field imparts sufficient energy to these two types of particle that they too can produce more electron-ion pairs by collision. The rate of production of ions depends mainly on the electron mean free path which itself is a function of the pressure of the particular gas between the electrodes. At a certain value of voltage therefore the ionization increases abundantly and at this point the path becomes highly conducting and a spark travels between the electrodes. The supply of ions is not diminished and further spark discharges are then able to occur at lower voltages. Sparking ceases when the voltage falls sufficiently.

The actual voltage at which a spark will occur under any particular set of conditions is difficult to assess especially in view of the considerable effect of the *shape* of the electrodes. Experimental work however gives us a good guide, for example for dry air at normal pressure. Between two parallel plates, for a spark to occur:

a gap of 1 mm requires about 4.1 kV (= 4.1×10^6 V/m)
a gap of 1 cm requires about 35 kV (= 3.5×10^6 V/m)
a gap of 2 cm requires about 65 kV (= 3.25×10^6 V/m)

and these figures are reduced to approximately one-third if the electrodes are sharp points.

(* Flashover >> Ionization, Collision, Mean Free Path, Gas Discharge, Arc)

SPARK QUENCH is usually required when a switch or electromagnetic relay contacts interrupt the current flowing in an inductive circuit. Rapid collapse of the magnetic field induces a high voltage into the circuit. As the switch contacts begin to part it is more than likely that an unwanted spark will jump across the tiny gap, unwanted because it burns away the contacts due to the intense heat generated over a small area. Sparks or *arcing* arise when a sufficiently high voltage between the contacts is impressed across a small air-gap, then even electrons which are normally tightly bound to their atoms are forced away, ionizing the air and forming a conducting path. A current then flows with sufficient heat to maintain the miniature arc.

There are several types of spark quench circuit, one of the simplest and least expensive being the connection of a voltage-sensitive resistor or diode rectifier across the contacts. The higher the voltage between the opening contacts, the greater the current by-passed by the resistor or rectifier, resulting in the reduction of the voltage to a small fraction. If this type of resistance has undesired effects on the remainder of the circuit then a single capacitor may be used instead although this is more expensive. As the contacts open, current flows into the capacitor, i.e. the energy previously stored in the inductance is transferred to the capacitor rather than being dissipated as a spark. However, when the contacts close again, the capacitor discharges through them with the danger of contact welding. This problem is reduced by connecting a resistance in series with the capacitor. Typical values for a CR spark quench suitable for a small relay are $C = 0.5\ \mu F$, $R = 510\ \Omega$.
(* Spark, Voltage-Sensitive Resistor >> Ionization, Inductance, Rectifier, Diode, Capacitor)

SPUTTERING is a technique of depositing metal by using high velocity ions. In *cathode sputtering* for example, a cathode of the metal to be deposited is fitted into a gas-discharge tube filled with argon at low pressure. Within the tube is also the item to be coated (e.g. a substrate to be used in a thin film process), connected as an anode. A high voltage (several kilovolts) between cathode and anode ionizes the argon and the positive ions are accelerated towards the (negative) cathode. When the ions strike the cathode, atoms or molecules of the metal are released. These have acquired a negative charge and are therefore accelerated to the anode to which they adhere. The metal of the cathode is therefore deposited

(or sputtered) onto the anode (or substrate). The deposited film density is high and adhesion good.
(* Hybrid Integrated Circuits >> Gas Discharge, Ionization, Impact Ionization, Cathode, Anode)

SQUARE-LAW DETECTOR is a detector or demodulator which has an output voltage which is directly proportional to the square of the input voltage over the working range of the device.
(>> Demodulation)

STABILIZATION is a term used in at least three different design processes:

(1) The operating point of an active device such as a transistor needs stabilization so that the mean collector current remains at the design value. A workable arrangement is shown in Figure S10(i) in which any increase in collector current reduces the collector voltage, hence less biasing current is provided via R_b. This reduces the collector current, tending to stabilize it. This is a simple arrangement and more complicated circuits are available giving considerably better stabilization.

(2) The voltage output of a power supply frequently requires stabilization so that it remains as close as possible to the design value. Rectification of an a.c. supply may produce a direct output containing appreciable ripple. Generally such outputs pass through a filter for further smoothing but some *ripple* remains. Many equipments require that the direct power supply voltage is maintained at a constant value irrespective of variations in a.c. input or load current, hence the requirement of a voltage stabilizer.

A zener diode has the characteristic in the reverse direction at breakdown of maintaining a substantially constant voltage across it even though the current varies considerably. A simple example shows how the circuit functions. Consider the circuit shown in Figure S10(ii) with currents and voltages labelled as shown. The series resistance R reduces V_S to V_L since $V_L = V_S - IR$. Now I is made up of I_Z and I_L, hence $V_S = V_L + (I_Z + I_L)R$

$$\therefore R = \frac{V_S - V_L}{I_Z + I_L} \quad \text{and} \quad V_L = V_S - (I_Z + I_L)R$$

thus should V_L try to increase, I_Z increases and creates a greater voltage drop across R to compensate and vice versa. More efficient circuits may contain two zener diodes or control by a transistor. Better still, V_L is compared by a *voltage comparator* against a

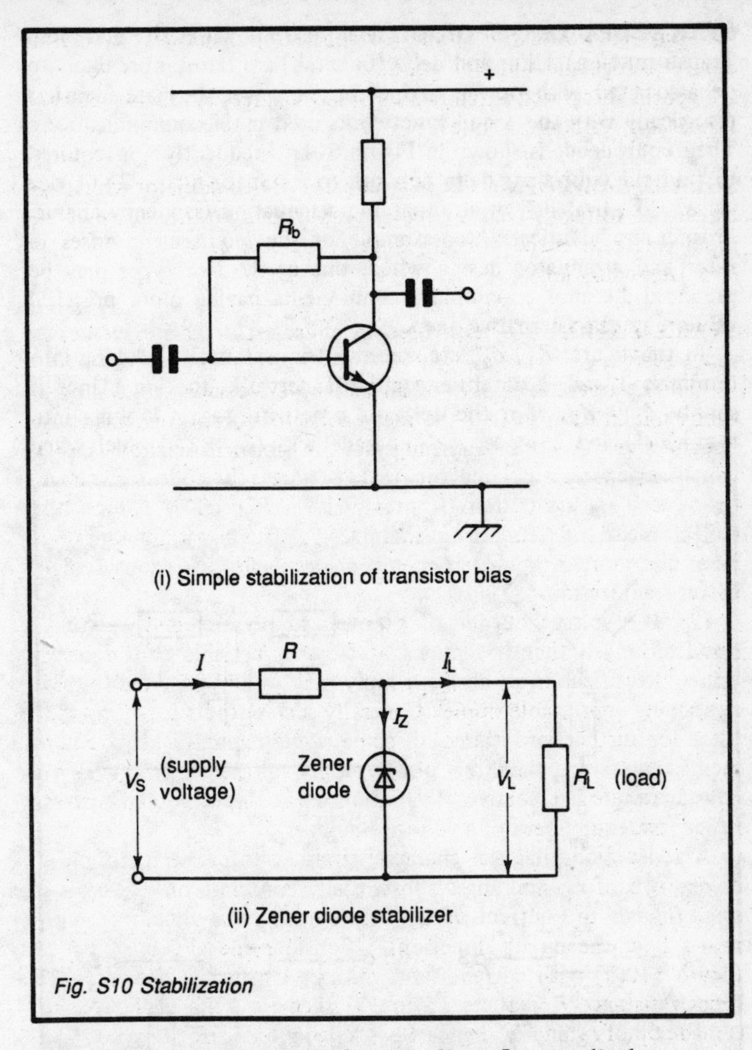

Fig. S10 Stabilization

voltage reference and a series element adjusts I_L accordingly.

(3) The term also refers to the use of negative feedback over for example, a high gain amplifier stage or stages containing inductance and capacitance which together resonate at a frequency within the amplifier range. The technique increases the damping sufficiently to prevent instability which may arise when any positive feedback present is sufficient to set the circuit oscillating.
(* Regulation, Ripple >> Transistor, Bias, Rectification, Filter, Zener Diode, Amplifier, Negative Feedback, Damping)

STAR-DELTA TRANSFORMATION (also known as the Star-Mesh Transformation). Star and delta (or mesh) are terms more likely to be associated with power engineering, however they are identical electrically with the T and π networks used in telecommunications. Their equivalence is shown in Figure S11. Frequently it is required to find the equivalent delta network to a star (or π to a T) or vice versa. "Equivalent" means that the attenuation/frequency characteristics are identical. An example of the requirement arises in filter and attenuator design where one of the two types may be preferred because it contains components having more practical values than the alternative one.

In the figure, Z_1, Z_2, etc. represent impedances. Looking into terminals 1 and 2 of either star or T network, the impedance is simply $Z_1 + Z_2$. For the delta or π network, again looking into terminals 1 and 2, we see Z_A in parallel with $(Z_B + Z_C)$ which when

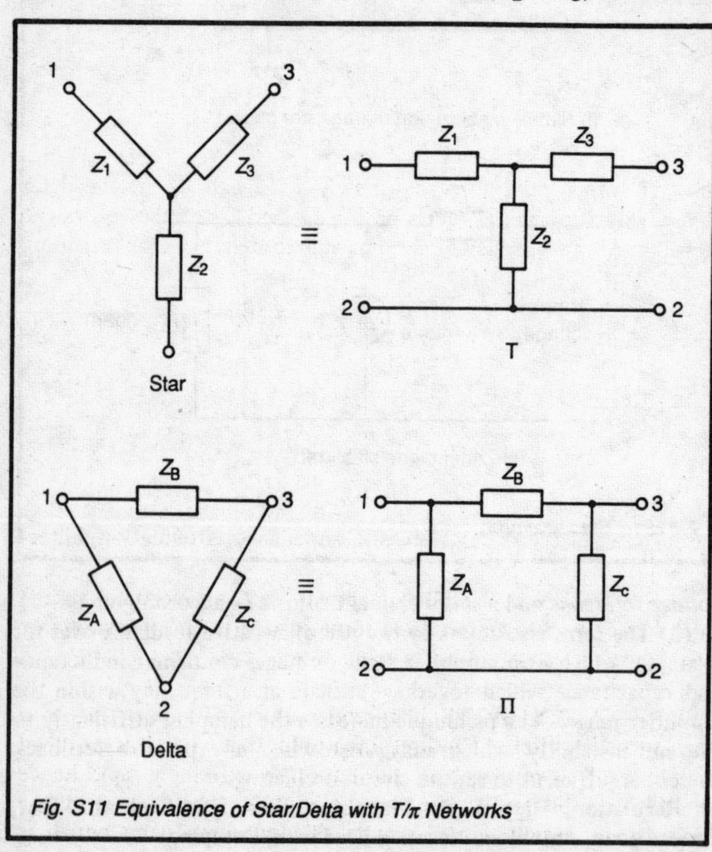

Fig. S11 Equivalence of Star/Delta with T/π Networks

sorted out becomes:

$$\frac{Z_A(Z_B + Z_C)}{Z_A + Z_B + Z_C}$$

For equivalence therefore:

$$Z_1 + Z_2 = \frac{Z_A(Z_B + Z_C)}{Z_A + Z_B + Z_C}$$

This can be repeated for terminals 1 and 3 and again for terminals 2 and 3 so giving 3 equations from which:

$$Z_1 = \frac{Z_A Z_B}{Z_A + Z_B + Z_C} \qquad Z_2 = \frac{Z_A Z_C}{Z_A + Z_B + Z_C}$$

$$Z_3 = \frac{Z_B Z_C}{Z_A + Z_B + Z_C}$$

This transforms delta to star for if Z_A, Z_B and Z_C of the delta network are known, the values of Z_1, Z_2 and Z_3 of the equivalent star network can be calculated. For star to delta, similar reasoning shows that:

$$Z_A = Z_1 + Z_2 + \frac{Z_1 Z_2}{Z_3} \qquad Z_B = Z_1 + Z_3 + \frac{Z_1 Z_3}{Z_2}$$

$$Z_C = Z_2 + Z_3 + \frac{Z_2 Z_3}{Z_1}$$

(* Equivalent Network >> Network, Impedance, Attenuation, Filter)

STEP FUNCTION is a mode of activity (e.g. an electrical signal) which has a value of zero until at some particular time it instantaneously jumps to a constant finite value.

STEP-RECOVERY DIODE is a semiconductor diode acting as a charge storage switch. The useful feature is that when it is switched from forward to reverse bias, the cut-off is extremely rapid hence the device can be used to generate an impulse. The diode structure consists of a heavily doped n-type silicon substrate on which is grown a thin layer of lightly doped n-type silicon. An upper region is then formed of heavily doped p-type silicon. This resembles a normal but heavily doped p-n diode but with an added thin lightly doped region in the centre.

Under forward bias charges are stored in the centre region. When reverse bias is applied the diode immediately conducts in the reverse direction while the stored charges are being dispersed. As the stored charge becomes depleted, the diode current then cuts off suddenly, in fact for some diodes, within less than 100 picoseconds (100×10^{-12} seconds). Such a fast change in current or voltage implies a waveform rich in harmonics hence the device can be used as an impulse or harmonic generator. This type of diode is also known as a *charge-storage diode*.

(* Impulse Generator >> P-N Junction, Diode, Charge Carrier, Doping, Fourier Analysis, Harmonic)

STEREOPHONIC BROADCASTING Monophonic broadcasting in a way is equivalent to listening with one ear only. On the other hand a stereophonic system gives a more pleasant spatial feeling because it is equivalent to listening with sound arriving at both ears from all directions. Stereophonic broadcasting aims to give the illusion of space but by using two microphone channels only. At the receiver the sound is delivered by using two similar loudspeakers operating in phase. The system generally in use transmits the two stereo signals, labelled LEFT (L) and RIGHT (R) or frequently A and B, using frequency modulation (FM Stereo).

It is essential that monophonic radio receivers are able to receive the stereophonic transmissions and for this the two signals must first be combined to give (L+R). For stereophonic reception (L–R) is also required and a simple method of combining the L and R signals to obtain (L+R) and (L–R) is given in Figure S12(i). Resistive networks may also be used. These two composite signals must now be transmitted on an f.m. carrier in such a way that they can eventually be separated in the receivers.

In (ii) of the figure is shown how the complete stereo baseband signal is assembled. The (L+R) signal occupies the lower frequency end of the band so that it is available to monophonic receivers. It covers the frequency range from say, 30 Hz to 15 kHz which is therefore classed as high quality. The (L–R) signal amplitude modulates a 38 kHz carrier in a balanced modulator hence with an output of the lower and upper sidebands but no carrier. The two sidebands therefore occupy the frequency range (38 – 15) to (38 + 15), i.e. 23 to 53 kHz as shown. A *pilot* carrier is added for ease of demodu-

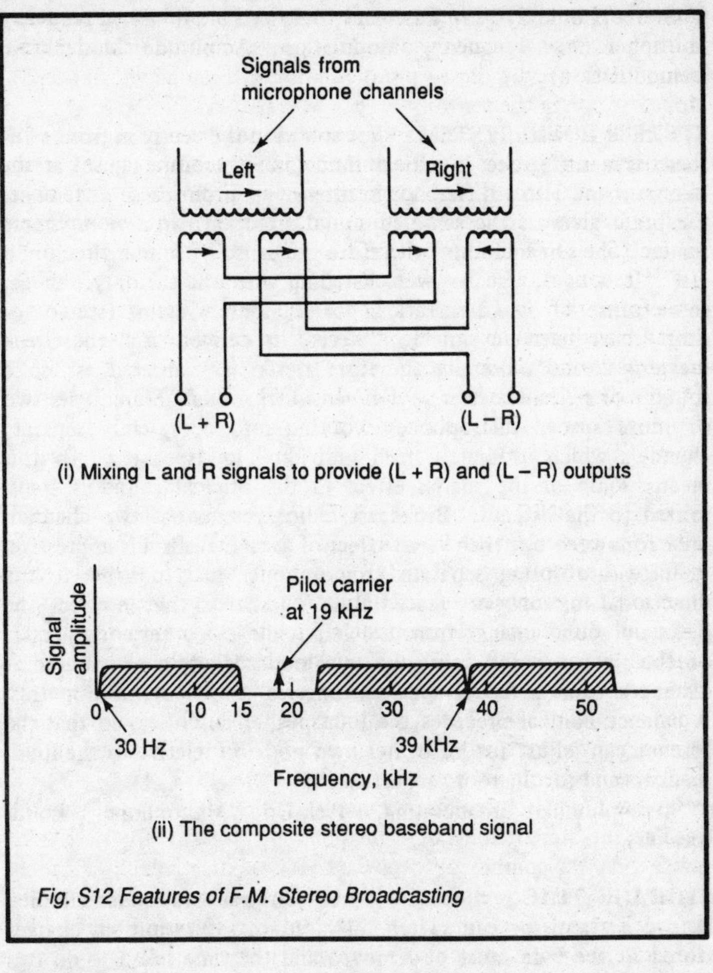

Fig. S12 Features of F.M. Stereo Broadcasting

lation in the receiver. This composite signal frequency-modulates the transmitter.

In the receiver the stereo signal is first regained from the incoming radio frequency signal. Next the (L+R) signal, (L–R) sidebands and pilot carrier are separated by filters. The 19 kHz pilot carrier is frequency doubled and applied with the (L–R) sidebands to a demodulator to extract the (L–R) signal. The (L+R) and (L–R) signals go through a process of addition and subtraction to recover the original L and R signals which are then amplified and fed to the appropriate loudspeakers. Monophonic reception requires the (L+R) signal only.

(* Stereophonic System, Baseband, Balanced Modulator, Frequency Multiplier >> Frequency Modulation, Amplitude Modulation, Demodulation)

STEREOPHONIC SYSTEM For sounds not directly in front of us there is a difference in arrival time (and therefore phase) at the two ears and also a difference in intensity. From these differences the brain gives us the sense of sound direction. In a *monophonic* system (one channel only) therefore the sense of sound direction is lost. It is as though we were listening with one ear only. To get some sense of sound direction, stereophonic systems (stereo for short) have been developed. "Stereo" is derived from the Greek meaning "solid", literally therefore stereo is translated as "solid sound" or perhaps better as *3-dimensional sound.* Stereo uses two or more spaced microphones working into completely separate channels which ultimately feed individual loudspeakers. By this means some of the spatial effect in the original sound is transmitted to the listener. Broadcast radio systems use two channels only for stereo but the overall effect of greater realism is impressive.

Instead of using separated microphones it is possible to use directional microphones placed close together so that in effect one picks up sound mainly from the left while the other concentrates on the right. In the home the two loudspeakers are separated at distances from a few tens of centimetres to one or more metres. A balance control precedes the loudspeaker amplifiers so that the listener can adjust for his or her own position relative to the loudspeakers and for the room acoustics.
(* Stereophonic Broadcasting, Pick-Up, Microphone, Loudspeaker)

STORAGE TIME is a feature of bipolar transistor pulse circuits. Before a transistor can switch fully out of saturation, all charges stored in the base must be removed and the time taken to do this is known as the storage time. It is perhaps best illustrated as shown in Figure S13 which shows how an input pulse which has been applied to a common-emitter switching transistor results in an output pulse delayed by the switching time.
(* Switching Transistor >> Carrier Storage, P-N Junction, Transistor, Charge Carrier, Pulse)

STORAGE TUBE is an electron tube capable of storing information which can be extracted later. Both input and output can be electrical or visual, hence dividing storage tubes into four different classes. A general idea of how such tubes function can be gained

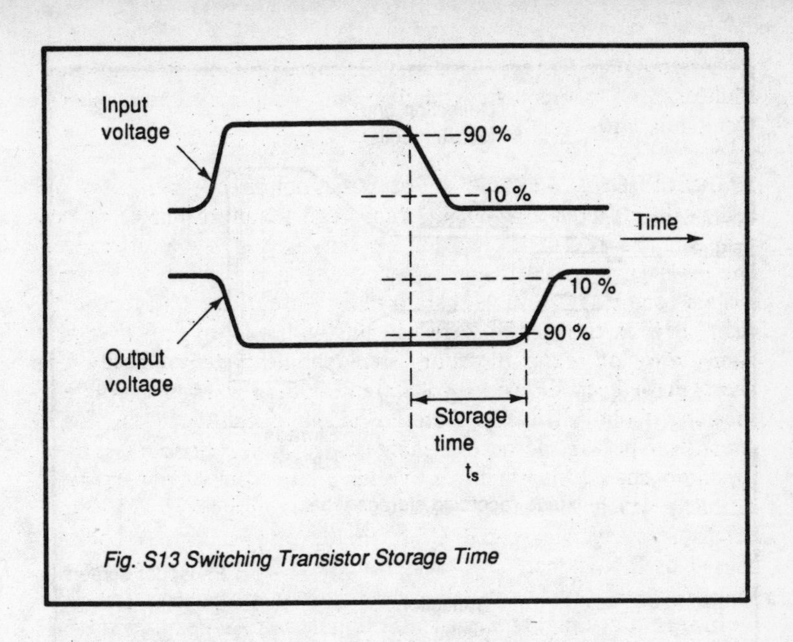

Fig. S13 Switching Transistor Storage Time

from the descriptions of just two types as given below.

An example of the electrical input – electrical output class is given by the *image recording storage tube*, the essential features of which are sketched in Figure S14(i). This is a *charge-storage tube* in which the information is stored on a target plate. The information signal to be stored modulates the intensity of the electron beam produced by the electron gun. The beam is made to scan the target and the electron velocity within the beam at any instant depends on the amplitude of the input signal, hence emission of secondary electrons from the target does also. This leaves an electrostatic charge pattern on the target. Reading is accomplished without affecting the stored charge pattern by using a constant current beam which divides between the collector and the storage mesh according to the value of the charge on the target. The output is taken from the collector.

Frequently encountered in the electronics laboratory or workshop is the *storage cathode-ray tube*, an example of the electrical input – visual output class. A sketch of a typical tube is given in (ii) of the figure. The screen (or target) is made up of tiny phosphor particles so that any area can be "written into" without affecting neighbouring areas. At the back of the phosphor screen is a glass plate coated with a transparent conducting material which acts as the collector.

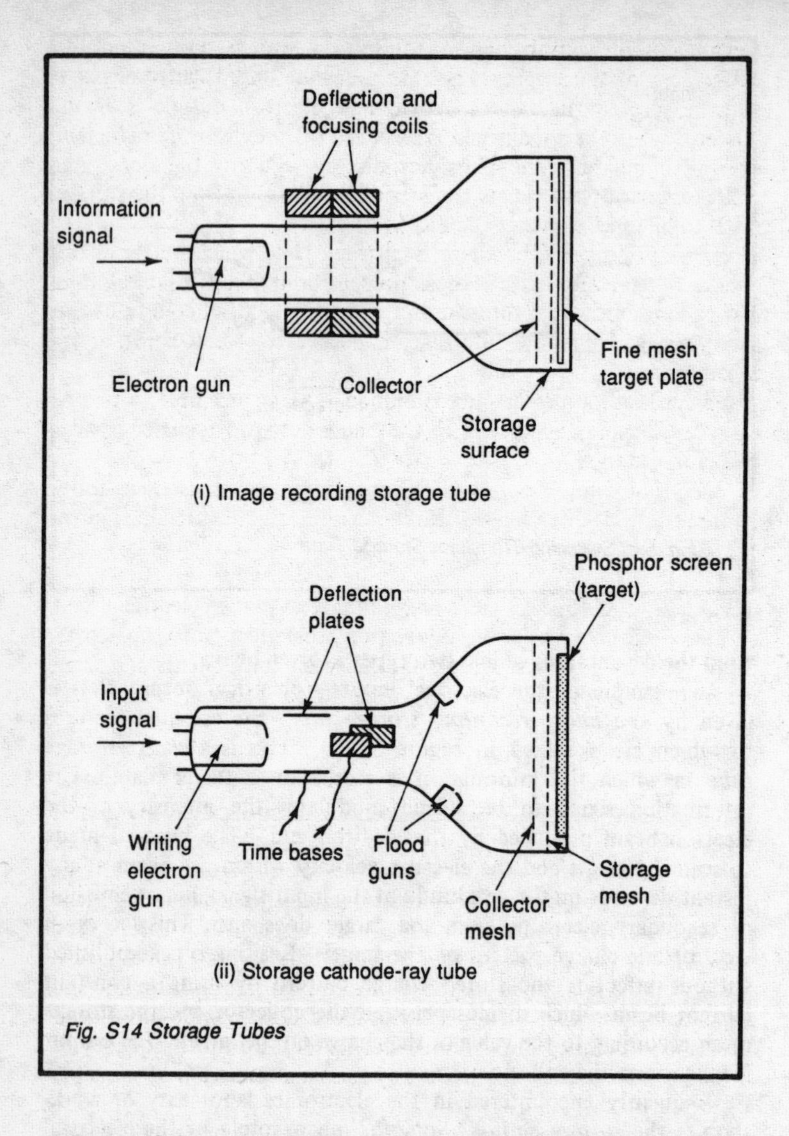

Fig. S14 Storage Tubes

Some of the primary electrons from the writing gun are intercepted by the storage mesh and secondary electrons are released. The secondary emission ratio is greater than unity and the secondary electrons are attracted to the positively held collector mesh. Through its loss of (secondary) electrons at any point the storage mesh goes positive hence on each scan the display is held on the storage mesh as a positive charge image. The flood guns are continually on and having no deflection system they flood the entire area of the target. Their cathodes are only slightly negative with respect to the target, hence their electron output is small, however when the writing gun is switched off they provide sufficient energy to maintain the phosphor display. Pulsing the flood gun collectors negatively causes the secondary emission from the storage mesh to be repelled hence the display is erased.

For any storage tube there is a *decay time* which indicates the period of time for which the stored information is usable. It is difficult to define and measure but generally is considered to be the time during which the information decays to 1/e (0.368) of its initial value.

Visual input types are less common. As an example, a photo-emissive film may be used with the photoelectrons focussed upon a grid storage target.
(* Electron Gun, Flood Gun, Scanning, Long Persistence Tube, Cathode-Ray Tube >> Secondary Emission, Photoemission, Photoelectric Effect)

STRAY CAPACITANCE is the capacitance within an electric circuit or device which arises from any source other than from capacitors. Stray capacitances exist within and between components and from wires running parallel to each other, also between wiring and components with a chassis.
(>> Capacitance, Capacitor)

STRIP TRANSMISSION LINE is used for short distance, low power applications and consists of a printed conductor sandwiched between two earthed conducting planes as in Figure S15 for the microstrip version but with an additional earthed conducting plane on the top. The conductor is usually of copper which is separated from the earthed planes by thin polyethylene sheets. The electrical characteristics are similar to those of a coaxial transmission line and typically a line with a copper strip about 0.5 cm wide has a characteristic impedance of 50 ohms and is useful up to a frequency of around 5 GHz and at this frequency has an attenuation of some 0.5 dB/metre.

The *microstrip transmission line* is of simpler construction compared with the strip line, it consists essentially of a single earthed conducting plane and strip as sketched in Figure S15. The metallic strip is bonded to a dielectric sheet on the other side of which is bonded the metallic plate. This miniature type of line is used in ultra-high frequency and microwave applications. The attenuation is greater than that for the strip line and the power handling capacity

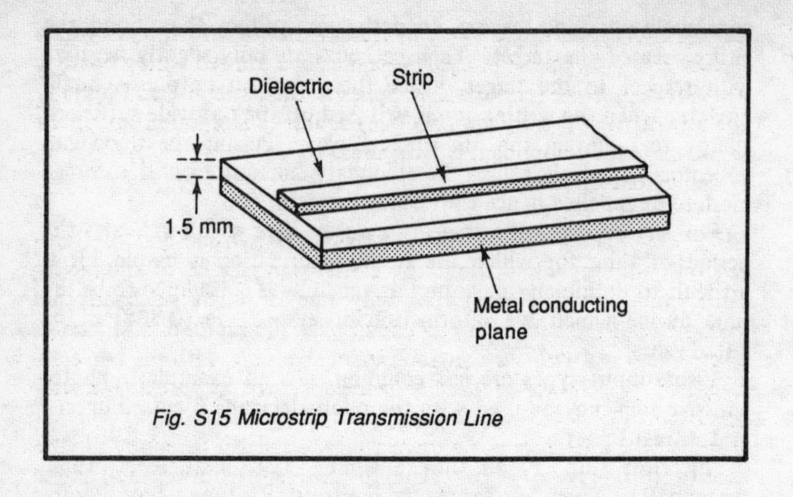

Fig. S15 Microstrip Transmission Line

is less. Typically for a microstrip of width 4 mm and a dielectric of thickness 1.5 mm the characteristic impedance is about 50 ohms, decreasing as the strip width increases. Microstrip lines are suitable up to around 10 GHz.
(* Coaxial Cable >> Transmission Line, Characteristic Impedance, Attenuation)

STUB, STUB MATCHING is mainly used with antennas so is described here as such. For an antenna feeder or transmission line to deliver maximum power to the antenna the line must be terminated in a pure resistance equal to its own characteristic impedance. This avoids reflection of energy with consequent standing waves on the line. In a few words, the line must be matched to the antenna. Generally an antenna has reactance so it is necessary to introduce a reactance of equal and opposite sign so that the antenna reactance is cancelled out. This is conveniently accomplished by connecting a section of transmission line known as a *stub* in parallel with the feeder. The stub has a length of up to half a wavelength and is short-circuited or open-circuited at the end remote from the antenna according to the reactance required. Theoretically stubs are capable of providing positive or negative reactances up to infinity. Besides cancelling reactance, matching of the antenna and feeder impedances is required hence the process is complicated and so is usually carried out by the "cut and try" method until standing waves on the feeder are reduced to a minimum.
(* Antenna, Matching >> Antenna, Transmission Line, Characteristic Impedance, Standing Wave, Reactance)

SUBSTRATE is a single block of material having a surface on which circuit elements can be printed. Technically a printed wiring board is a substrate but the term usually applies to the basic material (usually silicon) on which a *monolithic* (single block) integrated circuit or semiconductor component is fabricated.
(* Integrated Circuit)

SUPPRESSED CARRIER TRANSMISSION is a method of transmitting radio signals without the carrier component of the modulated wave being present, i.e. only one or both sidebands are transmitted. If there is one sideband only the method is known as *single sideband with suppressed carrier* (s.s.b.s.c.), with the two sidebands it is known as *double sideband with suppressed carrier* (d.s.b.s.c.).

When the carrier is not present a local oscillator is required in the receiver to regenerate the carrier in correct frequency and phase otherwise accurate demodulation is not possible. This is known as *synchronous detection.*

See also Single Sideband Transmission.
(* Balanced Modulator >> Carrier Wave, Sideband, Modulation)

SURFACE ACOUSTIC WAVE DEVICE is one in which an acoustic wave is propagated along the surface of a piezoelectric material which is separated by a very small gap from a thin film of semiconductor. The wave generates an electric field which interacts with conduction electrons in the semiconductor. Depending on a bias potential applied to the semiconductor, the conduction electrons either give up energy to the wave (amplification) or extract energy from it (attenuation) – see Acoustic Wave Device.

SWEEP is the regular movement of the electron beam across the screen of a cathode-ray tube – see Time Base.

SWITCH is a device used for completion or interruption of an electric circuit. Switches take many forms and appear in most electronic equipments. The simplest is the *single-pole* with metal contacts which completes or interrupts one wire only, the *double-pole* acts similarly on two separate wires at the same time. Switches may also be used to select one of several circuit options, e.g. the wave-change selector on a radio receiver.

Switches which function by placing two metal contacts together present almost a short-circuit (only a tiny fraction of one ohm) when "on". When "off" they introduce almost a complete disconnection. Unfortunately metal–metal contacts in time may suffer

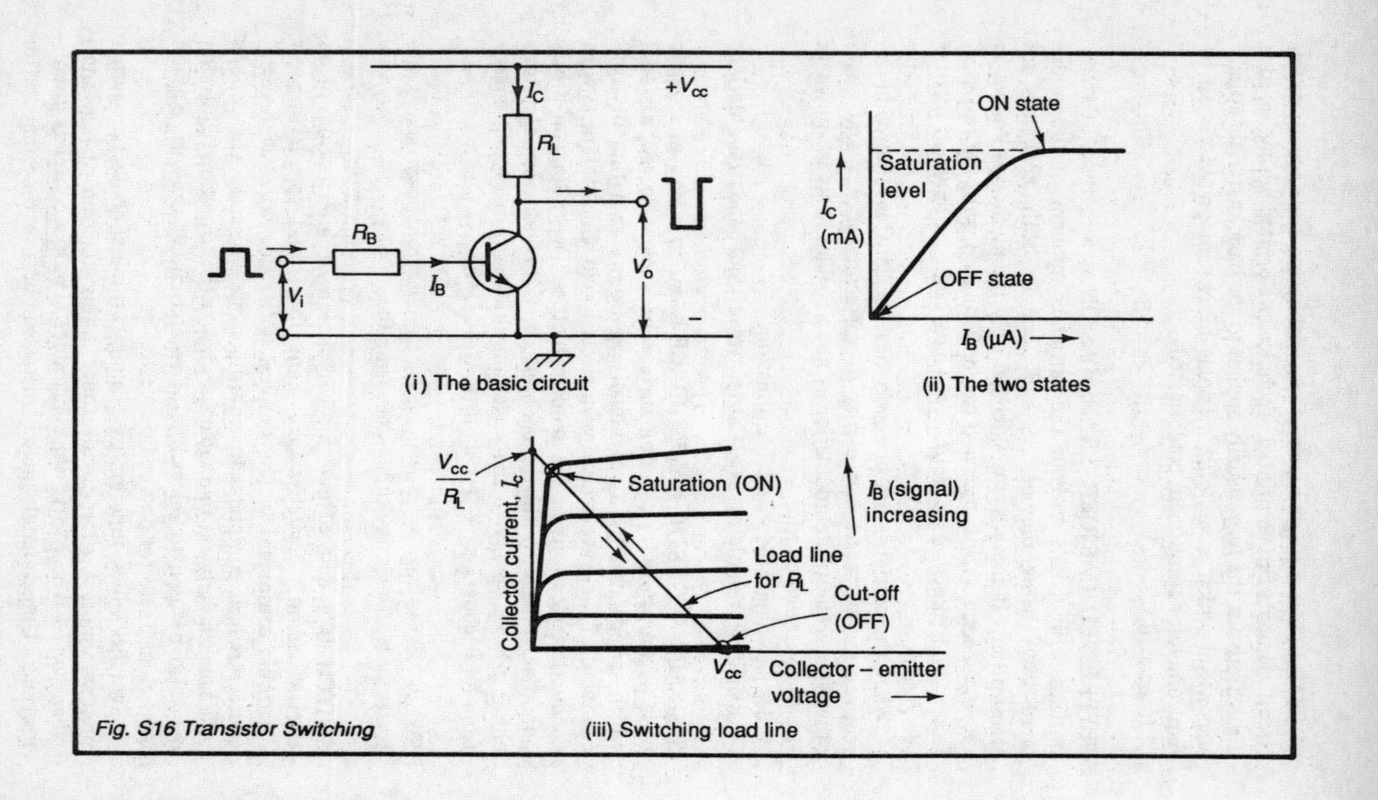

Fig. S16 Transistor Switching

from burning or corrosion but less if plated with a noble metal (e.g. gold or platinum). They may be remotely controlled as with a relay.

Semiconductor switches on the other hand do not have the clean short-circuit or disconnection of the metal contact type, their speed of operation and reliability are however very much greater. For this reason they are essential for the very fast switching required in computer, digital logic and similar circuits.
(* Relay, Switching Transistor)

SWITCHING TRANSISTOR Of the many different uses found for transistors, switching ranks as one of the more important. As an on/off switch a transistor has not the clean disconnection and short-circuit of the metal to metal contact but it makes up for this by its fast operation, an essential in computer systems and digital transmission.

The basic circuit arrangement for a bipolar switching transistor is shown in Figure S16(i). It is similar to the common-emitter amplifier except that there is no base biasing simply because the transistor is to be operated at its extremes of little or no collector current (the *cut-off* or "off" state) and maximum collector current (the *saturated, bottomed* or "on" state). These two states are indicated on the collector current (I_C) versus base current (I_B) characteristic shown in (ii) of the figure. This does not tell the complete story however for what we are more interested in is the maximum change in v_0 in the circuit of Figure S16(i) when the transistor switches between the two states. Obviously then R_L must be taken into consideration. This change is obtained from the appropriate load line for R_L drawn on the output characteristics as shown in (iii).

Consider the input signal to be at 0 volts, the transistor is then held "off" with a collector current no more than the normal collector leakage current. The voltage dropped across R_L is therefore negligible, i.e. v_0 is maximum and almost equal to the supply voltage, V_{CC}. Now if the input signal changes in amplitude to a value equal to or greater than that which creates saturation, the transistor changes to "on", i.e. the operating point travels the whole length of the load line. With the transistor conducting heavily, a large voltage is dropped across R_L, hence v_0 falls to its minimum value. Approximately therefore the output voltage swings between zero and V_{CC} and we see from (i) of the figure that the input waveform has been inverted.

Although Figure S16 shows a bipolar transistor, many other types, e.g. f.e.t. and m.o.s.f.e.t. may be used, all specially manufactured for the switching function and many thousands may be packed into an integrated circuit.

Possibly the most important facility demanded of a switching transistor is the extremely short switching time, i.e. the time taken for it to transverse the load line completely. Generally switching times are of the order of a few hundred nanoseconds with the time for an f.e.t. somewhat longer than that for a bipolar transistor. (* Switch, Common-Emitter Connection, Load Line, Operating Point >> Transistor, Field-Effect Transistor)

SYNCHRONOUS DETECTION is the technique employed for demodulating a suppressed carrier transmission – see Suppressed Carrier Transmission.

SYNCHRONOUS MOTOR is an electric motor in which the rotor runs at the same speed as that of the rotating magnetic field of the stator [see Fig.E1(i) – this shows only one pair of stator poles but in practice there are more]. Put simply, the rotor is energised by an external d.c. supply to become equivalent to several permanent magnets. The N-poles of these magnets are attracted to the S-poles of the rotating field and similarly with the rotor S-poles. Provided that the pull between the attracted poles is sufficient, the rotor then runs at the same speed as the rotating field, i.e. it is in synchronism. As mechanical loading on the rotor increases the rotor lags on the rotating field and if the loading becomes excessive, synchronous speed cannot be maintained and motor action ceases.

Synchronous speed (i.e. the speed of flux rotation) $n_s = f/p$

where f is the supply frequency in Hz and p is the number of pairs of (stator or rotor) poles. Accordingly a synchronous motor with two pairs of poles on a 50 Hz supply runs at 50/2 revolutions per second = 1500 revs/minute.
(* Electric Motor >> Magnetism, Magnetic Pole)

SYNCHROTRON is a particle accelerator used for producing pulses of very high energy electrons or protons for nuclear bombardment. The particles travel in a circular evacuated tube so that they are in an orbit of constant radius. Around the tube is a series of electro-magnets. Between the magnets are cavities and radio frequency energy is fed into these to accelerate the particles. As the energy and therefore the velocity of the particles increases, the magnetic field is increased to keep the particles in their appointed path. Electron energies as high as 10 GeV are possible.
(>> Particle, Electron, Proton, Energy, Kinetic Energy, Electron-Volt)

T

TELECOMMUNICATION SYSTEM is a world-wide network of interlinked communication channels with built-in switching arrangements so that any subscriber to the system can be connected to any other. An approximate idea of the system layout is given in Figure T1. Each of the links between any two switching centres may be made up of several minor links, not necessarily of the same type but capable of transmitting the desired frequency range, e.g. for telephony from 300 – 3400 Hz but for high speed digital transmission from several kilohertz up to megahertz depending on the speed of transmission required.

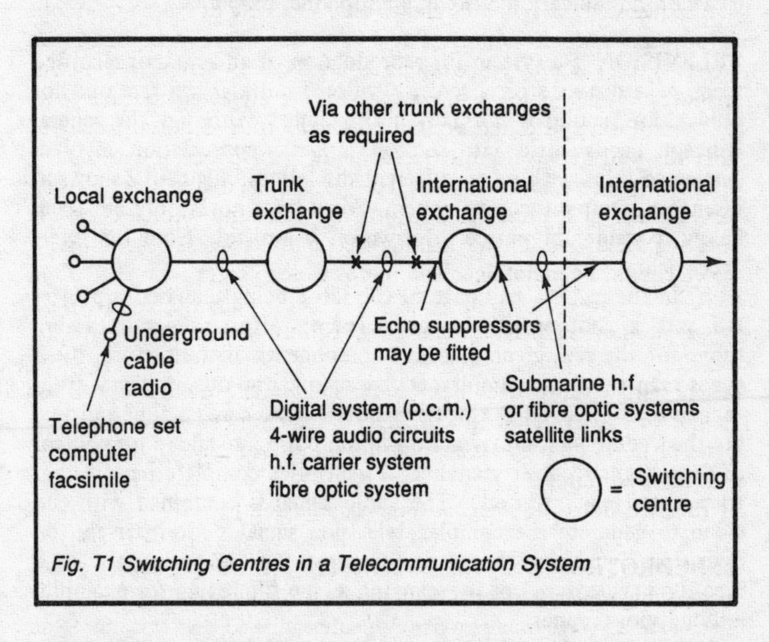

Fig. T1 Switching Centres in a Telecommunication System

Switching via modern exchanges is electronically achieved and controlled, a *register–translator* within the local exchange memorizes the dialling code received from the caller, translates it to the required routing code and controls the progress of the connection link by link.
(* Telephone Set, Computer, Four-Wire Circuit, Facsimile Transmission, Fibre Optic Transmission, Satellite, Pulse Code Modulation)

TELEPHONE SET needs little introduction, it consists essentially of a microphone and earphone (receiver) assembled in a *handset* connected to the telephone line via an *antisidetone* circuit. This circuit reduces *sidetone* which is the degree to which sounds picked up by the microphone are reproduced by the earphone. Too little attenuation between microphone and earphone (high sidetone) causes the talker to lower the voice and noise in the room may be troublesome. On the other hand with no sidetone the instrument appears "dead". A balance is therefore provided.

Signalling elements are also included, these are a tone ringer or bell for indicating that an incoming call is waiting and a pad of 0 – 9 plus one or two ancillary buttons for signalling requirements to the exchange. A *gravity switch* disconnects the instrument from the telephone line when the handset is replaced.
(* Telecommunication System, Microphone, Earphone)

TELEVISION is a system for reproduction of an actual or recorded scene at a distance on a screen, "vision from afar" in fact but not only vision, sound is normally also included. Although the general concept needs little introduction, a basic appreciation involves getting to grips with many different disciplines. Figure T2 shows in essence a complete colour system. Very brief notes only are given below, considerably more information is available from the references below.

(i) In the camera an image of the scene being televised is projected onto a photosensitive target. There are three separate camera tubes for the red, green and blue components of the picture, these tubes scan the image simultaneously so that the output signal from each is generated from the same point. The camera tube outputs are then combined and synchronization pulses are added for control of the distant receiver scanning. Twenty-five complete pictures are transmitted each second. The audio signal is combined with the video to generate the complex television signal. Alternatively the television signal may be generated directly from a magnetic tape recording (videotape) or by scanning a ciné film using for example, a flying-spot scanner.

(ii) The signal is transmitted either by land line or via a microwave link (or both) to the transmitter. Here it amplitude modulates a carrier at u.h.f. for broadcast over a terrestrial link or frequency modulates a carrier at s.h.f. for a satellite link.

(iii) Receiving antennas (Yagi type for terrestrial distribution, probably parabolic dish for satellite distribution) pick up the signal which is then amplified. On demodulation the television signal has to be sorted out. The luminance and chrominance components

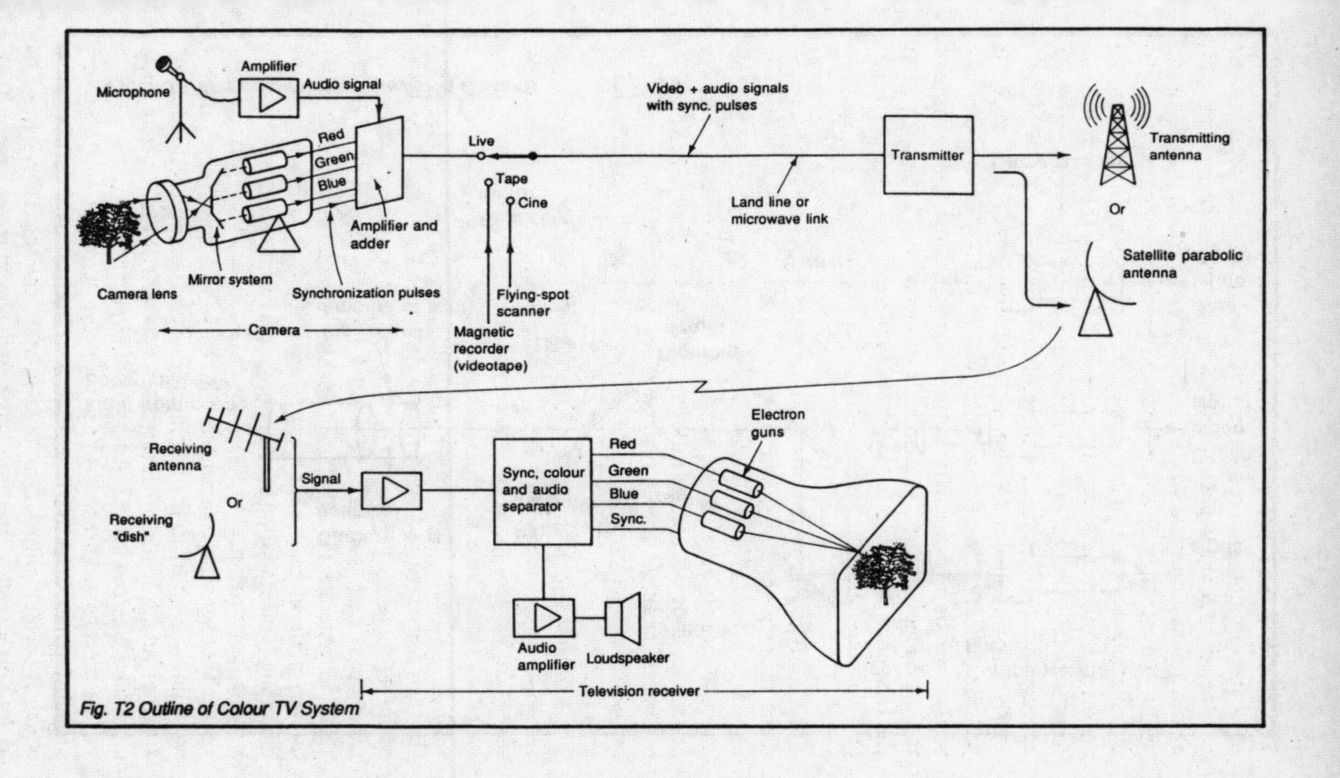

Fig. T2 Outline of Colour TV System

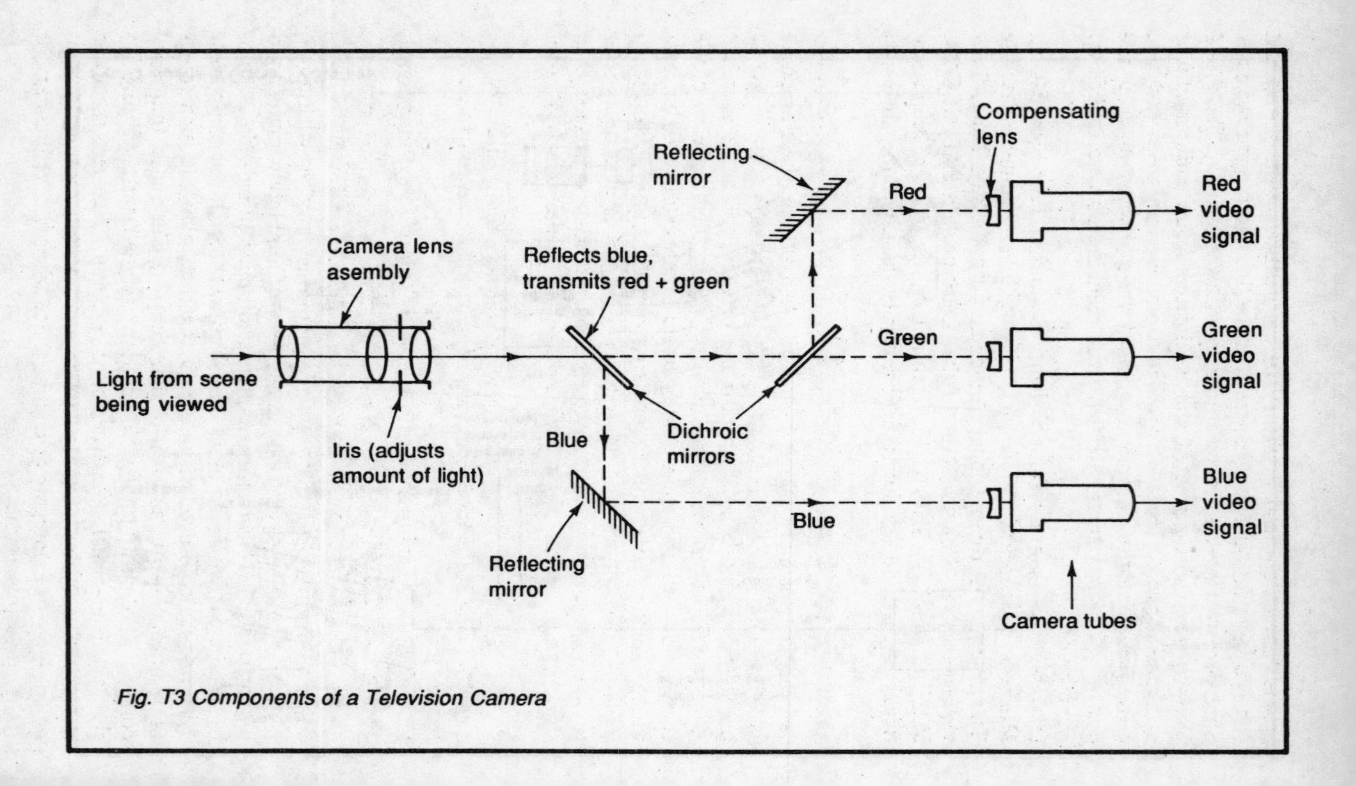

Fig. T3 Components of a Television Camera

control the colour and brightness of the picture on the screen and the synchronization pulses ensure that the line and frame time bases of the receiver operate in synchronism with the camera. The sound component is also extracted and is directed to an audio amplifier and loudspeaker. Three electron guns aim the red, green and blue components of the chrominance signal via a shadow mask at the screen. This in conjunction with the scanning process, builds up the picture.
(* Television Camera, Camera Tube, Scanning, Television Signal, Magnetic Recording, Videotape, Flying-Spot Scanner, Satellite Transmission, Antenna, Yagi Antenna, Cathode-Ray Tube, Television Receiver, Colour Picture Tube, Loudspeaker, PAL, SECAM, MAC, Scrambling, SHF, UHF, Transmitter >> Colour, Frequency Band, Amplitude Modulation, Frequency Modulation, Antenna)

TELEVISION CAMERA Colour television requires the generation of three primary signals for red, green and blue, these originate in the colour television camera. How light from a scene which is being transmitted is split up into the primary colours is sketched in Figure T3. Dichroic mirrors are used to direct light of each of the three colours to the appropriate camera tube as shown. The scanning systems of the camera tubes are maintained in synchronism to ensure that at any instant the outputs of all the camera tubes refer to the same point. The red, green and blue video signals are then combined to form the composite colour signal which is then amplified.

The luminance signal may be derived from the outputs of the camera tubes but is more likely to be generated by a fourth camera tube.
(* Television, Dichroic Mirror, Camera Tube, Television Signal, Television Receiver >> Colour)

TELEVISION RECEIVER The ubiquitous "box" is with us all, it is used and enjoyed by so many – yet completely understood by so few for its electronic circuitry is complicated indeed. Accordingly here we can do no more than see how the essential component systems of a colour television set fit together, omitting such things as remote control, automatic gain control, automatic frequency control, automatic tuning, integration, teletext, etc. Figure T4 shows the essential constituents of a colour receiver, each one comprising complex circuitry and several together frequently combined into one integrated circuit. See also the references for additional explanations.

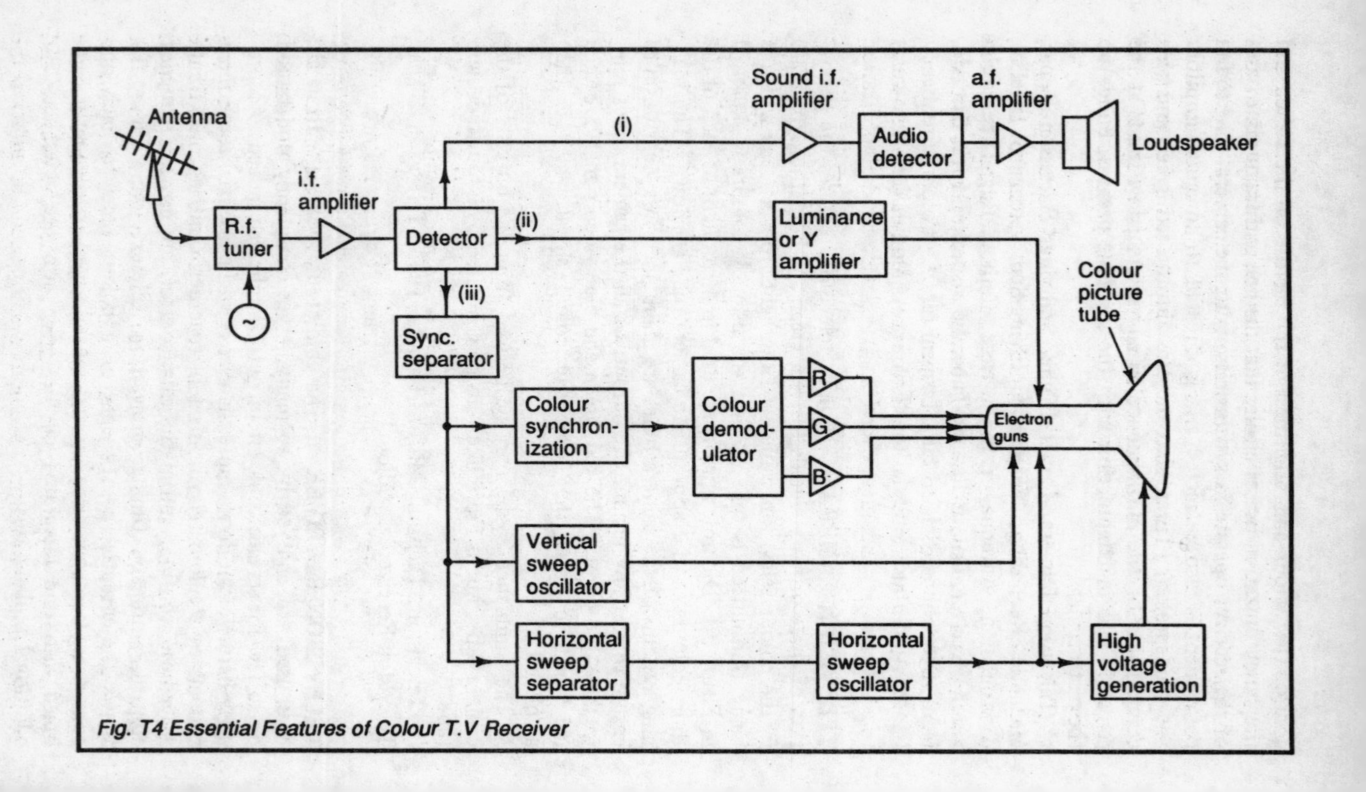

Fig. T4 Essential Features of Colour T.V Receiver

From the antenna the several signals received first meet the radio frequency tuner. Here the selected channel is first tuned in and amplified. A local oscillator heterodynes with the signal to produce the intermediate frequency (i.f.) signal. Then follows an i.f. amplifier and detector (demodulator). The output of this unit contains the t.v. signal containing both vision and sound [see Fig.T5(ii) and (iv)]. From the detector there are three separate paths taken by the television signal:.

(i) The *sound channel* – the audio and video carriers are separated by several MHz, depending on the actual system (for the UK, 6 MHz). The frequency modulated sound i.f. signal therefore appears as a sideband of the vision carrier, accordingly it is demodulated, amplified and fed to the loudspeaker.

(ii) The *video section* – the luminance amplifier (also known as the Y amplifier) includes several stages of wide-band amplification with a small time delay so that the information reaches the tube at the same time as the colour information which experiences delay in the colour demodulator. The colour demodulator itself employs two synchronous detectors to separate out the red, green and blue colour components. The colour sub-carrier is compared with the reference signal from the colour synchronization section. The red, green and blue components are each amplified and applied to the electron guns of the picture tube.

(iii) The *synchronization section* – the sync. separator removes the sync. pulses from the detector output, these are then used to control the starting of the saw-tooth waveforms for the scanning process. The horizontal fly-back pulses are stepped up, rectified and filtered to provide the high voltage required by the tube.

A black and white receiver follows the general ideas given above but of course, has no requirement of the colour circuits, nor of a colour tube.

(* Television, Television Signal, Antenna, Colour Picture Tube, Automatic Gain Control, Automatic Frequency Control, Scanning, Integrated Circuit, Aspect Ratio, Direct Current Restoration >> Superheterodyne Reception, Demodulation, Frequency Modulation)

TELEVISION SIGNAL can have several meanings but here it refers to the graphical representation (as seen on an oscilloscope) of the waveform appearing at the output of a television camera, the signal later to be used to drive a television receiver cathode-ray tube. In a black and white system the signal contains not only the luminance information required for one line of the picture itself but also the synchronization (sync.) signals essential to keep the cameras and receivers in synchronism. A colour system needs in addition the

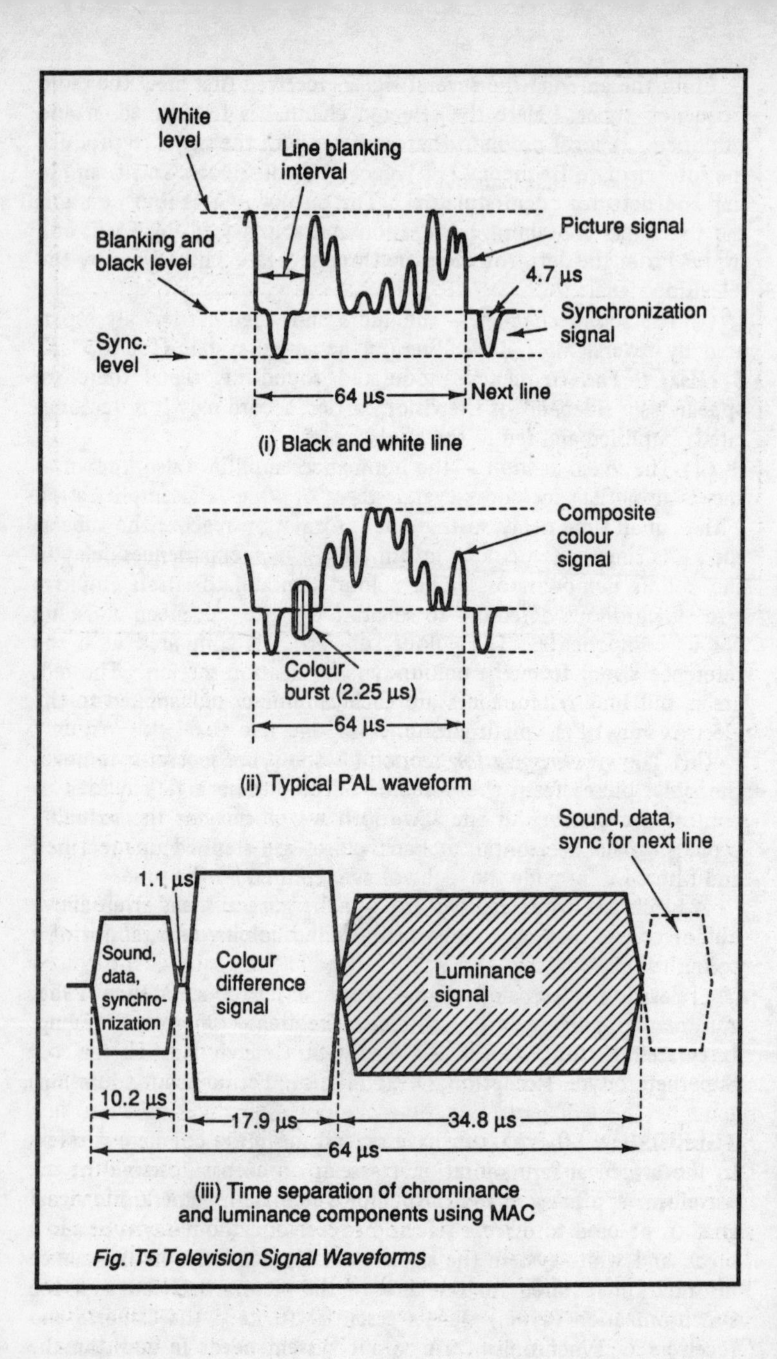

Fig. T5 Television Signal Waveforms

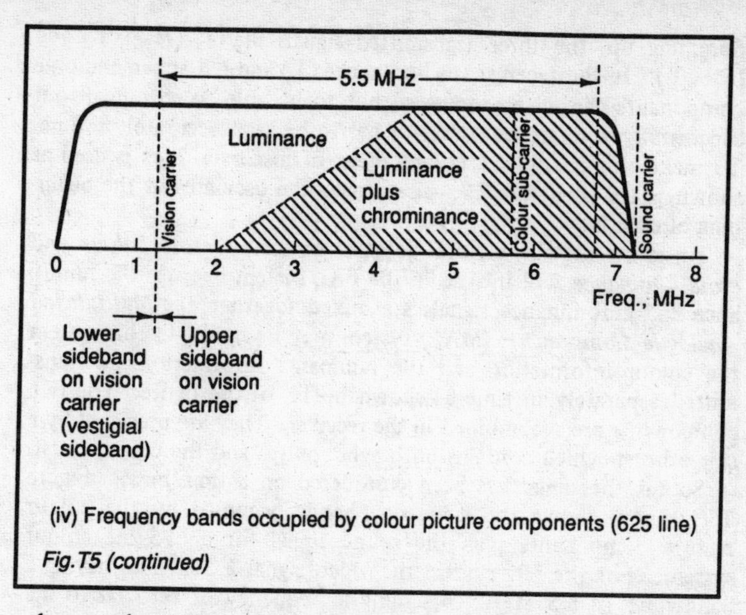

(iv) Frequency bands occupied by colour picture components (625 line)

Fig. T5 (continued)

colour or chrominance information.

In a 625-line system for example, this number of lines occupies 1/25 seconds, from which the time for one line is 64 μs. Within this time a sync. signal (a triggering pulse) and the picture information for one line must be transmitted. The pulse is a tiny burst of energy which causes the line time base in the receiver to start, so moving the spot across the screen. It is actually only of some 5 μs duration.

Figure T5(i) shows the waveform of a typical black and white line including the sync. signals. Note the line blanking interval during which the signal is held at black level so that the subsequent sync. pulse is easily recognized by the receiver. Extra pulses are required after each complete picture to trigger the frame time base. When colour is added, the chrominance information is included. The video signal then becomes quite complex. The system does not transmit separately the red, green and blue components which originate in the camera even though they contain not only the colour but also the luminance information. Instead to conserve bandwidth, a matrixing or mixing system is employed based on a luminance signal, Y which is a mixture of the basic colour components in certain proportions according to how each contributes visually to the luminance ($Y = 0.3R + 0.6G + 0.1B$). Having generated Y, two other *colour-difference* signals are obtained for the red and blue, $(R - Y)$ and $(B - Y)$. The third, $(G - Y)$ can be derived from these.

Summing up, the three transmitted signals are Y, $(R - Y)$ and $(B - Y)$. In the receiver the luminance (Y) and red, green and blue components can all be separated but to be able to sort it all out successfully a reference oscillator has to be kept accurately in line. To make this possible, a *colour burst* of just over 2 μs is used as shown in (ii) of Figure T5, this corrects the oscillator at the beginning of each line.

To avoid certain picture defects, especially *cross colour* and *cross luminance* which arise in the PAL system because the luminance and chrominance signals are mixed together, the *Multiplexed Analogue Components* (MAC) system may be used. In this system the colour information and the luminance information are transmitted separately in time as shown in (iii) of the figure. The two components are recombined in the receiver. They are preceded by a single burst which contains both sync. pulses and the colour burst.

So far the signal has been considered on a time basis. Figure T5(iv) now shows the frequency bands occupied by the colour picture components plus the sound signal for a 625-line colour system. For the UK system the video signal is taken as having a bandwidth of 5.5 MHz. Assigning a frequency of zero Hz to the bottom end of the total band as shown in the figure, the vision carrier arises at 1.25 MHz. Vestigial sideband transmission is employed with a full upper sideband therefore extending to 1.25 + 5.5 = 6.75 MHz and an abbreviated lower sideband extending from the carrier by only 1.25 MHz. The total vision frequency components therefore extend over a frequency range of 5.5 + 1.25 = 6.75 MHz. Above this is the sound frequency modulation carrier at 7.25 MHz. Allowing for the bandwidth required by the sound, for this particular system the television signal requires a total bandwidth of 8 MHz.

Generally, although use of the vestigial sideband technique economizes noticeably in the requirement of bandwidth, more cheese-paring goes on and in practical systems the compromise between perfection and economics frequently arrives at a figure of some 6 – 7 MHz.

(* Television, Television Receiver, Television Camera, Trigger, Scanning, Time Base, Vestigial Sideband Transmission, PAL, SECAM, NTSC, MAC >> Colour, Modulation)

TERMINATING SET is used at the end of a 4-wire circuit as sketched in outline in Figure T6(i). The send and receive pairs cannot be connected directly to the 2-wire line because this would couple the output of one amplifying system to the input of the other so producing a positive feedback arrangement which is unstable. To avoid

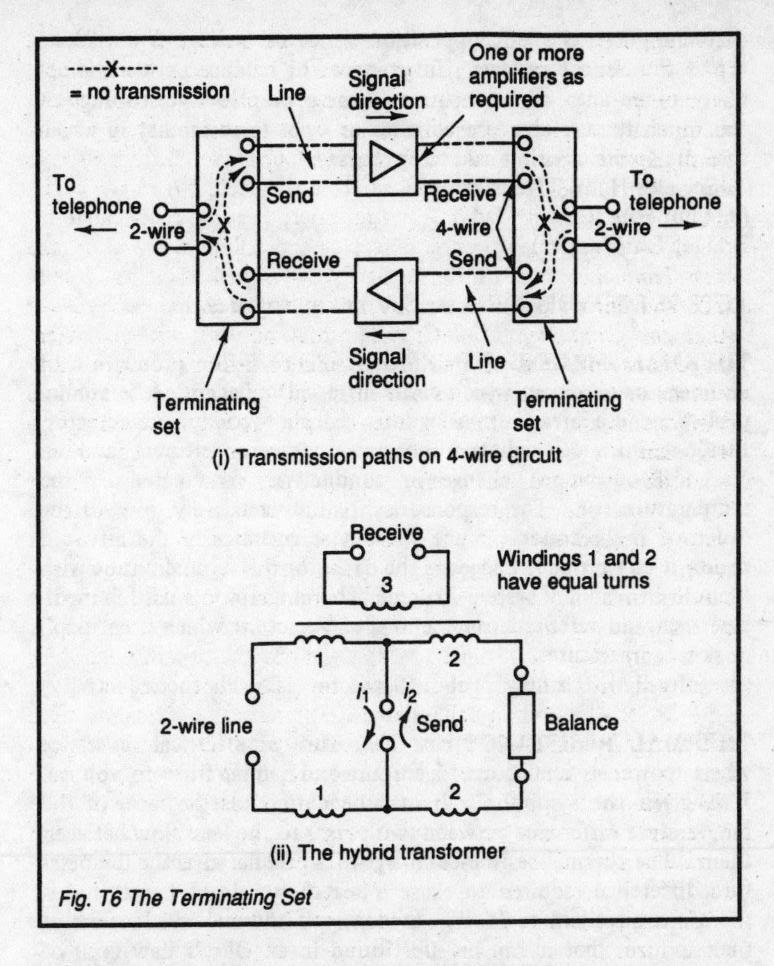

Fig. T6 The Terminating Set

such instability a *4w/2w terminating set* is inserted at each end. At each end of the circuit therefore there should be a low loss path 2-wire to Send and also Receive to 2-wire. The path Receive to Send should be of high attenuation. A Wheatstone bridge resistive network can be employed, however it is lossy consequently a *hybrid transformer* is almost invariably used.

The principle is illustrated in (ii) of the figure. The balance is ideally a network having the same impedance/frequency characteristic as that of the 2-wire line. In this case it is evident that the conditions required are fulfilled especially in that a voltage on the Receive terminals produces equal currents i_1 and i_2 in the networks on each side. The transformer windings 1 and 2 are so connected so that the currents are in opposition hence no voltage is developed across the Send terminals. In practice the balance network is not likely to be an accurate match so some power does get through, if too much it may give rise to echo or even to instability in which case the 4-wire circuit is said to be *singing*.

See also Hybrid Transformer.
(* Four-Wire Circuit, Echo >> Amplifier, Feedback, Wheatstone Bridge, Transformer)

TETRODE THYRISTOR – see Silicon Controlled Switch.

THERMAL IMAGING (THERMOGRAPHY) is the production of an image of an object which emits infra-red radiation. It is accomplished by use of a thermal or infra-red photoconductive detector. Incident infra-red radiation heats the detector element and an electrical output or change in conductivity is created by the temperature rise. The response is naturally relatively slow, of the order of milliseconds. Since the device operates in the infra-red region it can produce images in the dark, for this a camera tube with its built-in scanning system is used. Thermography is used in medicine using an infra-red camera to give a picture which is a "map" of skin temperature.
(* Infra-Red, Camera Tube, Scanning >> Photoconductivity)

THERMAL RESISTANCE has the nature of electrical resistance where power is analogous to current and temperature to voltage. It is given the symbol θ. It may be defined as the ratio of the temperature difference between two points to the heat flow between them. The thermal resistance of a path is calculated as the temperature difference required to cause a heat flow rate of 1 watt and is therefore measured as °C/W. Evidently if thermal resistance is of such a form that it can be substituted in an Ohm's Law type of equation, then separate paths may be considered in series and parallel in the normal resistance manner. This is a very useful concept, especially for the design of heat sinks for power transistors. Consider a junction power transistor as an example. There are two different heat loss paths in series (i) from the junctions to the case and (ii) from the case to the air. There is also one in parallel with the latter if a heat sink is fitted. Each path will have its own different thermal resistance which is assessed by laboratory measurements.

As a very simple example of the practical use, suppose the maximum junction temperature, T_j for a particular transistor is 175°C and the manufacturer quotes the overall thermal resistance, θ as being 90° C/W when the recommended heat sink is fitted. Is it safe to use this transistor with a junction dissipation of 2 watts at an ambient (room) temperature, T_{amb} of 20°C? Let the junction power dissipation allowable with θ = 90°C/W be P watts, then:

$$\theta = \frac{T_j - T_{amb}}{P} \quad \text{i.e.}\ P = \frac{T_j - T_{amb}}{\theta} \quad P = \frac{175 - 20}{90} = 1.75\ \text{W},$$

showing that the rate of heat transference away from the junction is too small, therefore risking breakdown. In fact the method also allows us to calculate what the junction temperature is likely to become in this case:

$$2 = \frac{T_j - 20}{90} \quad \therefore 180 = T_j - 20 \quad \therefore T_j = 200°\text{C},$$

well above the limit.
(* Heat Sink, Safe Operating Area >> Ohm's Law, Power, Transistor)

THERMAL RUNAWAY (THERMAL BREAKDOWN) is a process which especially affects semiconductors and in which heat generated by current in the device under working conditions gives rise to an increase in current. This increases the temperature still further so evidently there is a cumulative effect which if not checked may destroy the device. Semiconductors are particularly prone to this because p-n junctions are minute and therefore are easily destroyed. *Heat sinks* are used to carry surplus heat away from a p-n junction especially in power transistors but it is also possible to stabilize the operating point by use of a d.c. stabilizing circuit.
(* Heat Sink, D.C. Stabilization, Thermal Resistance >> Semiconductor, P-N Junction)

THERMISTOR This term is an acronym for *therm*ally sensitive res*istor* which in fact describes clearly the characteristics. It is a form of resistor made from semiconducting metal oxides formed into rods, beads or discs and having a very large temperature coefficient of resistance which can be made either positive (p.t.c.) or negative (n.t.c.). The n.t.c. type was the first to arrive with its resistance decrease as temperature rises. This is the opposite of how most metals behave. To provide a positive temperature coefficient greater than that for metals, p.t.c. thermistors were subsequently developed. Generally thermistors are used for sensing temperature or as a stabilizing element.

Most thermistors are unencapsulated and are self-supporting on the two leads, the bead itself being heated by the current through it. They can however be indirectly heated. For the n.t.c. type the resistance at a given temperature is given by:

$$R_{T(ntc)} = Ae^{(B/T)}$$

where T is the thermodynamic (absolute) temperature in kelvin and A and B are constants for the particular material. Resistance changes of more than 100 : 1 are easily achieved.

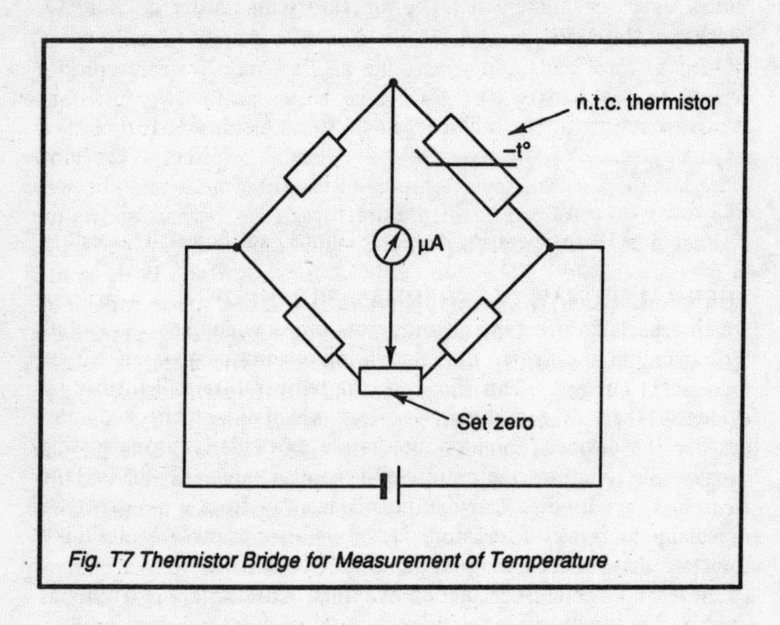

Fig. T7 Thermistor Bridge for Measurement of Temperature

For the p.t.c. type the relationship between resistance and temperature is more complex because the p.t.c. characteristic applies only over a certain temperature range. For this range only:

$$R_{T(ptc)} = A + Ce^{BT}$$

where A, B and C are constants for the material.

As an example of the use of an n.t.c. thermistor for measuring temperature, Figure T7 shows a typical bridge circuit. If the bridge is balanced at a particular temperature, then any change of temperature alters the resistance of the thermistor and the bridge becomes unbalanced.

Simple current stabilization may be achieved using a p.t.c. thermistor. If the circuit current also passes through the thermistor and it increases then the bead temperature rises. This increases the thermistor resistance, hence decreasing the circuit current.
(>> Resistance, Temperature Coefficient of Resistance, Thermodynamic Temperature, Wheatstone Bridge)

THERMOAMMETER A general term embracing ammeters which measure current through its heating effect – see Thermocouple Meter, Hot-Wire Ammeter.

THERMOCOUPLE comprises two dissimilar metals (usually wires) joined at their ends and generating an electromotive force proportional to the temperature difference between the two junctions. This arrangement is used in various thermocouple instruments to take advantage of the thermoelectric (Seebeck) effect. The most common application is in temperature measurement and the way the effect is used can be seen from Figure T8(i) which shows the elements of a thermocouple thermometer, often simply known as a "thermocouple". The two dissimilar metals A and B are joined at the probe end, the second junction is within a meter capable of indicating small voltages, hence temperature levels at the probe are translated into voltages read off the meter. The meter is usually mounted remotely from the probe and a differential amplifier can be added if required as shown for example in Figure T8(ii).

Various pairs of materials are used for thermocouples, much depending on the range of temperature to be measured and the sensitivity required. Typically a copper/Constantan combination develops some 40–60 μV per °C of temperature difference but is limited to temperatures up to about 300°C because of oxidation of the copper at temperatures above this (Constantan is a copper-nickel alloy). On the other hand a carbon/silicon carbide combination can reach over 250 μV per °C and work at temperatures up to 2000°C. As might be expected, the source resistance of the "hot" junction is low, typically a few ohms.

Thermocouples are also used for measuring small values of power from the heat developed in a metallic strip or wire. They are also connected in series for greater output, such a group is known as a *thermopile*.
(* Thermocouple Meter, Differential Amplifier, Operational Amplifier >> Thermoelectric Effect)

THERMOCOUPLE METER is an ammeter based on the heating effect of current in a wire, the amount of heat being expressed as

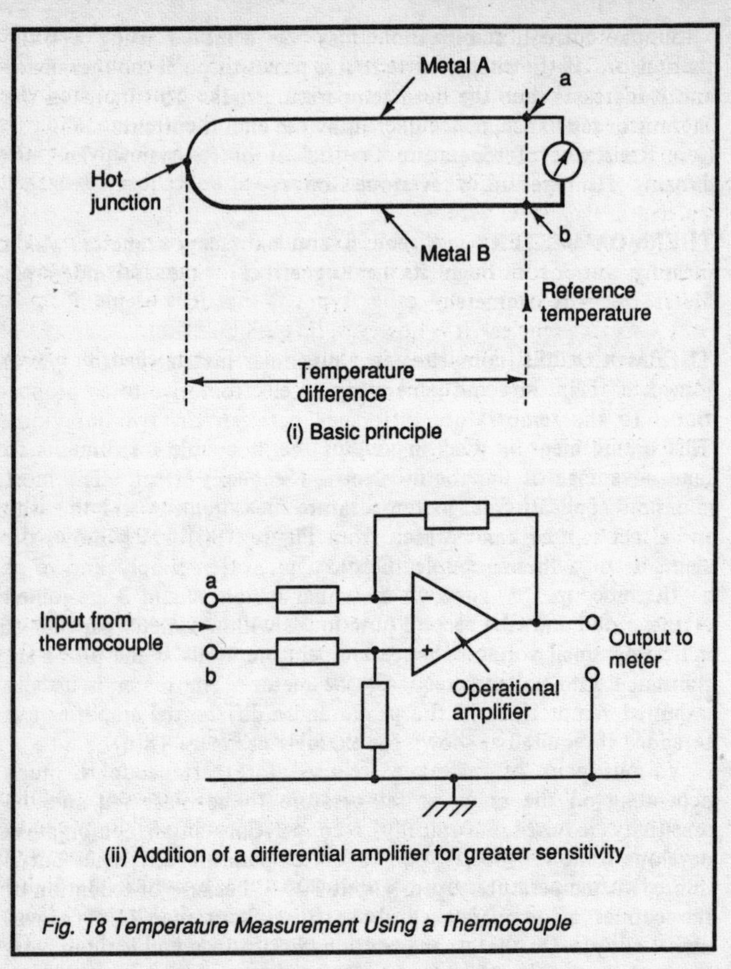

Fig. T8 Temperature Measurement Using a Thermocouple

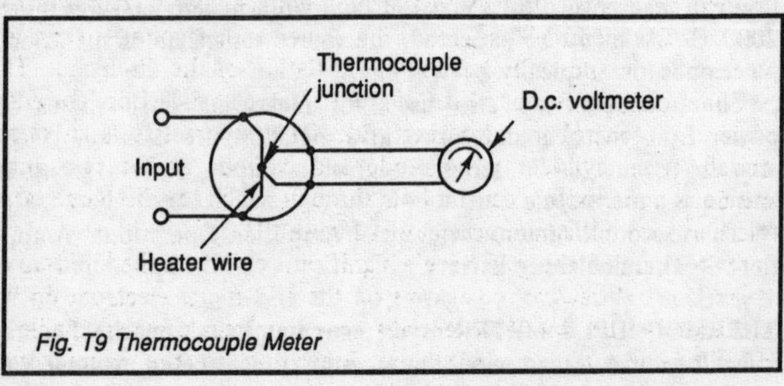

Fig. T9 Thermocouple Meter

an electromotive force by a thermocouple. The essential features of such an instrument are sketched in Figure T9. The current to be measured flows through the heater wire. To the centre of this wire is attached the thermocouple junction and the thermocouple is connected directly to an ordinary d.c. meter, probably of the moving-coil type. The scale can therefore be calibrated against current in the heater wire.

This type of meter is suitable for both d.c. and a.c. On a.c. the readings are of root mean square values and the main advantage the instrument has over many other types is that it is usable at up to very high frequencies. It is however, sluggish in action.
(* Thermocouple, Moving-Coil Meter >> Thermoelectric Effect, Ammeter, Root Mean Square)

THERMOPILE – see Thermocouple.

THICK FILM CIRCUITS are those in which components and wiring are deposited on a substrate. The film is at least 10 micrometres thick – see Hybrid Integrated Circuits.

THIN FILM CIRCUITS are those in which components and wiring are deposited on a substrate. The film is only a few micrometres thick – see Hybrid Integrated Circuits.

THREE-PHASE SYSTEM – see Polyphase System.

THYRATRON is a triode (advanced forms are tetrode) gas-filled tube in which the main current flow is triggered "on" by a change in potential on a grid which then loses its control. The operation follows that of a normal gas-discharge tube in which gas at low pressure is ionized to the degree that a plasma is formed when a sufficiently high voltage is applied between anode and cathode. The current flow is then high and the tube voltage, low. The thyratron has a heated cathode so requiring lower anode voltages than are needed for a cold-cathode tube for initiation of the discharge. The major difference in operation of the thyratron arises from the addition of a control or triggering grid. This in practice is an open-ended metal cylinder with anode and cathode at the two ends. Inside is a disc with a central hole through which the discharge takes place as shown diagrammatically in Figure T10(i).

Potentials on the grid have a significant effect on the build-up of ionization. A few volts negative on the grid repels electrons until a sufficiently high anode potential (some hundreds of volts) is able to overcome the effect and cause ionization in the normal way

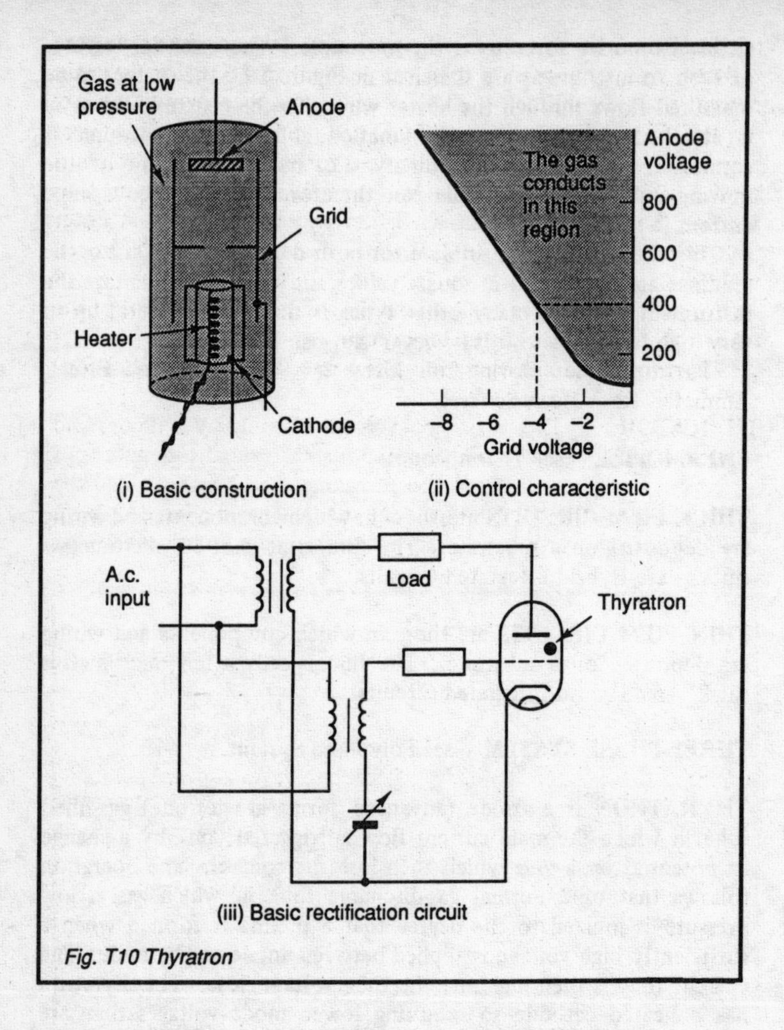

Fig. T10 Thyratron

whereupon a heavy current is then able to flow. Now the grid loses its influence because being negative it becomes surrounded by positive ions which neutralize its effect. Accordingly the current flow continues until the anode voltage is reduced or removed. How the voltage on the grid affects initial firing or *striking* of the tube is shown typically in Figure T10(ii). As an example, at a grid voltage of −4, the anode voltage must be 400 or more for conduction. The thyratron therefore acts as a switch because it is able to "switch on" a large current by a small voltage change on its grid. It is an efficient power rectifier and a basic circuit for this is shown in (iii) of the figure, in this the a.c. supply also triggers the thyratron.

With mercury vapour a tube can take up to 10 μs for the main current to be established and the deionization or *recovery* time (i.e. the time required to remove all ions) can be up to 1 ms. For faster working therefore hydrogen gas is used to replace mercury vapour. In this case the recovery time can be reduced to as low as 1 μs because the ions are very much lighter and therefore travel faster (the mercury atom is about 100 times heavier than the hydrogen molecule).

For many low power applications the solid state equivalent of the thyratron, the thyristor, is taking over.

(* Thyristor >> Ionization, Gas Discharge, Plasma, Rectification)

THYRISTOR This is one of a range of multilayer diodes and consists basically of a four-layer p-n-p-n structure with connections as shown in Figure T11(i). The p region at one end is called the anode, the n at the opposite end, the cathode (names handed down from thermionic valve days). There are three p-n junctions labelled

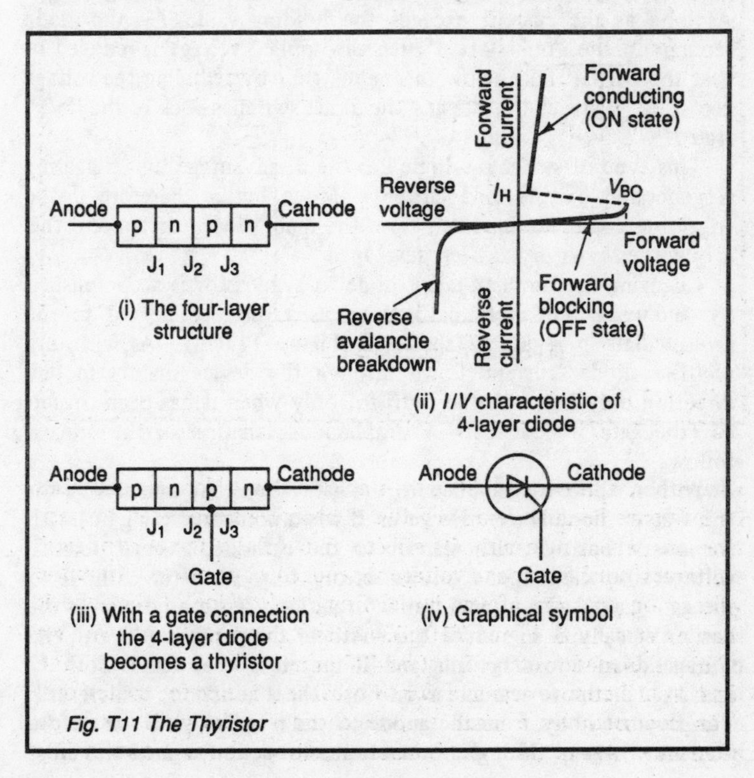

Fig. T11 The Thyristor

as shown. Consider a voltage to be applied with positive to the anode and negative to the cathode. Junctions J_1 and J_3 are then forward biased with their depletion layers of low resistance. There is only a small voltage drop across these two junctions, therefore most appears across J_2 which is reverse biased and so goes to high resistance. The diode current is therefore limited to the reverse saturation current through J_2 and the resistance of the whole diode is high. This is its "off" state which as shown in (ii) of the figure exists over the *forward-blocking* part of the current/voltage characteristic.

Next let the applied forward voltage be increased steadily. As shown above it is actually a reverse voltage across J_2 and eventually avalanche breakdown suddenly occurs in this junction. J_2 therefore goes to low resistance, accordingly the whole diode suddenly conducts, i.e. changes to the "on" state. It then has a normal diode forward characteristic shown as "forward conducting" in (ii) of the figure. The voltage at which the diode changes from forward blocking to forward conducting is known as the *breakover voltage*, V_{BO}. As long as the current exceeds the holding value, I_H, the diode remains in the "on" state. When the applied voltage is reduced so that the current falls below this value, thereby reducing the voltage across J_2, avalanche ceases and the diode switches back to the "off" state.

This type of switching diode has the disadvantage that triggering is generated by the load current. Much better therefore if the triggering could be separated from the main diode current and this is how the *thyristor* has been developed.

Changing the simple 4-layer diode to a thyristor is accomplished by adding a third terminal known as a *gate*, connected to the intermediate p region as shown in Figure T11(iii). As with any rectifier diode, current flows through the device mainly in one direction only but with the thyristor only when it has been triggered (the gate is opened). A simplied explanation of the process follows.

With no potential applied to the gate, the diode operates as for the 4-layer diode above. However, if when non-conducting but with the anode positive with respect to the cathode, a small positive voltage is applied to the gate, electrons flow from the cathode to the gate via J_3. By normal transistor action, electrons also cross the barrier at J_2 and so reduce the width of the depletion layer. The voltage drop across J_2 falls and it therefore rises across both J_1 and J_3, i.e. the forward bias on both these junctions is increased. The flow of holes from the anode to the n region via J_1 therefore increases. Again, through normal transistor action, some holes cross

J_2. This further reduces the width of the J_2 depletion layer so reducing the voltage dropped across it and thereby increasing that across J_1 and J_3 further. Current flow therefore increases and the effect is cumulative, in fact until the depletion layer of J_2 almost disappears. Now that the thyristor is fully conducting and the current flow is self sustaining, no potential is needed on the gate. The triggering pulse therefore need only be of short duration. The thyristor is turned "off" when the current falls to a value below the holding current, I_H.

Summing up: the thyristor is a *controlled* diode. It only conducts with a sufficiently positive anode (1–2 V) and when a short positive pulse is applied to the gate. The semiconductor material used is invariably silicon, hence the alternative name, the *silicon controlled rectifier*, SCR.

Thyristors are especially useful in power applications for series control of lamps and motors using alternating current. By varying the timing of the trigger the diode controls the proportion of the positive half-cycle which is allowed to pass. The negative half-cycle follows and turns the diode off. This avoids the power loss normally experienced with series resistance control. To control both half-cycles of the wave, two thyristors are employed back-to-back. This arrangement is known as a *triac*. Thyristors can handle currents up to 1000 A.

(* Trigger >> Semiconductor, P-N Junction, Avalanche Breakdown, Transistor, Electron, Hole)

TIME BASE is a voltage or current changing in such a way that when applied to the deflection system of a cathode-ray tube, the spot traverses the screen in a predetermined manner. One full traverse of the screen is known as a *sweep*. Following each sweep the spot is returned to its starting position as quickly as possible, this is known as *flyback*. Frequently and in television especially the spot is suppressed during flyback so as not to interfere with the visual display. Time bases are basic to television tubes and to oscilloscopes.

Television employs time bases to move the spot from left to right (as seen by the viewer) horizontally across the screen (the *line* time base) and also from top to bottom of the picture (the *frame* time base). Television always requires a linear sweep, non-linearity anywhere produces a distorted picture.

An oscilloscope uses a time base as the x-axis of the graph of the waveform to be displayed and generally the sweep required is also linear although *expanded* sweeps are sometimes required for examination of a waveform in greater detail.

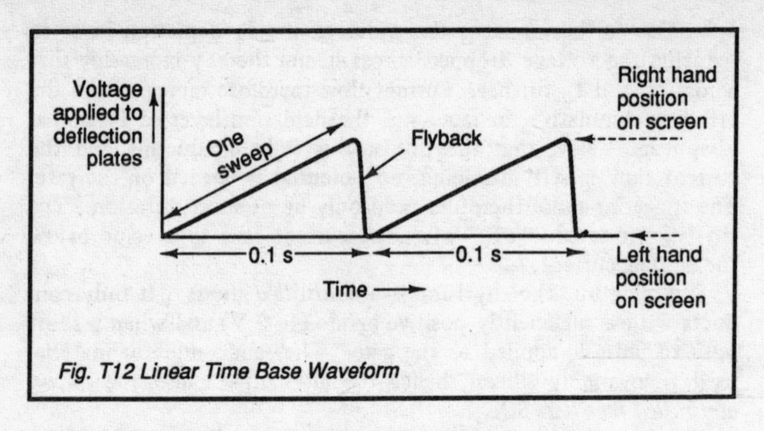

Fig. T12 Linear Time Base Waveform

A linear time base waveform is shown in Figure T12. This is how it appears when displayed on an oscilloscope, itself using a similar time base but with a different *sweep frequency* (the repetition rate). In the case of Figure T12 the time base being examined has a sweep time of 0.1 seconds so to display two full sweeps the oscilloscope time base has a sweep time of 0.2 seconds. The particular graph shown is known appropriately as a *saw tooth waveform.*

Time bases can be *free running* or what is more likely, *triggered*, i.e. the generator provides one sweep only following receipt of a trigger pulse. In an oscilloscope this occurs at the beginning of the waveform being measured in this case one sweep is made followed by flyback whereupon the generator awaits the next trigger. In television the incoming signal contains both the line and frame trigger pulses, there are fed to the line and frame time base generators. This arrangement keeps the picture in synchronism with the studio camera.
(* Cathode-Ray Tube, Oscilloscope, Trigger, Time Base Generator, Relaxation Oscillator, Sawtooth Waveform, Television Signal)

TIME BASE GENERATOR This is the equipment required for generating time base voltage (or current) waveforms for use mainly in oscilloscopes and television receivers. Generally a linear waveform is required as shown in Figure T12 and the main problem with this is obtaining true linearity, i.e. the sweep voltage (or current) must rise linearly with time. Many circuits have been developed with this in mind and the basis of a large number of these is the slow charge (sweep) and discharge (flyback) of a capacitor. Unfortunately a capacitor charges at an exponential rate which is anything but linear except while charging to about the first 20% of the final voltage. If this part of the characteristic only is employed the linearity is better but still unlikely to be good enough. Further improvement can be obtained if the current supply to the capacitor is from a constant current source for if the current is constant then the voltage across a capacitor varies linearly with time.

One method of generation of a suitable waveform is by a *relaxation oscillator* which can generally be described as one which delivers a peak output immediately the discharge of a capacitor takes place, this being followed by a "relaxation" period during which the capacitor is recharged.

Considerably more complicated circuits are available capable of providing a high degree of sweep linearity. Many are built around the *operational amplifier.* The Miller integrator is an example of a circuit used to improve linearity.
(* Constant Current Source, Operational Amplifier, Miller Integrator, Relaxation Oscillator, Sawtooth Waveform >> Time Constant)

TIME DIVISION MULTIPLEX A multiplex system in which a common transmission channel is made available at regular intervals to each of several input signals in turn for a short duration of time only – see Multiplex System.

TOLERANCE is a measure (usually expressed in percentage terms) of the degree to which the actual value of a component may vary from the design or nominal value. When many types of component are manufactured (especially resistors and capacitors) the product will have a range of values varying above and below the intended one. The tolerance quoted for a component is therefore the maximum expected variation from the nominal value. For example, purchase of a 1000 Ω ± 10% resistor gives no guarantee that the resistance value is 1000 Ω, in fact the label is stating that the value could be any between 900 and 1100 Ω although it is most likely to be near the centre of this range.

When the tolerances are not the same above and below the nominal value, they are expressed separately, e.g. +20%, –10% as happens with some types of electrolytic capacitors.

Small components such as resistors and capacitors usually have their tolerances indicated by a coloured band or spot.
(* Colour Code, Resistor >> Capacitor)

TONE CONTROL Listeners to electronic sound reproducing systems usually have their own ideas as to what constitutes good tonal balance. Accordingly we find that most systems, i.e. the power amplifier plus loudspeaker or earphones, have tone controls fitted in the shape of knobs or slider controls which can be

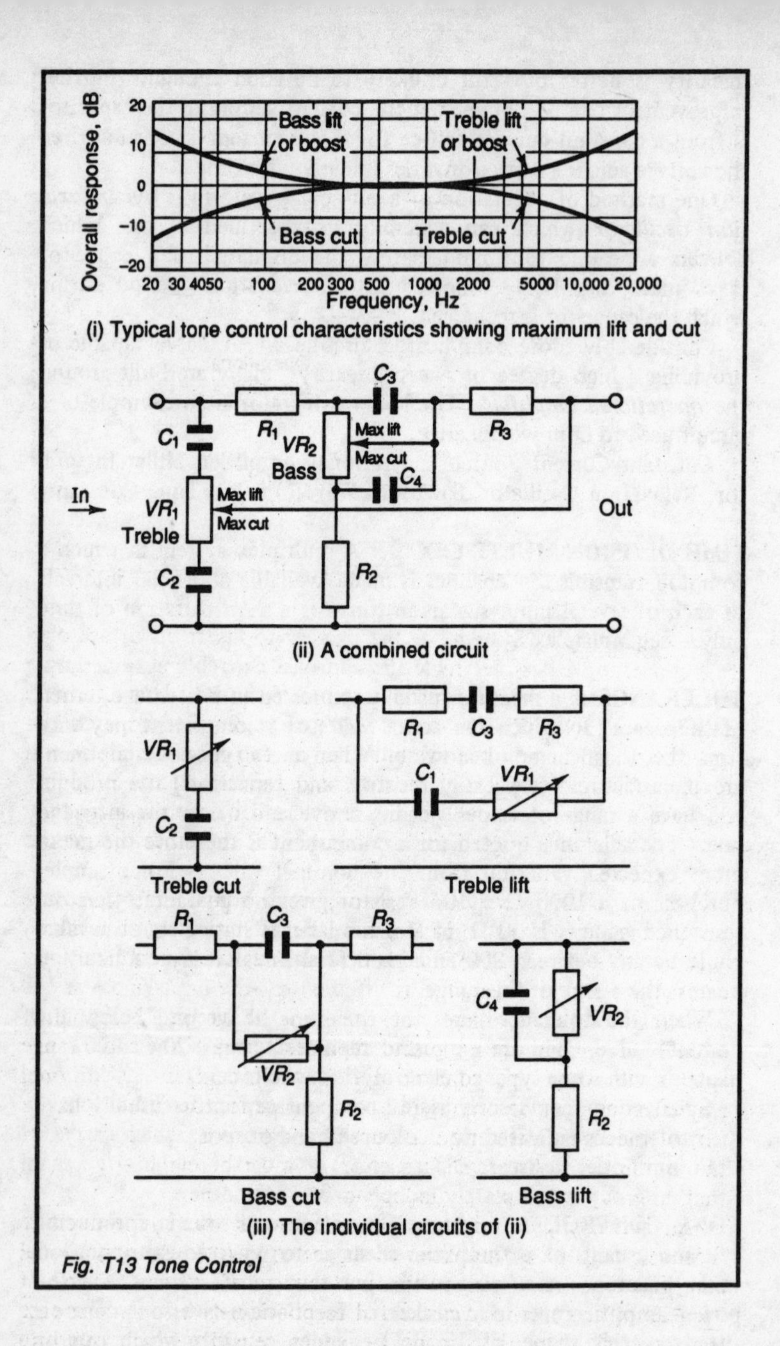

Fig. T13 Tone Control

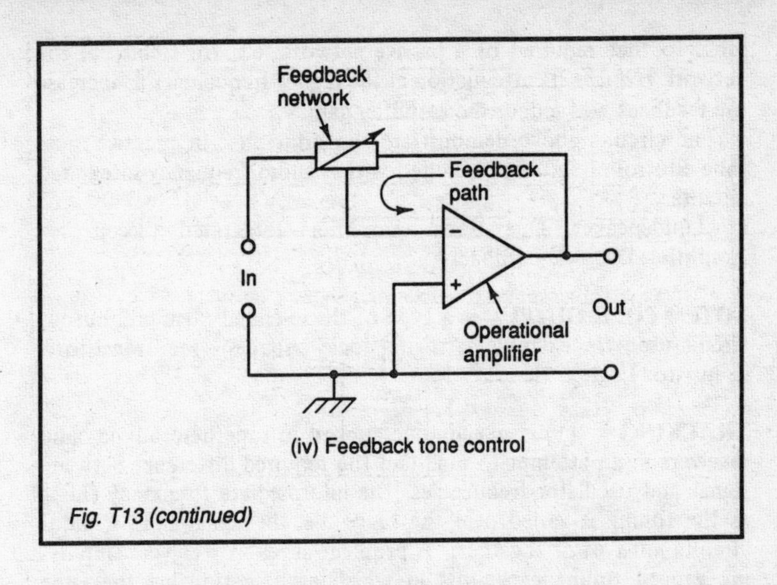

Fig. T13 (continued)

twiddled. The aim is to allow the listener to insert his or her own requirements of bass or treble lift and bass or treble cut, as shown more technically on the typical response/frequency characteristics of Figure T13(i). The amount of lift or cut required depends not only on the listener's hearing but also on the room acoustics and loudspeaker response. High quality sound systems embody highly complex controls but small radio receivers for example, may only provide treble cut in the form of a simple *CR* series network across the signal path.

There are many ways of building tone control into a sound reproducing system. A typical passive circuit providing all facilities is shown in Figure T13(ii). Each network does not function entirely on its own and the response is affected by the impedances at the input and output terminals, nevertheless the circuit is capable of some 15 dB maximum lift or cut at the extremes of the audio range with none when the controls are at their centres. Additional amplification may be required to compensate for the circuit loss. In (iii) of the figure the various groups of components which carry out the appointed tasks are picked out. It must be emphasized again that no group is completely independent of the others.

An active circuit might employ a network within the negative feedback path of an amplifier as suggested in (iv). An operational amplifier lends itself well to this particular mode of use because of its need of an externally connected feedback network. In this case the feedback network is made frequency sensitive in the opposite sense to that required of a passive network, e.g. for treble cut the network *reduces* its attenuation at the higher frequencies to increase the feedback and reduce the amplifier gain.

The circuits above demonstrate the principles, in practice most tone control circuits are included within audio frequency integrated circuits.

(* Loudspeaker, Operational Amplifier, Integrated Circuit >> Amplifier, Decibel, Feedback)

TOTEM-POLE OUTPUT is a type of single-ended push-pull output circuit used for example in digital logic circuits – see Transistor–Transistor Logic.

TRACKING (1) is a technique applied in superheterodyne radio receivers in an attempt to maintain the required difference between signal and oscillator frequencies [the intermediate frequency (i.f.)] as the tuning is varied over the range, i.e. the signal and oscillator circuits must *track* together. A problem arises in receivers employing ganged tuning capacitors in which each section has the same capacitance range. In the simplest arrangement one section of the variable capacitor tunes the signal frequency circuit and the second section tunes the oscillator frequency circuit. The ratio of maximum to minimum capacitance required from the two capacitor sections is different, for example using a 460 kHz i.f. for medium wave reception, the signal frequency range is $1600/550 = 2.9$ whereas for the oscillator it is $(1600 + 460)/(550 + 460) = 2.0$. By adjustment of trimming capacitors (i.e. small variable capacitors connected in parallel with the main capacitor) it is possible to choose two points at which the tracking of oscillator and signal frequency circuits is accurate as shown in Figure T14(i), this is known as *two point tracking* and clearly leaves much to be desired.

Better tracking is obtaining if the alignment is made correct at three points (*three point tracking*) and it is achieved by reducing the value of the main oscillator tuning capacitor by means of a series *padding* capacitor. This is the technique most commonly employed and the receiver may be aligned by injection of a modulated r.f. test signal at the antenna terminal, then the trimmers and padder are adjusted for maximum overall sensitivity at various frequencies over the range. A typical tracking characteristic is shown in Figure T14(ii) and the improvement gained by the addition of the padding capacitor can be judged by comparison with (i). For a medium wave receiver with an i.f. around 460 kHz trimmer capacitors might have a maximum value of 47 pF with a padding capacitor of maximum value between 500 and 1000 pF.

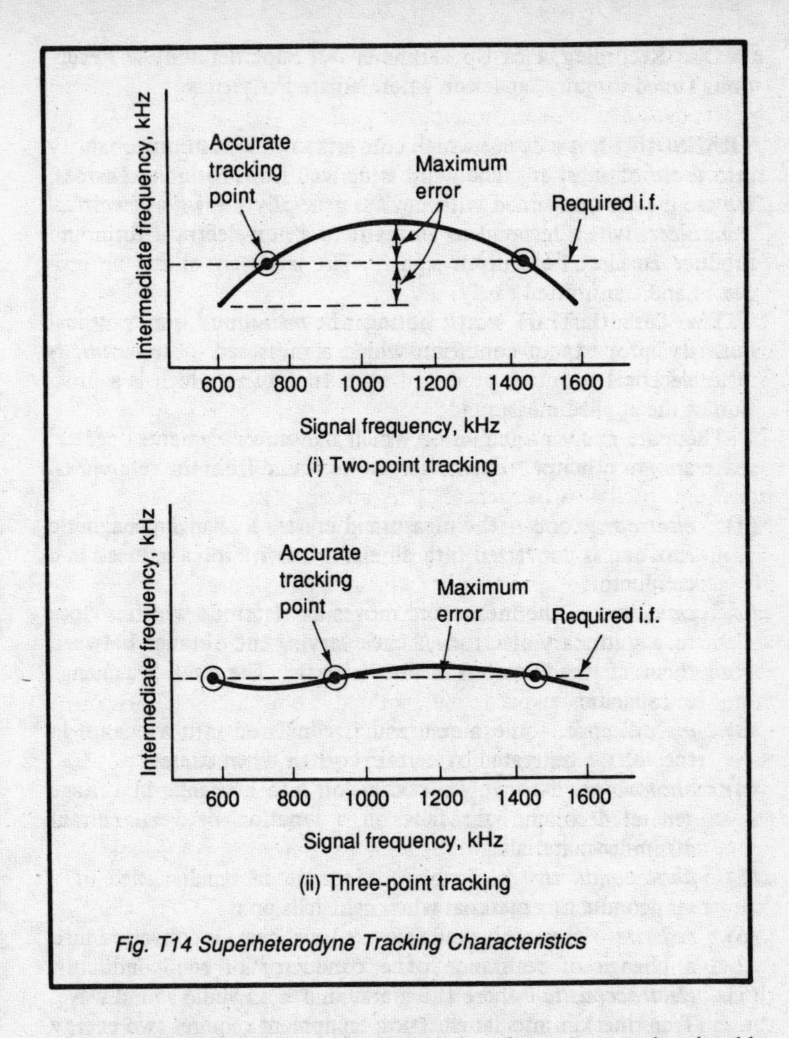

Fig. T14 Superheterodyne Tracking Characteristics

(2) In disc playback it is preferable that the pick-up stylus should be made to vibrate in a direction at right angles to the groove. This condition cannot be maintained accurately as the pick-up moves across the disc and so gives rise to *tracking error*. This error is normally minimized by various adjustments to the pick-up mounting.

(3) Unwanted conducting paths may be formed on the surface of an insulator between points across which a high voltage is maintained, e.g. between tags or terminals on an insulating board. The surface becomes carbonized and current flows through the carbon track, hence the term *tracking*.

(* Disc Recording, Pick-Up, Trimmer >> Superheterodyne Reception, Tuned Circuit, Capacitor, Intermediate Frequency)

TRANSDUCER is a device which converts variations of one quantity into those of another. The word is derived from Latin, *lead across.* We are mainly concerned with devices generally known as *electrical transducers* which respond to an input of a non-electrical form and produce an electrical output signal. The latter signal can be processed and transmitted easily.

Two definitions are worth noting: the *measurand* is a "physical quantity, property or condition which is measured", the *output* is "the electrical quantity produced by a transducer which is a function of the applied measurand".

There are many principles on which transducer elements operate, some are given below. Examples can be found from the references.

(1) *electromagnetic* – the measurand creates a changing magnetic flux and is converted into an electromotive force induced in a conductor;
(2) *capacitive* – the measurand moves an electrode which is close to a stationary electrode, hence varying the distance between them, i.e. the thickness of the dielectric. The result is a change in capacitance;
(3) *piezoelectric* – the measurand is converted into a change in the voltage generated by certain crystals when stressed;
(4) *photovoltaic* – involves conversion into a change in voltage generated when light falls on a junction between certain dissimilar materials;
(5) *photoconductive* – involves a change in conductance of a semiconducting material when light falls on it;
(6) *resistive* – the measurand (for example, heat) is converted into a change of resistance of a conductor or semiconductor;
(7) *electroacoustic* – here the measurand is an audio sound wave. Transduction into its electrical equipment requires two energy conversions, firstly from sound wave energy into the mechanical energy given to a diaphragm then from some other form of transduction (e.g. electromagnetic, piezoelectric, etc.) to convert the mechanical energy possessed by the vibrating diaphragm into its electrical analogue. Microphones are all in this class because this is their function. Loudspeakers are also electroacoustic transducers although they do not conform to the definitions above. For these the transduction process is reversed, i.e. the measurand is electrical and the output acoustical.

(* Microphone, Loudspeaker >> Electromagnetism, Electromagnetic Induction, Capacitance, Piezoelectric Effect, Photoemission, Photovoltaic Effect, Photoconductivity)

TRANSDUCTOR is an acronym derived from *transfer inductor.* It consists of two or more windings on a ferromagnetic core arranged so that the impedance of one winding is controlled by the current in another winding. The device can be used as a flux-controlled switch or as the basis of a magnetic amplifier – see Saturable Reactor.

TRANSISTOR–TRANSISTOR LOGIC (TTL) One of the difficulties encountered with diode–transistor logic circuits (DTL – see Fig.D9) is that R_b needs to be of low value for fast switching of T_1 but this reduces the input resistance of the gate. To overcome this, the input diodes are replaced by transistors in what is known as transistor–transistor logic. Transistors are almost as easy to produce in integrated circuits as are diodes.

A typical TTL NAND circuit configuration is shown in Figure T15(i) which can be compared with Figure D9(i) for DTL. The difference is simply that in this particular circuit the diodes have been replaced by the two p-n-p transistors, T_1 and T_2. Because TTL is more favoured, circuit improvements have been added as for example in (ii). T_1 is now a *multi-emitter* transistor, more complicated but it can do the job of several standard transistors. T_3 and T_4 work in a form of push-pull to obtain the benefit of a very low output impedance, a particularly useful feature when the gate is followed by another or several in parallel. This type of push-pull is known as a *totem-pole output* and its output swings between the positive supply voltage and zero volts. The versatility of TTL is such that many different types of logic element may be fabricated, for example logic gates as described above, flip-flops and memory units.
(* Digital Logic, Logic Gate, Push-Pull Operation, Multivibrator >> Diode, Transistor)

TRANSMITTER In general this term is used for any device which sends an electrical signal over a channel to its receiving end. More specifically the term is used to describe an arrangement of electronic equipment for producing radio frequency energy which is controlled by the information to be transmitted and which is radiated. As such it consists basically of a preamplifier to raise the level of the baseband input, carrier oscillator and modulator to impress the baseband on a carrier wave, followed by the necessary filters and a power amplifier. The latter has a signal power output varying from a few

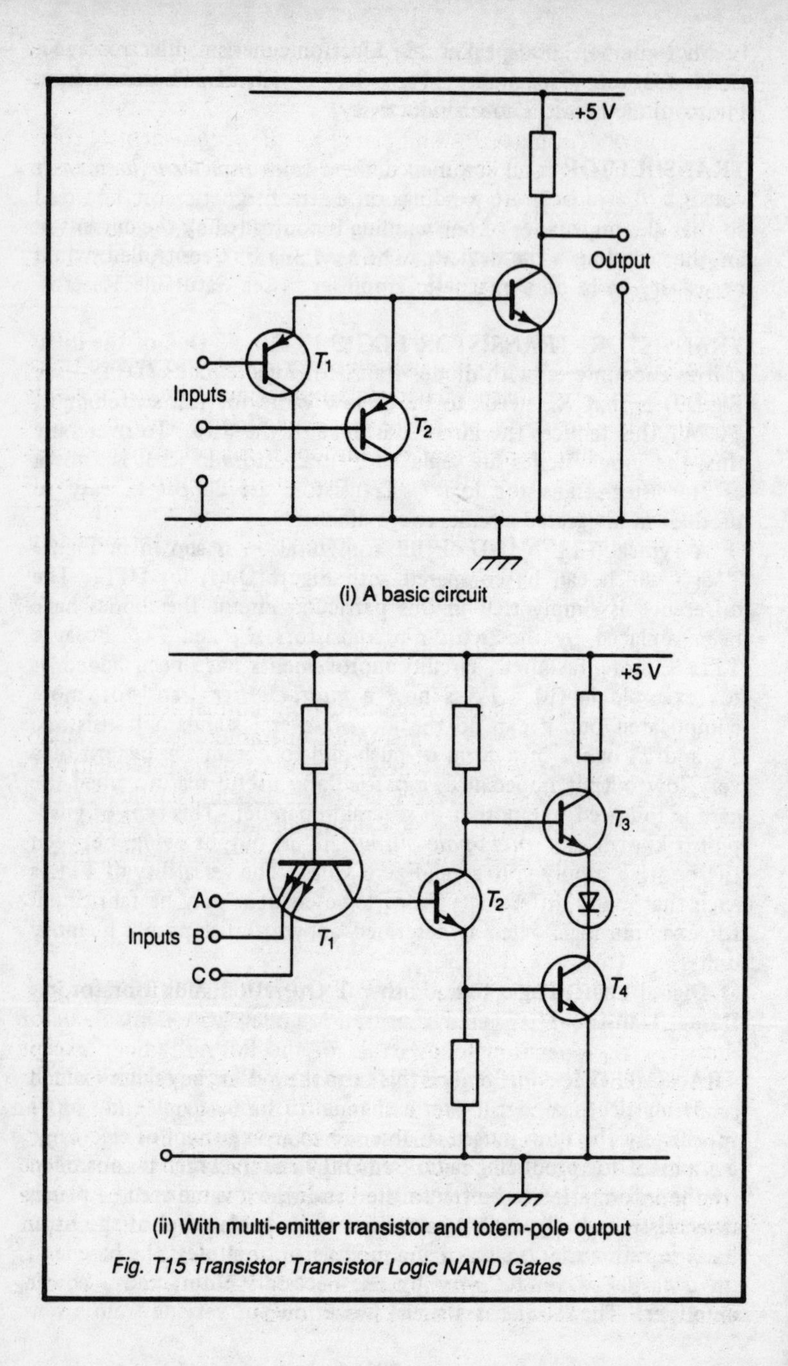

Fig. T15 Transistor Transistor Logic NAND Gates

watts to perhaps many kilowatts, depending on the application. The radio frequency signal is then fed over a transmission line or waveguide to the antenna which radiates it.

Design of transmitters is dominated by the requirement of transmitted frequency stability hence the carrier oscillator (the *master* oscillator) is most likely to be crystal controlled.
(* Baseband, Master Oscillator, Antenna, Crystal Oscillator >> Amplifier, Carrier Wave, Modulator, Crystal, Transmission Line, Waveguide)

TRANSPONDER (1) is a radio receiver coupled to a radio transmitter arranged so that an incoming trigger signal (the *interrogating* signal) causes the device to radiate an *acknowledging* signal.

(2) In satellite transmission a transponder is an electronic system in a satellite which receives a transmission from earth, changes its frequency, amplifies it and then transmits it back to earth. For satellite television a satellite may contain 10 – 20 transponders, each handling one programme.
(* Radio Receiver, Transmitter, Trigger, Satellite Television >> Amplifier)

TRANSPUTER is a radical departure from normal computer practice designed to achieve extremely high operating speeds. Normally a microprocessor carries out the program instructions sequentially. The transputer employs several microprocessors in a parallel arrangement so that in a way, they are doing the job together and so by sharing the work, take less time. Two or more transputers may be coupled for even faster operating speeds.
(* Computer, Microprocessor)

TRAPATT DIODE The acronym TRAPATT stands for TRApped Plasma Avalanche Triggered Transit; it is a microwave semiconductor device. The operation follows that of the IMPATT diode except that by allowing a higher diode current the avalanche region expands sufficiently so as to fill the drift region [the i-region in Fig.I4(i)]. The density of the charge is high and becomes rather like the plasma of a gas discharge. The electric field then extracts the plasma hence the junction voltage returns to the breakdown value and the plasma then reforms. TRAPATT oscillators are capable of yielding output powers of up to 500 watts at frequencies up to 10 GHz.
(* IMPATT Diode, Cavity Resonator >> P-N Junction, Charge, Electric Field, Plasma, Avalanche Breakdown)

TRAVELLING-WAVE TUBE (t.w.t.) is a microwave amplifier capable of operating over a wide frequency band, up to two octaves or more. These amplifiers are used especially in microwave telephony systems and in communication satellites. Basically amplification arises from the continuous interaction between an electromagnetic wave travelling along a *slow-wave structure* and an electron beam travelling through the structure. Figure T16 shows the main features of a tube. An electron gun generates an electron stream which travels axially along the tube to a collector at the remote end. The slow-wave structure is a helix which is spaced closely around the electron beam. The radio frequency (r.f.) signal to be amplified is coupled to the helix at the electron gun end. The signal propagates around and along the helix so that its axial velocity is approximately the same as that of the electrons in the beam. Both are controlled so that the velocity is of the order of one or more tenths of the speed of light, hence the term "slow-wave".

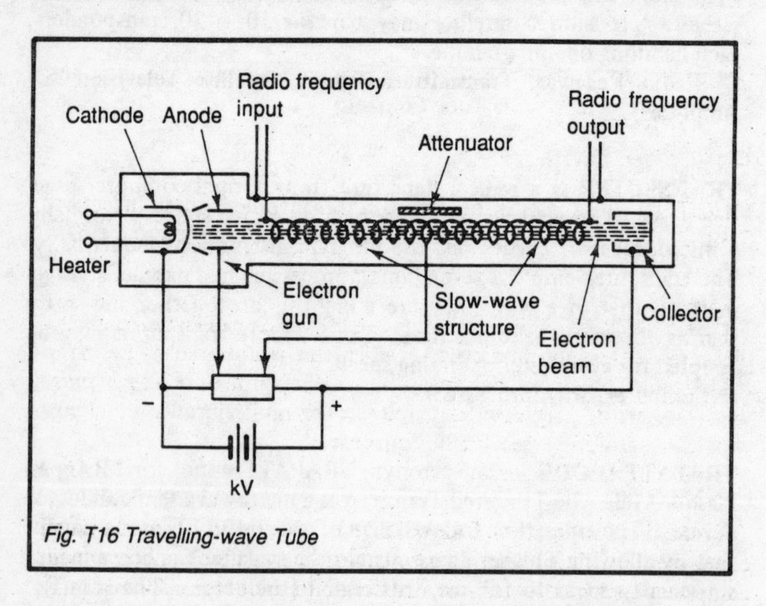

Fig. T16 Travelling-wave Tube

The axial component of the incoming radio frequency wave interacts with the electron beam because it is travelling in approximate synchronism with it. Depending on the polarity of the wave at any instant some travelling electrons are accelerated, some decelerated, hence the electron stream is modulated at the frequency of the r.f. wave. The electrons in turn add energy to the wave on the helix and the process of mutual interaction continues as the wave and the electron beam progress along the tube. The electron stream can be considered as a flow of direct current energy, some of this is transferred to the radio frequency wave which is therefore amplified. The output of the tube is taken from the end of the helix near the collector.

So that the electron beam is confined to the helix and not allowed to diverge because of the mutual repulsion of the electrons in it, a magnetic field is provided along the outside of the tube (not shown in the figure). The attenuator which is shown in the figure is a region in which some r.f. energy is absorbed so that it does not propagate in the reverse direction and give rise to instability, in fact turn the tube into a *backward-wave oscillator.*

See also Crossed-Field Device.
(* Electron Gun, Backward-Wave Oscillator >> Amplifier, Electromagnetic Wave, Microwave, Velocity Modulation, Attenuation)

TREBLE CUT is attenuation of the higher frequencies in a sound reproducing system – see Tone Control.

TREBLE LIFT is emphasis of the higher frequencies in a sound reproducing system – see Tone Control.

TRIAC – see Thyristor.

TRIGGER A means of setting an electronic circuit in action. Generally it consists of a pulse or other stimulus applied to a circuit which then changes its state and remains so.

TRIGGER CIRCUIT is a two-state circuit which can switch between the states either automatically or when this is initiated by an external signal. The circuit has an output in the form of a *trigger pulse* which is used to trigger other circuits. The multivibrator is a circuit which is commonly used for this purpose.
(* Multivibrator, Trigger)

TRIMMER (TRIMMING CAPACITOR) Generally this is a small component used for fine adjustment of the value of another main component such as a resistor, capacitor or inductor. The term is most likely to be found describing a small variable capacitor connected in parallel with a section of a ganged tuning capacitor in a radio receiver. The trimmers are separately adjusted to balance the capacitances of the main capacitor or they may be part of the tracking system in a superheterodyne receiver.
(* Radio Receiver, Tracking >> Capacitor, Superheterodyne Reception)

TRUTH TABLE lists all possible combinations of input signals to a logic function or gate and for each combination gives the output – see Digital Logic.

TUNED AMPLIFIER is one with a very narrow pass band. Quite frequently it is necessary to restrict the operating bandwidth of an

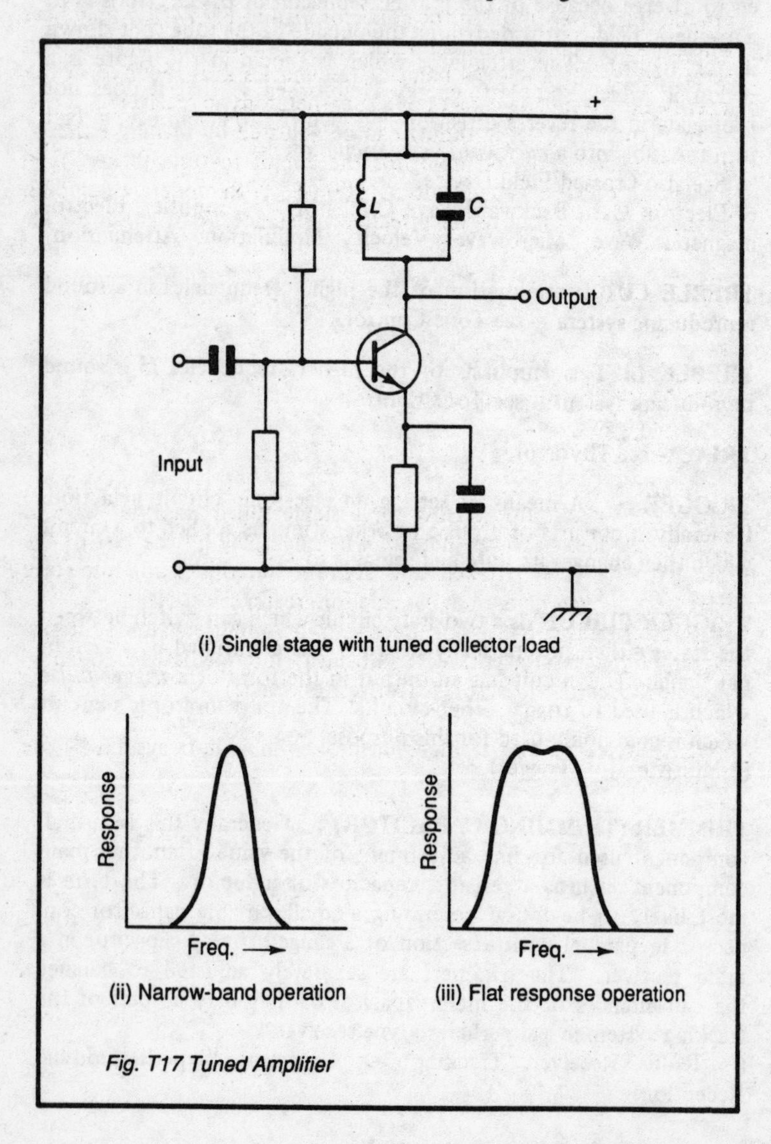

Fig. T17 Tuned Amplifier

amplifier especially in radio and television reception where high selectivity is essential. It is also a means of restricting noise. Such operation is readily achieved by use of a tuned amplifier for example by use of a parallel tuned circuit collector load of an amplifying transistor as shown in Figure T17(i). The collector circuit may be very sharply tuned as in (ii) or by use of coupled circuits [as for example in the collector load in Fig.F4(ii)] may have a response/frequency characteristic slightly flattened as in (iii). This caters better for a narrow band of frequencies as is required in the intermediate frequency stages of a superheterodyne receiver.

In Figure T17(i) the tuning can be adjusted by making either L or C variable. For example, for the circuit to tune to say, f_r = 1 MHz, L could be 250 μH with C, 100 pF. With moderate damping in the circuit leading to an effective resistance, R of about 10 Ω:

$$Q = \frac{1}{2\pi f_r CR} = 160 ,$$

hence the bandwith is equal to:

$$f_r/Q = 6.25 \text{ kHz} ,$$

which in fact is quite narrow for a single tuned amplifier stage at 1 MHz. It does however increase when damping by the rest of the circuit or the load is taken into account but this is for one stage only, several may be used in cascade for greater selectivity.
(* Radio Receiver, Television Receiver >> Amplifier, Tuned Circuit, Superheterodyne Reception, Bandwidth, Intermediate Frequency, Coupled Circuits, Q Factor, Effective Resistance)

TWEETER The treble loudspeaker in a hi-fi system – see Loudspeaker.

UHF is an abbreviation of *Ultra High Frequency.* This refers to the band of frequencies extending from 300 MHz to 3 GHz (decimetric waves).
(>> Frequency Band)

ULTRASONIC DELAY LINE – see Delay Line.

VACUUM EVAPORATION is a technique used for depositing a coating of metal onto a substrate. The substrate is placed in a vacuum near the metal to be deposited and the latter is heated above its vaporization temperature. Because there are few gas molecules present to create collisions, the metal molecules are able to radiate directly onto the substrate on which they form a thin layer.
(* Hybrid Integrated Circuits >> Molecule, Collision)

VAN DE GRAAFF ACCELERATOR is a particle accelerator capable of generating particles of very high energy – see Van de Graaff Generator.

VAN DE GRAAFF GENERATOR is a device for producing a high electrostatic potential, it is named after the American physicist who developed it, Robert Van de Graaff. The use of the generator is mainly for the acceleration of charged particles for nuclear research and also to operate high voltage devices such as certain x-ray tubes. The generator is based on the fact that if a charge is placed on the inside of a hollow conductor it will be transferred to reside on the outer surface irrespective of the magnitude of the charge already present. Accordingly charge can be built up continuously, the only losses being by leakage.

In use a generator delivers a potential of 1 – 2 kV to the metal points system P_1 as shown in Figure V1. A spray of charge (positive

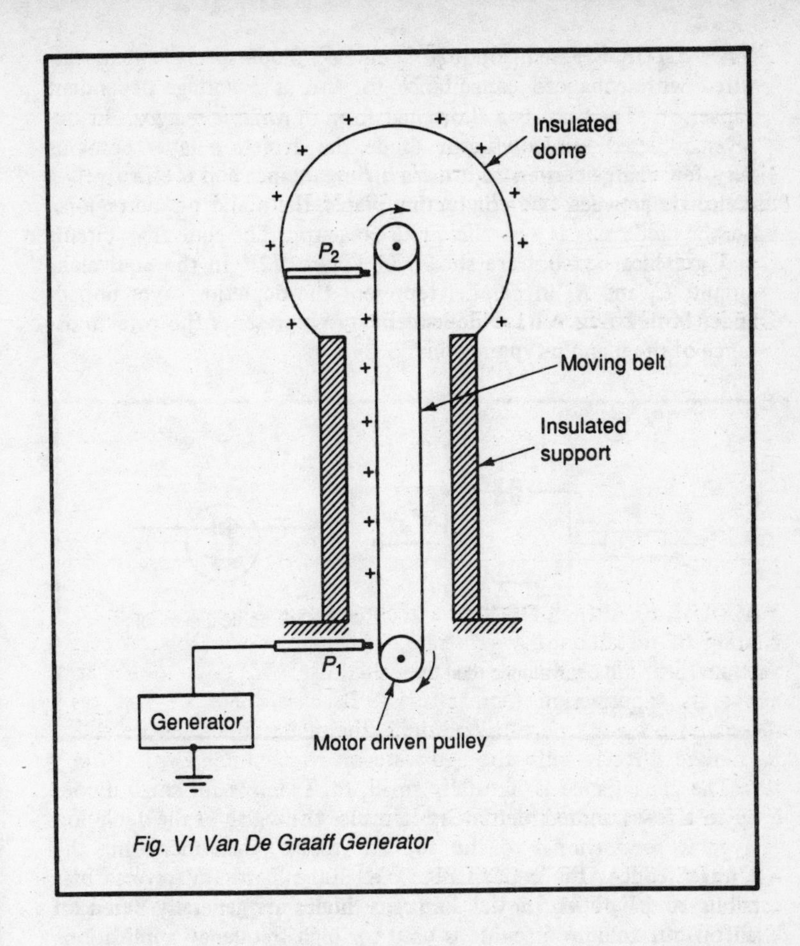

Fig. V1 Van De Graaff Generator

in this figure) is transferred onto the insulated moving belt. The charge is carried upwards to the insulated dome and is collected at points P_2 whereupon it transfers to the outside of the dome. The charge can eventually reach a potential of several millions of volts. It is also possible to use two generators charged to opposite potentials to develop even higher potential differences.

The generator can be arranged to go one step further as a *Van de Graaff accelerator*. The generator is used as a source of charged particles which are injected into a special accelerating tube to produce an emerging beam of high ion or electron intensity with currents approaching one milliampere at several megavolts.
(* Linear Accelerator >> Charge, Electron, Ion, Gauss's Theorem, Electrostatic Induction)

VARACTOR is a semiconductor junction diode specially manufactured with enhanced capacitance for use as a voltage dependent capacitor. The term is a shortened form of *variable reactor.* In any reverse biased semiconductor diode the depletion layer contains very few charge carriers so it has a high resistance and is effectively a dielectric between two conducting plates, the n and p-type regions, i.e. the diode acts as a parallel plate capacitor. The equivalent circuit and graphical symbol are shown in Figure V2. In the equivalent circuit, C_j and R_j in parallel represent the depletion layer impedance, both being voltage dependent. R represents the total resistance of the n and p-type regions.

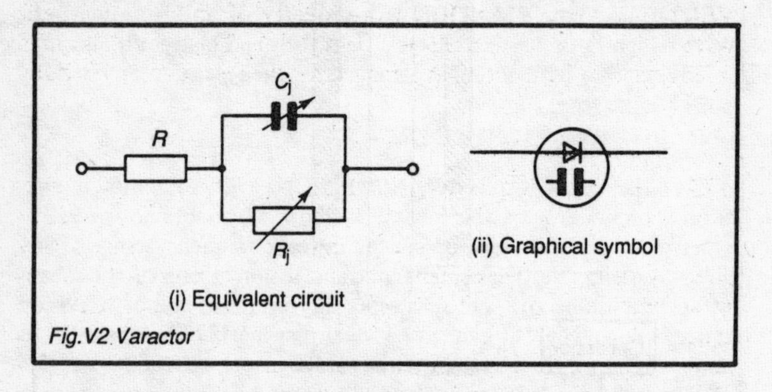

Fig. V2 Varactor

The capacitance is naturally small, for example for small diodes up to a few hundred picofarads. Because the width of the depletion layer is proportional to the applied voltage, then increasing the voltage reduces the capacitance, e.g. 300 pF at 3 V reverse bias falling to 27 pF at 15 V. Varactor diodes are generally based on silicon but gallium arsenide is used for high frequency applications above about 20 GHz.

Varactors are used in microwave oscillators, parametric amplifiers and low power ones as electronically controlled tuning capacitors in radio and television receivers.
(* Parametric Amplifier, Automatic Frequency Control >> P-N Junction, Diode, Capacitance, Depletion Layer, Impedance)

VARIABLE RELUCTANCE MICROPHONE A type of microphone based on variations in reluctance of an air-gap – see Microphone.

VARIABLE RESISTANCE MICROPHONE A type of microphone in which sound waves vary its resistance – see Microphone.

VARISTOR A shortened form of *variable resistor*, one which has a pronounced non-linear current/voltage characteristic. Most are basically p-n junction diodes and may be made polarity reversible by connecting two oppositely poled diodes in parallel.
(>> Resistor, Diode, P-N Junction)

VDU Abbreviation of Visual Display Unit – see this term.

VELOCITY MICROPHONE is a microphone which has an output proportional to the instantaneous particle velocity of the incident sound wave – see Pressure Gradient Microphone.

VERTICAL POLARIZATION is a property of an electromagnetic wave which has a vertical electric field vector. The term is also used in conjunction with antennas arranged for the reception of vertically polarized waves.
(>> Electromagnetic Wave)

VESTIGIAL SIDEBAND TRANSMISSION It is essential in electronic communication that channel bandwidth should be as small as possible so that much can be packed into the frequency range of any given system. Vestigial sideband transmission is one of the means of accomplishing this and it is especially useful in colour television transmissions where it can save several megahertz of bandwidth. As an example, a colour system with a video signal extending over 5.5 MHz would with conventional amplitude modulation require a bandwidth of twice this, i.e. 11 MHz. In practice one of the two sidebands is reduced in bandwidth from 5.5 to 1.25 MHz, so reducing the total bandwidth requirement for transmission of the video signal from 11 MHz to 6.75 MHz. The name "vestigial" arises from the Latin, a *footprint*, i.e. a sign or trace.

There is of course a price to pay in that on demodulation some distortion arises but the system is workable because the distortion, which is of the vision signals only, is not noticed by most viewers.

Other methods which economize even more in bandwidth such as single-sideband or single-sideband with pilot carrier cannot be employed in colour television transmission because the receiving equipment becomes over complicated.
(* Television Signal, Single Sideband Transmission >> Frequency, Bandwidth, Modulation, Amplitude Modulation, Sideband, Distortion)

VHF is an abbreviation of *Very High Frequency*. This refers to the band of frequencies extending from 30 to 300 MHz (metric waves).
(>> Frequency Band)

VIBRATOR This is a term used mainly to describe an electromechanical device which produces alternating current by periodically interrupting an input direct current. Many different types are available, the one sketched in Figure V3 shows the basic principle.

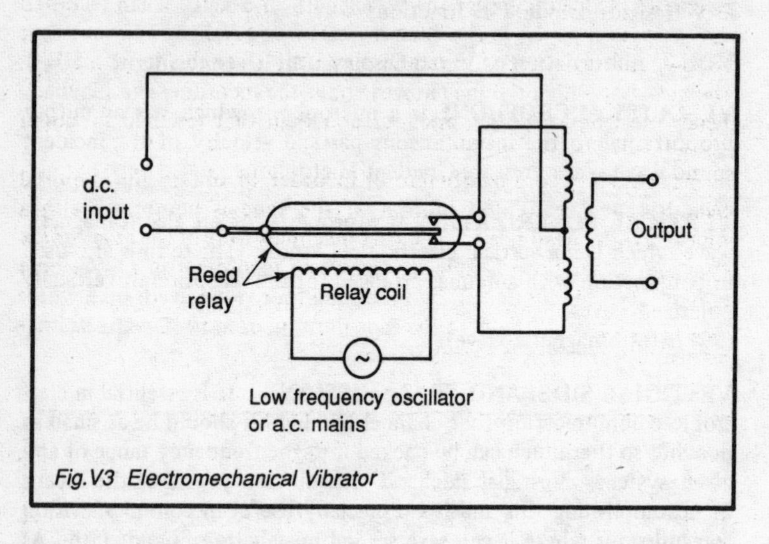

Fig.V3 Electromechanical Vibrator

In this particular one a reed relay is employed with its coil energised by for example, the a.c. mains. As the armature vibrates the d.c. supply is switched through alternate halves of the centre-tapped transformer. The alternating flux induces an electromotive force in the secondary winding, this is the a.c. output. The coil can be energised at any suitable frequency or by using an extra pair of contacts, be made self-vibrating as with a trembler bell.

A vibrator as above may be employed as a chopper in a chopper amplifier system for the production of high voltage d.c. from a low voltage supply such as a battery.

(* Chopper Amplifier, Relay, Reed Relay >> Transformer)

VIDEO FREQUENCY is a term used to describe any component of the output of a television camera. The video frequency range is from about 10 Hz to several megahertz.

(* Television, Camera Tube >> Frequency)

VIDEO SIGNAL describes the complete output of a television camera. It includes the video frequencies within the picture signal usually with line and frame synchronizing pulses added.

(* Television, Camera Tube >> Frequency)

VIDEOTAPE is a special form of magnetic recording tape used for recording television signals – see Magnetic Recording.

VIDEOTAPE RECORDING A fundamental requirement in magnetic recording is that the wavelength of a signal when recorded on the tape must be longer than the effective head gap. From this it follows that to obtain the required bandwidth (upwards of 5 MHz), the speed at which the tape moves under the recording and playback heads must be very high, much greater than that required for audio work.

For video recording therefore, in order to obtain the required head-to-tape speeds, the motion of the tape is combined with a motion of the head itself. The first machines were of the *quadruplex* type, in these the principle of transverse recording on a wide tape is used and this is effected by mounting four video heads on a wheel rotating perpendicularly to the tape motion, each head being switched into operation as it begins to scan the tape.

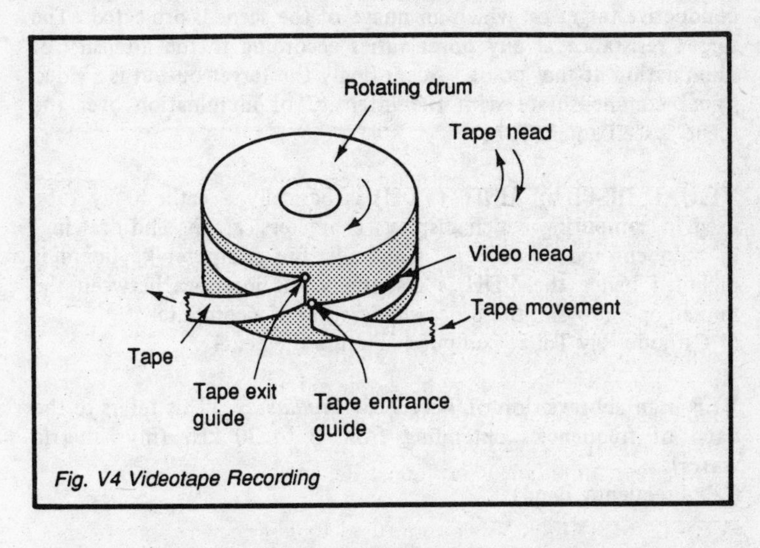

Fig. V4 Videotape Recording

A later development is the ***helical*** machine which has one or two video heads mounted on a drum rotating at field (or frame) rate. The tape is wrapped round the drum in the form of a helix as pictured in Figure V4. It is known as the Ω-wrap for as the figure shows, the tape is held in the shape of this Greek letter. There is one recording track per revolution of the drum and this runs at only a few degrees relative to the tape edge, each track or scan being equal to one field of the video signal.

Typically a video effective head gap (l) might be about 1 μm and with a head-to-tape speed (v) of say, 21 m/s, the frequency at which zero output occurs is v/l = 21 MHz with maximum output at half this. With equalization a reasonable frequency response up to around 14 MHz is therefore possible.

The helical system lends itself well to editing, slow motion and stationary pictures, as an example, the last is automatically obtained when the tape is stationary but the drum is still rotating. The angle of scan changes slightly so that the head then traces out a path which continually traverses the same two tracks.

Sound tracks on all systems are recorded longitudinally using conventional audio techniques.
(* Magnetic Recording, Video Frequency, Video Signal, Equalization)

VIDICON is a device which contains the electronics section of a television camera. It employs an electron beam to scan a photoconductive target on which an image of the scene is projected. The target resistance at any point varies according to the intensity of illumination at that point. Accordingly the target output is a video signal commensurate with the intensity of illumination over the scene – see Camera Tube.

VISUAL DISPLAY UNIT (VDU) is basically a cathode-ray tube used in computing which displays characters, graphs and drawings in monochrome or colour. Generally the computer keyboard is included hence the VDU is essentially the interface between the human operator and the processing section of a computer.
(* Cathode-Ray Tube, Computer, Picture Element)

VLF is an abbreviation of *Very Low Frequency*. This refers to the band of frequencies extending from 3 to 30 kHz (myriametric waves).
(>> Frequency Band)

V.L.S.I. (VERY LARGE SCALE INTEGRATION) is one of the most remarkable semiconductor technological developments. The number of transistors which can be squeezed into a single integrated circuit is well in excess of one million – see Integrated Circuit.

VOLTAGE-DEPENDENT RESISTOR (v.d.r.) A non-linear resistor which falls in resistance value as the voltage across it increases – see Voltage-Sensitive Resistor.

VOLTAGE DOUBLER is a rectifying circuit not unlike that of a full-wave bridge circuit except that capacitors are substituted for two of the diodes as shown in Figure V5. It is these capacitors which provide the voltage doubling. This type of circuit is particularly suitable where a higher d.c. voltage supply is required but at a moderate current.

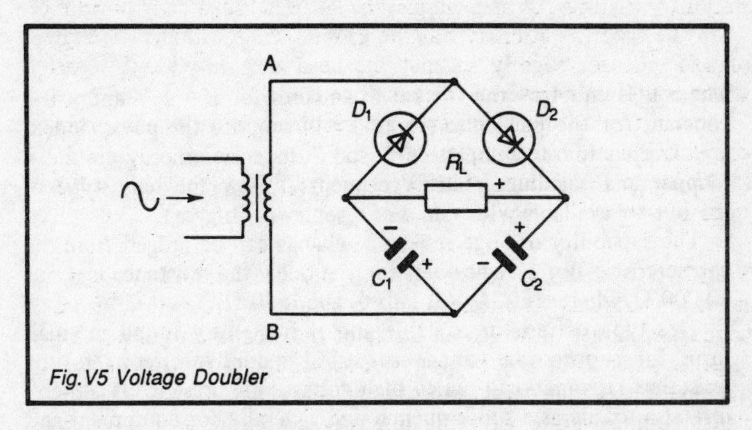

Fig. V5 Voltage Doubler

When A is negative to B, electron flow is through D_1 to charge up C_1. D_2 at this stage is reverse-biased and makes no contribution. On the alternate half-cycle C_2 is charged via D_2. After a few cycles from switching on therefore both capacitors are charged. As the figure shows, they are in series-aiding hence the total voltage across them approaches twice the maximum secondary voltage and this is the voltage applied to the load, R_L. The degree to which the voltage falls short of the maximum depends on the load current drain for the particular capacitance values employed, these should therefore be high (e.g. 100 microfarads or more).

Voltage Multiplication to a greater degree (e.g. ×3 or ×4) is feasible but the circuits become more complex hence use of a greater step-up in the transformer may be more economical.
(>> Rectification, Diode, Capacitor)

VOLTAGE MULTIPLICATION – see Voltage Doubler.

VOLTAGE REGULATOR – see Voltage Stabilization.

VOLTAGE-SENSITIVE RESISTOR (also known as a Voltage-Dependent Resistor). This is a non-linear resistor, the value of which depends on the voltage applied. The resistor consists of a mixture of silicon carbide and a ceramic binder formed into a disc or rod. This is then fired to produce a hard, solid compound. Connections to the material are made by spraying with a metal. If a voltage, V is applied directly to the resistor then the current, I through it is given approximately by:

$$I = kV^n$$

where k is equal to the current in amperes for $V = 1$ V and n is a constant for the particular material. In practice the power index, n is limited to values between 3 and 7, most commonly around 4 (copper and selenium rectifier elements follow the same type of law but are available with values of n somewhat higher).

The capability of large resistance change can be judged from the characteristics for a typical resistor. At 0.2 V the resistance is about 80 000 Ω, whereas at 2.0 V it falls to about 80 Ω.

This type of resistor is stable and is frequently found in small form for suppressing voltage surges in inductive circuits for its resistance falls markedly when high voltages are present. It is therefore also usable as a spark quench and generally for equipment and component protection against excessive voltages.

For the graphical symbol, see Figure N2.

(* Non-Linear Element, Spark Quench, Voltage Stabilization >> Resistance)

VOLTAGE STABILIZATION is the process through which the voltage output of a device is maintained substantially constant, i.e. as far as possible it is made independent of variations in the load current or input voltage. A *voltage stabilizer* or *voltage regulator* is therefore a unit inserted between a power supply and a load so that the load "sees" a constant voltage source. Generally the requirement is met using a semiconductor circuit, the simplest employing a zener diode which is essentially a constant-voltage device as shown in Figure V6. This gives moderately good regulation for a simple low cost circuit. The diode effectively clamps the supply rail at a voltage near its breakdown value. The supply to be stabilized must exceed the stabilizer output by several volts because the stabilizer itself creates a voltage drop.

If the load current falls the voltage drop across R decreases, hence the zener current increases and so compensates. If the load current rises then the zener current falls to compensate. On the other hand if the supply voltage, V_S increases, the zener current increases to bypass the extra current from the load and if the supply voltage

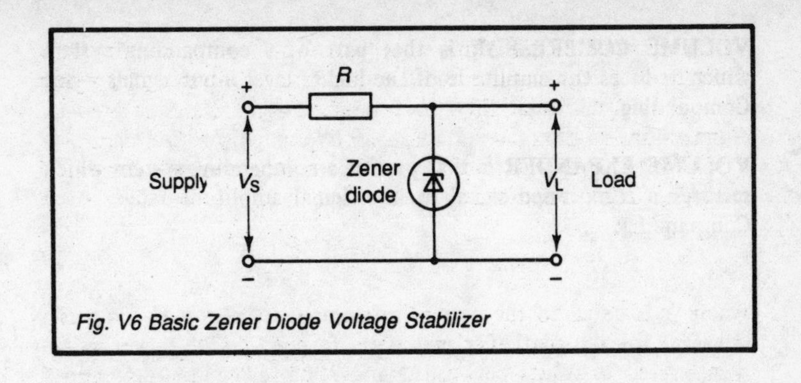

Fig. V6 Basic Zener Diode Voltage Stabilizer

decreases then the zener current falls so that a greater share of the lower current is available to the load. In each case the voltage drop across R is such that V_L remains substantially constant.

For greater stabilization many integrated circuits (IC's) are available, specially designed for this purpose. A typical IC voltage regulator comprises 3 main sections: (i) a voltage reference; (ii) an error detector and amplifier which senses the difference between the voltage reference and the output voltage; and (iii) an element in series with the load which adjusts its resistance according to the signal received from the error detector.
(* Constant Voltage Source, Integrated Circuit >> Zener Diode, Resistance, Ohm's Law)

VOLTAGE STABILIZER – see Voltage Stabilization.

VOLTMETER is an instrument for measuring d.c. and/or a.c. voltages. There are several different ways of indicating the value of an input voltage, especially by (i) a pointer moving over a scale as with a moving-coil meter, (ii) a numerical display e.g. by a digital meter, (iii) the degree of deflection on a cathode-ray oscilloscope.

A voltmeter which draws an appreciable current from the source being measured will give an incorrect reading especially if the source has a high impedance. This is because the current drawn by the instrument creates a voltage drop in the source. It follows therefore that a good voltmeter should draw very little current, i.e. it must have a high input impedance. There are exceptions to this, for example when measuring the voltage of a secondary cell for such cells have very low internal resistance.

See also Moving-Coil Meter, Digital Voltmeter, Electrostatic Voltmeter, Oscilloscope.
(>> Voltage, Impedance)

VOLUME COMPRESSOR is that part of a companding system which reduces the amplitude of the higher level input signals – see Companding.

VOLUME EXPANDER is that part of a companding system which restores a compressed signal to its original amplitude range – see Companding.

WATT-HOUR METER is one which measures and records energy consumption – see Induction Meter.

WATTMETER is an instrument for the measurement of electrical power. A type commonly found is the *electrodynamometer*, also known as the *electrodynamic wattmeter* or *dynamometer wattmeter.* This particular instrument has two coils which set up interacting magnetic fields. One field is proportional to the supply voltage, the other to the current, hence the two fields together indicate the power in watts, kilowatts, etc. – see Electrodynamometer.

WAVEMETER is an instrument for measuring the frequency of a radio wave. The wave under test may be induced into a coil which is tuned by a variable capacitor calibrated to read frequency or wavelength. Resonance is indicated by a small lamp or meter. This type is known as an *absorption wavementer* since it absorbs power from the wave for its operation.

Alternatively the heterodyne principle may be employed. The output of a calibrated variable frequency oscillator is combined with the incoming radio wave. When the oscillator frequency is very close to that of the wave under test a beat frequency is produced in the audio range and can therefore be heard on headphones or a loudspeaker. If now the oscillator frequency is adjusted for zero beat, its frequency is almost the same as that of the radio frequency under test (at "zero" beat the two frequencies could differ by a few hertz). The oscillator tuning dial is usually calibrated directly in frequency and wavelength. However by not tuning for zero beat

but by measuring the beat frequency and calculating accordingly, an exact result is given.
(* Frequency Meter >> Frequency, Wavelength, Electromagnetic Wave, Resonance, Beat Frequency)

WEIGHTING NETWORK is one with a specified attenuation/frequency characteristic. Such networks are perhaps most frequently used in the measurement of noise, one of the problems of which is the production of objective measurements having good correlation with subjective assessments. In a noise-measuring instrument therefore there is likely to be a weighting network so designed that the instrument reading simulates the annoyance or interfering effect of the noise.

Weighting networks are also to be found in sound-level meters usually with switchable characteristics so that very different types of sound (compare a pneumatic drill with an orchestra) can be made to produce measurements commensurate with the loudness as would be determined by human listeners.
(* Psophometer, Sound-Level Meter >> Attenuation, Noise)

WOOFER The bass loudspeaker in a hi-fi system – see Loudspeaker.

WORD is a term used in digital computer technology and refers to the basic unit of binary digits on which the processor operates. In everyday language our words are of various lengths but in the more disciplined world of the computer each model is designed around a particular word size. The longer the word, the greater the capabilities of the machine. Most personal computers use an 8-bit word (e.g. 10110101), this is known as a *byte*. However, note that the computer 8-bit word represents one letter (or numeral) only, the English language word is nearly always made up of several letters. More powerful machines use words of 16 bits, 32 bits and above. The now almost defunct 4-bit word is known as a *nibble*.
(* Computer, Binary, Binary Code, Digital Logic)

WOW is a colloquial term which applies to sound reproduction systems. It is used for unwanted slow pitch fluctuations of one up to a few hertz which are therefore most perceptible in sustained musical notes. The effect usually arises from an uneven motor drive. The term is frequently associated with *flutter* which is similarly an unwanted frequency modulation but at a higher frequency.
(* Disc Recording, Magnetic Recording, Flutter)

X

XEROGRAPHY (Greek, *xero* = dry, *graphos* = writing) is a dry copying process in which black or coloured *toner* particles or powder adhere to charged areas on the surface of a plate, the powder is then transferred onto paper. The complete process can be subdivided as follows:

(i) a rotating drum of photoconducting material (e.g. a metal drum coated with selenium) is charged to a high positive surface potential (up to 1000 V) by the deposition of ions on the surface. The process is carried out in the dark to avoid partial discharge;

(ii) the sensitized photoconductive drum is exposed to light reflected from the document to be copied. Photon absorption at the surface according to the intensity of the light creates electron-hole pairs, neutralizing the surface charge and so an image charge is built up. Thus for white areas of the document, the charge disappears and dark areas are represented by an electrically charged image;

(iii) toner particles of for example carbon black are charged to a polarity opposite to that on the drum surface (i.e. negative), these accumulate on the positively charged image;

(iv) a sheet of paper is held in contact with the drum and a positive charge is sprayed onto the back side, this causes the toner to transfer to the front side, it is then fixed by a heat treatment.

(>> Charge, Photoconductivity, Ion, Ionization, Selenium, Photon, Electron-Hole Pair)

YAGI ANTENNA was developed by H. Yagi and S. Uda (Japanese engineers) and is an advance on the basic dipole by the addition of directors and reflectors. In a receiving installation the Yagi system increases not only the signal pick-up but also the directivity. A plan of a typical Yagi horizontal antenna is shown in Figure Y1. The

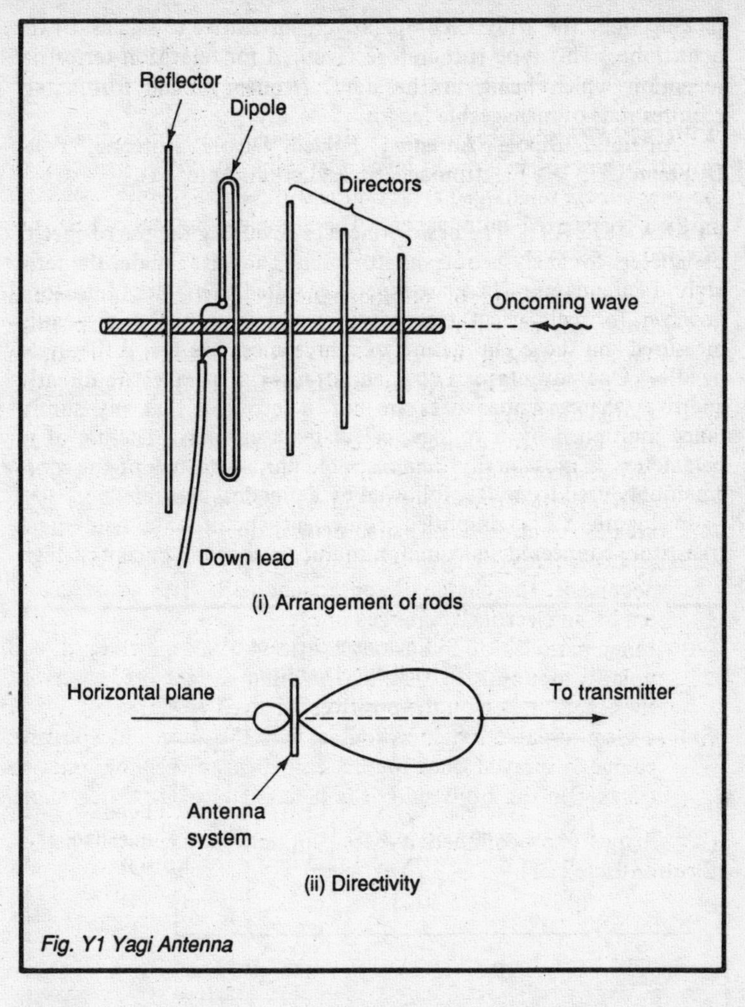

Fig. Y1 Yagi Antenna

dipole is shown folded but it could equally consist of a single rod approximately half a wavelength long. Although here we are considering reception, the antenna is equally useful for transmitting.

The dipole is assisted by a *reflector* behind it and one or more *directors* in front as shown in the figure. These are simply rods which are excited by the oncoming wave and their spacings from the dipole are such that they re-radiate the signal energy to arrive at the dipole in the desired phase.

Figure Y1 shows how sharply directional the array is. Such directivity is useful for the reduction of interference and noise

pick-up since the array is comparatively insensitive to signals off the main lobe. This type is therefore favoured for television terrestrial reception which being in the u.h.f. frequency band fortunately requires rods of manageable length.
(* Antenna, Dipole Antenna, Folded Dipole Antenna, Polar Diagram, UHF >> Electromagnetic Radiation, Antenna)

***y*-PARAMETERS** The basic principles governing the use of special parameters for analysis of transistor circuits are given under the term Hybrid Parameters. These are especially suited to bipolar transistors, however for field-effect transistors, *y*-parameters which are easily measured and have the nature of admittances are less difficult to handle. One advantage is that admittances in parallel are directly additive whereas impedances are not, a second is that any admittance multiplied by a voltage, calculates a current. The use of *y*-parameters is most easily demonstrated through a few of the most commonly used formulae, followed by a practical example.

In Figure Y2 a simplified equivalent circuit of a field-effect transistor, connected in common-source, is shown. Except at high

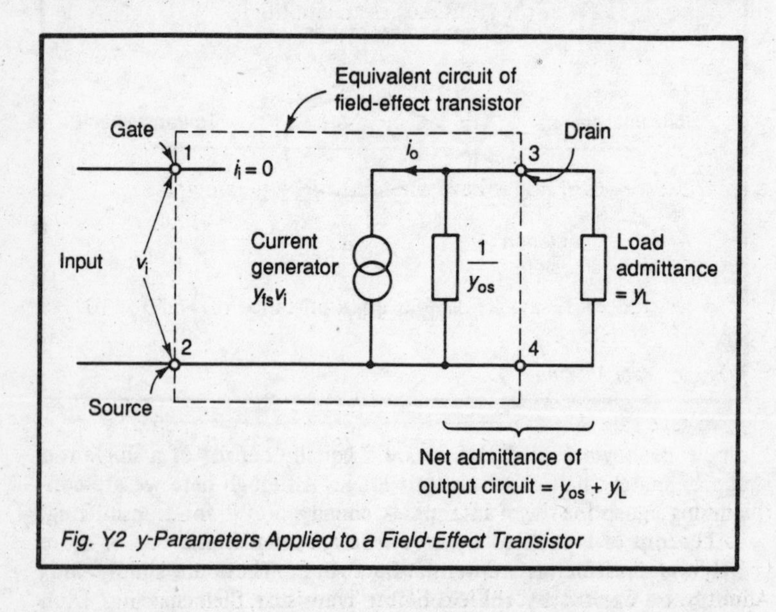

Fig. Y2 y-Parameters Applied to a Field-Effect Transistor

frequencies when internal capacitances must be taken into account, we can consider that there is little or no physical connection between the gate at terminal 1 and the rest of the circuit so no current flows into this terminal due to the voltage, v_i.

y_{fs} is the *forward transfer admittance* (the s subscript denotes *common-source*), measured under specified conditions. We sometimes find the term *mutual conductance* (g_m) used instead. Whether labelled y_{fs} (siemens) or g_m (mA/V), it is simply the ratio of the current generated in the transistor output circuit to the input voltage producing it. The transistor can therefore be considered as a current generator driving a current $i_o = y_{fs}v_i$ into the output circuit.

y_{os} is the *output admittance*, hence the net admittance of the output circuit is $(y_{os} + y_L)$ as shown in the figure.

The remaining y-parameters are y_i, the *input admittance* and y_r, the *reverse transfer admittance*, neither is required in this simplified explanation.

Then: output voltage, $v_o = i_o/Y$ where Y is the total admittance of the output circuit, i.e.

$$v_o = \frac{-y_{fs}v_i}{y_{os} + y_L}$$

and the voltage gain of the transistor as an amplifier,

$$K_v = \frac{v_o}{v_i} = \frac{-y_{fs}}{y_{os} + y_L}$$

A practical transistor might have the following y-parameters:

$$y_{fs} = 5 \times 10^{-3}\ \text{S} \qquad y_{os} = 25 \times 10^{-6}\ \text{S}$$

A load resistance of, say 20 kΩ has an admittance of $1/(20 \times 10^3) = 5 \times 10^{-5}$ S. Hence:

$$\text{voltage gain}, K_v = \frac{-5 \times 10^{-3}}{(25 \times 10^{-6}) + (5 \times 10^{-5})} = -66.67$$

the minus sign indicating a 180° phase change.

Other formulae exist to cover most design calculations.

(* Hybrid Parameters, Common-Source Connection, Load >> Admittance, Conductance, Field-Effect Transistor, Siemens)

Z

ZINC-AIR CELL This is a primary cell which differs from most others in that one of its electrodes (the positive) is in fact oxygen from the air. Dispensing with a metal or compound electrode therefore enables the cell to be smaller than otherwise. The negative electrode is zinc with an electrolyte of potassium hydroxide. The electrolyte is separated from the air electrode by a plastic film membrane which therefore prevents it from escaping from the cell. An advantage of the cell is that the air vent can be sealed until the cell is about to be used, accordingly shelf-life can be very high.

A zinc-air cell has a voltage of 1.4 and it is capable of higher current output for longer periods than would be obtained from another cell of the same size.
(>> Cell, Primary Cell, Electrolyte)

ZINC CHLORIDE CELL A primary cell which is usually found as a dry cell. It is similar to the popular Leclanché type dry cell but capable of heavier current output and because the cell must be sealed to prevent air reacting with the electrolyte, this type is leakproof with a high life expectancy. It is similar in construction and operation to a Leclancé cell except that the electrolyte is zinc chloride. Voltage 1.5.
(>> Cell, Primary Cell, Electrolyte, Leclanché Cell)

***z*-PARAMETERS** These are used for circuit analysis, mainly involving transistors but for this they are encountered less frequently than *h*- or *y*-parameters. They are in the nature of impedances and are therefore the inverse of the *y*-parameters. The four *z*-parameters are:

z_f = forward transfer impedance
(measured with open-circuited output)
z_i = input impedance
(measured with open-circuited output)
z_r = reverse transfer impedance
(measured with open-circuited input)
z_o = output impedance
(measured with open-circuited input)

For the basic principles see Hybrid Parameters.
(* Black Box, *y*-Parameters >> Transistor)

Index

A

Absorption Wavemeter – *see* Wavemeter 418
Accelerating Electrode 1
Accelerator 1
Acoustic Feedback 2
Acoustic Wave Device 2
Active Load 3
Aerial – *see* Antenna 7
Afterglow – *see* Persistence 281
Air Gap 4
Air Isolation – *see* Isolation 198
Alkaline Cell (Alkaline-Manganese Cell) 4
Alternator 4
ALU – *see* Arithmetic Logic Unit 10
American Standard Code for Information Interchange (ASCII) 6
Ampere-Hour 6
Analogue-to-Digital (A/D) Conversion 7
AND Gate – *see* Digital Logic 93
Antenna 7
Appleton Layer – *see* Ionosphere 196
Arc Lamp 10
Arithmetic Logic Unit (ALU) 10
Armature 10
Artificial Antenna 10
ASCII – *see* American Standard Code for Information Interchange 6
Aspect Ratio 11
Astable Multivibrator – *see* Multivibrator 255
Attenuation Equalizer 11
Attenuator 11
Audiometer 13
Automatic Frequency Control (a.f.c.) 13
Automatic Gain Control (a.g.c.) 14
Automatic Grid Bias 14
Autotransformer 15

B

Backward Diode 17
Backward-Wave Oscillator 17
Baffle 17
– *see also* Loudspeaker 219
Balanced Circuit 18
Balanced Modulator 19
Balancing Transformer – *see* Balun 20
Ballast Resistor 20
Balun 20
Barretter 21
Barrier-Layer Photocell 22
Baseband 22
Bass Cut – *see* Tone Control 395
Bass Lift – *see* Tone Control 395
Baud 23
Beat Frequency Oscillator 23
Beating 23
Bidirectional Transistor 24
Bifilar Winding 24
Bimetallic Strip 24
Binary 25
Binary Code 25
Binary Notation 26
Bistable Multivibrator – *see* Multivibrator 255
Bit 26
Black Box 26
Blanking – *see* Electron Gun 124
Blocking Capacitor 27
Blocking Oscillator 27
Bode Diagram 28
Boolean Algebra 28
Bootstrapping 29
Bottoming 30
– *see also* Switching Transistor 371
Breakover Voltage – *see* Thyristor 391
Bridged-T Network 30
Bridge Rectifier 30
Broadside Array 31
Bucket-Brigade Device (BBD) 31
Buffer 32
Bunching 32
Butterworth Filter 32
By-Pass Capacitor 32
Byte 32

C

Camera Tube 33
Capacitor Microphone – *see* Microphone 241
Carbon-Granule Microphone – *see* Microphone 241
Cathode-Ray Tube (c.r.t.) 35
Cathode Sputtering – *see* Sputtering 357
Cavity Magnetron – *see* Magnetron 230
Cavity Resonator 38
CCD – *see* Charge-Coupled Device 40
Central Processing Unit (CPU) 39
Ceramic 39
Ceramic Capacitor 40
Cermet – *see* Ceramic 39
Channel 40

Charge-Coupled Device (CCD) 40
Charge-Storage Diode – *see* Step-Recovery Diode 361
Charge-Storage Tube – *see* Storage Tube 364
Charge Transfer Device (CTD)
– *see* Bucket-Brigade Device 31
– *see* Charge-Coupled Device 40
Chebyshev Filter 42
Chip 42
Choke 43
Chopper 43
Chopper Amplifier 45
Chrominance 45
Chrominance Signal
– *see* Television 374
– *see* Television Signal 379
Circuit-Breaker 45
Circulator 45
Class A Amplifier 46
Class AB Amplifier 46
Class B Amplifier 49
Class C Amplifier 49
Clipping – *see* Limiter 206
Clock 50
Clock Pulse 50
Closed-Loop Control System 50
CMOS – *see* Complementary Metal-Oxide-Semiconductor 64
Coaxial Cable 51
Coincidence Circuit 53
Cold Cathode 53
Colour Burst – *see* Television Signal 379
Colour Cell – *see* Colour Picture Tube 55
Colour Code 53
Colour Picture Tube 55
Colour Television
– *see* Television 374
– *see* Television Receiver 377
– *see* Television Signal 379
Colpitts Oscillator – *see* Oscillator 269
Common-Base Connection 57
Common-Collector Connection 57
Common-Drain Connection 60
Common-Emitter Connection 60
Common-Gate Connection 60
Common-Mode Rejection Ratio
– *see* Differential Amplifier 89
Common-Source Connection 61
Communications Satellite – *see* Satellite 332
Commutator 61
Compact Disc – *see* Disc Recording 104
Companding 61
Comparator 63
Complementary Metal-Oxide-Semiconductor (CMOS) 64
Complementary Transistors 64
Compressor – *see* Companding 61
Computer 65
Condenser Microphone – *see* Microphone 241
Constant Current Source 67
Constant-k Filter 69
Constant Voltage Source 69
Control Electrode 72
Conversion Conductance 72
Core-Type Transformer 72
Counter 72
CPU – *see* Central Processing Unit 39
Crossed-Field Device 74
Cross Modulation 74
Crossover Distortion 74
Crossover Network 75
Crosstalk 78
Cryotron 79
Crystal Filter 79
Crystal Microphone – *see* Microphone 241
Crystal Oscillator 79
Current Feedback 81
Current Transformer 81
Cyclotron 81

D

Dark Current 81
Darlington Pair 82
D.C. Amplifier – *see* Direct-Coupled Amplifier 102
D.C. Coupling – *see* Direct-Coupled Amplifier 102
D.C. Restorer – *see* Direct Current Restoration 103
D.C. Stabilization 83
Debunching 84
Decay Time 84
Decoding 84
Decoupling 85
De-Emphasis – *see* Pre-Emphasis 297
Deflection Coils 86
Deflection Plates 86
Deflection Sensitivity 86
Degassing 87
Dekatron 87
Delay Equalizer 87
Delay Line 87
Detector 88
Dichroic Mirror 88
Dielectric Heating 88
Dielectric Isolation – *see* Isolation 198
Differential Amplifier 89
Differential Galvanometer 89

Differential Resistance 91
Differential Winding 91
Differentiating Circuit 91
Diffusion 92
Digital Computer – *see* Computer 65
Digital Logic 93
Digital-to-Analogue (D/A) Conversion 95
Digital Transmission 97
Digital Voltmeter 98
Digitron 98
Diode Detector 98
Diode Isolation – *see* Isolation 198
Diode-Transistor Logic (DTL) 99
Dipole Antenna 100
Direct-Coupled Amplifier (D.C. Amplifier) 102
Direct Coupling – *see* Direct-Coupled Amplifier 102
Direct Current Restoration 103
Direct Voltage 103
Discharge Lighting 103
Disc Recording 104
Diversity System 106
Dividing Network – *see* Crossover Network 75
DMOS 107
Doppler Effect 107
Double-Balanced Modulator – *see* Ring Modulator 326
Double-Base Diode 107
Double-Diffused Metal-Oxide-Semiconductor (DMOS) 107
Double-Sideband Transmission 108
Double Superheterodyne Reception 108
Drift Space – *see* Klystron 203
Drift Transistor – *see* Graded-Base Transistor 160
Driver (Driver Stage) 109
Dropping Resistor (Dropper) 109
Dry Cell 109
Dummy Antenna – *see* Artificial Antenna 10
Dust Core – *see* Ferrite 140
Dynamo – *see* Generator 157
Dynamometer Wattmeter – *see* Electrodynamometer 117
Dynode 110

E

Earphone 111
Earth 112
Earth Leakage Circuit-Breaker – *see* Residual Current Circuit Breaker 322
Earth Return 112
Echo 112
Eddy Current Heating – *see* Induction Heating 185
Effective Height (Effective Length) 113
EHF 113
EHT 113
Electret 113
Electret Microphone 114
– *see also* Microphone 241
Electric Lamp 114
Electric Motor 115
Electric Screening (Electrostatic Screening) – *see* Screening 341
Electroacoustic Transducer – *see* Transducer 400
Electrocardiogram 117
Electrode A.C. Resistance 117
Electrodynamic Wattmeter 117
Electrodynamometer 117
Electroencephalogram (e.e.g.) 119
Electrolytic Capacitor 119
Electromagnet 120
Electromagnetic Deflection 121
Electromagnetic Focusing 122
Electromagnetic Lens 122
Electromagnetic Relay – *see* Relay 318
Electrometer 122
Electron Beam Focusing 122
Electron Gun 124
Electron Microscope 126
Electron Multiplier 127
Electroplating 128
Electrostatic Deflection 129
Electrostatic Focusing – *see* Electron Beam Focusing 122
Electrostatic Generator – *see* Van de Graaff Generator 408
Electrostatic Lens – *see* Electron Beam Focusing 122
Electrostatic Loudspeaker – *see* Loudspeaker 219
Electrostatic Microphone – *see* Microphone 241
Electrostatic Voltmeter 130
Emitter-Coupled Logic (ECL) 131
Emitter Follower 131
Encryption – *see* Scrambling 341
End-Fire Array 132
Energy Meter – *see* Induction Meter 185
Enhancement Mode 132
Epitaxy 134
Equalization, Equalizer 134
Equivalent Circuit 134
Equivalent Electric Circuit 136
Equivalent Network 136
Excitation 137
Exclusive-NOR Gate – *see* Digital Logic 93
Exclusive-OR Gate – *see* Digital Logic 93

Expander – *see* Companding 61

F
Facsimile Transmission 137
Fading 138
Failure/Failure Rate 138
Fall Time 139
Faraday Cage, Faraday Screen 139
Fast-Recovery Diode 139
Feedback Control Loop – *see* Closed Loop Control System 50
Feeder 140
Ferrite 140
Ferrite-Rod Antenna 140
Fibre Optic Transmission 141
Field Coil – *see* Electromagnet 120
Field Emission Microscope 142
Filament 142
Film Resistor 142
Flashover 143
Flip-Flop – *see* Multivibrator 255
Floating 143
Floating-Carrier Modulation 143
Flood Gun – *see* Storage Tube 364
Fluorescent Lamp – *see* Discharge Lighting 103
Flutter 143
Fluxmeter 145
Flyback – *see* Time Base 393
Flying-Spot Scanner 145
Folded Dipole Antenna 145
Four-Layer Diode – *see* Thyristor 391
Four-Wire Circuit 146
Frame Antenna – *see* Loop Antenna 217
Free-Field 147
Free Space Path Loss 147
Frequency Changer 149
Frequency Discriminator 149
Frequency Divider 151
Frequency Division Multiplex – *see* Multiplex System 253
Frequency Meter 152
Frequency Multiplier 153
Frequency Response Characteristic 153
Frequency Shift Keying (Frequency Shift Modulation) 153
Frying 154
Full-Scale Deflection (f.s.d.) 154
Fuel Cell 154
Fuse 154

G
Gain Control 155
Galactic Noise 156
Gas-Filled Tube 156
Gas Focusing – *see* Electron Beam Focusing 122
Gate 156
Geiger Counter 156
Generator 157
Geostationary Orbit 159
– *see also* Satellite 332
Getter – *see* Degassing 87
Glow Discharge 159
Goniometer 159
Graded-Base Transistor 160
Grid 160
Ground Wave 161

H
Half-Power Point 162
Hall Probe 162
Hardware 162
Harmonic Distortion 162
Harmonic Distortion Analyser 163
Harmonic Generator 163
Hartley Oscillator – *see* Oscillator 269
Head
– *see* Magnetic Recording 225
– *see* Disc Recording 104
Head Gap – *see* Magnetic Recording 225
Hearing Aid 164
Heater 165
Heat Sink 165
Heaviside-Kennelly Layer 166
– *see also* Ionosphere 196
Heterodyne Wavemeter – *see* Wavemeter 418
HF 166
H-Network 166
Horizontal Polarization 166
Horn Loudspeaker – *see* Loudspeaker 219
Hot-Wire Ammeter 166
h-Parameter – *see* Hybrid Parameters 168
Hum 167
Hybrid Integrated Circuits 167
Hybrid Parameters (h-Parameters) 168
Hybrid Transformer 171
Hydrophone 173
– *see also* Sonar 354

I
IC – *see* Integrated Circuit 187
Iconoscope 173
Igniter 174
Ignition Coil 174
Ignitron 175
IIL (I^2L) – *see* Integrated Injection Logic 191
Image Converter 176
Image Frequency 176
Image Intensifier 177

Image Interference – *see* Image Frequency 176
Image Orthicon 178
– *see also* Camera Tube 33
Image Tube 178
IMPATT Diode 178
Impedance Matching 180
Impulse 180
Impulse Generator 181
Impulse Noise 181
Impulse Voltage 182
Incandescent Lamp – *see* Electric Lamp 114
Indirectly Heated Cathode 183
Indirect Wave 183
Induction Coil 183
Induction Heating 185
Induction Meter 185
Induction Motor – *see* Electric Motor 115
Inductive Coupling 186
Infra-Red 186
Insertion Gain/Loss 187
Instability 187
Instrument Transformer 187
Integrated Circuit 187
Integrated Injection Logic 191
Interelectrode Capacitance 191
Interference 192
Intermodulation Distortion 193
Inverter 193
Ionization Chamber 195
Ionization Pressure Gauge 196
Ionosphere 196
Isolating Transformer 198
Isolation 198
Isotropic Antenna 199

J

Jitter 200

K

Kell Factor 201
Kennelly-Heaviside Layer – *see* Ionosphere 196
Kilowatt-Hour 201
Klystron 203

L

Lamination 204
Large-Scale Integration (LSI) – *see* Integrated Circuit 187
Latching 204
Lavalier Microphone – *see* Microphone 241
Lead-Acid Cell 204
Leading Edge 205
Leakage Current 205
LF 205
Lightning 205
Lightning Conductor 206
Limiter 206
Linear Accelerator 206
Linear Induction Motor – *see* Electric Motor 115
Liquid Crystal Display (LCD) 208
Lissajous Figures 210
Litzendraht (Litz) Conductor 212
– *see also* Skin Effect 350
LNB (Low Noise Block) Converter 213
– *see also* Satellite Television 334
Load 213
Loading 213
Load Line 213
Local Oscillator 214
Locking 214
Logic 215
Logic Gate 215
Logic Level 216
Long Persistance Tube 217
Long-Tailed Pair 217
– *see also* Differential Amplifier 89
Loop Antenna 217
Loose Contact Microphone – *see* Microphone 241
Loss 219
Loss Factor 219
Loudspeaker 219
LSI – *see* Integrated Circuit 187
Luminance 222
Luminance Signal – *see* Television Signal 379

M

MAC 222
Magnetic Amplifier 223
– *see also* Saturable Reactor 337
Magnetic Bubble 223
Magnetic Core 225
Magnetic Damping 225
Magnetic Deflection – *see* Electromagnetic Deflection 121
Magnetic Memory 225
Magnetic Recording 225
Magnetic Screen – *see* Screening 341
Magnetic Tape 229
Magnetostrictive Transducer 230
Magnetron 230
Mains Hum – *see* Hum 167
Maintaining Voltage 232
Master Oscillator 232
Matching 232
Matrix 233
m-Derived Filter 235
Mean Time Between Failures (MTBF) – *see* Reliability 320
Medium-Scale Integration (MSI) – *see* Integrated Circuit 187

Memory 236
Mercury Arc Rectifier 238
Mercury Vapour Rectifier 239
Mesa Transistor 239
Metal-Film Resistor 240
Metal Rectifier 240
Meter 240
MF 240
Microelectronics 240
Microphone 241
Microprocessor 246
Microstrip Transmission Line – *see* Strip Transmission Line 367
Microwave Heating 246
Miller Integrator 247
Mismatch 247
Mixer 248
Modem 249
Monochrome 250
Monostable Multivibrator – *see* Multivibrator 255
MOS Capacitor 250
MOS Integrated Circuit 251
Moving-Coil Meter 251
Moving-Coil Microphone – *see* Microphone 241
Moving-Iron Meter 253
Multiplexed Analogue Components – *see* MAC 222
Multiplex System 253
Multivibrator 255
Muting 258

N

NAND Gate – *see* Digital Logic 93
Negative Logic 258
Neon Tube 258
Neutral 258
Neutralization 258
NICAM (Stereo) 259
Nickel-Cadmium Cell 260
Nickel-Iron Cell 260
Noise Factor 260
Noise Figure 261
Noise Generator 261
Noise Limiter 261
Non-Linear Element 262
NOR Gate – *see* Digital Logic 93
NOT Gate – *see* Digital Logic 93
NTSC 263
Nyquist Diagram 263

O

Octave 265
Ohmic Contact 265
Ohmmeter 265
Open Circuit 265
Open-Circuit Voltage 265
Operating Point 266
Operational Amplifier 266
Optical Isolator 268
OR Gate – *see* Digital Logic 93
Oscillator 269
Oscilloscope 272
Overshoot 274

P

Pad – *see* Attenuator 11
Padding Capacitor (Padder) 275
– *see also* Tracking 398
Pair 275
PAL 275
Parabolic Antenna 275
Parallel Connection 277
Parameter 277
Parametric Amplifier 277
Parasitic Oscillation 278
Parasitic Stopper 279
Parity Bit 279
Parity Checking 279
PCM – *see* Pulse Code Modulation 301
Peak Inverse Voltage (p.i.v.) 280
Permanent Magnet 280
Permeability Tuning 280
Persistence 281
Phase Discriminator 281
– *see also* Frequency Discriminator 149
Phase-Shift Oscillator – *see* Oscillator 269
Phase Splitter 282
Photolithography 282
Photomultiplier 284
Photoresist – *see* Photolithography 282
Phototube 285
Pick-Up 285
Picture Element 286
Piezoelectric Microphone – *see* Microphone 241
Piezoelectric Oscillator – *see* Oscillator 269
Piezojunction Microphone – *see* Microphone 241
Pilot (Pilot Carrier) 288
– *see also* Single Sideband Transmission 350
Pink Noise 288
Pixel – *see* Picture Element 286
Planar Process 288
Plane of Polarization 289
Polar Diagram 289
Pole 290
Polyphase System 290
Positive Logic 293
Potential Divider 293
Potentiometer 294
Powder Core (Powdered-Iron Core) 296
Power Amplifier 296

Preamplifier 296
Pre-Emphasis 297
Preferred Values 297
Pressure-Gradient Microphone 299
– *see also* Microphone 241
Printed Circuit 299
Printed Wiring 299
Probe 300
Program 300
Programming Language 300
Proportional Counter – *see* Geiger Counter 156
Psophometer 301
Pulse Code Modulation (p.c.m.) 301
Push-Pull Operation 303

Q

Quantization 305
Quantization Distortion 305
Quantization Noise 306
Quarter-Wave Line 306
Quarter-Wave Transformer 308
Quenching 308

R

Radar 308
Radiation Resistance 310
Radio Receiver 310
RAM – *see* Computer 65
Ratio Detector 314
Read-Only Memory (ROM) 315
– *see also* Computer 65
Receiver 315
Rectifier Instrument 315
Redundancy 316
Reed Relay 317
Regeneration 317
Regenerator – *see* Pulse Code Modulation 301
Regulation 317
Relaxation Oscillator 317
Relay 318
Reliability 320
Repeater 321
Reservoir Capacitor 321
– *see also* Ripple Filter 328
Residual Charge 321
Residual Current Circuit Breaker 322
Resistance-Capacitance Coupling (R-C Coupling) 322
Resistance-Capacitance Oscillator – *see* Oscillator 269
Resistance Thermometer 323
Resistor 324
Resistor-Transistor Logic 326
Rheostat 326
– *see also* Potentiometer (2) 294
Ribbon Microphone – *see* Microphone 241
Ring Modulator 326
Ripple 328
Ripple Factor 328
Ripple Filter 328
ROM – *see* Read-Only Memory 315
Rubylith – *see* Photolithography 282

S

Safe Operating Area 331
Sampling 332
Satellite 332
Satellite Television 334
Saturable Reactor (Transductor) 337
Saturation 338
SAW – *see* Acoustic Wave Device 2
Sawtooth Waveform 338
Scanning 339
Schmitt Trigger 339
Scintillation Counter 341
Scrambling 341
Screening 341
Screening Can 343
SECAM 343
Second Channel Interference – *see* Image Frequency 176
Selenium Rectifier 343
Self-Capacitance 344
Sensitivity 344
Series Connection 344
Servomechanism – *see* Closed-Loop Control System 50
Seven-Segment Display 344
Shadow Mask – *see* Colour Picture Tube 55
Shelf-Life 345
Shell-Type Transformer 345
SHF 345
Shift Register 345
Shock Excitation 347
Short-Circuit 347
Short Wave 347
Shunt 347
Signal Generator 348
Signal-to-Noise Ratio 348
Silicon Controlled Rectifier – *see* Thyristor 391
Silicon Controlled Switch (S.C.S.) 348
Silvered Mica Capacitor 349
Silver-Zinc (Silver Oxide) Cell 349
Singing 350
Single Sideband Transmission 350
Skin Effect 350
Skip Distance 351
Sky Noise 351
Sky Wave 352
– *see also* Ionosphere 196
Slew Rate – *see* Operational Amplifier 266

Slide Wire 352
Slip Ring – *see* Generator 157
Slow-Wave Structure – *see* Travelling-Wave Tube 404
Slug 352
Smoothing Circuit – *see* Ripple Filter 328
Software 352
Solar Cell 353
Solenoid 353
Solid-State Camera 354
Solid-State Device 354
Sonar 354
Sound-Level Meter 355
Spark 356
Spark Quench 357
Sputtering 357
Square-Law Detector 358
Stabilization 358
Star-Delta Transformation 360
Step Function 361
Step-Recovery Diode 361
Stereophonic Broadcasting 362
Stereophonic System 364
Storage Time 364
Storage Tube 364
Stray Capacitance 367
Strip Transmission Line 367
Stub, Stub Matching 368
Substrate 369
Suppressed Carrier Transmission 369
Surface Acoustic Wave Device 369
– *see also* Acoustic Wave Device 2
Sweep – *see* Time Base 393
Switch 369
Switching Transistor 371
Synchronous Detection – *see* Suppressed Carrier Transmission 369
Synchronous Motor 372
Synchrotron 372

T

Telecommunication System 373
Telephone Set 374
Television 374
Television Camera 377
Television Receiver 377
Television Signal 379
Terminating Set 382
Tetrode Thyristor – *see* Silicon Controlled Switch 348
Thermal Imaging (Thermography) 384
Thermal Resistance 384
Thermal Runaway (Thermal Breakdown) 385
Thermistor 385
Thermoammeter 387
– *see also* Hot-Wire Ammeter 166
Thermocouple 387
Thermocouple Meter 387
Thermopile – *see* Thermocouple 387
Thick Film Circuits – *see* Hybrid Integrated Circuits 167
Thin Film Circuits – *see* Hybrid Integrated Circuits 167
Three-Phase System – *see* Polyphase System 290
Thyratron 389
Thyristor 391
Time Base 393
Time Base Generator 394
Time Division Multiplex – *see* Multiplex System 253
Tolerance 395
Tone Control 395
Totem-Pole Output – *see* Transistor-Transistor Logic 401
Tracking 398
Transducer 400
Transductor 401
– *see also* Saturable Reactor 337
Transistor-Transistor Logic (TTL) 401
Transmitter 401
Transponder 403
Transputer 403
Trapatt Diode 403
Travelling-Wave Tube (t.w.t.) 404
Treble Cut – *see* Tone Control 395
Treble Lift – *see* Tone Control 395
Triac – *see* Thyristor 391
Trigger 405
Trigger Circuit 405
Trimmer (Trimming Capacitor) 405
Truth Table – *see* Digital Logic 93
Tuned Amplifier 406
Tweeter – *see* Loudspeaker 219

U

UHF 408
Ultrasonic Delay Line – *see* Delay Line 87

V

Vacuum Evaporation 408
Van De Graaff Accelerator 408
Van De Graaff Generator 408
Varactor 410
Variable Reluctance Microphone – *see* Microphone 241
Variable Resistance Microphone – *see* Microphone 241
Varistor 411
VDU – *see* Visual Display Unit 414
Velocity Microphone – *see* Pressure Gradient Microphone 299
Vertical Polarization 411
Vestigial Sideband Transmission 411
VHF 411

Vibrator 412
Video Frequency 412
Video Signal 412
Videotape – *see* Magnetic Recording 225
Videotape Recording 413
Vidicon 414
– *see also* Camera Tube 33
Visual Display Unit (VDU) 414
VLF 414
V.L.S.I. (Very Large Scale Integration) – *see* Integrated Circuit 187
Voltage-Dependent Resistor (v.d.r.) – *see* Voltage-Sensitive Resistor 415
Voltage Doubler 415
Voltage Multiplication 415
Voltage Regulator – *see* Voltage Stabilization 416
Voltage-Sensitive Resistor 415
Voltage Stabilization 416
Voltage Stabilizer – *see* Voltage Stabilization 416
Voltmeter 417
Volume Compressor – *see* Companding 61
Volume Expander – *see* Companding 61

W

Watt-Hour Meter – *see* Induction Meter 185
Wattmeter 418
– *see also* Electrodynamometer 117
Wavemeter 418
Weighting Network 419
Woofer – *see* Loudspeaker 219
Word 419
Wow 419

X

Xerography 420

Y

Yagi Antenna 420
y-Parameters 422

Z

Zinc-Air Cell 424
Zinc Chloride Cell 424
z-Parameters 424

Notes

Notes

Notes

Notes

Notes

Notes